D1207180

High Performance
Liquid Chromatography
in Biochemistry

© VCH Verlagsgesellschaft mbH, D-6940 Weinheim (Federal Republic of Germany), 1985

Distribution:

VCH Verlagsgesellschaft, P.O. Box 1260/1280, D-6940 Weinheim (Federal Republic of Germany)

USA and Canada: VCH Publishers, 303 N.W. 12th Avenue, Deerfield Beach, FL 33442-1705 (USA)

ISBN 3-527-26057-9 (VCH Verlagsgesellschaft)
ISBN 0-89573-066-9 (VCH Publishers)

High Performance Liquid Chromatography in Biochemistry

Edited by
Agnes Henschen, Klaus-Peter Hupe,
Friedrich Lottspeich, Wolfgang Voelter

VCH

Editors:

Dr. Agnes Henschen
Max-Planck-Institut für Biochemie
D-8033 Martinsried

Dr.-Ing. Klaus-Peter Hupe
Hewlett-Packard GmbH
D-7517 Waldbronn 2

Dr. Friedrich Lottspeich
Max-Planck-Institut für Biochemie
D-8033 Martinsried

Prof. Dr. Wolfgang Voelter
Abt. für Physikalische Biochemie
Physiologisch-chemisches Institut der Universität
D-7400 Tübingen

Editorial Director: Dr. Hans F. Ebel
Production Manager: Dipl.-Ing. (FH) Hans Jörg Maier

Library of Congress Card No. 85-5053

Deutsche Bibliothek Cataloguing-in-Publication Data

High performance liquid chromatography in biochemistry / ed. by Agnes Henschen ... −
Weinheim; Deerfield Beach, Florida; Basel: VCH, 1985.
  ISBN 3-527-26057-9 (Weinheim, Basel)
  ISBN 0-89573-066-9 (Deerfield Beach)
NE: Henschen, Agnes [Hrsg.]

Composition: Filmsatz Unger, D-6940 Weinheim
Printing: betz-druck GmbH, D-6100 Darmstadt-Arheiligen
Bookbinding: Wilhelm Osswald + Co., D-6730 Neustadt
Printed in the Federal Republic of Germany

Preface

It is hard to imagine what it would mean to research in biochemistry if chromatography were not available as an analytical tool.

Liquid chromatography, in all it's various modes, has become particularly indispensable. Above all, the high performance version of liquid chromatography (HPLC) has brought completely new dimensions to the analytical work of this and all other areas of chemistry. The features most important for the analysis (separation efficiency, speed of analysis and lower level of detection) have all gained improvement of at least one order of magnitude over the last 10 years. The method can now be carried out on a microscale, with small amounts of sample.

The roots of what is today called high performance liquid chromatography go back to the early 1960s. It was then that two crucial elements of the technique came together: 1. A better understanding of the kinetics and thermodynamics of the separation process, leading to column packings and columns of much higher selectivity and efficiency. 2. The development of instrumentation which turned the sequential steps of the analysis process (previously carried out separately and manually) into a continuous, automated procedure. The first instruments to appear on the market as a result of this trend were an Amino Acid Analyser, which was developed by Moore et al. [*], and a Nucleic Acid Analyser, based on work by Horvath et al. [*]. Biochemistry can thus be regarded, from an instrumental and application point of view, as the cradle of HPLC. From there it grew and spread out over almost all areas of chemistry.

Today the technique has matured to such an extent that it can be applied routinely with a high degree of reliability and reproducibility even to the very complex analytical problems typical for biochemistry. This has initiated the use of HPLC by an ever increasing number of biochemists, a trend which is likely to continue. The time therefore seems right for a self-contained appraisal of the technique with special regard to its application in biochemistry.

In this book it has been our aim to give an introduction to the theoretical and instrumental principles of HPLC, followed by a detailed treatment of its application to the various groups of compounds of biochemical interest.

München, Waldbronn and Tübingen,
October 1984

A. Henschen
K.-P. Hupe
F. Lottspeich
W. Voelter

---

[*] Bibliography at end of Chapter 1.

Contents

List of Contributors

Bauer, Hermann, Dr.
Abt. für Physikalische Biochemie
Physiologisch-chemisches
Institut der Universität
Hoppe-Seyler-Straße 1
D-7400 Tübingen
Chapter 8

Engelhardt, Heinz, Prof. Dr.
Angewandte Physikalische Chemie
der Universität des Saarlandes
Bau 9
D-6600 Saarbrücken
Chapter 2

Henschen, Agnes, Dr.
Max-Planck-Institut für Biochemie
D-8033 Martinsried
Chapter 4

Hostettmann, Kurt, Prof. Dr.
Ecole de Pharmacie
Université de Lausanne
Place du Château
CH-1005 Lausanne
Chapter 14

Hostettmann, Maryse, Dr.
Ecole de Pharmacie
Université de Lausanne
Place du Château
CH-1005 Lausanne
Chapter 14

Hupe, Klaus-Peter, Dr.-Ing.
Hewlett-Packard GmbH
Postfach 1280
D-7517 Waldbronn 2
Chapters 1, 3

Kronbach, Thomas, Dr.
Biozentrum der Universität
Klingelbergstraße 70
CH-4056 Basel
Chapter 12

Liebich, Hartmut, Dr.
Medizinische Klinik
der Universität
Otfried-Müller-Straße
D-7400 Tübingen
Chapter 13

Lottspeich, Friedrich, Dr.
Max-Planck-Institut für Biochemie
D-8033 Martinsried
Chapter 4

Meyer, Hans Detlef, Dr.
Institut für Klinische Chemie
der Ludwig-Maximilians-Universität
Klinikum Großhadern
Postfach 701 260
D-8000 München 70
Chapter 10

Müller, Hartmut, Dr.
Dynamit Nobel
Forschung und Entwicklung
Geb. 50
D-5210 Troisdorf
Chapter 2

Rozing, Gerard, Dr.
Hewlett-Packard GmbH
Postfach 1280
D-7517 Waldbronn 2
Chapter 3

Schön, Uwe, Dr.
Dynamit Nobel
D-5216 Niederkassel
Chapter 2

Schott, Herbert, Prof. Dr.
Institut für Organische Chemie
der Universität
Auf der Morgenstelle 18
D-7400 Tübingen 1
Chapter 9

Schrenker, Helge, Dipl.-Ing.
Hewlett-Packard GmbH
Postfach 1280
D-7517 Waldbronn 2
Chapter 3

Steinmüller, Dirk
Botanisches Institut der Universität
Lehrstuhl für Pflanzenphysiologie
Kaiserstraße 12
D-7500 Karlsruhe
Chapter 7

Tevini, Manfred, Prof. Dr.
Botanisches Institut der Universität
Lehrstuhl für Pflanzenphysiologie
Kaiserstraße 12
D-7500 Karlsruhe
Chapter 7

Voelter, Wolfgang, Prof. Dr.
Abt. für Physikalische Biochemie
Physiologisch-chemisches
Institut der Universität
Hoppe-Seyler-Straße 1
D-7400 Tübingen
Chapters 5, 8, 11, 12

Zech, Karl, Dr.
Byk Gulden Lomberg
Byk-Gulden-Straße 2
D-7750 Konstanz
Chapter 6

List of Chromatographic Symbols

A_s	asymmetry factor
A_c	free cross-sectional area of the column
B_0	column permeability
c	concentration
c_M	solute concentration in the mobile phase
c_S	solute concentration in the stationary phase
dp	particle size
D_M	diffusion coefficient in the mobile phase
E	extraction constant
F	flow-rate
h	height equivalent to a theoretical plate (HETP)
h_{min}	minimum plate height
H	height equivalent to one effective plate
k	capacity ratio (capacity factor, mass distribution ratio)
K	distribution coefficient, partition coeffient
K^*	adsorption coefficient
l	column length
n	number of theoretical plates
N	number of effective plates
Osp	specific surface area
r	column radius
R	gas constant
R_D	response factor
R_S	resolution
t_M	solvent hold-up time (dead time)
t_R	retention time
t_R'	adjusted retention time
T	absolute temperature
u	linear flow velocity
u_{min}	flow velocity at minimum plate height
u_x	linear migration velocity
Vol%	volumetric mixing ratio
V	peak volume
V_D	detector volume
V_e	elution volume (SEC)
V_g	gradient volume
V_M	void volume, volume of mobile phase
V_p	pore volume (volume within the particles)
V_R	retention volume
V_S	volume of stationary phase
V_z	interstitial volume (volume between particles)
W	peak area

w_b	width of a peak at its base
w_i	width of peak at height of inflection point
α	separation factor (selectivity)
β	phase ratio
γ	geometry factor
ΔP	pressure drop along the column
ε_0	eluting strength in eluotropic series
ε_T	total porosity
η	eluent viscosity
λ	Eddy diffusion coefficient, packing factor
σ	peak standard deviation
σ^2	peak variance
σ_l	peak standard deviation in units of length
σ_t	peak standard deviation in units of time
σ_v	peak standard deviation in units of volume
τ	detector time constant
ρ	packing density
ϕ	average pore diameter
Ψ	column resistance factor
ω	geometry factor

List of Abbreviations

DAD	Diode Array Detector
ECD	Electrochemical Detector
GC	Gas Chromatography
GLC	Gas Liquid Chromatography
GPC	Gel Permeation Chromatography
HETP	Height Equivalent to a Theoretical Plate
HPLC	High Performance Liquid Chromatography
IEC	Ion Exchange Chromatography
IPC	Ion Pair Chromatography
HMDS	Hexamethyldisilane
LC	Liquid Chromatography
LLC	Liquid Liquid Chromatography
LLD	Lower Limit of Detection
LSC	Liquid Solid Chromatography
MAK	Maximale Arbeitsplatzkonzentration
MCS	Moisture Control System
ODS	Octadecylsilane
PEG	Polyethylene Glycol
PHE	Phenylalanine
PIC	Paired Ion Chromatography
PTH	Phenylthiohydantoin
RI	Refractive Index
RPC	Reverse Phase Chromatography
SD	Standard Deviation
SEC	Size Exclusion Chromatography
THF	Tetrahydrofuran
TLC	Thin Layer Chromatography
TLV	Threshold Limit Value
TEA	Triethylamine
TMCS	Trimethylchlorosilane
VWD	Variable Wavelength Detector

1 Fundamental Chromatographic Relationships

by *Klaus-Peter Hupe*

1 Fundamental Chromatographic Relationships

1.1 Introduction

This chapter gives a brief introduction to the formal relationships of the liquid chromatographic process and explains the terms and definitions used in this book. It shows how the performance of a system can be evaluated and enables the reader to define and to describe the conditions so that an analysis can be reproduced by other laboratories. Additionally, it will provide a basis for understanding the thermodynamic and kinetic mechanisms of the various chromatographic modes and phase systems dealt with in Chapter 2.

For in-depth study of the theory of liquid chromatography, the reader is referred to text books on this subject [1, 2, 3].

Nomenclature and symbols used throughout this book are in accordance with the recommendations of the American Society for Testing and Materials (ASTM) [4] as commented on in detail by L. S. Ettre [5].

1.2 Retention

Chromatography is a separation process. The analysis is accomplished by first separating a mixture into its individual components and then monitoring these with a detector for quantitative determination and/or qualitative identification. Optimizing the chromatographic process implies generating sufficient resolution between adjacent components as quickly as possible. In practice, the technical limitations of the pump and equipment available add a third variable: the column back-pressure.

The individual constituents of a mixture are separated as a result of their different physical and chemical interactions with the mobile phase (the solvent) and with the stationary phase (the column packing).

Times and volumes are connected via the mobile phase volumetric flow-rate (F):

$$F = \frac{V_R}{t_R} = \frac{V_M}{t_M} \quad \text{(mL/min)} \tag{1}$$

The velocity at which the mobile phase moves through the column is called the linear flow velocity (u) and is interrelated with the flow-rate (F) via the free cross-sectional area (A_c) of the column:

$$u = \frac{F}{A_c} = \frac{l}{t_M} \tag{2}$$

where l is the column length.

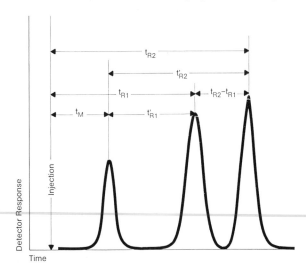

Figure 1-1. Definition of chromatographically relevant times.

According to Figure 1-1,

t_R the retention time (the time elapsed between injection and elution of a particular component);

V_R the retention volume (the volume of mobile phase passed through the column during t_R);

t_M the hold-up time (the time taken for the unretarded solvent front to elute from the column);

V_M the void volume of the column accessible to the solvent molecules.

On their way through the column, the solute molecules continually fluctuate between the mobile phase (solvent) and the stationary phase (column packing). While in the mobile phase they move at the linear velocity u in the stationary phase they do not move at all. Their apparent mean migration velocity is defined as:

$$u_x = \frac{l}{t_R} .$$

(3)

Consequently, the retention time (t_R) can be divided into the time that the molecules spend in the mobile phase (t_M) and in the stationary phase (t'_R):

$$t_R = t_M + t'_R .$$

(4)

The ratio between t'_R and t_M is an important characteristic describing the thermodynamic relationship between a solute and a given chromatographic system (where system is equal to mobile phase plus stationary phase). Under equilibrium conditions, this ratio also indicates the relative numbers of solute molecules to be found in the stationary and mobile phases. For this reason, it is called the mass distribution ratio; unfortunately, it is more commonly known as the capacity ratio or the capacity factor (k):

$$k = \frac{t'_R}{t_M} = \frac{t_R - t_M}{t_M} = \frac{V_R - V_M}{V_M} \ . \tag{5}$$

Rearranging equation (5) shows more clearly the relationship between retention time and capacity factor:

$$t_R = t_M(k + 1) \ . \tag{6}$$

t_R is a characteristic value for a given compound and can, for a given flow-rate, be used for its identification.

The capacity factor is interrelated with the distribution coefficient via the phase ratio. The distribution coefficient (K) is defined as the ratio of the concentration (c) of a solute in the stationary (S) and mobile (M) phases respectively:

$$K = \frac{c_S}{c_M} \ . \tag{7}$$

The phase ratio equals the interstitial volume of the mobile phase (V_M) divided by the stationary phase volume (V_S):

$$\beta = \frac{V_M}{V_S} \ . \tag{8}$$

For adsorption chromatography, V_S can be replaced by the surface area of the stationary phase.

It follows that:

$$K = k \cdot \beta \ . \tag{9}$$

The capacity factor also determines the ratio between the linear flow velocity (u) of the mobile phase and the mean migration velocity (u_x). Combination of equations (2), (3) and (6) gives:

$$\frac{u_x}{u} = \frac{1}{k + 1} \ . \tag{10}$$

k can vary between 0 and infinity. For $k = 0$ it follows that $u_x = u$, i. e. the solute passes the column unretained. For $k = \infty$, equation (10) gives $u_x = 0$, i. e. the solute is absorbed irreversibly and will not be eluted under the chosen conditions.

The ratio of the capacity factors of two solutes 1 and 2 is called the separation factor α, sometimes also referred to as selectivity:

$$\alpha = \frac{k_2}{k_1} \quad (k_2 > k_1) \ . \tag{11}$$

1.3 Separation

According to Figure 1-1, the separation of the maxima of two adjacent components increases with the time difference $(t_{R2} - t_{R1})$ between their maxima as they elute from the column. Applying equation (6) to two adjacent compounds, 1 and 2, and subtracting the first equation from the second gives:

$$t_{R2} - t_{R1} = t_M (k_2 - k_1) . \tag{12}$$

Substituting t_M from equation (2) leads to:

$$t_{R2} - t_{R1} = \frac{1}{u} (k_2 - k_1) \cdot l . \tag{13}$$

This relationship shows that the retention time difference necessary for separation increases with an increasing difference in the capacity factors of compounds 1 and 2; and, for a given velocity, with increasing column length (l).

1.4   Dispersion

1.4.1 The Characterization of Zone Spreading

The separation process described in the previous chapter has an antagonistic effect due to the dispersion of the individual solute zones during their migration through the column.
According to Figure 1-2, this effect is commonly characterized by the width (w_b) of a peak at its base (intersection of tangents through inflection points and base line) or at the height of the inflection points (w_i). For a Gaussian peak:

$$w_b = 2 \cdot w_i = 4\sigma \tag{14}$$

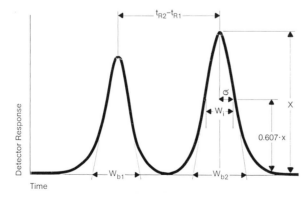

Figure 1-2. Terms describing separation and dispersion.

where σ is the standard deviation of the emerging peak measured in units of length, time or volume [6]. It should be noted that the graphical determination of the standard deviation for a peak in a given chromatographic trace gives accurate results only for truly Gaussian peaks. For the majority of peaks found in practice, which tend to be non-Gaussian, this value must be calculated via the second central moment.

Both theory and practice show that the peak width increases with the square root of the distance migrated within the column. For a completely eluted substance this distance is the column length (l), so that:

$$\sigma \approx \sqrt{l}\,; \quad \sigma^2 \approx l \tag{15}$$

where σ^2 is the peak variance.

In order to turn this relationship into an equation, a proportionality factor has to be introduced, leading to:

$$\sigma^2 = h \cdot l\,. \tag{16}$$

Equation (13) and (16), respectively, feature the two basic phenomena of the chromatographic process: separation and dispersion. Both effects increase with column length. The corresponding proportionality factors, $(k_2 - k_1)$ and h, are of paramount importance for the understanding, description and optimization of any chromatographic analysis.

Factor h in equation (16) comprises all those effects which cause the individual molecules of a uniform solute band to migrate through the column with differing velocities. As a consequence of this increasing dispersion and dilution, the solute will elute from the column in a volume of mobile phase larger than that in which it was initially dissolved and with a lower concentration.

It is unfortunate that, in the evolution of chromatographic nomenclature, this factor has been named "the height equivalent to a theoretical plate" (HETP). This has confused students and teachers of chromatography since its introduction, because it has only a little in common with the separation plates found in distillation columns. A more appropriate name would be "dispersion coefficient".

From a theoretical point of view, however, the plate concept is very useful. It assumes that a chromatographic column is mathematically equivalent to a plate column where an equilibrium is established for the solute between the stationary and the mobile phase on each plate. The column length (l) can then be thought of as being made up of a number of theoretical plates (n), the height of which is h.

It then follows that:

$$n = \frac{l}{h}\,. \tag{17}$$

This equation gives the standard measurement of column efficiency.

It is an important goal for any chromatographic analysis to operate columns under conditions such that they yield a high number of theoretical plates for a given length and, therefore, a small plate height. The progress HPLC has made over the last 15 years can be appreciated by the fact that in 1965 a good "HP"LC-column had a theoretical plate height not less than 1 mm. Today one expects a good column to have an h-value of 20 μm or less, which represents a 50-fold improvement.

Substituting equation (16) into equation (17) leads to:

$$n = \left(\frac{l}{\sigma_l}\right)^2 = \left(\frac{t_R}{\sigma_t}\right)^2 \tag{18}$$

σ_l and σ_t being the standard deviation of the peak in units of length and time respectively.

In the theory of the chromatographic process, the retention time is defined as the time the solute spends in the column. If the retention time is to be determined from a chromatogram, it must be taken into account that the time between injection of the sample and its appearance in the detector also includes the time that the solute has spent outside the column in the flow paths of the system. Consequently, the time determined from the chromatogram is longer than the retention time, as is the dispersion determined as the standard deviation of the peak. The plate number which is obtained when these values are substituted into equation (18) is called the "apparent plate number" and is usually lower than the theoretical plate number.

According to equation (18), and based on the formal definition of the retention time, an unretained peak ($t_R = t_M$) generates a certain number of theoretical plates (n). However, t_M has the same value for all peaks in the chromatogram and so does not contribute to differential retention and separation. Therefore a term equivalent to n, but based instead on the adjusted retention time (t_R'), has bee defined:

$$N = \left(\frac{t_R'}{\sigma_t}\right)^2 \tag{19}$$

N is called the number of effective plates and

$$H = \frac{l}{N} \tag{20}$$

is the height equivalent to one effective plate.

Combining equations (18) and (19), and substituting the capacity factor from equation (5), leads to the relation between the theoretical and the effective plate number:

$$N = n \cdot \left(\frac{k}{k + 1}\right)^2 \tag{21}$$

For $k = 0$ it follows that $N = 0$.

1.4.2 The van Deemter Equation

There are three essential phenomena causing the dispersion of a chromatographic peak on its way through the column:

a) The multipath effect. Due to the tortuous nature of the flow through the packed bed, solute molecules taking different routes will become increasingly far apart. The best means of keeping this effect small is to pack columns carefully, with small particles of narrow size distribution, resulting in a packed bed of high uniformity.

b) Random molecular diffusion in the axial direction of the column. This effect is relatively small in liquid chromatography because of the small diffusion coefficients of liquids. It only becomes important when the solute spends a long time in the column due to a very low solvent velocity.

c) Diffusion and mass transfer resistance of molecules moving from one phase to the other, and the deviation from equilibrium accompanied by this transfer. Because of the latter, this effect is highly dependent on flow velocity. It can be minimized by reducing the flow velocity and by using packing with small particle sizes and an open pore structure, thus keeping the length of diffusion paths small. Working at elevated column temperatures normally acts in the same direction since this increases the diffusion coefficient and decreases viscosity.

Considerable theoretical and experimental effort has gone into the elucidation and quantification of these effects. They are usually expressed as individual and independent variances which can therefore be summed up to give the total variance of the emerging peak:

$$\sigma^2 = \sigma_1^2 + \sigma_2^2 + \sigma_3^2 = h \cdot l \tag{22}$$

Expliciting the theoretical plate height it follows that:

$$h = \frac{\sigma_1^2}{l} + \frac{\sigma_2^2}{l} + \frac{\sigma_3^2}{l} . \tag{23}$$

This is the famous "van Deemter" equation (7) which, for HPLC, can be given in the following form:

$$h = A + \frac{B}{u} + C \cdot u . \tag{24}$$

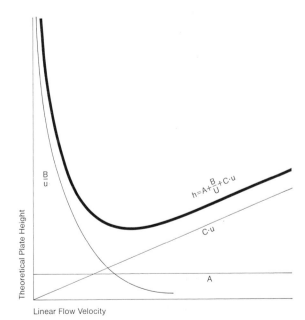

Figure 1-3. Plot of the van Deemter Equation and the component contributions to dispersion.

With some simplifying assumptions, the constants in equation (24) can be described by:

A $= 2 \lambda \, dp$

B $= 2 \gamma \, D_M$

C $= \omega \, dp^2 / D_M$

dp average particle diameter

D_M diffusion coefficient in the mobile phase

ω geometry factor

γ geometry factor

λ Eddy diffusion coefficient

In Figure 1-3, the individual dispersion contributions are plotted with their sum, the theoretical plate height, versus the flow velocity. This reveals the dependence of h on flow velocity and the fact that a minimum plate height can be achieved at a point where the contributions of the second and third terms of equation (24) are about equal. The dominant factors controlling plate height are: flow velocity; particle diameter (diffusion path length); packing structure; packing geometry and diffusion coefficient. These factors determine the position of the $h-u$-curve in the diagram, especially the steepness of the right hand part of that curve. They are commonly referred to as kinetic parameters and will be dealt with in detail in chapter 2.

1.5 Resolution

The optimization procedure for the chromatographic process as a whole has to take into account both the maximization of separation according to equation (13) and the minimization of dispersion according to equations (16) and (24) respectively. The ratio of these two effects leads to a term which serves as the ultimate criterion of optimization in chromatography. It is called resolution (R_S) and is defined as the ratio of the distance between the maxima of two adjacent peaks and the arithmetic mean of their base widths:

$$R_S = 2 \cdot \frac{t_{R2} - t_{R1}}{w_1 + w_2} \, . \tag{25}$$

A base line separation results in $R_S = 1$ (see also Figure 1-2). Assuming Gaussian peaks ($w = 4\sigma$) of equal size, with a negligible difference in their standard deviations ($\sigma_1 = \sigma_2$: $w_1 = w_2$), equation (25) takes the form:

$$R_S = \frac{t_{R2} - t_{R1}}{4 \cdot \sigma_t} \, . \tag{26}$$

Substituting equations (12) and (18) into equation (26) yields:

$$R_S = \frac{1}{4} \cdot \frac{k_2 - k_1}{k_2 + k_1} \cdot \sqrt{n} \tag{27}$$

(σ_t taken for peak 2 in time units).

Eliminating k_1 in this equation by substituting the separation factor (α) of equation (11), and deleting the subscript for k, results in the final expression for the resolution:

$$R = \frac{1}{4} \cdot \frac{\alpha - 1}{\alpha} \cdot \frac{k}{k + 1} \cdot \sqrt{n} \, . \tag{28}$$

This equation contains the three variables which ultimately control every chromatographic separation and which define the basic requirements for resolution:

- solutes must be retained, i.e. $k > 0$;
- solutes must be retained to different extents, i.e. $\alpha > 1$;
- the column must have a certain number of theoretical plates, n.

If the theoretical plate number (n) in equation (28) is substituted by the effective plate number (N) in equation (21) it follows that:

$$R = \frac{1}{4} \cdot \frac{\alpha - 1}{\alpha} \cdot \sqrt{N} \, . \tag{29}$$

When setting up the conditions for a chromatographic separation, the three variables of equation (28) are open for manipulation, within certain limits. Increasing resolution by an increase in the capacity factor has two limitations: Firstly, according to equation (6), an increase in k results in an increase in retention time, making the analysis slow. Secondly, as shown in Figure 1 – 4, the term $(k/k + 1)$ very quickly approaches its limiting value of unity. This means that k-values above 5 do not contribute very much to further increases in resolution. In practice,

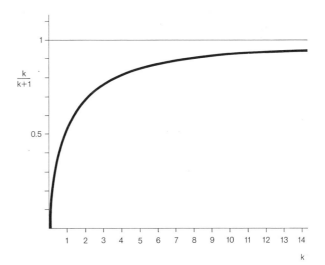

Figure 1-4. The term $\dfrac{k}{k + 1}$ of equation (28) as a function of k.

one tries to choose the conditions such that the capacity factors are between 1 and 5. The highest number of effective plates per unit of time is obtained if $k = 2$.

The real key to the optimization of resolution is the separation factor (α), which has to be made as large as possible by choosing the appropriate phase system and conditions. More than 50% of all research papers published on liquid chromatography over the last few years have been dedicated to this subject. It is the great strength of liquid chromatography (and its main advantage over gas chromatography) that the capacity factor and the separation factor can be changed and adjusted easily by changing the composition of the mobile phase. This, of course, is limited by the fact that certain substances show a high degree of chromatographic similarity, resulting in small α-values, and that one often has to deal with extremely complex mixtures of closely related compounds.

According to equation (28) the plate number must have a certain minimal value. For $R_s = 1$ and $k = 1$, figure 1-5 shows the dependence of the required plate number on the separation factor, revealing the fact that α-values below 1.1 necessitate the use of columns with very high plate numbers.

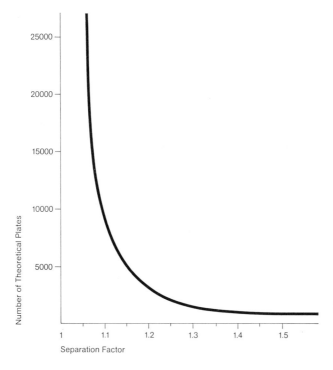

Figure 1-5. Dependence of the required plate number from the separation factor according to equation (28) $(R_s = 1; k = 1)$.

In the process of optimizing a chromatographic analysis, it must therefore be a prime goal to select conditions which give high separation factors, fully exploiting the different interactions between the different solutes and the phase system. The variables affecting capacity factor and separation factor are different for the different modes of liquid chromatography. They are commonly referred to as thermodynamic parameters and will be dealt with in detail in Chapter 2.

In order to keep the considerations carried out above simple, the chromatogram was reduced to only two peaks. In practice one usually has to deal with a larger number. The optimization then has to be based on the pair of compounds which is most difficult to separate.

It often happens that, for a given mobile phase, the components of a mixture to be separated exhibit an inconveniently large range of retention. In such a situation the first eluted peaks typically are poorly separated, while the last peaks take a very long time to elute from the column. It is then necessary to change the polarity of the mobile phase during the separation process so that the capacity factors of the first eluting peaks are increased, while those of compounds eluting towards the end of the chromatogram decrease. This is accomplished, either by using several eluents sequentially, or by changing the composition of the eluent (by mixing two or more solvents in a pre-programmed way). This technique is called gradient elution, the change of eluent being carried out stepwise or continuously. In contrast, the normal operation mode, with a uniform solvent, is called isocratic elution.

1.6 References

[1] J. C. Giddings: *Dynamics of Chromatography,* Part **1**. Dekker, New York 1965.
[2] L. R. Snyder, and J. J. Kirkland: *Introduction to Modern Liquid Chromatography*. Wiley, New York 1974.
[3] R. P. W. Scott: *Contemporary Liquid Chromatography*. Wiley, New York 1976.
[4] *Am. Soc. Test. Mater.* Publication **E 682** (1979).
[5] L. S. Ettre, *J. Chromatogr.* **220,** 29 (1981).
[6] A. S. Said: *Theory and Mathematics of Chromatography*. Huethig, Heidelberg 1981.
[7] J. J. van Deemter, F. J. Zuiderweg, and A. Klinkenberg, *Chem. Eng. Sci.* **5,** 271 (1956).
[8] S. Moore, D. H. Sparkman, and W. H. Stein, *Anal. Chem.* **30,** 1185 (1958).
[9] D. H. Sparkman, W. H. Stein, and S. Moore, *Anal. Chem.* **30,** 1190 (1958).
[10] C. Horvath, B. Preiss, and S. R. Lipsky, *Anal. Chem.* **39,** 1422 (1967).

2 The Column

by *Heinz Engelhardt, Hartmut Müller* and *Uwe Schön*

2 The Column

2.1 Dispersion Mechanism

2.1.1 Introduction

As already discussed in the previous Chapter, two processes in chromatography are counteracting: the separation of two solutes, due to differences in their thermodynamic interactions with the stationary phase; and the dispersion of the solute zones during their movement through the packed bed. The theory of chromatography mainly describes zone dispersion, also called peak broadening [1 to 6]. The theory of the thermodynamics of the separation process is not yet so advanced. Explanations of the separation process are therefore more or less pragmatic and descriptive. The two processes which finally result in the resolution of two peaks are discussed independently. A prerequisite of each separation is a good and efficient column, with minimal dispersion.

2.1.2 Optimization of Column Performance

For characterization of a column, the plate height h (or the number of plates n generated) is used as a measure of column performance. As already discussed in Chapter 1, Section 1.4, the h-values depend on the particle size, the flow-rate of the eluent, its viscosity, the diffusion coefficient of the solute and how well a column has been packed. The influence of these chromatographic parameters on the h-value can be described empirically by the van Deemter equation (see Chapter 1, Section 1.4.2). On the other hand, this equation can be used to test a given chromatographic column for its efficiency [7].

The van Deemter equation in its simplest form can be written as follows [for detailed discussion see 5, 8, 9]:

$$h = 2\lambda dp + \frac{2\gamma D_{M}}{u} + \omega \cdot \frac{dp^2}{D_{M}} u .$$

(1)

As can clearly be seen from the equation, and as also demonstrated in Figure 2-1, column efficiency and, consequently, peak resolution increase with decreasing particle diameter dp.

The principle dependence of h on particle size can be ascribed to two factors: the *Eddy diffusion* term [A-term, first term in eq. (1)] and the *mass transfer* term [C-term, third term in eq. (1)]. The Eddy diffusion term describes the peak broadening caused by the differences of the individual flow paths, inducing contrary currents and whirlpools around and between particles, and should be independent of flow-rate. The coefficient λ, which usually has a numerical value close to 1, is sometimes described as the "packing factor".

In the chromatographic model, transport of molecules through the column happens only in the moving part of the eluent between the particles. The pores of the particles are, of course, also filled with stagnant eluent, where no transport in the axial direction of the column occurs. All

This discussion becomes clearer if the efficiency and the speed of analysis of different columns packed with 10 μm, 5 μm and 3 μm particles are compared. Typical experimental values obtained with efficient columns are summarized in Table 2-1. In a 25 cm column packed with 10 μm particles, around 10000 plates can be generated. This plate number can also be achieved with 3 μm particles in a 10 cm column. However, the analysis time at $k = 3$ is reduced from 17 to 3.5 min. This demonstrates that the main advantage offered by very small particles is the high speed of analysis, measured as plates generated per unit of time. For 3 μm particles, 50 plates per second can easily be achieved. Table 2-1 also demonstrates for short columns packed with 3 μm particles that h-values decrease with increasing k-values due to instrumental variables (volumes of sampling valve, connecting tubes and detector cell, time constants of detector and recorder).

Table 2-1. Levels of Efficiency Available in HPLC with 10 μm, 5 μm and 3μm Particles. – Chromatographic Conditions: stationary phase: RP C_{18}; eluent: methanol.

dp	u	h $k = 0$	h $k = 3$	l	n $k = 0$	n $k = 3$	ΔP	n/t $k = 0$	n/t $k = 3$	t_{anal}
(μm)	(mm/s)	(μm)	(μm)	(cm)			(bar)	(s^{-1})	(s^{-1})	(min)
				25	12500	8330	8			17
10	1	20	30	10	5000	3330	3.2	12	8	7
				3	1500	1000	1			2
				25	16670	15625	32			17
5	1	15	16	10	6670	6250	12.8	16	15	7
				3	2000	1875	3.8			2
				25	22730	25000	180			8.5
3	2	11	10	10	9090	10000	71	45	50	3.5
				3	2730	3000	21			1

dp particle diameter; u linear velocity; h plate height; l column length; n plate number; ΔP pressure drop; n/t speed of analysis; t_{anal} analysis time

For many separations in HPLC, 3000 plates are sufficient with retarded peaks. They can be realized at $k = 3$ in a 10 cm column packed with 10 μm particles. The analysis time is then 7 min and the pressure drop required is 3.2 bar. The same separation can be achieved with 5 μm particles, in a 5 cm column with an analysis time of about 4 min. and a pressure drop of 7 bar. With 3 μm particles, a 3 cm column is sufficient. With a pressure drop of 21 bar the analysis is finished within 1 min. However, peak width at $k = 3$ is only 4.4 s. Therefore a very high-speed detector and recorder is required [17]. Since peak height increases with decreasing peak width, concentration sensitive detectors give the highest response using the smallest particles. Therefore, for trace analysis, the shortest possible column, packed with small particles and offering the necessary plates for separation, should be used to obtain the smallest possible peak volume. However, with small particles another problem may arise with longer columns: the heat of friction generated along the column causes unwanted temperature and viscosity gradients within the column, destroying peak shape and influencing solute retention [18].

Discussions on the advantages and disadvantages of spherical vs. irregular particles in literature [6, 19 to 21] have shown no significant differences in achievable efficiencies, but spherical particles have the disadvantage of higher price per gram of column packing [20, 21]. On the other hand, columns packed with spherical materials have slightly better permeability.

For theoretical reasons, reduced plate heights and reduced velocities [5] are used, because then a single curve and equation is sufficient to describe column behaviour in different eluents independent of particle diameter [22 to 24]. From this equation, similar statements can be deduced [6] as discussed above about optimum particle diameter, minimum flow velocity and column packing performance.

2.1.3 Efficiency Evaluation of Columns

From the discussion above it is evident that the preparation or the purchase of "good" columns is essential for optimal analysis. The efficiency of columns is a function of the particle diameter, as discussed, of the particle size distribution of the sieve fraction, and how homogenously the bed of particles is packed. For column preparation, slurry packing techniques are used exclusively. For the preparation of home made columns, equipment, experience and skill are required to prepare efficient columns in a reproducible way. Narrow sieve fractions of most packing materials are available. The different packing procedures have been reviewed [1, 2, 25].

The following procedure describes a simple method, using easily measurable quantities, to determine, with respect to efficiency and pressure drop, whether a column performs as it should, as deduced from the particle size within the column [2, 7]. Consequently, together with the column, the performance of the equipment is also checked. The test should preferably be performed with easily-available solutes and pure eluents. Methanol or dichloromethane are commonly used for reversed phase or silica systems, respectively. Solutes with k-values between 0 (inert solute) and 3 have to be selected. With reversed phase systems and methanol, polyaromatic hydrocarbons are suitable test solutes. With silica and dichloromethane, monosubstituted benzene derivatives can be used.

Asymmetric peaks, especially the unretained ones or those weakly retarded ($k < 2$) are typical for poorly packed columns, if effects of inadequate instrumentation can be excluded or ignored. It can happen that columns show double peaks from a single solute. Such columns often show a hole at the top of the packing. Sometimes these can be repaired by adding packing material to fill up the hole. Asymmetry of retarded peaks in a column with a symmetric inert peak is due to isotherm non-linearity and/or overloading effects. By reducing sample size symmetric peaks can be achieved often in these cases.

Peak asymmetry is determined by dropping a perpendicular from peak maximum to the baseline and calculating the ratio of the rear to the front baseline segment in 10% of peak height. If the asymmetry factor A_s thus calculated exceeds 1.5, the column should be discarded.

The effective *particle size* within the column does not necessarily correspond to that quoted by the supplier. On the other hand, column contamination can lead to a much higher pressure drop than expected for a given particle diameter. Particle size, column length, flow-rate and pressure drop are correlated via column permeability as described above. For convenience, the following equation allows the calculation using the standard dimensions in chromatography:

$$dp = 23 \sqrt{\frac{F \cdot \eta \cdot l}{r^2 \cdot \Delta P}} \qquad (4)$$

Here dp is obtained in µm, F is expressed in mL/min, l in cm, η in cP, r in mm and ΔP in bar. The conversion factors for the SI units are contained in the constant.

The *linear velocity* has to be determined by injecting an inert solute. In Table 2-2 some references to suitable inert solutes are given. The problems involved in dead time determination in RPC are discussed in detail in Section 2.2.4.2. From t_M and the column length, the average linear velocity u of the eluent can be calculated.

Table 2-2. Inert Solutes for Silica and Reversed Phase Systems.

Stationary Phase	Silica		Reversed Phase			
			Eluent			
	n-C$_7$H$_{16}$	CH$_2$Cl$_2$	H$_2$O	CH$_3$OH	CH$_3$CN	CH$_2$CL$_2$
	n-C$_6$H$_{14}$ (RI)	CD$_2$Cl$_2$ (RI)	D$_2$O (RI)	CD$_3$OH (RI)	CD$_3$CN (RI)	CD$_2$Cl$_2$ (RI)
		CHCl$_3$ (RI)				CHCl$_3$ ((RI))
Inert Solutes (Detection)	C$_2$Cl$_4$ (UV, RI)	C$_2$Cl$_4$ (UV, RI)		CH$_3$NO$_2$ (UV, RI)	CH$_3$NO$_2$ (UV, RI)	C$_2$Cl$_4$ (UV, RI)
		CCl$_4$ (UV, RI)				CCl$_4$ (UV, RI)
		C$_6$H$_6$ (UV, RI)				C$_6$H$_6$ (UV, RI)
				D$_2$O/CH$_3$OH (RI)	D$_2$O/CH$_3$CN (RI)	
				Mixtures with eluent composition		

The theoretically achievable *plate height* as a measure of column performance can be determined from the effective particle diameter, calculated with equation (4), and the linear velocity by the following approximation [7, 13]:

$$h = 2\,dp + \frac{6}{u} + \frac{dp^2}{20}\,u\ .\qquad(5)$$

This equation, which is a simplified form of equation (1), gives h in µm when dp and u are substituted in µm and mm/s, respectively. It permits h to be calculated, but does not allow us to differentiate between the individual terms of the van Deemter equation. At linear velocities around 1 mm/s (u_{min} for 5 to 10 µm particles), the optimal h-value corresponds approximately to $3\,dp$. If the h-values are up to two times the values calculated in this way, packed columns yielding symmetrical peaks can be considered to be still working satisfactorily. This concept is only valid if low molecular weight solutes in low viscosity eluents are used (a diffusion coefficient of $3.5 \cdot 10^{-5}$ cm^2/s was assumed for the derivation of the above equation). In eluents of higher viscosity, or for high molecular weight solutes, higher h-values are observed. Also, secondary retention mechanisms like ligand exchange can cause additional band-broadening.

2.2 Retention Mechanism

2.2.1 Introduction

A prerequisite for a separation of two solutes is a difference in their free energy of sorption in the chromatographic system (stationary phase and eluent). The higher these differences are (the larger the relative retentions) the easier the resolution of the two peaks is to achieve and the fewer plates are necessary. Efficiency of columns stated by column manufacturers is usually determined with low viscous eluents and low molecular weight solutes and cannot be translated to biochemical applications.

In principle, it is possible to transfer the separation methods of classical – low pressure – column liquid chromatography to HPLC technology, if the stationary phases are identical, and stable against pressure, and if the eluent is compatible with HPLC detector requirements. The introduction of chemically-bonded phases extended the applicability of HPLC to the separation of water soluble substances. Nowadays about 90% of all separations in HPLC are performed with these chemically-bonded phases, mainly applying phases with bonded alkyl groups, called reversed phases (RPs). Gel filtration with soft gels like Sephadex etc. could not be transferred to HPLC. Silica can be prepared, however, with different pore size distributions, and its chemical modification allows high speed and high resolution size-exclusion chromatography (SEC). For ion-exchange chromatography, pressure stable resins as well as silica based ion-exchangers are available.

This schematic differentiation between sorption mechanisms can only describe the main processes involved. With biological samples, especially, several mechanisms may contribute to solute retention. On the other hand, interaction with the surface of a stationary phase is only possible when the sample is able to penetrate into the pores and has access to the surface area. With spherical particles (10 μm) less than 1% of the total surface area is the outer, geometrical surface. Surface inhomogeneity even with chemically-bonded phases may have a decisive contribution to solute retention, e. g. in Reversed Phase Chromatography (RPC), still-present silanol groups may cause ion-exchange or ion-exclusion in aqueous eluents. These contributions to solute retention are influenced differently by altering eluent composition. The exact knowledge of these different processes, their variation with eluent composition, and the impact of their contribution to total solute retention is essential for reproducible separations.

In developing a separation, two different aims may be pursued. One is the analytical approach, where separation, identification and quantitation is wanted. In this case, a separation system with sufficient resolving power, good reproducibility and precision may be used. If standards are available system optimization is easy. In this case conditions may even be applied which are destructrive to biological activity. More complicated system selection becomes necessary for preparative separations, especially if biological activity must be preserved during separation. Interaction with superimposed retention mechanisms may be the reason for bad solute recovery. Sorptive processes can sometimes lead to structure alterations, and therefore SEC seems to be the first choice. However, secondary interactions have also to be minimized, to assure high solute recovery.

2.2.2 Characteristics of Silica

In classical column liquid chromatography, alumina and silica had been used as stationary phases. With the advent of HPLC silica became the main stationary phase, used as such or as a carrier for chemically-bonded phases. In Figure 2-3 a schematic presentation of the application of silica as stationary phase and as carrier for bonded groups is given. In the discussion of retention mechanisms of chemically-bonded phases, one considers mainly the bonded groups, but the influence of the silica carrier can never be omitted. Therefore, a chapter describing general properties of silica must precede the discussion of the individual separation techniques.

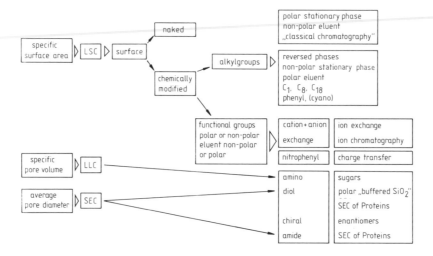

Figure 2-3. Porous silica based stationary phases.

Commercially available silicas differ in physical properties, such as specific surface area, average pore diameter and specific pore volume. Assuming open cylindrical pores these three variables are connected by

$$\phi = \frac{4 \cdot Vp}{Osp} \cdot 10^3 \tag{6}$$

where ϕ is the average pore diameter (nm), Vp the specific pore volume (mL/g) and Osp the specific surface area (m^2/g) [26]. The increase of the specific surface area consequently leads to narrower pore diameter, provided the pore volume is kept constant.

Silica commonly used in HPLC has a specific surface area around 300 m^2/g, an average pore diameter of 10 nm, resulting in a specific pore volume of 1 mL/g. Silicas with average pore diameters down to 5 nm are also available as packings for HPLC. These properties are normally sufficient for HPLC separating solutes with molecular weights below 5000. In this case, the solutes have access to more than 80% of the pore volume. If such a material is used for SEC molecules with molecular weights over 200000 (random coil) are totally excluded [27].

In chromatography, these specific values can only be compared with silicas prepared by identical methods. For the separation the surface area or the pore volume per unit column volume is more important. Silicas prepared especially for HPLC (e. g. spherical silicas) are more dense than silicas prepared by polymerization of silicic acid [28, 29]. The latter materials have packing densities around 0.35 g/mL, whereas spherical materials can have packing densities up to 0.6 g/mL. The properties of some commercially available silica gels used in HPLC as such or as carrier for bonded phases are summarized in Table 2-3.

Table 2-3. Properties of Some Commercial Silicas.

	Surface Area (m^2/g)	Pore Diameter (nm)	Pore Volume (mL/g)	Total Porosity	Packing Density (g/mL)	pH[a]	Particle Shape[b]
Eurosorb	400	9	1.0	0.84	0.35	6.7	I
Hypersil	180	11	1.1	0.78	0.53	9.0	S
LiChrosorb Si 100	320	10	1.0	0.83	0.34	7.0	I
LiChrospher Si 100	250	10	1.2	0.84	0.35	5.5	S
LiChrospher Si 500	60	27	0.8	0.85	0.38	9.9	S
Nucleosil 100	300	10	1.0	0.82	0.34	5.7	S
Partisil	400	9	0.9	0.84	0.35	7.5	I
Polygosil 60	500	6	0.8	0.83	0.37	8.0	I
Porasil	350	10	1.1	0.86	0.37	7.2	I
Servachrom Si 100	300	10	1.2	0.84	0.34	6.7	I
Spherisorb SW	220	8	0.6	0.77	0.61	9.5	S
Zorbax BP-Sil	300	6	0.5	0.71	0.60	3.9	S

[a] in 5% aqueous suspension   [b] I irregular, S spherical

The retention of small molecules on two materials with identical specific surface area $(300\ m^2/g)$, e. g. LiChrosorb Si 100 and Zorbax Sil, with identical eluent composition, can be quite different. If the columns were packed under identical conditions, higher k-values will be obtained with Zorbax than with LiChrosorb, because of the larger packing density of the former.

An increase of packing density from 0.34 to 0.60 g/mL is correlated with a decrease of the volume fraction of the eluent in the column. Its total porosity ε_T drops from 0.83 to 0.71. In standardizing sorption parameters, this decrease of eluent volume within the column cannot be neglected [30].

Generally it is assumed that silicas exhibit acidic surface properties [28, 29]. The pH of "pure" silica in aqueous suspension (5% w/w) should be between 4 and 5. Irregular silicas show values around neutral pH, whereas some spherical silicas have pH-values above 8 due to impurities from their preparation [30]. It is to be expected that these differences in surface pH may influence selectivity of bonded phases in polar aqueous eluents. However, it is surprising that even with nonpolar eluents, slight changes in surface pH can have a tremendous influence on solute retention and column efficiency, as demonstrated in Figure 2-4 for the separation of aromatic amines with dichloromethane as eluent. This behaviour may open another aspect for optimization of stationary phases for the separation of basic or acidic solutes in adsorption chromatography [31] as well as in separations with chemically-bonded phases [17, 32].

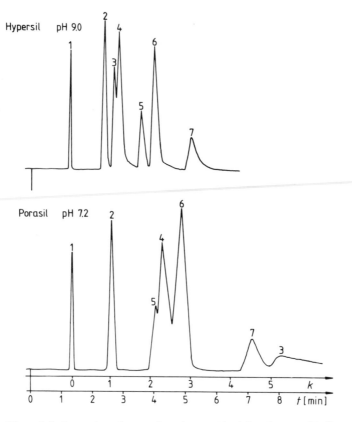

Figure 2-4. Separation of aromatic amines on "basic" and "neutral" silica with non-polar eluent [30]. Eluent: Dichloromethane. Solutes: 1 benzene; 2 o-nitroaniline; 3 N, N-dimethylaniline; 4 N-methylaniline; 5 p-nitroaniline; 6 m-nitroanilin; 7 aniline.

Silica or bonded phases based on silica are stable in aqueous solutions between pH 2 and 8 [28, 29]. Outside this range silica dissolves, or bonded groups are hydrolyzed. At room temperature, and with aqueous eluents at neutral pH, some long-term changes in k-values have been observed and ascribed to hydrolization. The solubility of silica in water is small and is around 100 ppm at room temperature [28]. It is proposed to install presaturation columns before the sample injector. For biochemical analysis it is generally recommended to install a guard column before the analytical column to remove polymeric, insoluble or colloidal materials from the sample and eluent. Thus the separation column is protected and its lifetime prolonged.

The pore diameter of standard silica can be widened by a hydrothermal treatment at elevated temperatures [28, 29]. By this wide pore diameter silica gels are prepared commercially, e. g. for polymer separation by sorption or exclusion chromatography. The properties of one of these wide pore silicas (LiChrospher Si 500) are included in Table 2-3. Their exclusion chromatographic properties will be discussed in Section 2.2.8. It should be mentioned that each heat treatment of silica in the presence of water or alcohols, e. g. drying of water wet silica at elevated temperatures, can lead to a change in silica pore structure, and generally results in a decrease of surface area [29].

The chemical nature of silica surface can be traced to the presence of silanol ($\equiv$ Si – OH) and siloxane ($\equiv$ Si – O – Si $\equiv$) groups. The silanol groups are mainly responsible for sorption or for reaction with silanes. It has been measured experimentally, and calculated from cuts through crystalline silicon dioxide modifications, that the surface concentration of silanols is between 7 and 8 μmol/m^2 [28]. From this it can be deduced that the average distance of silanol groups is between 0.4 and 0.5 nm. Drying silica at temperatures below 150 °C removes only physically adsorbed water, whereas at temperatures above 200 °C the concentration of silanol groups decreases due to loss of structural water. Of course, such silicas show different chromatographic properties.

2.2.3 Separation with Silica

In adsorption chromatography, a polar stationary phase, e. g. silica, and non-polar UV-transparent eluents, e. g. aliphatic hydrocarbons and dichloromethane, are used, eventually with additives such as alcohols, dioxane and tetrahydrofuran. Solutes not eluted with such eluent combinations are preferentially separated by RPC, where the stationary phases are non-polar and the eluent very polar, i. e. aqueous mixtures of acetonitrile or methanol. Because classical adsorption chromatography is of minor importance in biochemical analysis, only a short review of "silica chromatography" is given. As with every chromatographic system, it is difficult to determine the influence of a single parameter on separation for itself alone. The chromatographic milieu, the interactions of solutes, solvent and stationary phase has to be considered always as a whole. Nevertheless, to ease the description of the separation system each parameter, i. e. stationary phase, solvent polarity and solute structure and its influence on separation is considered independently.

2.2.3.1 Influence of Silica Properties

As stated above, surface silanol groups are considered to be mainly responsible for solute retention. Because of these acidic properties, basic solutes are more strongly retained than neutral or acidic ones. Retention increases with increasing surface area per unit column volume. In Figure 2-5 the separation of aromatic hydrocarbons is demonstrated on silicas with different specific surface areas.

Identical resolution is achieved with LiChrospher Si 100 and Hypersil despite their different surface areas. The higher packing density of Hypersil compensates for its smaller specific surface area. The fastest analysis with in this case still sufficient resolution is achieved with the silica having the smallest surface area (LiChrospher Si 500). Because of the different silica properties, shown in Table 2-3, a comparision of retention power is only possible if k-values are standardizied for differences in specific surface area (Osp), packing density (ρ) and volume fraction (ε_T) of the eluent in the column [31]:

$$K^* = k \cdot \frac{\varepsilon_\mathrm{T}}{O\mathrm{sp} \cdot \rho} \tag{7}$$

If the chemical surface properties of the silicas are identical the thus calculated "adsorption coefficient" (K^*) should be the same. Differences in K^* are caused by differences in the chemical nature of silica surface, especially the surface pH (compare Figure 2-4, Section 2.2.2).

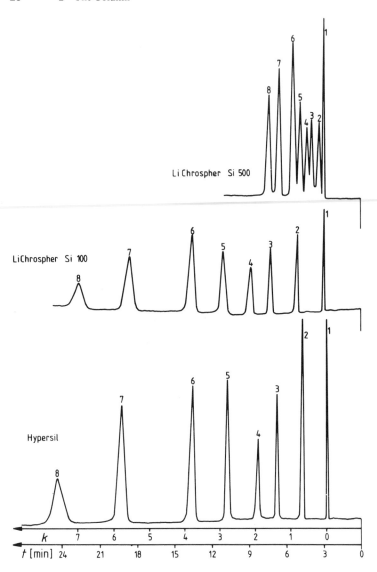

Figure 2-5. Influence of specific surface area and packing density on solute retention [31]. Eluent: n-heptane. Solutes: 1 C_2Cl_4; 2 benzene; 3 naphthalene; 4 acenaphthene; 5 anthracene; 6 fluoranthene; 7 chrysene; 8 3,4-benzfluoranthene.

2.2.3.2 Influence of Eluent. Eluotropic Series

The appropriate selection of the eluent usually affects a separation more than a change of stationary phase. Generally speaking, the more strongly the eluent is adsorbed on the stationary phase the higher is its elution power. There is always a competition between solute and eluent molecules for the adsorptive sites on the silica surface [33]. Because of the great excess of eluent molecules competing for the active sites, even relatively non-polar eluents can be used to elute polar substances. In classical adsorption chromatography, the organic solvents were ordered according to their eluting strength ε_0, in so-called eluotropic series [33]. Most of the solvents of these series are not compatible with HPLC photometric detectors. n-Alkanes with only slightly different elution strength than isoalkanes are to be preferred because of their lower viscosity. Dichloromethane and, to a lesser extent, chloroform can be used as a polar eluent component. Higher elution power can be generated by the addition of alcohols, ethers or acetonitrile. Because these eluents differ widely from alkanes and dichloromethane in their elution strength small amounts of them change elution power markedly. Even fractions of a percent can increase elution strength drastically. Since such eluent mixtures are difficult to prepare in a reproducible way, and also may change their composition during storage (selective evaporation), adsorption chromatography has acquired the reputation of having poor reproducibility.

It is possible to prepare solvent mixtures of identical elution strength by mixing either large quantities of solvents similar in elution power, or by adding a very small quantity of a strongly eluting solvent to the non-polar main eluent component. In Figure 2-6 a graphical scheme, where the elution strength of solvent mixtures can be compared, is given. As can be seen, the elution strength of a pentane-dichloromethane mixture 1:1 can also be achieved by adding 1% acetonitrile or approximately 0.3% methanol to pentane. This solvent strength scale gives only an approximation of the change of elution power with eluent composition. A final adjustment of eluent composition is often required to achieve the proper k-value. Changes of 0.05 in the elution strength scale result in a 3 to 4 fold change in k-values because of the logarithmic relationship of k on eluent composition. One should, however, not be surprised if the chromatographic selectivity is different according to whether an equal volume pentane-dichlo-

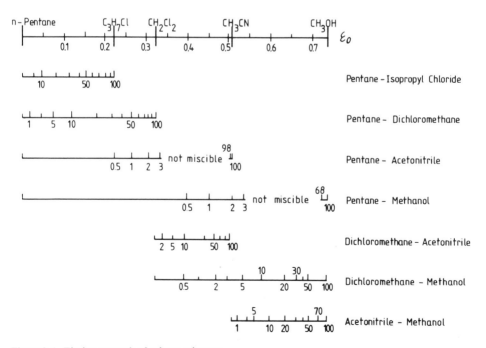

Figure 2-6. Elution strength of solvent mixtures.

romethane mixture or pentane with 1% acetonitrile is used. Selectivity for the separation of solutes with large polarity differences is usually better with the latter eluent mixture. Reproducibility, on the other hand, is generally better with 1:1 mixtures.

2.2.3.3 Influence of Water

Polar additives to the eluent strikingly influence retention and selectivity even in the very low concentration range where water is soluble in n-heptane (less than 100 ppm) and dichloromethane (less than 0.2%). Small changes, difficult to determine and control, effect retention and selectivity. An on-line moisture control system (MCS) has been described to adjust, control and maintain eluent and column moisture content [34]. The influence of moisture content is more pronounced in the non-polar eluents, becoming weaker with increasing polarity

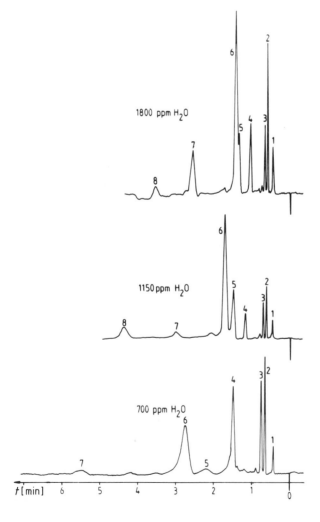

Figure 2-7. Influence of water concentration of the eluent on the separation of steroids [34]. Stationary phase: Spherisorb alumina; eluent: dichloromethane with MCS controlled moisture content; solutes: 1 Inert; 2 cholestenone; 3 progesterone; 4 17-methyl-testosterone; 5 estrone; 6 17-hydroxyprogesterone, 7 estradiol; 8 prednisolone.

Polarity

(increasing solubil͟   ͟romethane, the water content can be determined by Karl-Fischer titration and may vary for several ppm without significantly effecting absolute and relative retentions. In Figure 2-7, the influence of the water concentration in dichloromethane on the separation of steroids is demonstrated. Depending on the analytical problem, a high or a low water concentration gives optimum separation. It has been recommended that methanol or other alcohols should be used to overcome the problems with water content. However, the preparation and preservation of these alcohol-eluent mixtures is problematic, as already discussed. Additionally, the influence of the ever-present water cannot be neglected [35]. Even if the k-values of alcohol moderated systems are in the same region as those moderated with water, the selectivity of the system can be significantly different.

2.2.3.4 Partitioning

The attainment of equilibrium between the concentration of a polar compound such as water or alcohol dissolved in the eluent and adsorbed on the polar stationary phase can be used to load an active support with variable amounts of liquid stationary phase. Thus a column packed with an active support can be transformed into a "partition"column. Higher concentrations of the polar additives have to be used to go from "moderated" solvent systems to partition chromatography. With prepacked columns, this is the only way to coat a polar solid *in situ* with any desired liquid stationary phase [36, 37].

For partitions systems with polar solid phases, the use of ternary mixtures is recommended [38]. They consist of a non-polar eluent (e. g. heptane or dichloromethane) and a very polar one (usually water) to which a third component (e. g. a lower alcohol or another solvent miscible with both water and the non-polar component) is added. Since one works with a dynamic sorption equilibrium, and very often close to the limits of miscibility, exact temperature control is essential. Relatively high liquid loadings up to 0.5 gram liquid stationary phase per gram polar solid can be achieved dynamically [37]. It is difficult to predict the exact composition of the liquid stationary phase and of the mobile phase in equilibrium with it. Therefore, a renewal of the eluent can cause changes in solute retention, because the equilibrium concentration of the polar components changes.

One advantage of partition systems is that the same column can successively be coated by different liquid stationary phases. The previous coating can easily be removed by applying a pure eluent to flush out the polar components: Reestablishing the properties of the polar solid (e. g. drying the column with dry dichloromethane) and then recoating the system with a new ternary mixture.

The liquid-liquid systems have been used for the separation of steroids [38, 39], acids and their derivatives [40], phospholipids [41], nucleobases and nucleosides[42], etc.

The partition systems generated *in situ* are not restricted to polar solid phases. The same separation of eluent components into two different phases occurs with reversed phases, when e. g. aqueous methanolic solvents containing non-polar additives like tetrahydrofuran, dichloromethane, etc. are used as eluents (see Section 2.2.4.2). In Section 2.2.5.1 on ion-pair-chromatography partition systems are discussed as well. The separation of sugars on an amino-bonded phase with water-acetonitrile as eluent can also be achieved by a partition system generated *in situ* (see Section 2.2.9.2).

2.2.3.5 Influence of Sample Structure

Chromatography with silica as stationary phase should nowadays be restricted to the separation of solutes soluble in organic eluents. Of course, other more polar solutes have been and will be separated with such systems, but more efficient separations can, in many cases, be achieved more conveniently by using chemically bondes phases. Silica exhibits optimum selectivity for the separation of solutes different in kind and number of functional groups. In a first approximation, each functional group contributes to the strength of retention: the more polar a functional group, the higher its contribution ($-H < -NO_2 < COOR < =CO < -OH < -NH_2 < -COOH$) [33]. The separation of the different polyfunctional substituted benzene isomers, e. g. the different nitrophenols, is a good example of the capabilities of silica chromatography. Steric and resonance effects may strengthen or weaken the interaction of solutes with the "acidic" silica surface. Steroids with substituents in equatorial position are stronger adsorbed than those with the same functional groups in axial position.

2.2.3.6 Separation of Complex Mixtures. Gradient Elution

Complex mixtures containing components whose k-values differ considerably cannot be separated and eluted within a reasonable time by using a single eluent mixture under constant, isocratic conditions. To resolve both early eluting solutes and strongly retained ones equally well, and to elute them as easily recognizable peaks, the eluent composition has to be changed continuously. This programmed increase of solvent strength, known as gradient elution, increases speed of analysis but destroys resolution, which, however is usually higher than wanted in these cases. In gradient elution, each sample component is eluted under optimal conditions. Because of principal problems (slow achievement of equilibrium) gradient elution with silica as stationary phase is more difficult and problematic than with chemically-bonded phases. Because of its importance and complexity gradient elution will be discussed separately in Section 2.2.7.

2.2.4 Reversed-Phase Chromatography (RPC)

By chemical reaction of the surface hydroxyl groups on silica (silanols) with suitable reagents the chromatographic properties of silica can be altered. If the organic residue exerts no specific or selective effect, the k-values of such a support are always lower than on the bare silica. This statement, however, is valid only if the same non-polar eluent is used. The most important applications of chemically-bonded phases are, however, not in this region but in the area of polar eluents, where these stationary phases have a different non-polar, hydrophobic selectivity. Because of the reversal of the phase systems, where now the stationary phase is non-polar and the mobile phase is polar, they are called reversed systems (RP). (It would be more appropriate to speak about non-polar stationary phases). It is possible to introduce functional groups into the bonded organic residue. The selectivity of such stationary phases is different from those where only alkyl groups have been bonded to the surface. Therefore, they will be discussed in other sections, according to their selectivity or application (e. g. ion-exchange, size-exclusion, etc.). The chemically-bonded phases have certain advantages over silica and partition separation systems: equilibration time of column and eluent is short, eluent programming (gradient elution) causes less problems, and column lifetime is usually long.

Chemically-bonded phases were introduced by A. J. P. Martin into column liquid chromato-graphy for the preparation of hydrophobic partition systems [43]. Later, they were used in GC [44, 45] and in HPLC [46]. The advent of these chemically-bonded phases was responsible for the boom of liquid chromatography and especially for its application to biochemical problems.

2.2.4.1 Preparation and Properties of Reversed Phases

On the surface of silica gel the concentration of silanol groups is about 7 to 8 $\mu mol/m^2$ [28, 29]. By a chemical reaction of alkylsilanes containing reactive chloro or alkoxy groups, a new siloxane bond is formed on the surface, and the alkyl groups of the silanes are thus bonded. It is impossible to react all the silanol groups initially present. An optimal 50% can be reacted. Because alkylsilanes can have one, two or three functions to react with the acidic silanol group, discussions arose about the advantages and disadvantages of "monomeric" and "polymeric" surface coverages. If silica is treated with monochloro — or monoalkoxysilanes and three alkyl groups (mostly two methyl groups and a longer alkyl chain), the reaction between the silanes and the silanols is unequivocal. No polymerization can occur, a monomeric coverage is achieved. If di—or trifunctional alkylsilanes are used, it is impossible for these groups to react simultaneously with the surface. On an average, about 1.5 of the two or three chlorides (or alkoxy groups) are able to react [47]. Besides bonding to the surface, the silanes can polymerize

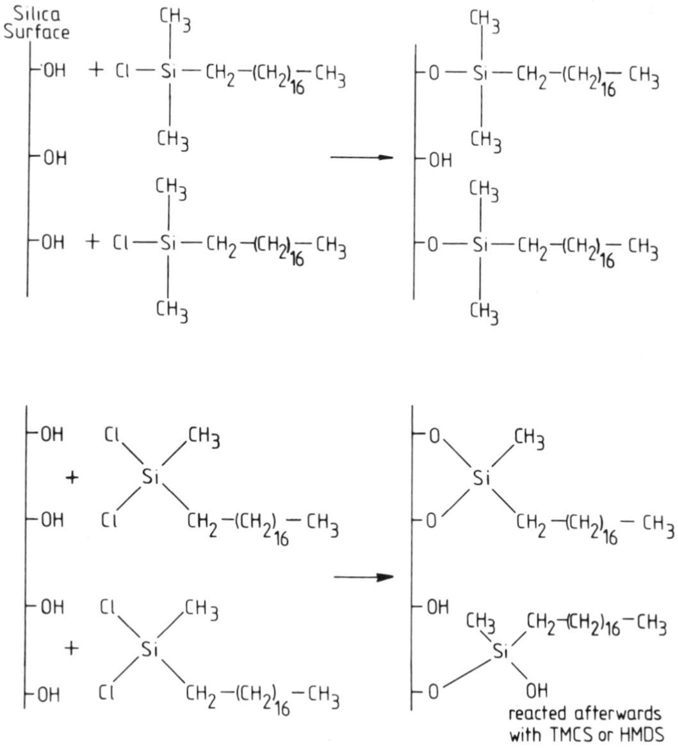

Figure 2-8. Reaction scheme for the preparation of reversed phases.

to polysiloxanes, both on the surface and (if water has not been strictly excluded) in solution. The polymers can also be bonded to the surface. On the other hand, bonded polymeric siloxanes reduce column efficiency substantially [48].

The achievable column efficiency with bonded phases compared to silica of identical particle size can be used to differentiate between "monomeric" and "polymeric" bonded phases. If efficiency similar to silica is achieved the bonded phase can be regarded to be "monomeric". If polysiloxanes are bonded onto silica, column efficiency becomes worse by a factor of 3 to 4 [49].

In Figure 2-8 the reaction scheme of silanes with silica is shown. The unreacted chlorides of the silanes have to be removed in a second reaction after hydrolysis by a treatment with an effective silanizing reagent like trimethylchlorosilane (TMCS) or hexamethyldisilazane (HMDS). This secondary silanization, sometimes called end-capping, is indispensable if good and reproducible reversed phase separations are wanted. It is recommended that this secondary silanization should also be used for reversed phases prepared with monofunctional silanes. This procedure can be done in a packed column by flushing it with a solution of HMDS or another active silanizing reagent in toluene at room temperature. In Figure 2-9 the influence of this resilanization is demonstrated. It should be noted that the total carbon content and the relative reten-

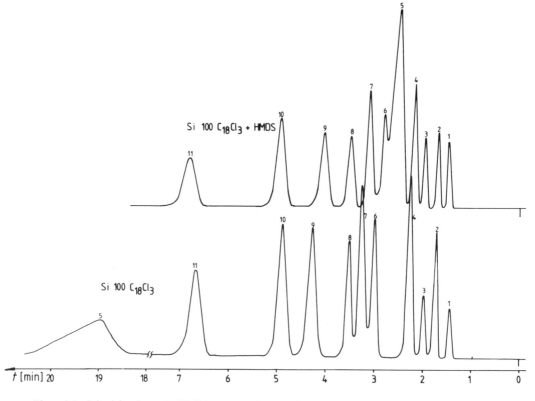

Figure 2-9. Selectivity change by HMDS treatment [32]. Stationary phase: RPC$_{18}$ before and after HMDS treatment; eluent: methanol/water (65.4/35.6, w/w); flow: 1 mL/min; solutes:1 D$_2$0; 2 benzamide; 3 phenol; 4 2-phenylethanol; 5 aniline; 6 nitrobenzene; 7 benzoic acid methylester; 8 benzene; 9 benzoic acid ethylester; 10 toluene; 11 ethylbenzene.

tions of the hydrocarbons are not affected by this treatment, whereas the relative retention of all other medium-polar solutes are changed. The most striking change is observed for the basic solute aniline, whose retention and peak shape is effected markedly.

The coverage of silica with alkylgroups is calculated from the carbon content of the bonded phase determined by organic analysis [47, 50] Under optimum conditions, the amount of bonded silane can approach a surface concentration around 4 μmol/m^2. This value decreases if bulkier silanes or those with longer alkyl groups are reacted with the surface. With the most commonly used reversed phase, reacted with octadecylsilane (RP C$_{18}$), surface coverages between 3.0 and 3.5 μmol/m^2 can be achieved. Each C$_{18}$ group covers in average 0.5 nm^2 on the surface; this means that the distance of two adjacent C$_{18}$ groups is around 0.7 nm. It should be remembered that the place requirement of a silanol group is around 0.2 nm^2 resulting in a distance of 0.4 nm between neighbouring silanol groups. From this comparision, it is clear that silanol groups which cannot be reacted may still be accessible to sample molecules, and participate in solute retention.

The reproducibility of surface coverage is good as long as the same batch of silica is used [51]. Because of the colloidal properties of the silica, and because of processes involved in its production and storage, reproducible preparation of bonded phases is sometimes difficult. Blending of different batches may help to overcome these problems with respect to reproducible carbon content. But differences in silica properties and silanol concentration may cause unwanted irreproducibilities. Therefore, some manufacturers do not aim for maximum coverage, but prepare reversed phases with a defined amount of bonded carbon. However, with such reversed phases the amount of silanol groups may vary. On the other hand, it is not surprising that separations developed with stationary phases with maximum coverage cannot be transferred to a reversed phase with a lower but well defined coverage. These problems are familiar to everyone who has tried to compare a separation carried out on identically labeled phase materials from different manufacturers. Figure 2-10 may be a warning to those who start to work in RPC of the problems which may arise.

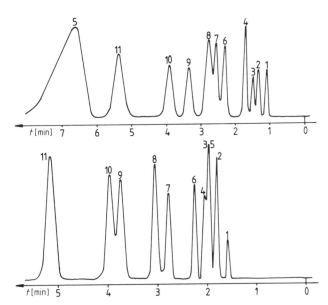

Figure 2-10. Comparision of commercial RP C$_{18}$ phases [32]. Conditions and Solutes as in Figure 2-9.

The properties of reversed phases discussed so far are the result of their preparation from silica and alkylsilanes. The influence of the bonded alkyl group is summarized in the term hydrophobic selectivity.

In a first approach, the k-values of solutes increase with increasing bonded carbon per unit column volume. If the surface coverage is identical, absolute retention increases with increasing chain length of the bonded alkyl group. High absolute and relative retentions can be achieved with bonded octadecyl groups. These phases are preferable when solubility of solutes in the aqueous eluent is limited. With RP C_{18} about 10% more of an organic component can be added to the eluent than with a RP C_8 in order to achieve approximately the same k-values. If the separation of the members of a homologous series is the problem, it is always better to use RP C_{18}, because the selectivity for the separation of neighbouring members is highest. On the other hand, if large molecules with hydrophobic properties and limited solubility in organic rich eluents have to be separated the use of short chain reversed phases is recommended.

The observed high selectivity is also a function of eluent composition. In organic rich eluents (more than 50% methanol or acetonitrile) the stationary phase is completely wetted and the relative retention in a homologous series increases with the chain length of the bonded alkyl groups. In pure water these differences are no longer noticeable. The relative retentions are identical but the absolute retentions increase with increasing chain length due to the higher carbon content [50]. In Figure 2-11 the separations of some coffee acids on a RP C_4 and a RP C_{18} in water rich eluents are compared. The relative retentions are identical in both systems. To compensate for the higher carbon content of RP C_{18} about 10% more organic solvent, in this case acetic acid, had to be added to get similar k-values.

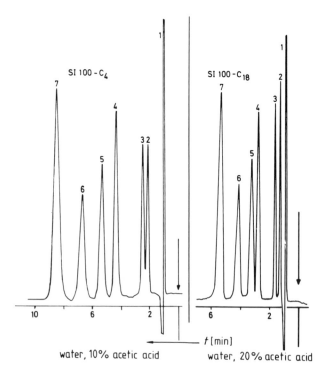

Figure 2-11. Comparision of RP C_4 and RP C_{18}. Separation of Caffeic acids [52]. Stationary phase: LiChrosorb Si 100, RP C_4 and RP C_{18}; eluent: water/acetic acid (10 or 20 Vol%); solutes: 1 china acid; 2 chlorogenic acid; 3 caffeic acid; 4 p-coumaric acid; 5 m-coumaric acid; 6 o-coumaric acid; 7 coumarin.

It has already been discussed for silica gel columns (Section 2.2.3.1) that if different columns have to be compared, the retention values must be normalized. This is also true for bonded phases. The k-values do not correspond to the weight percentage of bonded carbon but to the amount of carbon per unit column volume. For this, the packing density has to be known. This can only be obtained from the manufacturer or by destroying (unpacking) the column. The packing densities of bonded phases are higher than those of the initial silica gel because of the amount of carbon within the pores, e. g. the packing density of LiChrosorb Si 100 is around 0.34 g/mL, whereas that of RP C_{18} (18% C w/w) based on this support is around 0.47 g/mL.

Many types of bonded reversed phases are available commercially. RP C_{18} is by far the most extensively used reversed phase system. It can be used for separation of non-polar substances, like fatty acid esters as well as for water soluble solutes. RP C_8 seems to be the second choice in selecting reversed phases. It can be used in place of RP C_{18} as discussed above. In some separations, short-chain reversed phases prepared with dimethyl- or trimethylchlorosilanes have been used. These phases are excellent for the separation of large molecules whose retention would become too high with RP C_8 and RP C_{18}. These phases may be superior, especially for protein separation.

Nomenclature of reversed phases is not consistent. Usually the largest alkyl group is taken for characterization and it is ignored whether one or two methyl groups are introduced additionally with e. g. an octadecyl group. All these phases are labeled RP C_{18}. According to this, reversed phases prepared with dimethyl- or with trimethylsilyl groups should be called methyl phases or RP C_1. Some suppliers, however, call these phases RP C_2 or RP C_3.

Besides phases with bonded alkyl groups, reversed phases with bonded phenyl groups or with alkylnitrile groups have also been used. These phases exhibit in aqueous eluents exclusively reversed phase properties. Some specific selectivities ascribed to these phases especially if used in non-polar water free eluents may be caused by differences in surface coverage. The very specific selectivity of nitrile phases in gas chromatography has not to date been verified in liquid chromatography.

2.2.4.2 Influence of Eluent Composition

In RPC the k-values increase exponentially with increasing water content of the eluent. The highest retentions are always obtained in pure water as eluent. Water miscible eluents such as methanol, acetonitrile, higher alcohols and dioxane or tetrahydrofuran (THF) are used as aqueous mixtures to accelerate elution. The elution power of these solvents increases in the order given above and corresponds to the strength of their retention on reversed phase with water as eluent [52]. Acetic acid can also be used to decrease retention, as discussed above.

Because sorption of organic solutes is strongest out of water solutions, reversed phases are well suited for the collection of traces of organic components from water [53]. This trace enrichment is usually followed by a stepwise or programmed increase of elution strength of the eluent, causing the accumulated organic solutes to be separated and eluted. It is advantageous to perform the two steps, i. e. collection and separation, on different columns and transfer only the fraction of interest of the trace enrichment step to the analytical column by applying the column switching technique.

Whether methanol, acetonitrile, propanol or tetrahydrofuran should be used, depends on the degree of solubility of the solutes and some specific selectivities correlated to the eluent. Identical k-values for benzene were achieved with RP C_{18} and water-methanol $1:1$ (v/v) or water-acetonitrile $7:3$ (v/v) or water-THF $3:1$ (v/v). The selectivities for polar benzene derivates were quite different [54, 55]. The retention of aromatic amines, phenols and carboxylic acids are significantly increased in the THF system compared to the methanol or acetonitrile system. The selectivity for polar functional groups in the solute molecule is also considerably increased.

For water-methanol and water-acetonitrile mixtures, a more or less linear dependence of $\log k$ vs. % of organic component is usually obtained. With other water miscible eluents, deviations of this linearity have been observed. Going from water to methanol, the k-values decrease by a factor of 10^3 to 10^4. This means that slight changes in eluent composition effect k-values markedly. As a rule of thumb, a 10% increase of organic eluent component reduces the k-value by a factor of 2. Therefore, eluent mixtures have to be prepared carefully. In our experience, it is best and simplest to prepare eluent mixtures gravimetrically. In this case the reproducibility of eluent composition is better than 0.1%. In literature, very often only the ratio of eluent composition is given, while the exact statement whether volume or weight ratios have been used is omitted.

Table 2-4 demonstrates for a $1:1$ mixture of methanol-water the deviations which may occur. Also demonstrated is the consequence of a mistake sometimes made by using only one graduated cylinder in preparing the mixtures. Depending on which component is introduced first and which is used to fill up, striking differences in k-values are obtained because of the volume contraction with methanol/water mixtures.

Table 2-4. Preparation of a $1:1$ Eluent Mixture. – Chromatographic Conditions: stationary phase: RP C_{18}; eluent: methanol/water.

Preparation	Procedure	% H_2O (w/w)	k-values of Catechol	Phenol	p-Cresol
$1:1$ (w/w)	50 g CH_3OH + 50 g H_2O	50.0	0.33	0.72	1.36
$1:1$ (v/v)	50 mL CH_3OH + 50 mL H_2O	55.9	0.47	1.03	2.05
$1:1$	50 mL H_2O filled up with CH_3OH to 100 mL	54.7	0.44	0.97	1.90
$1:1$	50 mL CH_3OH filled up with H_2O to 100 mL	57.0	0.51	1.11	2.24

With proteins and polypeptides at higher organic solvent content, anomalous elution behaviour in RPC is observed [56]. With the addition of organic components to the aqueous eluent the k-values first decrease, as expected. At an organic solvent content above 30% (e. g. with acetonitrile), however, the k-values increase again. A typical example for this behaviour is shown in Figure 2-12. The slope of the curves is very steep. Reproducible analysis is therefore only possible by an exact preparation of the eluent mixtures. The reason for this increase of k-values at higher organic solvent composition is not yet clear. Silanophilic interactions between solutes and stationary phase have been discussed. Another possible explanation may be structural changes of the solute molecules at high organic solvent concentrations, such as unfolding, thus creating a larger surface of the solute molecule for possible interaction with the hydrocarbonic surface of the reversed phase. Of course, for very large biomolecules denaturation and precipitation may cause difficulties at high organic solvent concentrations and may lead to a loss of resolution and reduce recoveries. Such disadvantages can in part be avoided by using propanol as a second eluent component. Due to its greater elution strength smaller concentrations are required.

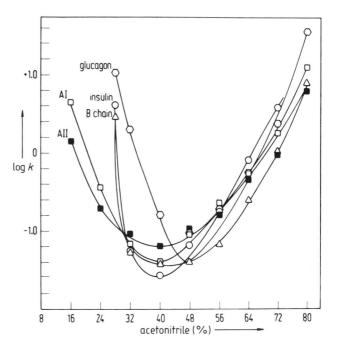

Figure 2-12. Anomalous retention behaviour of proteins with increasing solvent strength [57]. Stationary phase: µ-Bondapak RP C$_{18}$; eluent: Buffer-acetonitrile mixtures (Buffer: 15 mmol Triethylammonium phosphate, pH 2.95); solutes: angiotensin 11 (A 11); angiotensin 1 (A 1); bovine insulin B chain; bovine insulin; porcine glycagon.

Typical imperfect behaviour of mixtures is also shown for the viscosity of water-alcohol or water-acetonitrile mixtures. The viscosity of methanol-water passes through a maximum of 1.84 mPa · s (at 20 °C) at 40% (w/w) methanol. With n-propanol the viscosity increases over 3 mPa · s as shown in Figure 2-13. This behaviour does not effect solute retention, but column back pressure and column efficiency as discussed in Chapter 2.1.2. Of course, by increasing column temperature the viscosity can be lowered.

Changes in temperature, however, effect absolute and relative retentions, because of differences in heat of sorption of the solutes. In standard separation systems ($0.5 < k < 3$) the heat of sorption is between 10 and 20 kJ/mol. In these cases a temperature change of 1 °C leads to changes in k-values between 1% and 2.5%. Therefore, the temperature of the eluent, of the sampling system and of the column has to be controlled in order to obtain reproducible results.

The addition of a second organic component to a water-methanol eluent can be used to alter relative retentions [54, 55, 58]. Tetrahydrofuran or dichloromethane have been used as a third component. The reversed phase selectively adsorbs from the aqueous eluent (50% methanol in water) the non-polar component and the properties of the bonded phase are changed. In Figure

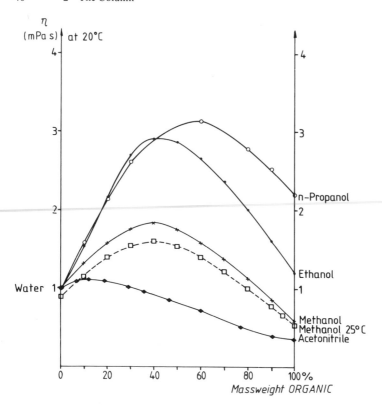

Figure 2-13. Viscosity of aqueous eluent mixtures [2].

2-14 the influence of the addition of a third component to the eluent for the separation of PTH amino acids is demonstrated [59].

Solvent selection and optimization is still a problem, especially for beginners in HPLC. Gradient elution offers a quick test for selection of optimum isocratic eluent composition (see Section 2.2.7.2). In the literature, different approaches to optimize eluent composition have been described [60 to 62]. In every case, with standard eluent mixtures (e. g. water-methanol, water-acetonitrile, water-THF), preliminary separations have to be performed. The composition has to be adjusted until the k-values are in the required or wanted region. Resolution can then be optimized by mixing the different organic eluents for their donator, acceptor or dipole properties. This optimization procedure gives clear results, if all components of the mixture are known. With every optimization method, problems arise for mixtures, where the number of components is not known. In this case, additional information for peak identification is required to be able to differentiate whether peaks are overlapping or not.

So far the discussion has been restricted to the optimization of eluent composition for solutes which are not dissociated in ions. If acids or bases have to be separated additional eluent optimization is necessary. The problem to be solved is demonstrated in Figure 2-15 for the separation of two isomers of aristolochia acid (a derivative of nitrophenanthrene carboxylic acid). In pure methanol, the isomers are only partially separated and slightly retarded. As discussed, it should be expected that an addition of 20% water would increase retention and improve separation.

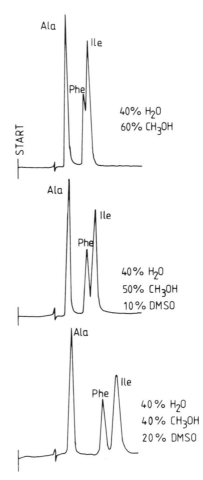

Figure 2-14. Ternary eluent mixtures. Separation of PTH amino acids [59].

However, the acids are eluted before the inert sample and are hindered from penetrating the pores. The reasons for this are the unreacted but dissociated silanols within the pores, which cause solute exclusion by the Donnan potential [63]. By the addition of 1 % acetic acid the dissociation of both the silanols and the carboxylic acid is repressed and the carboxylic acids are retarded and separated.

The silanols can also interact with basic substances in an ion-exchange mechanism. Of course, the (in this case) unwanted ion-exchange can be repressed by applying the law of mass action and adding either a base to the eluent or an acid to form salts. In Figure 2-16 the striking influence of the addition of triethylamine (TEA) in the ppm range on the efficiency of the separation of strongly basic solutes is shown. The problems with tailing peaks of basic or acidic solutes are not restricted to HPLC, they are familiar to everybody using paper or thin layer chromatography. Such problems can be solved by adding acids or bases to the mobile or stationary phase.

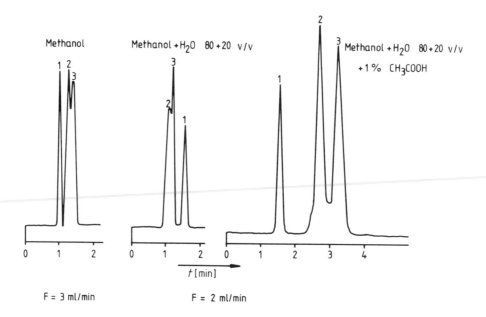

Figure 2-15. Exclusion and Retention in RPC [50]. Separation of aristolochia acids (two isomers 2 and 3; 1 inert).

By adding neutral salts to the eluent, the influence of silanols on elution behaviour of dissociable solutes can be minimized. This addition increases the polarity of the eluent, and causes the k-value of non-polar organic molecules to rise. This "salting out" of organic molecules into the stationary phase can be used to adjust solute retention (see Section 2.2.5 and 2.2.6).

Besides minimizing the dissociation by adding inorganic or organic electrolytes due to the law of mass action, the use of organic acids or bases with higher hydrophobicity also results in diminished dissociation. However, additional formation of ion pairs may occur. These are retarded by another mechanism and thus different selectivity may be observed. Since the formation of ion pairs as a separation method has gained wide application in HPLC, it will be discussed separately in Section 2.2.5.

In RPC it is sometimes difficult to determine the dead time of the column [2, 64, 129]. Precise knowledge of t_M is essential for the exact determination of the volume of mobile phase in the column, its velocity and for the calculation of the retention parameters k and α. Usually t_M is defined as the breakthrough of eluent molecules injected with the sample. Deuterated eluent molecules are the first choice, but a differential refractometer is required for their detection. With aqueous organic eluents two peaks are sometimes seen. In this case the use of a mixture of the organic eluent component with D_2O of identical concentration results in a single peak showing t_M. The use of UV-absorbing tracers for t_M determination is restricted to pure organic eluents, where nitromethane can be used as inert solute. Of course, the dead time determined in organic eluents can be used also in aqueous systems, because silica based stationary phases do not change their packing and pore structure by changing the eluent from organic to aqueous media and vice versa. In Table 2-2 (see Section 2.1.3) some suggestions for the determination of

t_M are summarized. Because of the additional ionic interaction with silanol groups, colored anions or cations are not suitable for t_M measurements.

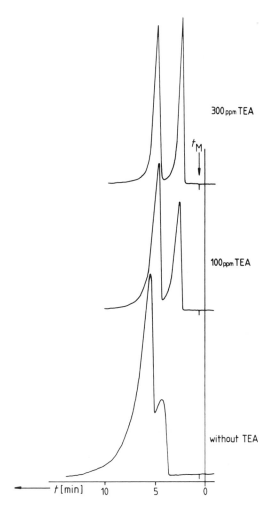

300 ppm TEA

t_M

100 ppm TEA

without TEA

Figure 2-16. Influence of silanol groups on retention and their masking by TEA. Stationary phase: LiChrosorb Si 100 RP C_{18}, HMDS treated; eluent: methanol/ water (0.01 mol/L KH_2PO_4) (2/8, v/v) with different amounts of triethylamine; solutes: procain amide, N-acetyl procainamide.

t [min]   10   5   0

2.2.4.3 Influence of Solute Structure on Retention

The influence of solute structure on retention in RPC is more easily understood than with plain silica. To a first approximation, solute retention increases with diminishing solubility in water, i. e. with decreasing polarity. Within a homologous series each methylen group contributes to solute retention. The increase of free energy of sorption per methylen group is around 600 J/mol under normal chromatographic conditions. Samples with branched alkyl groups are less retained than those with straight chains. The higher the branching, the earlier the isomer is eluted. Unsaturated solutes are eluted before the saturated ones. The influence of functional groups on the retention behaviour of phenols is demonstrated in Figure 2-17. With water as the eluent, the introduction of two methyl groups or one ethyl group gives an identical contribution. Similar effects are noticed with the chlorophenols. One nitro group also leads to an increase of k, but the addition of a second or third nitro group reduces k substantially, because picric acid and dinitrophenols are readily soluble in water. Identical behaviour can be observed for the hydroxyphenols.

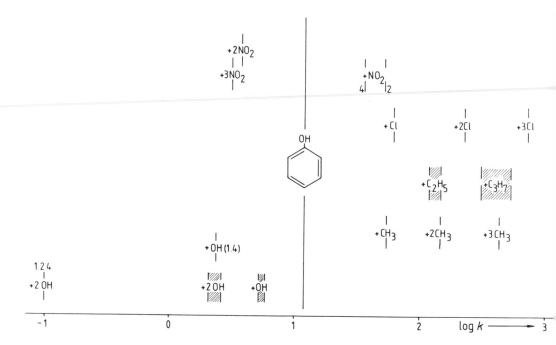

Figure 2-17. Influence of solute structure on retention [2]. Stationary phase: RP C_{18}; eluent: water; solutes: derivatives of phenol.

Similar rules are valid for the retention behaviour of steroids and other groups of compounds. Hydroxysteroids are eluted prior to those with carbonyl groups in the same position. Acetylation of the hydroxyl group increase the retention of the steroid.

Ionized groups usually do not contribute to solute retention. This can be used to change the elution order e. g. of dipeptides just by changing the pH of the eluent. For example at high pH Trp-GlyO$^-$ will elute after Gly-TrpO$^-$ since the ionized portion of the molecule is more highly solvated and cannot interact closely with the hydrophobic stationary phase. At low pH the part of the peptide with the protonated amine will be higher solvated and thus H$^+$ Gly-TrpOH will elute after H$^+$ Trp-GlyOH. At the pH of their isoelectric point the zwitter-ions cannot be separated [65].

For further discussions of hydrophobic or solvophobic interactions and their theoretical treatment reference to literature is given [4, 66].

2.2.5 Secondary Equilibria in RPC

2.2.5.1 Ion-Pair Chromatography

The separation of samples that dissociate in aqueous solution can be optimized, as in paper or thin layer chromatography, by adjustment of the pH of the eluent or of the stationary phase, in order to suppress the dissociation. Sharper zones are then achieved, resulting in highly efficient separations with symmetrical peaks – as with neutral solutes. On the other hand, organic acids or bases, which are able to act as "counter-ions" for the solutes to be separated can be added. In this separation system an "organic" phase is always present, either as eluent or as stationary phase. The formation of dissociated "ion-pairs", which are extracted into the "organic" phase, can thus be assumed. These "ion-pairs" alter the retention behaviour of ionic compounds substantially, whereas that of non-ionic substances is not affected. Therefore, an additional parameter becomes available to optimize the separation or to identify ionic species in a complex mixture by a peak shift technique.

The principles of ion-pair chromatography (IPC) have been deducted from classical extraction procedures of ionic compounds via ion-pair formation from aqueous solutions into organic solvents [67]. These fundamental principles have been transferred to chromatography and, depending on the phase systems used, various names have been given to this method. Besides IPC, the synonyms extraction chromatography, liquid ion-exchange, paired-ion chromatography (PIC) and soap chromatography have been used [66, 68]. The last two synonyms are preferable when reversed phases are used as stationary phases.

The first HPLC application of IPC used columns packed with silica gel which had been coated with aqueous solutions of buffers and ion-pair forming salts. In a descriptive example the sodium salt of naphthalenesulfonic acid was applied as an ion-pair forming component in the aqueous stationary phase by coating it onto the silica. Chloroform was used as eluent and aliphatic amines or dipeptides were separated. The solutes formed ion-pairs, via their amino groups, with naphthalenesulfonic acid and these were extracted into the mobile phase. The aliphatic solutes could be detected in the form of their ion-pairs by UV adsorption [69].

IPC has found much broader applications with reversed phase systems because equilibrating a prepacked silica column with an aqueous salt containing liquid phase and changing this coating are both very difficult. Here, with the aqueous eluent mixtures, it is easy to adjust the pH, the concentration, and the kind of counter-ions in the eluent, and thus to optimize separation conditions. Because aqueous sample solutions can be applied directly, another application area for IPC is in biochemical separations.

The mechanism of IPC can be described by the two extremes: In aqueous eluents, the counter-ions and solute ions form dissociated ion-pairs in the mobile phase which are selectively retarded and separated. At the other extreme, the counter-ions are adsorbed by the stationary phase, the solute ions interact with these adsorbed counter-ions, are retarded and consequently separated. Depending on the counter-ions and their hydrophobicity, the amount of organic component in the eluent, the hydrophobic or hydrophilic nature of the solute, one or the other mechanism predominates.

In the simplest case, the sorption of an organic acid as ion-pair with tetrabutylammonium ions, ionic species should be present only in the eluent, and the ion pairs sorbed exclusively [8].

$$(RCOO^-)_{aq} + (TBA^+)_{aq} \rightleftarrows (RCOO^- TBA^+)_{org} . \tag{8}$$

One can describe the sorption process by an extraction constant E:

$$E = \frac{[RCOO^- TBA^+]_{org}}{[RCOO^-]_{aq} \cdot [TBA^+]_{aq}} . \tag{9}$$

The equilibrium and the extraction depends on the pH of the aqueous eluent, the ionic strength, the temperature, the organic component and the kind of organic counter-ion used. In chromatography one uses the k-value as a measure for solute retention. It is proportional to the extraction constant and the concentration of the counter-ion in the aqueous mobile phase:

$$k \sim E \cdot [TBA^+]_{aq} . \tag{10}$$

Equation [10] shows that the k-value increases with increasing extraction constant and increasing counter-ion concentration. This is not, however, as simple as it seems. The retention behaviour in IPC can also be influenced by other ions introduced with the counter-ion or with the sample, by the type of buffer used, by the ionic strength in the eluent, by the type of organic eluent component and, among other things, by the temperature. These variables can be manipulated so as to optimize IPC and to demonstrate the wide range of separation capabilities. Some general principles of IPC will be discussed in the following section.

2.2.5.1.1 Type of Counter-Ion

As discussed, the k-value should increase proportionally with the concentration of the counter-ion. As shown in Figure 2-18, this is true for the extraction of adrenaline with short chain alkylsulfates at low pH. For longer chain alkylsulfates, the k-values level off at higher concentration. For decylsulfate the k-value first rises with increasing counter-ion concentration and then decreases [51]. This anomalous behaviour can be explained by a saturation of the stationary phase with alkylsulfate, which acts as a liquid ion exchanger. On the other hand with the soap-like decylsulfate, a micel formation of the soap could be causing the decrease of k-values. This behaviour is restricted to hydrophobic ion pairs in water rich eluents. Hydrophilic ion pairs show a less pronounced dependence of k on counter-ion concentration. Of course, similar relationships are noticed for the extraction of acids with quarternary ammonium ions differing in hydrophobicity.

2.2.5.1.2 Influence of pH

Ionization control is essential in IPC. The influence of pH on the k-values of valine and anthranilic acid is shown in Figure 2-19. The retention of valine is minimal at intermediate pH, where it is in its zwitter ionic state. The k-value at low pH is higher than at high pH. The contribution of the undissociated carboxylic group to retention seems to be higher than that of the unprotonated amino group. Anthranilic acid is uncharged at intermediate pH and strongly retained. The charged species at low and high pH show smaller k-values. As can also be seen from Figure 2-19, the k-values change significantly if the pH of the eluent is close to the pK-value of the acid or base. Because valine and anthranilic acid are either an acid or a base, this change happens at low as well as at higher pH.

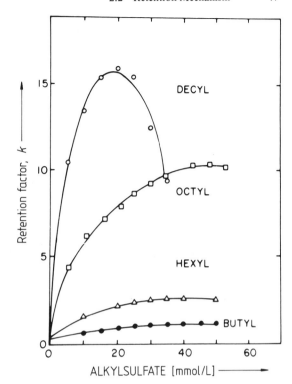

Figure 2-18. Retention as a function of counter-ions and their concentration [51]. Stationary phase: Partisil ODS; eluent: 0.05 mol/L phosphate in water, pH 2.55, containing various concentration of counter-ions; solute: adrenaline.

The pK_l-value of unknown solutes can be determined from the dependence of k on pH [71, 72]. The selectivity for separation of acids and bases is highest in the region of their pK_l-values. However, because of the high dependence of k on the pH, in this region, system reproducibility is bad. Additional problems arise if the organic component of the eluent is changed, because pH- and pK_l-values depend on the proportion of an organic solvent in the eluent mixture. Generally a

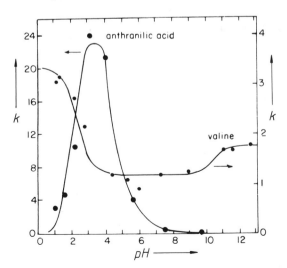

Figure 2-19. Retention of ampholytes at different pH [70]. Stationary phase: cross-linked polystyrene.

change of pH $\approx$ 0.1 can cause a 10% relative change in k-values. Temperature also affects the pH- and pK-value, therefore, in IPC, in addition to pH control, good temperature control is required.

2.2.5.1.3 Influence of Eluent Compositions

It is very seldom that pure aqueous buffer solutions give suitable mobile phases in IPC. The pH of a buffer is affected by the addition of an organic solvent. If the amount of the organic component is below 25% no correction of pH is necessary. In the region of 25 to 50% of organic solvent the effective pH is around 0.1 to 0.2 units below that measured with the glass electrode in aqueous solutions [68]. It is still valid to talk about pH, dissociation and buffer capacity at larger organic solvent concentrations?

The pK_I-values are significantly influenced by the amount of the organic component in the eluent [68]. The reasons for this are that the dielectric constant of the eluent changes and the solute molecules interact with the eluent components. For organic acids the pK_I-values increase steadily with increasing methanol concentration. However, the expected reciprocal relationship to the dielectric constant is not observed. The changes in pK_I-values are very significant if the methanol concentration exceeds 80% (v/v). The pK_I of benzoic acid changes by an order of magnitude if the methanol concentration increases from 20% to 60% (v/v). ($\Delta pK_I \approx 0.4$ with an increase from 20% to 40% methanol). For cationic acids, such as anilinium compounds, the change in pK_I-value with the methanol concentration shows a minimum around 80% methanol.

Increasing the ionic strength of the eluent also affects pK_I-value, because dissociation increases due to the law of mass action [72]. Changing the temperature between 20 °C and 60 °C has a minor influence on the pK_I-value ($\Delta pK_I \approx 0.1$).

The selection of the organic component follows the same rules as discussed for RPC (see section 2.2.4.2). Acetonitrile is preferable to methanol because it has some advantages in the solvation behaviour of ions. Tetraalkylammonium compounds are better solvated in acetonitrile; therefore, if these compounds are used in IPC, they show a stronger dependence on eluent composition compared to methanol mixtures. For the solvation of cationic species, dimethylsulfoxide has a higher solvation capacity than water. The use of ternary eluent mixtures in IPC may bring additional advantages for optimization.

Column equilibration with the eluent and the counter-ions sometimes takes longer than in RPC, especially if counter-ions with large alkyl groups are used in high concentrations. By decreasing their concentration, the equilibration time can be reduced to 1 hour. If a reversed phase column is used in the ion-pair mode, it is difficult, and sometimes very problematic, to regenerate the column to its initial state because quarternary ammonium compounds may be irreversibly adsorbed on surface silanol groups.

IPC is an excellent method for the analytical separation of dissociable solutes. They are eluted as sharp peaks; the achievable column efficiency corresponds to that obtained with neutral solutes. The simple ionic mechanisms involved often make the retention behaviour predictable. Ionic species can be shifted easily to areas of the chromatogram where no neutral solutes are eluted. The separation potentialities can be increased and affected tremendously. The use of IPC is restricted to analytical separations because it is very difficult to remove the ubiquitous counter-ions from the eluent and from the separated samples.

2.2.5.2 Other Secondary Equilibria

Complexation and chelatization in the mobile and/or in the stationary phase can also be used to enhance selectivity. The use of silver nitrate to selectively alter the retention of unsaturated organic compounds is well known. If silver nitrate is added to the eluent the unsaturated hydrocarbons form polar complexes and are eluted considerably earlier than they are without the salt in the eluent [73]. If silver nitrate is fixed on the stationary phase (e. g. on silica or on cation exchanger) the unsaturated compounds are, of course, more strongly retarded than on the same column without silver ions [74].

Metal chelate additives have also been used to develop selective separations. Metal chelate involving a triamine functionality and zinc or cadmium metal ions were found to have improved selectivity in the IP separation of aromatic acids [68]. When chiral tridentate amines were used, the enantiomeric separation of dansyl amino acids was possible [75]. Other systems, with metal chelates, were also described for chiral separation of amino acids [76]. Here, an optical pure amino acid was used as an additive in the presence of copper(II) ions.

2.2.6   Ion-Exchange Chromatography

The separation of amino acids is the main application of ion-exchange chromatography in biochemical analysis. The amino acids are adsorbed on a cation-exchanger (a polymeric matrix with sulfonic acid groups) and are eluted by changing the pH and the ionic strength of the aqueous eluent. The classical ion-exchangers are swollen gels with a limited pressure stability which prevents their use under HPLC conditions. The pressure stability can be improved by increasing the crosslinking. However, this causes the average pore diameter to decrease. Pressure-stable ion-exchangers for HPLC sometimes have too narrow pores for application in biochemical analysis [77]. Because of their matrix properties, they shrink or swell by changing the pH and/or the ionic strength of the eluent.

2.2.6.1 Properties of Silica-Based Ion-Exchangers

Since the early beginning of HPLC, attempts have been made to prepare pressure-stable ion-exchangers. The first ones described were the so-called "pellicular ion-exchangers" with a thin ion-exchanger film deposited on an impenetrable glass bead [78]. These ion-exchangers lacked sufficient capacity. Nowadays ion-exchangers are available which are prepared by chemically bonding suitable silanes onto the surface of silica gel with ion-exchange groups. Cation-exchangers, with phenyl- or alkylsulfonic groups, and weak or strong anion-exchangers, with amino or quarternary ammonium groups, are both available. The ion-exchange capacity of these materials is sufficient. Because of the higher packing densities of silica-based materials, the exchange capacity per mL column volume is only half that achieved with polystyrene-based ion-exchangers, whereas the specific exchange capacities (mmol/g) differ by a factor of 4 or even more. There are silica based materials available with capacities up to 1 mmol/g, but also with 0.1 mmol/g (all data are refered to 1 ionic equivalent). In addition to the desired ion-exchange properties, the selectivity of the system may also be influenced by ionic exclusion caused by the Donnan potential [63], and by hydrophobic interaction of the solutes with the organic spacers.

The higher the ion-exchange capacity, the larger the k-values are, provided that the solutes are present as exchangeable ions. In Figure 2-20 the dependence of k on pH for purine and pyrimidine bases on a cation-exchanger is shown [79]. At low pH the protonated ammonium groups can interact with the sulfonic acid groups. As discussed for IPC the largest change of k with pH occurs around the pK_I-values of the bases.

Uracil and thymine are not ionized in this pH-range and cannot interact with the ion-exchanger. Their retention and the still measurable retention of the other bases at high pH is caused by hydrophobic interaction with the organic groups bonded to the silica.

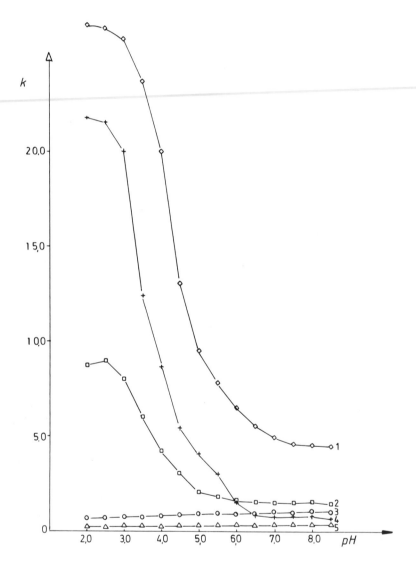

Figure 2-20. Retention of nucleobases at different pH on cation-exchanger. Stationary phase: Nucleosil 10 SA; eluent: phosphate buffer (ionic strength I = 0.1 mol/L); solutes: 1 adenine, 2 guanine, 3 thymine, 4 cytosine, 5 uracil.

The retention of nucleotides (monophosphates) on a strong basic anion-exchanger with quaternary ammonium groups is shown in Figure 2-21 [79]. At low pH the phosphoric acid is protonated and cannot interact with the bonded ammonium groups. By increasing the pH the phosphoric acid group dissociates, retention is possible. At pH-values above 7 the amount of hydroxyl groups which are able to compete with the phosphates for the ion-exchange groups increases. The hydroxyl ions displace the solute molecules from the ion-exchanger and the k-values of the nucleotides decrease. It is easy to separate the three groups of nucleotides by ion-exchange chromatography because di- and triphosphates are more strongly retained.

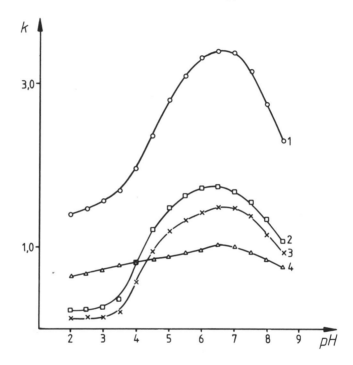

Figure 2-21. Retention of monophosphates on an anion-exchanger. Stationary phase: silica-based quaternary ammonium chloride; eluent: phosphate buffers (I = 0.1 mol/L); solutes: 1 GMP, 2 AMP, 3 CMP, 4 UMP.

2.2.6.2 Optimization of the Separation

As already discussed in the previous section, the pH of the eluent is an important parameter in adjusting and controlling retention in IEC. The change in the ionic strength of the buffer affects retention much more than pH changes. Due to the law of mass action the ion-exchange can be suppressed by the addition of neutral salts. An increase of the ionic strength causes the k-values to decrease. If k is plotted vs. the reciprocal ionic strength, straight lines originating at zero should be obtained if ion-exchange is the only retention mechanism. For an anion-exchanger with a propyl spacer group between the silica and the quaternary ammonium group this could be verified, as shown in Figure 2-22 [79].

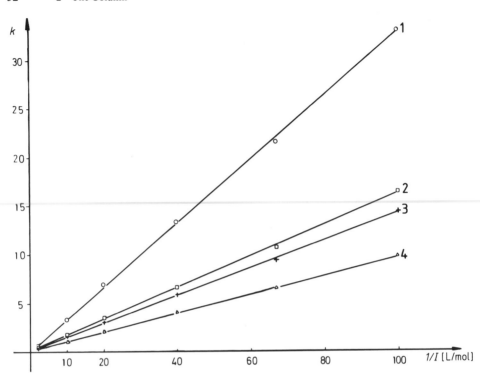

Figure 2-22. Retention and ionic strength with anion-exchanger (Conditions as in Figure 2-21.); pH 7.0; ionic strength adjusted with NaCl.

It is more difficult to explain solute retention as a function of the ionic strength if hydrophobic interaction is taking place. Here, two mechanisms may be concurrent: the ion-exchange mechanism, which causes the k-value to decrease with increasing ionic strength, and the salting-out mechanism (see Section 2.2.4.2), which causes the k-values to increase with increasing ionic strength. This is demonstrated in Figure 2-23 for the separation of amino acids on a cation-exchanger at two different ionic strengths [79]. At low ionic strength phenylalanine (PHE) is eluted as the first peak, directly after the inert solute, with a k-value of 1.33. Increasing the ionic strength, under otherwise identical conditions, from 0.1 to 0.5 changes the elution order. In this case PHE is eluted as the last but one peak. The k-values of the other amino acids are diminished considerably (e. g. arginine from 7.2 to 2.1) whereas the k-value of PHE increases slightly to 1.44. The hydrophobic amino acid PHE is salted out into the organic stationary phase.

Hydrophobic interactions are reduced by adding an organic component to the eluent (see Section 2.2.4.2). This can also be applied with ion-exchangers. It should be mentioned, that such systems, of an ion-exchanger with aqueous methanolic eluents, can be used for the separation of neutral compounds like sugars [80] by a partition mechanism (Section 2.2.9.2).

Buffer transparency at low wavelength in the UV region puts serious limitations on the proper buffer selection, especially if wavelengths below 230 nm have to be used. Polyphosphates in a phosphate buffer may cause base-line shifts even at 254 nm. The selectivity of the separation can also be affected by the proper selection of the buffer composition. As with adsorption

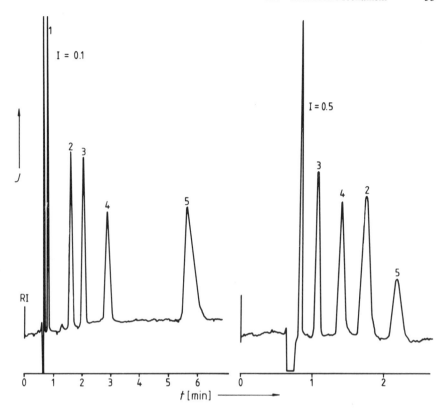

Figure 2-23. Hydrophobic interaction of amino acids with ion-exchanger. Stationary phase: silica-based cation-exchanger; eluent: citrate buffer, pH 4.8, with NaCl to ionic strength 0.1 and 0.5; solutes: 1 D_2O (inert), 2 PHE, 3 LYS, 4 HIS, 5 ARG.

chromatography, the elution power of cations and anions increases with their increasing sorption on the particular ion-exchanger, e. g. a lithium citrate buffer is a weaker eluent than a sodium citrate buffer in amino acid analysis. In classical ion-exchange chromatography, series of anions and cations have been established, demonstrating the elution power of the different ions.

For a strongly basic anion-exchanger the elution power decreases in the following order:

$$citrate > oxalate > J^- > HSO_4^- > NO_3^- > Br^- >$$
$$Cl^- > formiate > acetate > OH^- > F^-$$

For a strongly acidic cation-exchanger the elution power decreases:

$$Fe^{3+} >$$
$$Ca^{2+} > Cu^{2+} > Zn^{2+} > Mg^{2+} >$$
$$Ag^+ > Rb^+ > K^+ > NH_4^+ > Na^+ > H^+ > Cu^+$$

Of course, additional selectivity may arise from specific interactions of the solutes with cations or anions in complexation reactions.

2.2.6.3 Ion-Exchange of Amino Acids

Amino acids in their zwitterion state are not retarded by an ion-exchange mechanism. The differences in their isoelectric points can be used for the separation of amino acids on a cation-exchanger. In Figure 2-24 the dependence of the k-value on eluent pH is shown [79]. The separation of all amino acids is only possible if a buffer gradient is used. The problems generally encountered in gradient elution are discussed in Section 2.2.7.

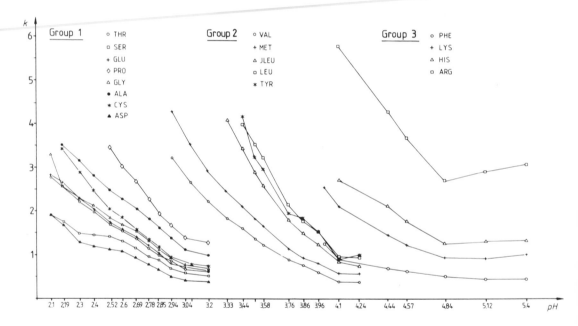

Figure 2-24. Retention of amino acids at different pH. Stationary phase: silica- based cation-exchanger; eluent: sodium citrate buffer, ionic strength 0.1.

Additional detection problems arise with amino acids that show no significant adsorption in the UV range. In classical ion-exchange analysis of amino acids the ninhydrine reaction is used for a colorimetric detection after the separation [81, 82]. For HPLC this reaction is too slow and peak broadening in the reaction system is untolerably high. Therefore, different reactions and reaction detectors are used [83 to 86]. The use of pressure-stable ion-exchangers, together with highly sensitive and selective reaction detection allows highly efficient separation of amino acids and peptides e. g. in urine. The lower level of detection with o-phthaldialdehyde and fluorescence detection is in the picomol range [86]. A separation of amino acids in human urine by direct injection of a 25 μL sample is shown in Figure 2-25. No sample pretreatment was required in this case. All components with primary amino groups were retarded by cation-exchange and could be separated and detected by this system.

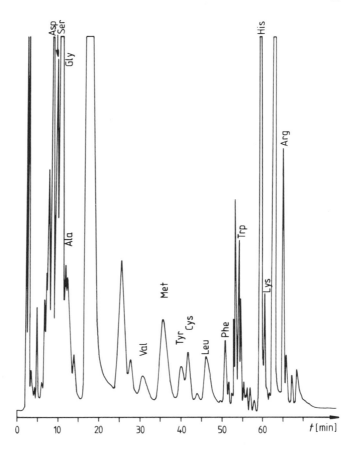

Figure 2-25. Amino acids determined in human urine with gradient elution and reaction detection. Stationary phase: silica based ion-exchanger; eluents: A: Lithium citrate, pH 2.0, I = 0.1 mol/L; B: Lithium citrate, pH 7.5, I = 0.1 mol/L; program: 0 to 50 min: 5 to 35% B; flow: 1.0 mL/min, 50 to 55 min: 35 to 100% B, flow: 2.0 mL/min, after 55 min: 100% B, I = 0.5 mol/L, flow: 2.0 mL/min; reactor: 900 cm, 0.5 mm i. d. "knitted" tube; reagent flow: 1.0 mL/min; reaction time: 40 to 60 sec; temperature: 30°C; reagent: o-phthaldialdehyde in borate-buffer, pH 10.0.

2.2.7 Gradient Elution

With silica chromatography, as well as with RPC and IEC, only part of the solutes are separated under optimal isocratic conditions if solute polarities differ widely. The programmed change of eluent solvent strength, called gradient elution, allows the separation of non-polar as well as polar solutes in a single run. Gradient elution always leads to a reduction in analysis time and helps to sharpen solute zones. The resolution of sample zones is always poorer for programmed than for isocratic analysis [2, 87]. This is, however, not a problem, because, in the cases where gradient elution should be applied, resolution is always greater than required.

In gradient elution, apart from the stationary phase, the following additional variables can be selected: eluent composition at the beginning of analysis, shape of gradient, the eluent composition at the end of analysis, flow-rate and programm time.

2.2.7.1 Selection of Gradient Conditions

The sample determines the selection of the stationary phase. The polarity range of the solutes determines the choice of the two eluents and their composition at the beginning and at the end of the programmed analysis. As a result one should get a good resolution of the early eluted peaks, while the most strongly retarded sample constituents should be eluted in reasonable time.

The increase in concentration of the second eluent component as a function of time can be described by concave, linear or convex curves. A linear gradient curve should be chosen first, especially in RPC and IEC. The actual and effective gradient is only partially dependent on the program type. It is always a function of the differences in elution strength of the two components. With two solvents of large differences in elution strength, even small amounts of the polar component produce a sharp rise in elution strength, thus generating an effectively convex gradient. Such a gradient shape is rarely desirable because the components are always eluted close together at the beginning of a separation.

A linear increase in solvent strength is optimum for the separation of a homologous series, because all peaks of the members of the homologous series are then eluted with equal distances in elution time, and show indentical peak width. Therefore, the detection limits are identical for all members. With RPC a linear increase in solvent strength corresponds to a linear increase of organic eluent component with methanol and acetonitrile. In Figure 2-26 for the separation of phenacylesters of fatty acids the influence of solvent strength in gradient elution is demonstrated. With methanol the distance between the homologous fatty acids decreases progressively during the analysis because of a larger increase in solvent strength. Whereas almost equal distances between the members of the homologous are noticed with acetonitrile as the stronger eluting component. At the beginning (with high initial concentration of B) the distance is smaller, whereas at the end (elution after final conditions have been reached) the distance increases again. With stronger eluting organics, such as propanol, the elution strength increases, at least at the beginning, in a convex form. In ion-exchange, where pH or ionic strength gradients are used, linear gradients are highly recommended. With silica as stationary phase and a gradient from hexane to dichloromethane, a linear increase in solvent strength can be simulated by applying a slightly concave gradient. If these parameters are chosen there are still two variables to select: the flow-rate and the program time. The product of both can be defined as the gradient volume V_g, i.e. the volume of eluent pumped through the system during the programmed run.

2.2.7.2 The Gradient Volume Concept

At constant gradient volume both flow-rate and program time can be varied, but the sample components will always elute at the same eluent composition at column outlet [88]. This eluent composition is a function of the gradient volume. The larger the gradient volume, the lower the concentration of B at which a solute is eluted. The gradient volume with normal analytical columns (25 to 30 cm length, 0.4 cm i. d.) should not be below 10 mL or, expressed in volume units of the empty column, it should be at least 2.5 times the volume of the empty column. The

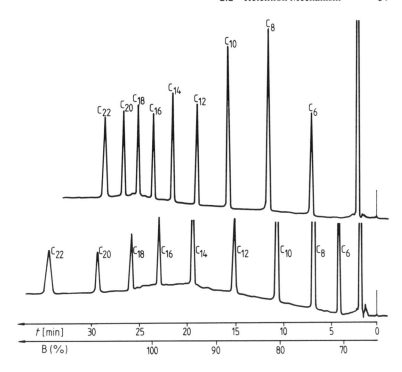

Figure 2-26. Demonstration of linear solvent strength gradient elution [117]. Separation of phenacylesters of fatty acids. Gradient 70% B to 100% B; Gradient volume: 40 mL; upper chromatogram: B methanol; lower chromatogram: B acetonitrile.

number of components that can be separated with such a small gradient volume is also small. With columns of 10 μm particles about 30 peaks can be separated. For multicomponent analysis, large gradient volumes of about 30 empty column volumes should be applied. With such a system it is no problem to separate up to 100 peaks. At an optimum flow-rate of 2 mL/min, the analysis takes 60 minutes. Optimum gradient volumes are around 10 to 15 empty column volumes, where around 70 peaks can be separated.

Peak volumes are, of course, a function of flow-rate. Instrumental limitation, however, restrict the minimum flow-rate. 2 mL/min was found to be the optimum; at smaller flow-rates pumping precision may cause problems. Increasing the flow-rate from 1 mL/min to 2 mL/min reduces the peak capacity at constant gradient volume by about 10% but cuts analysis time in half. At flow-rates above 4 mL/min, mixing of the two eluent components is problematic.

The gradient volume concept also allows the fast determination of optimal eluent composition for isocratic analysis. At a given gradient volume, the eluent composition at which a sample elutes from the column during a gradient run has to be known. Because of dead volumes in the system, and the eluent volume in the column, the effective eluent composition at column outlet is always delayed for several mL relative to that indicated by the instrument setting. A way to determine the eluent composition at column outlet will be discussed in Section 2.2.7.3. If the eluent composition at which a peak elutes in the gradient run is taken as the eluent mixture for isocratic analysis, the k-value of that solute will be around 1. Of course, this holds true only for gradient volumes between 5 and 15 empty column volumes. Larger isocratic *k*-values are observed when larger gradient volumes are used with this approach.

2.2.7.3 Practical Aspects of Gradient Elution

The instrumental aspects of gradient elution are discussed in Section 2.3. Special demands must be placed on solvent purity. The separation column acts as a collector of impurities in the solvents, which may consequently be eluted as sharp zones, mostly at the end of the program and may be mistaken for sample components. It is therefore advisable to run the gradient blank (without a sample) to recognise the impurity peaks. Figure 2-27 shows the blank gradients obtained with different commercial brands of methanol under identical conditions [88]. Not only the impurities of the first (weaker eluent) are collected on the column, but also those contained in the stronger solvent, which were not eluted at the beginning because of the low initial elution strength of the eluent mixture. The number of impurities collected is also a function of column flushing volume between two runs. It is therefore good practice to keep regeneration times or flush volumes constant before each analysis. A blank gradient elution is always advisable if new batches of eluents are used.

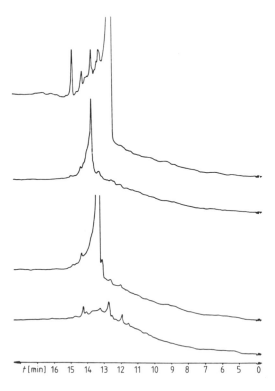

Figure 2-27. Blank gradients with different brands of methanol. Collection of eluent impurities on a   RP C_{18}.

Column regeneration, i.e. the reestablishment of initial conditions by removing the polar eluent component requires a long time with silica stationary phase. With chemically bonded phases the original conditions are achieved after passing through at least 10 empty column volumes of eluent. However, the regeneration time should also be standardized, as the impurities in water or methanol are enriched on the column.

The following procedure is recommended as a means for testing the equipment, and for determining:

● the true gradient shape;
● the delay of the gradient caused by dead volumes;
● the eluent composition at column outlet.

The system should be set up, including the column. As eluent A, pure methanol should be used, and as eluent B, methanol containing about 100 ppm toluene as a UV tracer. This concentration was selected so that with usual detector sensitivity (0 to 0.5 AU full scale) the gradient from 0 to 100% B can be observed. The gradients obtained with two different types of commercial equipment are shown in Figure 2-28. The lower diagram shows a typical high pressure gradient generated with two pumps; the upper shows a gradient generated at the low pressure side of a single pump including a mixing chamber, causing also a deformation of the gradient shape. The delay of the gradient can also be determined from this diagram. The final gradient conditions have not yet reached the end of the column (i. e. the end of separation and elution), when the instrument already shows their achievement. The start of the ascent of the UV trace corresponds to 0% B at column outlet, the end of the ascent to 100% B. The distance between the points corresponds to the change from 0% B to 100% B. From this the eluent composition at column outlet can be determined. The concentrations thus obtained can be used with the gradient volume concept to determine the optimum eluent composition for isocratic analysis.

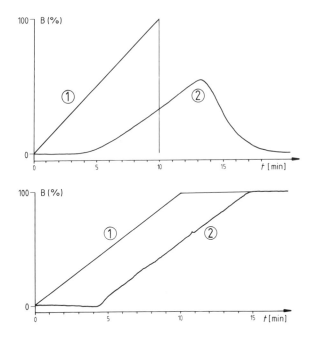

Figure 2-28. Test of two commercial equipments for gradient generation. Curve 1: gradient profile electronically generated; curve 2: real gradient profile at column outlet.

2.2.8 Size-Exclusion Chromatography

Unlike the separation systems discussed so far, size-exclusion chromatography (SEC) involves a single unambigous mechanism. In the absence of interactions (by definition) between the sample and the stationary phase, the elution order should be exclusively a function of the molecular size in the eluent. For synthetic linear polymers which are present in solution as random coils, the size can be directly related to the molecular weight. For molecules with an ordered structure the usual plot of the logarithm of molecular weight vs. elution volume does not describe their behaviour in SEC properly. Size-exclusion chromatography is a synonym for the classical processes of gel filtration and gel permeation chromatography. Cross-linked gels whose pore structure is generated by a swelling process in the eluent cannot be applied under conditions of HPLC. The bed structure, and hence the pore structure, are a function of gel cross-linking and eluent composition. The flow rates usually applied in HPLC compress the bed and the soft gels. Therefore, semi-rigid organic gels and rigid silica-based stationary phases with small particle diameters are now used. The advantages of modern SEC over gel-filtration chromatography is demonstrated in Figure 2-29 for the separation of dextranes. The introduction of rigid silica gels with small particles has reduced the time of analysis by a factor of 20. The speed of analyses (plates per second) with silica stationary phases is increased by a factor of 400.

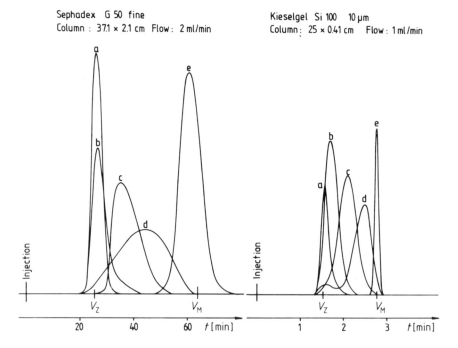

Figure 2-29. SEC with soft gels and with silica. Stationary phase: Sephadex G 50 and silica Si 100; eluent: water; solutes: dextranes with MW 70000 (a), 40000 (b), 10000 (c), 5000 (d) and xylose (e).

2.2.8.1 Fundamentals of SEC

The elution volume V_e of a polymeric solute should depend solely on the size of the molecule in solution and on its relationship to the pore size distribution of the stationary phase. The volume of the mobile phase V_M in the column can be determined from the elution volume of an eluent molecule, or another small molecule, not interacting with the surface, but penetration all the pores of the stationary phase (for rules in determinating t_M and V_M see Table 2-2, Section 2.1.3). The volume V_M includes the eluent volume between the particles, the interstitial volume V_Z (Zwischenkornvolumen) and the eluent volume within the pores V_p of the stationary phase in the column. V_Z can be measured with a totally excluded, high molecular weight sample unable to enter the pores, and is identical for all molecules. Depending on the pore size distribution of the stationary phase and on the size of the molecule, only part of the pore volume will be accessible for penetration. The sample is always eluted with

$$V_e = V_z + K_{GPC} \cdot V_p \tag{11}$$

where K_{GPC} is the fraction of the pore volume accessible for the component, which by definition in SEC never exceeds unity ($1 \geq K_{GPC} \geq 0$). Therefore, the elution volume is always smaller

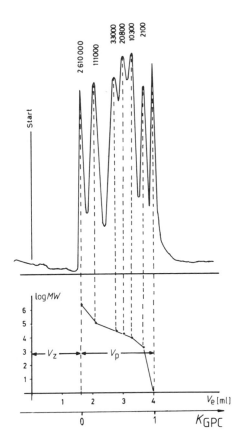

Figure 2-30. Illustration and calibration of SEC. Upper portion: Separation of polystyrenes with molecular weights from 2100 to 2600000 (benzene was used as the smallest molecule). Lower portion: The calibration curve derived for SEC. Stationary phase: silica; eluent: dichloromethane [2].

than or equal to V_M and the end of separation is, therefore, predictable. In retentive chromatography, however, the elution volume V_R of a retarded solute is always greater than V_M ($V_R = V_M(1 + k)$). In Figure 2-30 the relationships of V_e, V_Z and V_P with log M_w are demonstrated for polystyrenes, which can be used to characterize the pore size distribution of a stationary phase [27].

Resolution in SEC depends, as in retentive chromatography, on column efficiency, expressed in plates generated within a column at a given flow-rate. The smaller the slope of log M_w vs. V_e the higher the resolution ($\triangle V_e$ or $\triangle K_{GPC}$) of two peaks with closely related molecular weights. The third parameter important for resolution is the relationship between the pore volume (volume required for separation) and the interstitial volume, where no separation takes place. The resolution of two peaks (1 and 2) can be calculated as:

$$R = \frac{1}{4} \cdot \frac{V_p}{V_z} \cdot \frac{K_{GPC,2} - K_{GPC,1}}{1 + K_{GPC,2} \cdot V_p/V_z} \cdot \sqrt{n_2} \,. \tag{12}$$

In comparing the separation shown in Figure 2-29 under the aspects of this equation, the resolution with Sephadex is good because of the large ratio of V_p/V_z ("capacity ratio") of 1.5 compared to 0.8 for silica. The efficiency (n) achievable with the silica column (small particles) compensates for the smaller V_p/V_z relationship of this system.

2.2.8.2 Stationary Phases

The knowledge of the average pore diameter, the pore diameter distribution and the effective pore volume is necessary for optimization of SEC separations. Rigid stationary phases can be used in organic as well as in aqueous eluents, their pore structure is independent of the eluent. These materials can easily be characterized by applying the inversal size-exclusion chromatographic method using polystyrene standards [27, 77]. This procedure has the advantage that over the whole range of SEC, polymer standards with defined and narrow polydispersity ($P < 1.1$) are available. In Figure 2-31 the calibration curves of different silicas with polystyrenes are shown, demonstrating the applicability and the required average pore diameter for a given range of molecular weights. Such calibration curves can be obtained with each polymer, provided that narrow standards of the polymer are available and that the eluent composition is adjusted so that no sorption or interaction with the stationary phase influences the elution volume. Water soluble polymers often interact with the silanol groups on the silica surface. Surface-modified silicas have been described and are commercially available for application in biochemical analysis [89].

For modification glycols, other hydroxylated silanes and acetylaminopropyl silanes have been used, and are commercially available as LiChrospher DIOL, SynChropak GPC, TSK SW columns, Waters I-125, Aquapore, etc. from various suppliers [89 to 93].

For calibration in aqueous systems dextranes, sulfonated polystyrenes and polyethylene glycols can be used as well as protein standards. In any case with water soluble polymers and silica-based stationary phases, the absence of sorption processes has to be evaluated carefully.

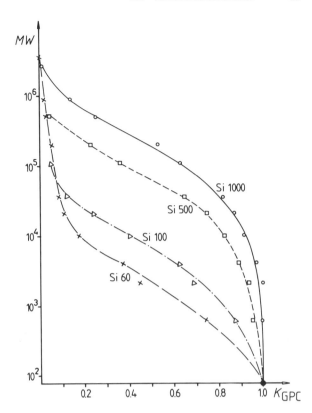

Figure 2-31. Calibration curves of different silicas. Stationary phase: LiChrosorb Si 60, Si 100, Si 500, Si 1000; eluent: dichloromethane; solutes: polystyrenes.

2.2.8.3 Optimization of SEC Separations

As discussed generally for bonded stationary phases based on silica, those silanols which cannot be covered by chemical bonding may influence solute retention, especially in aqueous systems. Ionic interaction with acidic or basic solutes can decrease or increase solute elution behaviour (see Section 2.2.4.1). These effects are also noticeable with SEC, especially with proteins. Deviations from predicted elution sequence may also be noticed because even chemically bonded phases with short alkyl groups and polar functional groups have some hydrophobic properties.

Two different ionic interactions of proteins with the stationary phase can be discussed:
a) Proteins positively charged in the applied buffer solution (pI > pH) are retarded by an ion-exchange mechanism, and are eluted at higher V_e-values than expected from their molecular size.
b) Proteins which are negatively charged in the buffer solution are excluded from penetrating the pores by the Donnan potential [63], and are eluted earlier than expected. By adjusting the pH of the buffer the charge of the proteins can be altered. However, if enzymatic activity needs to be retained, the applicablility of this means of optimization is limited.

The ionic interaction can be diminished by applying the law of mass action and adding neutral salts to the buffer. This means of optimization is used in ion-exchange chromatography (see

Section 2.2.6.2). In Figure 2-32 the influence of the ionic strength of the eluent is demonstrated for different proteins. An increase of the ionic strength to 0.3 is sufficient to diminish the ionic exclusion effects. At this ionic strength the negatively charged proteins are eluted according to their size. To diminish the ion-exchange of positively charged proteins, an ionic strength of 0.5 is required. It should be mentioned that an increase of ionic strength causes hydrophobic substances to be retarded as shown in Figure 2-32, for the tripeptide (PHE)$_3$ and DNP-alanine. As already discussed, an increase of the ionic strength causes salting out of hydrophobic solutes. This modification of eluent composition to diminish ionic interaction is essential for all silica based SEC columns [90].

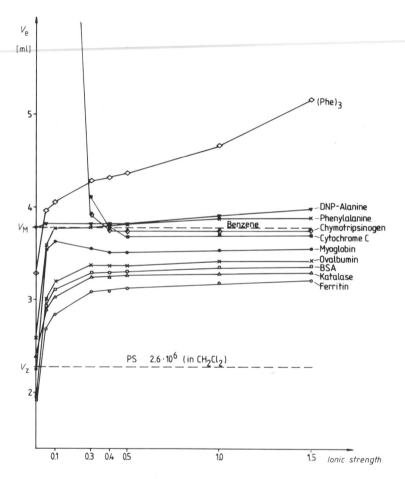

Figure 2-32. SEC of peptides and proteins. Elution volume and ionic strength [92]. Stationary phase: Amide bonded phase; eluent: 0.1 mol/l Tris-HCl-Buffer, pH 7.5, ionic strength adjusted with NaCl.

It is well known to biochemists that proteins can be denatured by changing the pH, by salting out and by hydrophobic interaction. The adjustment of chromatographic conditions should, therefore, be done carefully and be controlled if the column is exchanged. Ionic interaction has also been observed in gel filtration with Sephadex, which may contain carboxylic groups on the surface [94]. Under the chromatographic conditions described above, the recoveries for proteins are always better than 90%, even if the proteins are slightly retarded. The ionic strength should not be significantly higher than 0.5 [90].

2.2.8.4 Correlation of Elution Volume, Molecular Weight and Molecular Size

One advantage of silica based SEC columns is that pore size and pore volume are independent of the eluent. It is possible, therefore, to calibrate a column with polystyrene standards in dichloromethane , and then after switching to water or aqueous buffers, water soluble polymers and proteins can be separated by the same column.

If polymers exist in solution as random coils, the size of the random coil can be related to their relative molecular mass [95]. Additionally, the size of the coil in solution is a function of the solvation of the polymer. To obtain universal calibration plots in polymer chemistry, the molecular weight of the polymer is multiplied by its intrinsic viscosity, which compensates for differences in solvation [96].

In Figure 2-23 the calibration curve of a column system with modified silica is shown for polystyrenes in dichloromethane and for dextranes in water as well as for proteins in buffer solution. No compensation for differences in molecular structure is made. The dextranes are much more dense than polystyrenes of identical molecular mass; the volume of their random coil is smaller and, therefore, they are eluted with higher elution volumes. Proteins exist in solution with a distinct shape determined by the sequence of the amino acids. The tertiary structure of proteins is much more compact than random coil structures. Proteins are therefore eluted at higher V_e compared to polystyrenes and dextranes of identical molecular weight [92]. Myoglobin with a relative molecular mass of 17800 represents an ellipsoid with a longest axis of

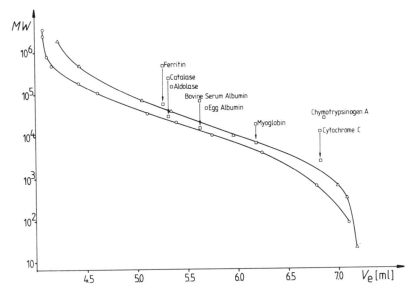

Figure 2-33. Correlation of elution volumes of proteins and polystyrenes [92]. For explanation see text.

4.4 nm. This size corresponds to a polystyrene random coil of 6700 [27]. If this relative molecular mass corresponding to the size of myoglobin is added in Figure 2-33 (as indicated by arrows), the calibration curve of proteins fits that of polystyrenes. This is also a confirmation of the absence of additional retention mechanisms other than size-exclusion. By inversion of this method SEC can be used to determine Stoke's radii for unknown proteins via the calibration curve of polystyrenes [97]. Proteins can differ in the geometry of their tertiary structure, despite having the same molecular weight. They may also differ, therefore, in their elution volume.

2.2.9 Stationary Phases with Other Functional Groups

Silica can be reacted with alkylsilanes and with silanes which have functional groups bonded via a spacer to the silicium. The introduction of functional groups in already surface-bonded organosilanes is difficult and never gives good and reproducible stationary phases [98]. It is very difficult to determine specific selectivity introduced by functional groups. All bonded phases exert hydrophobic selectivity. Bonded phases where functional groups decrease this hydrophobic character have been discussed as stationary phases in aqueous SEC. Bonded N-acetylaminopropyl, glycidoxypropyl groups are used in aqueous SEC of proteins (see Section 2.2.8). Very strong interaction between solutes and functional groups are common with ion-exchangers (see Section 2.2.6). These systems may also demonstrate how hydrophobicity influences solute retention despite the strong ionic interactions.

In this case the differentiation between desired and noticed selectivity is easy. With other functions the discussion of selectivity becomes much more sophisticated, because it is difficult to obtain identical surface coverages with silanes differing in functions. Differences in hydrophobic selectivity, differences in the surface coverage and, consequently, differences in concentration of silanol groups make it complicated to attribute a noticed selectivity solely to the functional groups already introduced. The selectivities described e. g. for cyanopropyl- or phenyl-bonded phases are not specific to these bonded groups, but can also be explained with different hydrophobic polarity and/or differences in the surface coverage. It would otherwise be difficult to explain how an amino and a nitrile phase of different suppliers show similar selectivities, when the nitrile phases are very dissimilar [99]. It is imprudent and unprofitable to compare bonded phases and to describe their selectivity with different eluents. In chromatography the whole system, i. e. the stationary phase, the eluent composition and the solute have to be considered when selectivity is discussed [32].

Because of these problems, only a few examples of specific applications of stationary phases with bonded functional groups will be described, where the selectivity can clearly be attributed to the functional group.

2.2.9.1 Charge Transfer Phases

For the separation of aromatic hydrocarbons stationary phases with nitrophenyl groups [2, 100], nitrofluorenon and tetrachlorphthalic acid groups [101] have been described. With non-polar eluents, the selectivity of these phases is superior to that of bare silica.

2.2.9.2 Amino Phases

Stationary phases with propylamino groups in non-polar eluents show different selectivities compared to silica for the separation of aromatic hydrocarbons [2, 102]. In water they are weak anion-exchanger, whereas in water acetonitrile mixtures, they are excellent stationary phases for the separation of sugars [103, 104]. In Figure 2-34 the separation of sugars and sugar alcohols with an amino phase is shown. The mechanism of separation is partitioning [105]. The amino group does not, as such, interfere in solute retention. It causes the eluent to split and to form a water enriched stationary phase. The separation is caused by partitioning of the solutes between this water rich stationary phase and the eluent. A similar mechanism was described for the separation of sugars with aqueous methanol on ion-exchange resins [80]. By using a bifunctional amine (diamine) the amount of water within the pores increases from 0.13 g/g stationary phase to 0.23 g/g. With this diamine phase a higher water concentration in the eluent can be tolerated to achieve identical k-values. This helps sugar separation because solubility of sugars in the eluent may otherwise be a problem.

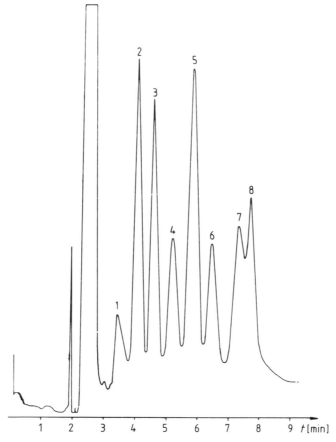

Figure 2-34. Separation of sugars and sugar alcohols on a bonded amino phase [105]. Stationary phase: Amino silane on LiChrosorb Si 100; eluent: acetonitrile/water (80/20, w/w); solutes: 1 desoxyribose, 2 rhamnose, 3 meso-erythritose, 4 arabinose, 5 fructose, 6 mannose, 7 sorbitose, 8 mannitose.

In Figure 2-35 the dependence of k on water content in acetonitrile for three different amino phases is shown. The introduction of the third amino group into the bonded silane has a minor influence on the amount of stationary water and hence on sugar retention [105].

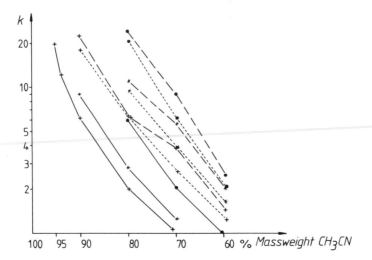

Figure 2-35. Comparision of different amino phases. Retention of fructose (+) glucose (∗) and saccharose (₀). Stationary phase: —— amine; - - - - - diamine; – – triamine; eluent: water/acetonitrile mixtures.

The diamine phase, being a weak ion-exchanger and causing a partition system for sugar separation, can be used in water to separate polyethylene glycols (PEG) according to their size [91]. The polyethylene glycols are strongly retarded, not only with reversed phase but also with bare silica [98]. The PEGs are also retarded with SEC phases for protein separation such as amide and glycol. This again demonstrates that stationary phase selectivity is a function of the chromatographic milieu and depends on the interaction of eluent and solute with the stationary phase.

2.2.9.3 Chiral Phases

Chiral separations have been discussed in LC since its early days. Successful and reproducible enantiomeric separations with soft gel matrices have been reviewed [106]. These "preparative" separations are "prepscale" only as regards column dimensions. The sample through-put per gram of stationary phase is, however, in the usual analytical range around 10^{-3} g of sample per gram of stationary phase. Analysis time and dilution is high because of the large and soft particles. Enantiomeric separations in organic eluent have also been achieved successfully with acetylated cellulose [107].

Highly efficient enantiomeric separations have been obtained with silica gel based bonded phases [108, 109]. Enantiomeric sulfoxides, amines, amino acids, alcohols, hydroxy acids, etc. were separated successfully in non aqueous eluents.

For the separation of amino acids and their derivatives chiral stationary phases with bonded amino acids on an organic polymeric matrix [110] as well as on silica have been used [111 to 116].

The separation can be achieved in aqueous acetonitrile mixtures or in plain water but chelating metals like copper have to be on the stationary phase and in the eluent. In Figure 2-36 the chiral separation of free amino acids is shown. Because of the slow mass transfer kinetics with ligand exchange, the efficiency of these columns is relatively low. The k-values depend strongly on the copper concentration, the eluent composition, temperature and, of course, on the bonded amino acid. Besides amino acids the enantiomeric separations of barbiturates and other pharmaceuticals have been described [116].

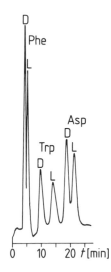

Figure 2-36. Chiral separation of free amino acids. Stationary phase: silica with bonded chiral proline; eluent: water, $7 \cdot 10^{-4}$ mol/L $CuSO_4$; temperature: 35°C.

2.2.10 Selection of a Separation System

In the previous sections the principles of the different separation mechanisms have been discussed. More than 100 different stationary phases are on the market, prepared by several manufacturers. Of course, several phases are identical but are sold under different trade names. As discussed for silica, for reversed phases and for other bonded phases, the selectivity is a function of the physical and surface characteristics. It is therefore not surprising that batch to batch reproducibility is a problem. It is also a problem to transfer a separation from one stationary phase to another from a different manufacturer, even if both phases are labeled identically.

For a newcomer it may be easy to select a separation system with respect to the principal separation mechanisms, because many separations are described in the handbooks of classical column liquid chromatography already [118 to 120]. Reference to this literature should always be the first task.

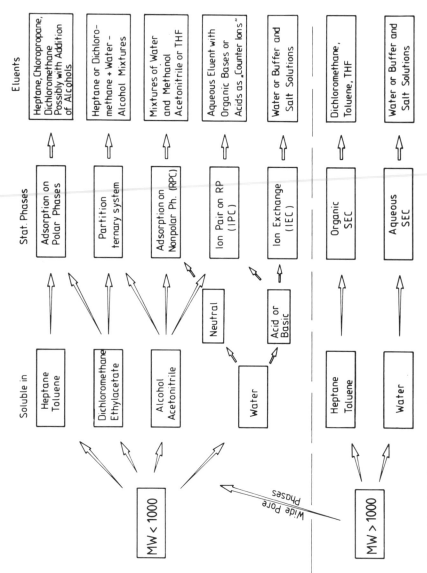

Figure 2-37. Selection of a separation system according to sample solubility.

A general scheme for the selection of a separation system according to the solubility of the samples is demonstrated in Figure 2-37. With some knowledge of sample composition and solute structure Table 2-5 may give some suggestions for the selection on an "optimal" system.

In chromatography, in addition to solute structure, the whole milieu, i. e. the stationary phase, the eluent and the solute have always to be considered together. As demonstrated in

Table 2-5. Selection of a Separation System according to Sample Structures Parameters.

Structure Parameter	Chromatographic Separation System				
	Adsorption		Partitioning	IEC	SEC
	SiO$_2$	RP			
Size	(+)	+	+		+ +
Homologous Series		+ +	+ +		(+)
Isomers: – steric (cris-trans)	+ +	+ +			
– positional	+ +	+			
– branching	(+)	+ +			(+)
– optical			with additives or special bonded phases		
Kind and Number of Substituent:					
– alkyl groups	(+)	+ +	+ +		
– non polar groups (aromatic, double bonds, halogen)	+ +	+ +	+		
– medium polar groups (nitro, carbonyl ester)	+ +	+	+		
– polar (phenolic, alkoholic, amide)	+	+ +		(+)	
			preferentially IPC		
– dissociable groups, acids and bases		IPC		+ +	

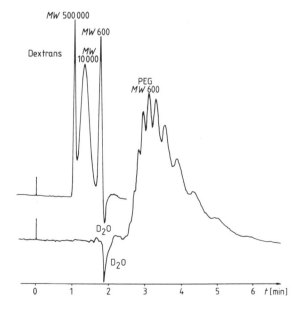

Figure 2-38. Exclusion and sorption of dextrans and PEG on a glycol phase [98]. Stationary phase: glycol bonded on LiChrosorb Si 100; eluent: water; solutes: dextran (MW 10000 and 500000), raffinose (MW 595), polyethylene glycol (MW 600); Inert: D$_2$0.

Figure 2-38 for two water-soluble, neutral polymers and a glycol-bonded phase, the dextranes are eluted before t_M and separated according to a size-exclusion mechanism, where as a polymeric standard (PEG 600) is retarded and partially separated into its polymolecular constituents.

Another guiding factor in system selection should be the aim of the separation. The optimum is a separation as complete as necessary, in the shortest time, with conditions as simple and easy as possible.

Water-soluble samples are best separated with RPC. Retention increases with increasing hydrophobicity, i. e. with decreasing solubility in water. To achieve elution, organic, water-miscible solvents are added to the aqueous eluent. Polar solutes may give asymmetric and distorted peaks. The addition of appropriate counter-ions to the eluent increases efficiency and effects system selectivity as discussed in the IPC section.

Dissociated solutes can be successfully separated in IEC. The separation is principally due to ionic interaction of solutes with the stationary phase. Retention can be affected via pH and ionic strength in the aqueous eluent. Hydrophobic interactions may be noticed, and can be controlled according to RPC rules. With these systems interaction between solute and stationary phase are essential. By sorption, especially in RPC, structural changes of solute molecules such as unfolding of protein chains may occur. For the elution of hydrophobic species a relatively high organic content in the eluent may be required. This also can effect protein structure and hence biological activity. For analytical purposes and qualitative identification gradient elution of peptides and proteins in RPC is an efficient and selective system of high separation capabilities. To overcome peak distortion counter-ions can also be added. In preparative separations the removal of the omnipresent counter-ions from the separated solutes may be problematic.

In SEC, by definition no interaction of solute and stationary phase occurs. Solute decomposition should be minimal. The separation is only due to differences in molecular size. The elution is already finished when retentive chromatography starts. The number of peaks that can be separated is, therefore, limited.

To sum up, for biological analysis, the separation capabilities of RPC are highest. However, the danger of solute structural changes of enzymes and proteins is also high. The problems are minimal with SEC, but then peak capacity is small.

2.2.11 Coupling of Separation Systems (Column Switching)

To improve resolution it may be necessary to separate a sample on a number of different stationary phases. This can be done by coupling different columns in series or in parallel. In contrast to GC the eluent plays an important role in the chromatographic system. It is difficult to change mobile phase composition during column switching. Therefore, this approach is limited to a variation of the column length (plate number) or variation of the phase ratio of the stationary phase (amount of liquid stationary phase, specific surface area, hydrophobicity of bonded phases, etc.).

In system selection, the main emphasis is on the compatibility of the different stationary phases with the eluents applied. Usually, a preseparation is carried out on a relatively short column, and fractions of this eluate are subsequently separated on other columns containing the same or other stationary phases. This column switching technique can be used to accelerate analysis, to improve selectivity and resolution, and to perform on-line sample preconcentration or on-line sample pretreatment.

It is difficult to give a general description of column switching because the application of this method depends strongly on the analytical aim and on the sample composition. The principles of operation of coupled column systems will, therefore, be explained with typical examples. Several companies offer equipment for column switching. Their application to the individual analytical problem requires endeavour and system optimization.

To speed up analysis when only a few solutes, in a multicomponent mixture, have to be determined, "box-car" chromatography may be helpful [121]: From the primary separation on a short column, the components to be determined are flushed to an efficient column, whereas the preceeding and following peaks are flushed to waste. In the second column several analyses are performed simultaneously, one after the other, as in a box-car.

Another possible application of column switching is optimization of column selectivity to improve resolution. Here also a preseparated mixture is separated on different columns either in parallel or successively. Because it is problematic to remove the eluent from the transferred segment, the applicability of this system is limited to columns tolerating the eluent of the preseparation. Examples of this type have been described [122, 123]. Columns with different amounts of stationary liquid phase (phase ratio) and stationary phases with different specific surface areas have been used at constant eluent composition. A schematic representation of this method is shown in Figure 2-39 a. The preseparation takes place in column I and segments can be flushed either to column II or III. Of course, if the later eluting components are separated sufficiently in column I, this column would be connected directly to the detector. System optimization has to be done very carefully. The switching is only possible at a time when no solute is eluted from column I. The practicability of this system can be improved if it is possible to optimize the eluent composition for each column by additional solvent delivery systems.

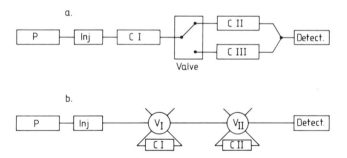

Figure 2-39. Schematic presentation of column switching. a: in series or parallel column switching; b: column switching for trace enrichment and preseparation (sample clean-up). Backflush pumps for C I or C II can be installed at valve V_I or V_{II}, respectively.

It often happens that only one or a few components in a complex matrix have to be determined. The column switching system can then be applied for on-line sample clean-up or trace enrichment out of dilute solutions [124 to 127]. With biological samples e. g. the removal of polymeric components, it is essential to preserve the analytical column and thus prolonging its life-time. In these cases, the requirements for the quality of the preseparating column are not very high.

Stationary phases with large particle diameter (inexpensive materials) can be used. Such a column switching set-up is shown schematically in Figure 2-39 b. Column I serves again for preseparation. The position of valve V_{II} is so that column I is directly connected to the detector and column II is bypassed. The efficiency of column I is not sufficient to separate the sample totally. A cut of the elution profile of column I containing the solutes to be determined is therefore brought onto column II. This cut can be from the beginning (front cut) or from an intermediate portion (heart cut) or from the end (end cut) of the preseparation. While the separation of the cut takes place in column II (the pump is now directly connected to column II and to the detector), column I can be cleaned and regenerated. This can be done by backflushing with solvent from a second pump. Peak broadening in the switching valves and connecting tubes can be ignored if the k-values of the solutes are higher on column II than on column I. In this case, the solutes will be concentrated at the top of column II. If possible, an eluent change at the beginning of elution on column II can accelerate this final separation.

A preconcentration can be done with the same set-up. Here, the diluted solution is flushed through column I. With aqueous solutions for the concentration of organic components, this column should be packed with reversed phase. At the end of this step, elution starts with a solvent change, and the desired cut is brought to the analytical column. During the separation the preconcentration column can be cleaned and regenerated. The optimization of the chromatographic conditions is very important (only a window is cut out) and requires a careful adjustment of eluent composition and separation conditions. An on-line concentration between the first and second column ensures good starting conditions for the separation in the second column.

To illustrate the column switching technique with eluent composition change and for rapid sample preparation, an example is shown in Figure 2-40 for the determination of cyclosporin A (CyA) in blood [128]. A similar set-up as in Figure 2-39 b was used. The sample is injected in a short precolumn packed with porous layer beads coated with RP C_8 (dp 30 to 40 μm). Polar sample components are eluted, at this stage, directly to the detector. The segment, including the interesting component and the internal standard cyclosporin D (CyD) are transferred with a slightly stronger eluent to column II packed with RP C_{18} (dp 5 μm). For a short period only, as indicated in Figure 2-40, both columns are coupled together for sample transfer. The k-values of the solutes on this column are larger, therefore, the zone is sharpened, and the final separation on the analytical column is achieved with another stronger eluent. No interfering components were eluted in a blank run (trace A), so that a low detection limit could be achieved. After this separation, column I is connected again to the detector, regenerated by an appropriate solvent flush and reconditioned with the initial eluent for a new injection. At the same time column II is regenerated for the next separation with a second pump. Because of the different zone sharpening processes, only 0.5 mL blood were required to achieve a detection limit as low as 20 ng/mL for the cyclosporin.

These examples may demonstrate that column switching is an excellent method to increase chromatographic selectivity, to concentrate dilute samples and to analyse isolated solutes from very complex mixtures. By applying the heart cut technique, column switching can be used to automate on-line sample pretreatment and cleaning procedures.

Figure 2-40. Column switching with eluent change for rapid sample preparation: heart-cut technique [128]. Analysis of cyclosporin A (CyA) in blood. A: blank blood; B: 100 ng/mL CyA; C: 1000 ng/mL CyA. Internal standard: 1500 ng/mL CyD. Detection: 210 nm, 0.02 a. u. f. s. For details see text.

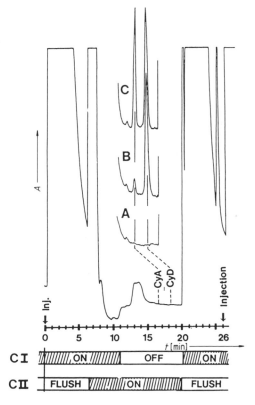

2.3 References

[1] L. R. Snyder, and J. J. Kirkland: *Introduction to Modern Liquid Chromatography.* Wiley-Interscience, New York 1979.

[2] H. Engelhardt: *High Performance Liquid Chromatography.* Springer, Berlin-Heidelberg-New York 1979.

[3] C. Horváth: *High Performance Liquid Chromatography, Advances and Perspectives,* Vol. **1** and **2**. Academic Press, New York 1980.

[4] A. M. Krstulović and P. R. Brown: *Reversed-Phase High Performance Liquid Chromatography.* Wiley-Interscience, New York 1982.

[5] J. C. Giddings: *Dynamics of Chromatography.* Dekker, New York 1965.

[6] G. Guiochon, in: C. Horváth (ed.): *High Performance Liquid Chromatography, Advances and Perspectives,* Vol. **2**, p. 1 – 56. Academic Press, New York 1980.

[7] I. Halász, *Z. Anal. Chem.* **277**, 257 (1975).

[8] A. B. Littlewood. *Gas Chromatography,* 2nd Ed. Academic Press, New York 1970.

[9] I. Halász, in: J. J. Kirkland (ed.): *Modern Practice of Liquid Chromatography,* Chapter 9. Wiley-Interscience, New York 1971.

[10] Courtesy of F. Eisenbeiss, E. Merck AG, Darmstadt.

[11] J. L. DiCesare, M. W. Dong, and L. S. Ettre, *Chromatographia* **14**, 257 (1981).

[12] D. E. Domalgaska, and C. R. Loscombe, *Chromatographia* **15**, 657 (1982).

[13] I. Halász, and G. Görlitz, *Angew. Chem.* **94**, 50 (1982).
[14] I. Halász, *Ber. Bunsenges.* **77**, 140 (1973).
[15] P. A. Bristow, *J. Chromatogr.* **149**, 13 (1978).
[16] R. Endele, I. Halász, and K. K. Unger, *J. Chromatogr.* **99**, 377 (1974).
[17] G. Ahr, Ph. D. Thesis, Universität des Saarlandes. Saarbrücken 1982.
[18] I. Halász, R. Endele, and J. Asshauer, *J. Chromatogr.* **112**, 37 (1975).
[19] K. K. Unger, W. Messner, and K. F. Krebs, *J. Chromatogr.* **149**, 1 (1978).
[20] R. Ohmacht, and I. Halász, *Chromatographia* **14**, 155 (1981).
[21] R. Ohmacht, and I. Halász, *Chromatographia* **14**, 216 (1981).
[22] G. J. Kennedy, and J. H. Knox, *J. Chromatogr. Sci.* **10**, 549 (1972).
[23] J. H. Knox, and J. Vasvari, *J. Chromatogr.* **83**, 181 (1973).
[24] J. H. Knox, and A. Pryde, *J. Chromatogr.* **112**, 171 (1975).
[25] H. Elgass, H. Engelhardt, and I. Halász, *Z. Anal. Chem.* **294**, 97 (1979).
[26] A. Wheeler, in: P. H. Emmett (ed.): *Catalysis,* Vol. **2**, p. 116. Reinhold, New York 1955.
[27] I. Halász, and K. Martin, *Angew. Chem., Int. Ed. Engl.* **17**, 901 (1978).
[28] R. K. Iler: *The Chemistry of Silica.* Wiley-Interscience, New York 1979.
[29] K. K. Unger: *Porous Silica.* Elsevier, Amsterdam 1979.
[30] H. Engelhardt, and H. Müller, *J. Chromatogr.* **218**, 395 (1981).
[31] H. Müller, and H. Engelhardt, in I. Molnar (ed.): *Practical Aspects of Modern HPLC,* p. 25. de Gruyter, Berlin 1982.
[32] H. Engelhardt, B. Dreyer, and H. Schmidt, *Chromatographia* **16**, 11 (1982).
[33] L. R. Snyder: *Principles of Adsorption Chromatography,* Dekker, New York 1968.
[34] W. Böhme, and H. Engelhardt, *J. Chromatogr.* **133**, 67 (1977).
[35] H. Engelhardt, *J. Chromatogr. Sci.* **15**, 380 (1977).
[36] B. L. Karger, H. Engelhardt, K. Conroe, and I. Halász, in: N. Stock (ed.): *Gas Chromatography,* p. 112. Institut of Petroleum, London 1971.
[37] H. Engelhardt, J. Asshauer, U. Neue, and N. Weigand, *Anal. Chem.* **46**, 336 (1974).
[38] J. F. K. Huber, C. A. M. Meijers, and J. A. R. J. Hulsman, *Anal. Chem.* **44**, 111 (1972).
[39] C. A. M. Meijers, J. A. R. J. Hulsman, and J. F. K. Huber, *Z. Anal. Chem.* **261**, 347 (1972).
[40] W. J. Th. Brugman, S. Heemstra, and J. C. Kraak, *J. Chromatogr.* **218**, 285 (1981).
[41] A. Nasner, and L. Kraus, *J. Chromatogr.* **216**, 389 (1981).
[42] W. J. T. Brugman, S. Heemstra, and J. C. Kraak, *Chromatographia* **15**, 282 (1982).
[43] G. A. Howard, and A. J. P. Martin, *Biochem. J.* **46**, 532 (1950).
[44] I. Halász, and I. Sebestian, *Angew. Chem.* **81**, 464 (1969).
[45] I. Halász, and I. Sebestian, *J. Chromatogr. Sci.* **12**, 161 (1974).
[46] J. J. Kirkland, *J. Chromatogr. Sci.* **9**, 206 (1971).
[47] K. K. Unger, N. Becker, and P. Roumeliotis, *J. Chromatogr.* **125**, 115 (1976).
[48] J. J. Kirkland, *J. Chromatogr. Sci.* **9**, 206 (1971).
[49] B. Lillig, Master Thesis, Universität des Saarlandes, Saarbrücken 1980.
[50] H. Engelhardt, and G. Ahr, *Chromatographia* **14**, 227 (1981).
[51] C. Horváth, W. Melander, and I. Molnar, *Anal. Chem.* **49**, 142 (1977).
[52] K. Karch, I. Sebestian, I. Halász, and H. Engelhardt, *J. Chromatogr.* **122**, 171 (1976).
[53] H. Engelhardt, and M. Aufsatz, *Ann. Univ. Saraviensis* **15**, 55 (1980).
[54] S. R. Bakalyar, R. McIlwrick, and E. Roggendorf, *J. Chromatogr.* **142**, 353 (1977).
[55] N. Tanaka, H. Goodell, and B. L. Karger, *J. Chromatogr.* **158**, 233 (1978).
[56] M. T. W. Hearn, in: J. C. Giddings, E. Grushka, J. Cazes, P. R. Brown (eds.): *Advances in Chromatography,* Vol. **20**, p. 1 – 82. Dekker, New York 1982.
[57] B. Grego, and M. T. W. Hearn, *Chromatographia* **14**, 589 (1981).
[58] E. Roggendorf, and R. Spatz, *J. Chromatogr.* **204**, 263 (1981).
[59] Courtesy of Spectra Physics GmbH, Darmstadt.
[60] J. L. Glajch, J. J. Kirkland, K. M. Squire, and J. M. Minor, *J. Chromatogr.* **199**, 57 (1980).
[61] L. R. Snyder, J. L. Glajch, and J. J. Kirkland, *J. Chromatogr.* **218**, 299 (1981).
[62] P. J. Schoenmakers, A. C. J. H. Drouen, H. A. H. Billiet, and L. de Galan, *Chromatographia* **15**, 688 (1982).
[63] F. Helfferich: *Ionenaustauscher.* Verlag Chemie, Weinheim 1959.
[64] R. M. McCormick, and B. L. Karger, *Anal. Chem.* **52**, 2249 (1980).

[65] G. W. K. Fong, and E. Grushka, *Anal. Chem.* **50**, 1154 (1978).
[66] C. Horváth (ed.), in: *High Performance Liquid Chromatography, Advances and Perspectives.* Vol. **2**, p. 113 – 318. Academic Press, New York 1980.
[67] G. Schill, in: J. A. Marinsky, and Y. Marcus (eds.): *Ion Exchange and Solvent Extraction,* Vol. **6**. Dekker, New York 1974.
[68] B. L. Karger, in: C. Horváth (ed.): *High Performance Liquid Chromatography, Advances and Perspektives,* Vol. **1**, p. 113 – 206. Academic Press, New York 1980.
[69] J. Crommen, and G. Schill, *J. Chromatogr.* **142**, 283 (1977).
[70] D. J. Pietrzyk, E. P. Kroeff, and T. R. Rotsch, *Anal. Chem.* **50**, 497 (1978).
[71] C. Horváth, W. Melander, and I. Molnar, *Anal. Chem.* **49**, 142 (1977).
[72] J. L. M. van de Venne, J. L. H. M. Hendrikx, and R. S. Deelder, *J. Chromatogr.* **167**, 1 (1978).
[73] G. Schomburg, and K. Zegarksi, *J. Chromatogr.* **114**, 174 (1974).
[74] R. Vivilecchia, M. Thiebaud, and R. W. Frei, *J. Chromatogr. Sci* **10**, 411 (1972).
[75] J. N. LePage, W. Lindner, G. Davies, D. E. Seitz, and B. L. Karger, *Anal. Chem.* **51**, 433 (1979).
[76] P. E. Hare, and E. Gil-Av, *Science* **204**, 1226 (1979).
[77] T. Crispin, and I. Halász, *J. Chromatogr.* **239**, 351 (1982).
[78] C. Horváth, B. Preiss, and S. R. Lipsky, *Anal. Chem.* **39**, 1422 (1967).
[79] P. Orth, Ph. D. Thesis, Universität des Saarlandes, Saarbrücken 1979.
[80] E. Martinsson, and O. Samuelson, *J. Chromatogr.* **50**, 429 (1970).
[81] D. H. Spackman, S. Moore, and W. H. Stein, *Anal. Chem.* **30**, 1190 (1958).
[82] S. Moore, and W. H. Stein, *J. Biol. Chem.* **192**, 663 (1951).
[83] M. Weigele, S. L. De Bernado, J. P. Tergi, and W. Leimgruber, *J. Am. Chem. Soc.* **94**, 5927 (1972).
[84] S. Udenfried, S. Stein, P. Böhlen, W. Dairman, W. Leimgruber, and M. Weigele, *Science* **178**, 871 (1972).
[85] H. Engelhardt, and U. D. Neue, *Chromatographia* **15**, 403 (1982).
[86] B. Lillig, Ph. D. Thesis, Universität des Saarlandes, Saarbrücken 1984.
[87] L. R. Snyder, in: C. Horváth (ed.): *High Performance Liquid Chromatography, Advances and Perspectives,* Vol. **1**, p. 207 – 316. Academic Press, New York 1980.
[88] H. Elgass, Ph. D. Thesis, Universität des Saarlandes, Saarbrücken 1978.
[89] H. G. Barth, *J. Chromatogr. Sci.* **18**, 409 (1980).
[90] E. Pfannkoch, K. C. Lu, F. E. Regnier, and H. G. Barth, *J. Chromatogr. Sci.* **18**, 430 (1980).
[91] H. Engelhardt, and D. Mathes, *J. Chromatogr.* **185**, 305 (1979).
[92] H. Engelhardt, and D. Mathes, *Chromatographia* **14**, 325 (1981).
[93] H. Engelhardt, G. Ahr, and T. W. Hearn, *J. Liq. Chromatogr.* **4**, 1361 (1981).
[94] B. A. Neddermeyer, and L. B. Rogers, *Anal. Chem.* **47**, 95 (1969).
[95] B. Vollmert: *Polymer Chemistry.* Springer, Berlin-Heidelberg-New York 1973.
[96] Z. Grubistic, R. Rempp, and H. Benoit, *J. Polym. Sci.* **5**, 753 (1967).
[97] K. Horiike, H. Tojo, T. Yamano, and M. Nozaki, *Biochem. Int.* **4**, 477 (1982).
[98] H. Engelhardt, and D. Mathes, *J. Chromatogr.* **142**, 311 (1977).
[99] C. W. Qualts, jr., and H. J. Segall, *J. Chromatogr.* **150**, 202 (1978).
[100] O. E. Brust, and I. Halász, *J. Chromatogr.* **83**, 15 (1973).
[101] W. Holstein, *Chromatographia* **14**, 469 (1981).
[102] L. R. Snyder, and T. C. Schunk, *Anal. Chem.* **54**, 1764 (1982).
[103] J. C. Linden, and C. L. Lawhead, *J. Chromatogr.* **105**, 125 (1975).
[104] R. B. Meagher, and A. Furst *J. Chromatogr.* **117**, 211 (1975).
[105] P. Orth, and H. Engelhardt. *Chromatographia* **15**, 91 (1982).
[106] G. Blaschke, *Angew. Chemie* **92**, 14 (1980).
[107] G. Hesse, and R. Hagel, *Chromatographia* **6**, 277 (1973).
[108] W. H. Pirkle, and D. W. House, *J. Org. Chem.* **12**, 1957 (1979).
[109] W. H. Pirkle, and J. M. Finn, *J. Org. Chem.* **46**, 2935 (1979).
[110] V. A. Davankov, in: J. C. Giddings, E. Grushka, J. Cazes, P. R. Brown (eds.): *Advances in Chromatography,* Vol. **18**, p. 139 – 196. Dekker, New York 1980.
[111] A. Foucault, M. Caude, and L. Oliveros, *J. Chromatogr.* **185**, 345 (1979).
[112] G. Gübitz, W. Jellenz, G. Löfler, and W. Santi, *J. High Resol. Chromatogr.* **3**, 145 (1979).
[113] H. Engelhardt, and S. Kromidas, *Naturwissenschaften* **67**, 353 (1980).
[114] W. Lindner, *Naturwissenschaften* **67**, 354 (1980).

[115] P. Roumeliotis, K. K. Unger, A. A. Kurganov, and A. V. Davankov, *Lecture*. Philadelphia (1982).

[116] S. Kromidas, Ph. D. Thesis, Universität des Saarlandes, Saarbrücken 1983

[117] H. Engelhardt, and H. Elgass, *J. Chromatogr.* **158**, 249 (1978).

[118] Z. Deyl, K. Măcek, and J. Janak (eds.): *Liquid Column Chromatography*. Elsevier, Amsterdam 1975.

[119] E. Heftmann: *Chromatography*, 3 rd Ed. Reinhold, New York 1975.

[120] O. Mikes: *Laboratory Handbook of Chromatographic and Allied Methods*. Wiley & Sons, New York 1979.

[121] L. R. Snyder, J. W. Dolan, and S. van der Wal, *J. Chomatogr.* **203**, 3 (1981).

[122] J. F. K. Huber, R. van der Linden, E. Ecker, and M. Oreans, *J. Chromatogr.* **83**, 267 (1973).

[123] R. J. Dolphin, F. W. Willmot, A. D. Mills, and L. P. J. Hoogeveen, *J. Chromatogr.* **122**, 259 (1976).

[124] F. Erni, H. P. Keller, C. Morin, M. Schmitt, *J. Chromatogr.* **204**, 65 (1981).

[125] H. Hulpke, and U. Werthmann, *Chromatographia* **12**, 390 1979).

[126] H. Hulpke, and U. Werthmann, *Chromatographia* **13**, 395 (1980).

[127] W. Roth, K. Beschke, R. Jauch, A. Zimmer, and F. W. Koss, *J. Chromatogr.* **222**, 13 (1981).

[128] K. Nussbaumer, W. Niederberger, and H. P. Keller, *HRC & CC* **5**, 424 (1982).

[129] A. M. Krstulović, H. Colin, and G. Guiochon, *Anal. Chem.* **54**, 2438 (1982).

3   Instrumentation

by *Klaus-Peter Hupe, Gerard Rozing* and *Helge Schrenker*

3 Instrumentation

3.1 Introduction

HPLC is a relatively young analytical technique. Suitable instrumentation did not become commercially available until about a decade ago. The related methods already in existence were classical column chromatography, gas chromatography and thin layer chromatography. The knowledge gained from these methods prooved to be very helpful in the development of the new technique. However, it very soon became apparent that practical experience of these methods could only partially be transfered to the design and construction of what at that time was called a "Modern Liquid Chromatograph". In particular, a number of specific criteria had to be met which put high demands on design and construction:

a) HPLC-Columns are filled with stationary phases of small particle diameter, generating high pressures at the kind of solvent flow-rates necessary to achieve short analysis times.

b) Detectors used in HPLC are sensitive to flow and pressure fluctuations (noise). Moreover quantitation with concentration dependant detectors requires high stability of effluent flow rate.

c) The separation process has an antagonistic effect, i.e. dispersion of the sample in the mobile phase, leading to remixing of separated components and a decrease of the maximum sample concentration in the eluting peak (detection), Dispersion occurs everywhere in the system from injector to detector.

d) Solvents used as mobile phases are often corrosive, particularly those used in reverse phase chromatography, which is the preferred method for biochemical applications.

These peculiarities of HPLC as an instrumental technique have to be taken into account for the proper design, construction and operation of the whole system. It has taken more than a decade of research and development to solve the technical problems encountered and to make instruments and components commercially available which are reliable, easy and safe to use and have an appropriate price/performance relationship. The recent trend to further miniaturize column dimensions, both with respect to length and diameter, is a new challenge for instrument design, especially with respect to points b) and c) above.

The aim of this chapter is:

- to clarify technical terms used in conjunction with HPLC instrumentation;
- to explain the basic operating principles of the most important elements of a liquid chromatograph;
- to give some insights into the relevance of important instrument specifications with respect to the qualitative and quantitative results of the analysis;
- and to give some hints for the effective use of the instrument.

Figure 3-1 is a schematic representation of the essential elements of a liquid chromatograph; a pump P delivers one or more solvents out of solvent containers A, B, C into the system. Proportioning valves a, b, c control the composition of the main stream. The sample is injected into the column C via a valve V. The column effluent is continuously monitored by a detector D, the signal of which is recorded or otherwise handled for quantitative and/or qualitative analysis. The effluent is finally collected in a waste bottle W.

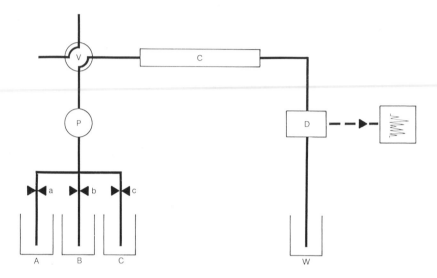

Figure 3-1. Schematic of a liquid chromatograph. A, B, C solvent containers; a, b, c proportioning valves; P pump; V injection valve; C column; D detector, W waste bottle.

3.2 Solvent Delivery

3.2.1 Solvent Storage

Two undesirable properties of solvents used as mobile phases require particular consideration with regard to storage and handling in an HPLC instrument.

a) Many solvents are toxic. The "threshold limit value" (TLV) or "maximale Arbeitsplatz-Konzentration" (MAK) indicates the maximum of its vapour concentration allowed in the working environment and can be found in relevant handbooks e.g. in [1] and [2]. The TLV of one of the most common solvents in RPLC, acetonitrile, is 40 ppm.

To prevent contamination of the working environment, the solvent containers in the LC instrument should be hermetically sealed. A small stream of inert gas through the vapour space of the containers (with the outlet leading into a suitable exhaust or fume hood) will prevent build-up of vacuum in the container and absorption of air into the solvent.

b) Solvents, as supplied, are usually saturated with air. This can impair instrument operation in several ways. Air-bubble formation by spontaneous deaeration, particularly in the inlet valve of the pump, can disturb or completely interrupt correct pump operation. This is enhanced, when the pump temperature is significantly higher than the solvent container temperature, because air solubility in aqueous solvents decreases by about 1% with every °C increase in temperature. Air-bubble formation may also occur when solvent mixing takes place up-stream of the pump, in particular when water and methanol are mixed (air solubility in the mixture is lower than in the individual solvents).

Gas-bubbles can also form in the detector cell, impairing detector baseline stability. This can usually be overcome by putting a small flow restrictor downstream of the detector. Less well known is the influence of dissolved gases on the signal of many LC detectors. Experimental data on the problems that dissolved air (oxygen) can cause in UV-absorbance and fluorescense detection are published in [3] and [4]. The refractive index of the mobile phase is also affected by the amount of dissolved gas. Detector drift may therefore occur if the gas concentration is changing (because of temperature changes in the solvent container).

Complete de-aeration of the mobile phase is vital when using an electrochemical detector in the reductive mode.

The most common de-aeration procedure used in HPLC instruments is sparging helium or nitrogen into the solvent(s). An initial flow of 100 mL/min, which can be reduced to about 10 mL/min after 10 minutes, is usually adequate for de-aerating 1 L of solvent. However, this method only replaces the air in the mobile phase with helium or nitrogen. When using a pump with inlet valves which are sensitive to gas-bubble formation, degassing by heat and vacuum might be advisable [5].

3.2.2 Solvent Pumps

The solvent pump has to supply "constant" flow of mobile phase at a pressure required to overcome the flow resistance of the column(s). Before discussing the commonly used principles to realize this task, the relevance of a "constant flow" for the qualitative and quantitative result of an LC analysis will be reviewed.

3.2.2.1 Flow Stability and Analysis Precision

A substance eluting from the column is distributed over a certain volume of the mobile phase, referred to as the peak volume V. Passing at a flow-rate F through the cell of a detector with a concentration dependent response, this peak volume is registered as a peak of width w_b on the recorder trace of the detector signal (measured in time units):

$$w_b = \frac{V}{F} \qquad (\text{if } F = \text{const}) .$$

Since peak area is determined by peak height and peak width, it becomes obvious that this most common measure for peak quantitation is directly influenced by flow-rate variations occuring while the associated substance band (peak) is passing through the detector cell.

A secondary effect of flow-rate on quantitation is its influence on column efficiency (plate height), which results in a certain dependence of peak height (and width) on flow-rate.

Peak retention time t_R, as the means of qualitative assessment of the substance band, is also dependent on flow-rate:

$$t_M = \frac{1}{F} \cdot V_M; \quad \text{and} \quad t_R = \frac{1}{F} \cdot V_M (1 + k).$$

V_M is the mobile phase volume in the column; t_M is the retention time of an unretained substance ($k = 0$).

According to their different effects on the analysis result, flow fluctuations can be subdivided into noise, wander and drift, which are characterized by their typical time behaviour relative to average peak duration and retention time [6].

Flow noise is characterized by dominant fluctuation periods which are short compared to average peak base width. It mainly affects detector baseline noise (particularly of RI- and EC-detectors) and therefore peak recognition by electronic integrators (in the region of low signal-to-noise ratios) and detection limits.

Flow wander is characterized by dominant fluctuation periods in the order of 1 to 10 times the average peak base width. It directly affects peak area precision. The magnitude of its effect is determined by the ratio of its dominant fluctuation period and the peak base width. This relationship is plotted in Figure 3-2, which indicates that flow wander reaches its maximum effect on peak area precision if the fluctuation period is 5 to 10 times the peak base width [6], [7].

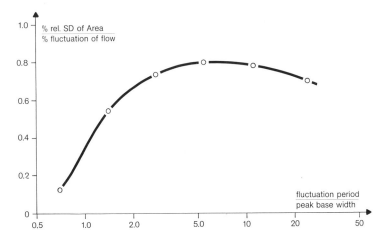

Figure 3-2. Contribution of flow wander to standard deviation of peak area reaches maximum, when period of flow fluctuation (inverse of fluctuation frequency) is about 5 to 10 times peak base width.

Flow drift is characterized by fluctuation periods larger than peak retention times. It affects both peak retention times and areas in the same direction: increasing flow-rate leads to decreasing retention times and areas and vice versa. The resultant quantitative errors become systematic, the longer the fluctuation periods are, i. e. the longer the flow is drifting steadily in one direction.

Frequent recalibration and the use of internal standards are suitable means to reduce such systematic errors.

3.2.2.2 Pump Operating Principles

For the reasons given above, an LC pump must deliver flow which is:
- pulseless (no noise);
- constant (no wander or drift);
- reproducible (from day to day).

Instrument manufacturers employ various operating principles in their pump designs to achieve this goal. Figures 3-3 through 3-8 give a survey of pump types in common use today.

Pneumatic amplifier pumps and high pressure syringe pumps (Figures 3-3 and 3-4), though no longer available in commercial HPLC equipment, can be found in older instruments still in use in many laboratories.

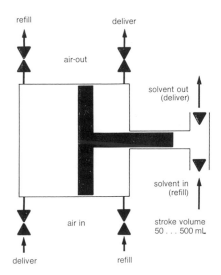

Figure 3-3. Pneumatic Amplifier Pump.
Delivers pulseless flow at constant pressure; flow rate through column depends on column resistance, i. e. flow is set through air pressure setting.

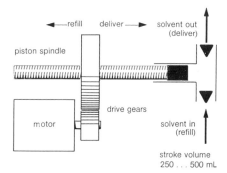

Figure 3-4. Syringe (positive displacement) Pump.
Delivers pulseless constant flow (if no pressure changes occur); flow-rate is controlled by piston drive speed.

The vast majority of HPLC pumps offered today are reciprocating single, dual or triple piston pumps, with or without diaphragm, all more or less approaching one of the operating principles shown in Figures 3-5 through 3-8.

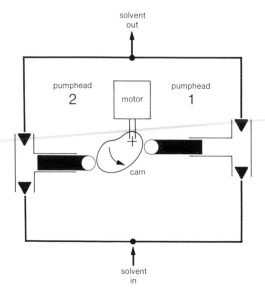

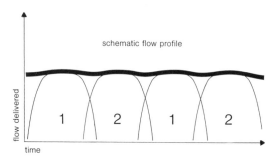

Figure 3-5. Cam driven, Dual Head Reciprocating Pump delivers constant flow (if properly roll-off compensated) with relatively low pulsation; flow-rate is controlled by cam rotation (stroke-frequency, typically 0.01 ... 1 Hz; further improvement of flow stability is possible by operating three parallel pump heads 120° out of phase.

These pump types all require some sort of flow control to maintain constant flow against variable pressures. They all have in common that, because of liquid compressibility, the delivery flow-rate decreases ("rolls off") when the pressure increases. Four different solutions are used to overcome this problem:

a) Roll-off compensation circuitry (found in pump types 3-5 and 3-6) corrects the pump drive, based on measurements of the pump outlet pressure.

b) Flow feed-back control (found in pump type 3-7). A flow sensor, operating independently from the pump, measures the flow-rate and, via feed-back circuitry, corrects the pump drive when the measured flow-rate deviates from the setting.

c) Constant pressure operation of the pump (realised in conjunction with pump type 3-6). A pressure regulator between pump and column maintains constant pump outlet pressure, independant of column resistance, flow rate and solvent.

Figure 3-6. Crank driven, Single Head
Reciprocating Pump.
Delivers constant flow (if properly roll-off
compensated) with medium pulsation
(pulse damper required); flow-rate is controlled by stroke frequency, typically 0.02
... 2 Hz; fast refill by speeding up motor
during refill phase.

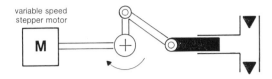

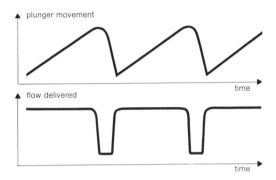

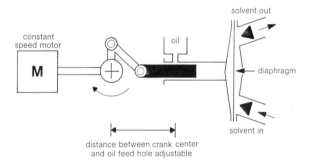

distance between crank center
and oil feed hole adjustable

Figure 3-7. Crank driven, Single
Head Diaphragm Pump.
Piston movement is transfered to
pump chamber through oil and elastic steel diaphragm; delivers constant
flow (feed back flow control); stroke
frequency is constant (5 ... 10 Hz);
flow-rate is controlled by adjustment
of effective stroke volume; efficient
pulse damping is enhanced by high
and constant stroke frequency.

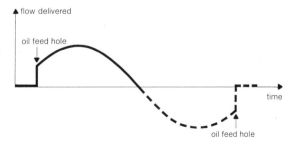

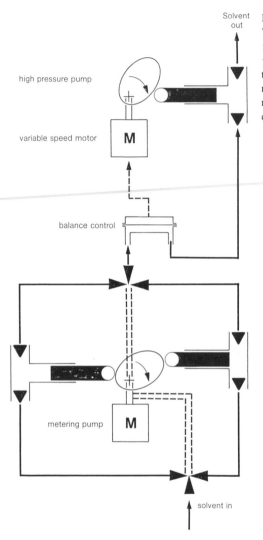

Solvent
out

Figure 3-8. Dual Stage Reciprocating Pump. The low pressure metering pump generates the flow; the (second stage) high pressure pump which is controlled by a balance controller between the two pumps, transfers that flow to the required pressure; inlet and outlet valve of the metering pump are synchronized with the pump drive.

high pressure pump

variable speed motor

balance control

metering pump

solvent in

d) Dual stage pumps (type 3-8), Two separate pumps operate in series; a low-pressure pump acting as the flow metering device; and a high-pressure pump forwarding to the column, at the required operating pressure, any liquid volume received from the low-pressure pump. Operation of the high-pressure ("slave") pump is controlled such that its flow intake is balanced against the flow delivery of the low pressure metering pump.

The flow delivered by a reciprocating pump is always pulsating in the rhythm of the piston movement. Although pulsation is minimized in single head pumps by making the refill time as short as possible (Figure 3-6) and in dual or triple head pumps by overlapping piston movement (Figure 3-5), additional pulsation damping is often required. A commonly found pulse damper is the hydraulic analog of a capacitor. In principle this is a small elastic vessel that "swallows" a part of the stroke volume delivered by the pump and dispenses solvent to the column while the pump is refilling.

3.2.3 Solvent Blending and Gradient Forming Devices

For many LC applications the mobile phase is a mixture of two or more solvents, the mixing ratio of which has to be easily changeable according to a time program during the analysis (gradient elution). Control of the mixing ratio is thus an additional task of the solvent delivery system.

3.2.3.1 Mobile Phase Composition, Stability and Analysis Precision

The influence of the precision of mobile phase composition on the qualitative and quantitative result of an LC analysis is less obvious than that of flow stability, particularly in gradient elution. For a given stationary phase and sample, the composition (and nature) of the mobile phase determines the partition equilibrium of the sample in mobile and stationary phase and thus the capacity factor k. This in turn determines the retention time t_R. For RPLC numerous data are available on the relationship between mobile phase composition and capacity factors, e. g. [8] and [9]. As a rule of thumb a 1% change in mobile phase composition will cause a 3 to 10% change in retention time in isocratic elution (smaller and larger influence is possible).

In gradient elution, deviations of the actual composition from the programmed gradient are generally more critical in the later part of the elution process. Furthermore, the demands on composition precision increase with decreasing column length, decreasing gradient steepness and increasing mobile phase velocity [7]. These rules can successfully be applied when analysis precision is unsatisfactory in conjunction with gradient elution.

3.2.3.2 Types of Solvent Blending and Gradient Devices

For automatic solvent blending and gradient generation two methods are in use:

a) One flow controlled pump is applied for each solvent. Mixing of the solvents occurs downstream of these pumps usually in a low-volume mixing chamber. The volumetric mixing

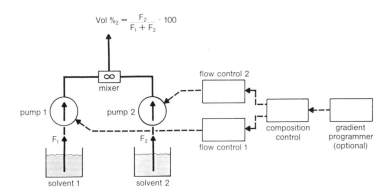

Figure 3-9. Example of a binary solvent blending device with two flow controlled pumps determining solvent mixing ratio (Vol %).

ratio of the resultant solvent mixture is determined by the ratio of the individual flow-rates $F1$, $F2$... of the pumps P 1, P 2... and the sum of the flow-rates of all pumps $\sum F_i$; (Figure 3-9):

$$\text{Vol}\% \ (\text{Solvent}_k) \ = \ \frac{F_k}{\sum F_i} \cdot 100 \ .$$

To relate the mixing ratio produced by such blending devices to solvent mixtures (made up in a single flask by adding corresponding volumes of the respective solvents) the flow control must be calibrated to match the intake flows of the pumps.

b) The inlet of the solvent pump is sequentially connected to solvent containers 1, 2... in a time sharing manner through proportioning valves, i.e. it sequentially pumps solvents 1, 2... for time intervals $\Delta t1$, $\Delta t2$... (Figure 3-10). Provided the pump intake flow-rate F is constant, then the volumetric mixing ratio is determind by the ratio of the individual opening intervals $\Delta t 1$, $\Delta t 2$... of the valves $V1$, $V2$... and the total intake time:

$$\text{Vol}\% \ (\text{Solvent}_k) \ = \ \frac{\Delta t_k}{\sum \Delta t_i} \cdot 100 \ .$$

Usually the opening intervals of the proportioning valves are synchronised with the intake period tp of the pump which is defined as the time period between opening and closing of the pump inlet valve; i.e. $\sum t_i = t$p. Therefore, the combination of an existing reciprocating pump with a proportioning valve device of different make will not result in acceptable blending precision, if this combination is not specifically recommended by the pump manufacturer.

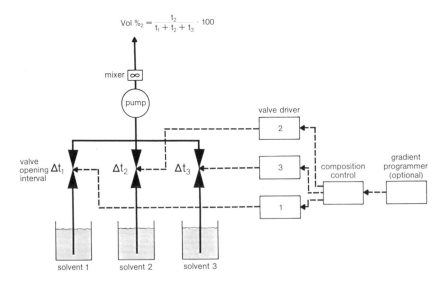

Figure 3-10. Example of a ternary solvent blending device with three (time-)proportioning valves determining solvent mixing ratio.

The blending method in either blending device is a "volume addition method", uncorrected for volume changes caused by the mixing process. This must be considered, particularly with water/methanol mixtures, when comparing results of isocratic separations on instruments with automatic solvent blending with those on instruments where the solvents have to be pre-mixed in the solvent flask. In order to make k-values comparable, all solvent volumes must be measured before mixing.

3.3 Sample Injection

3.3.1 Basic Considerations

Chromatography is a continuous process and from a hydrodynamic point of view the sample injection is a disturbance of the steady state flow conditions. Both the designer and the operator of the instrument must take care that this disturbance is kept as small as possible. To maintain the separation efficiency of the column, the sample must be injected in a narrow plug. A precise, quantitative result of the analysis requires injection of well defined sample volumes in a highly reproducible manner.

Beside these basic requirements there are a number of others a sample injection system has to fulfil:

- Injection of samples with variable volumes should be possible. For analytical purposes the range should be between 0.5 and 20 μL and for preparative applications between 0.1 and 5 mL.
- Carry over from one sample to the next, when injected consecutively, must be small.
- It should be suitable for automation.
- The design should be uncomplicated, so as to make operation easy and keep reliability high.

In practice it has turned out to be difficult to design systems serving all the above mentioned requirements equally well. Because of this, the instrumentation available is usually a compromise with certain advantages and disadvantages. The user has therefore to select the system most suitable for his purposes [10, 11].

3.3.2 Types of Sample Injectors

Sample injectors for HPLC can be classified in two groups: They either use the principle of a sluice or of a sample loop.

3.3.2.1 Injectors of the Sluice Type

With these injectors the sample is added to the mobile phase as a temporary flow increment by a syringe. The mobile phase flow is either maintained or stopped. At low pressure the sealing element through which the syringe needle is introduced into the system may be an elastomeric septum. For higher operating pressures various sealing and valve devices are available. Sluice type injectors were introduced into HPLC in the early stage of the method as an analogy of the injection technique commonly used in gas chromatography. Leak thightness at high operating pressure and chemical inertness of the sealing selements have proved to be difficult to control with these types of injectors. As a consequence, their usage is presently decreasing.

3.3.2.2 Injectors of the Loop Type

Figure 3-11 shows an injector with variable injection volume. The sample is first metered by a syringe and then introduced at port 4 of a 6-port rotary valve into the sample loop. This is accomplished at atmospheric pressure. Excessive solvent initially contained in the loop is displaced by the sample and passed through port 3 as waste. In the "Fill"-Position the mobile phase coming from the pump flows to the column via ports 1 and 6. Switching the valve to "Inject" causes the solvent to pass through ports 1 and 2 via the loop, sweeping the sample through ports 5 and 6 onto the column. The small portion of sample remaining between ports 4 and 5 is not injected during this procedure and must be flushed out before the next injection in order to avoid sample carry over.

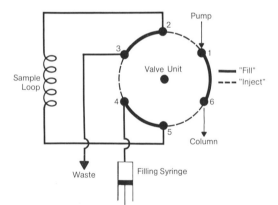

Figure 3-11. Injector of the loop type with variable injection volume.

In the injector described metering of the sample is accomplished by a syringe. The sample loop is generally only partially filled. Accuracy and precision of such a system when operated manually mainly depends on the skill of the operator. The same applies to the sample band broadening effects caused by syringe and valve manipulation. A system of this type therefore should be operated completely automatically as is shown in Figure 3-12. This avoids potential operator errors.

For manual operation, an injector valve is preferable, where the sample loop is filled completely and the complete loop volume injected. Sampling valves with internal or external loops are offered by various manufacturers. They also have the advantage of high accuracy and precision when operated manually. Their drawback is that the sample loop has to be exchanged for different sample sizes. Moreover it is necessary to flush the loop prior to the next injection with excessive sample in order to assure injection of undiluted sample. This is a disadvantage if only limited amounts of sample are available.

3.3.3 Automatic Injectors

Based on the valve arrangement described above Figure 3-12 shows an automatically operated loop injector. In the position shown solvent goes direct to the column, while the metering syringe is connected with the sample vial. The end of the sample loop is a stiff needle which can be moved up and down by an air-driven actuator. The motor-driven syringe draws a certain volume of sample up into the sample loop. The needle is raised, the vial is moved back and the needle pressed downwards against a metal seal. Switching the valve into the "Inject"-position which is accomplished pneumatically or by an electrical motor, causes the solvent to flow through ports 1 and 2 via the loop flushing the sample through ports 5 and 6 onto the column. During this procedure sample can penetrate into the channel between ports 5 and 4 by diffusion. To avoid sample carry over a valve is opened briefly before the next filling procedure and a small solvent stream flushes any residual sample out of the system through ports 5 and 4.

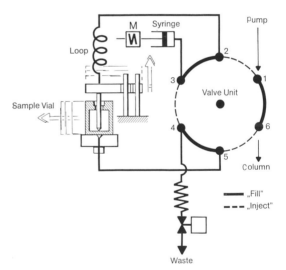

Figure 3-12. Automatically operated injection system.

A sample injector as shown in Figure 3-12 can easily be extended to a completely automatically operated injection system by transporting the sample vials automatically to the place were the sample is drawn into the sample loop. Systems like this, where the vials are either stored on racks or on chains can accomodate 100 or more different samples which can be analyzed in unattended operation.

3.4 Column Hardware

The part that is called a column in HPLC is divided into the bed of (small) particles of packing material and the hardware containing it. This hardware comprises the tube and the endfittings.

3.4.1 Column Tube

Most tubes for analytical HPLC columns are made of 316 stainless steel. This is a steel alloy according to an US standard defined by the American Institute for Standards in Industry (AISI). It is an alloy which shows an excellent resistance against corrosion. All steel parts of a chromatographic system which are in contact with liquids should be made of this alloy.

The roughness of the tube inner wall is a specification governed by the chromatography. As a rule of thumb the wall roughness − expressed as its peak-to-peak value − should be less than one tenth of the mean size of the particles packed in the column. This means that the wall roughness should be smaller than 0.5 μm, when 5 μm particles are packed into the column.

For this reason, glass-, polymer- or goldlined tubing is also being used. However it must be stated that steel tubing of the specification mentioned is very satisfactory.

Glass tubes were recently introduced [12, 13]. The excellent wall properties of glass were an incentive for this. Connection of endfittings can, however, be troublesome. An acceptable solution is offered by Merck [13].

Polyethylene tubing is used by Waters [14] for their radial compressed columns. These columns are fitted into a jacket in which they are pressurized from the outside. This causes a radial compression of the column which improves performance and stability.

Tube diameters used for analytical columns range from

4 to 8 mm i. d. − medium bore columns
2 to 4 mm i. d. − small bore columns
1 to 2 mm i. d. − microbore columns.

The terms given to the diameters are indications currently used for the columns and for their chromatographic application. The internal diameter of the column is a very important experimental factor which has to be selected properly to match the application. Columns within the above ranges of internal diameter are commercially available.

The columns are operated under high pressure. A certain wall thickness is therefore required for safety reasons. The 0.25″ tubing most often used has, with an i. d. of 4.6 mm, a wall thickness of 0.9 mm, which is sufficient. Thicker wall tubing, with the same i. d., is offered by some manufacturers. This allows them to fit the endfitting directly onto the tube (see below).

3.4.2 Column Endfitting

The endfitting and filter unit assembly together constitute the interface between HPLC instrument and packed bed. Its main function is to fix the bed position when it is operated under high pressure and to guard the bed against particulate matter in the mobile phase which can deteriorate the bed structure. In addition it must achieve a smooth transfer of the mobile phase from the connecting capillary (i. d. 0.1 to 0.2 mm) to the wide column bed. Therefore, the endfitting filter unit assembly plays a crucial role for overall column performance. In Figure 3-13 a schematic drawing of the column endfitting will illustrate its function.

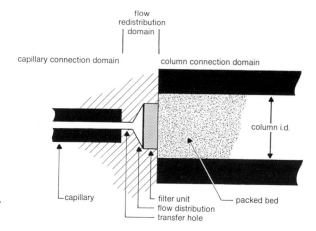

Figure 3-13. Schematic drawing of column endfitting.

The scheme divides the fitting in three prominent parts:

- the flow redistribution domain;
- the column connection domain;
- the capillary connection domain.

In the flow redistribution domain (Figure 3-14), the mobile phase stream carrying the sample components is transferred from the capillary end to the column bed through the transfer hole, the flow distributor and the filter unit. The flow distributor ascertains a homogenious distribution of the stream over the whole filter area.

The design ensures that the whole surface area of the filter unit is used and that the sample is distributed over the whole of the packed bed top surface. This avoids local overloading of the

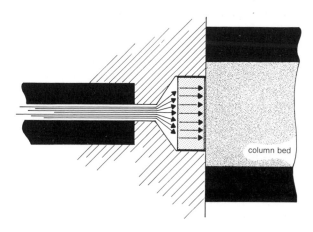

Figure 3-14. Function of the flow distributor.

column which can easily occur when the sample is introduced in the centre of the column bed [15]. Nevertheless the filter diameter chosen should be smaller than the column diameter to avoid the sample components entering the more loosely packed wall regions of the column bed.

It is obvious that the volume occupied by the transfer hole, flow distributor and the filter unit should be designed to match with the column volume to suppress bandspreading in the endfitting. As a rule of thumb, the dead volume in the endfitting should be less than 1% of the empty column volume. Within this restriction many variations are still possible with respect to the design of the flow distributor and to the aspect ratio of the filter unit. This has been the subject of extensive optimization studies [16, 17].

Preferably, there should be no difference between the inlet and the outlet fitting. The considerations shown in Figure 3-14 are also valid for the mobile phase leaving the packed bed. In addition, symmetrical design allows reversal and backflushing of the column, which can be very beneficial for removing deposits from the filter and from the column bed.

Filter units are made of porous 316 stainless steel discs (frits) or of porous teflon sheets (membranes). Because of their poor mechanical strength, these membranes are supported by metal screens, which can also contain flow distributors. The pores in frits and membranes should be smaller than the mean particle diameter of the packing material by a factor of between 5 and 10 (e. g. 2 µm for 10 µm particles).

Because the bed is operated under high pressure (up to 800 bar during column packing) the filter unit has to be packaged. This is done by a metal part, which is called fitting body, that on the one side fits to the outside of the column and on the other side allows connection of the capillary. An example is given in Figure 3-15.

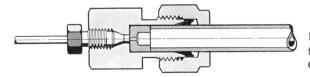

Figure 3-15. Assembled column end fitting (Courtesy of Hewlett-Packard Company).

It is at this point that the numerous variations of endfittings will become apparent to the user. Because of varying column outside diameter, the use of male or female threads on the fitting, or of male threads on the column outside (according to different standards), and the recently introduced reusable endfittings, there are almost as many column endfitting systems as there are column manufacturers.

The column is connected to the injection system and to the detector by capillaries. As it is very often neccessary to use columns from different manufacturers the lack of standardization in this domain has become troublesome.

High pressure resistant capillary connections are very well engineered. Crawford (Swagelok) has set the standard for this. Unfortunately, there are many Swagelok-type connections, which are not identical to the Swagelok standard. Therefore the user must be aware of the standard the column manufacturer uses for capillary connection. In Table 3-1 most of the important standards for capillary connection and the sources are summarized.

It must be emphasized that it is impossible for a user to use the different capillary connection standards interchangeably. The consequences are leakage, damage of the endfitting and performance loss.

Table 3-1. Standards for Capillary Connections.

Capillary o. d.	Manufacturer/Trade Name	Details
1/16'' (1.6 mm)	Crawford Fitting Company/Swagelok	front- and back ferrule; distance 1.6 mm[a]
	Parker Hannifin	one piece ferrule; distance 1.6 mm[a]
	Valco	one piece ferrule; distance 2.5 mm[a]
	Rheodyne	one piece ferrule; distance 4.5 mm[b]
1/32'' (0.8 mm)	Valco	one piece ferrule
(0.6 mm)	Hewlett-Packard	adapted to 1/16'' Swagelok Standard
(0.5 mm)	ANTEK/MICONN	–

[a] Distance from ferrule end to capillary end.
[b] Only used to connect sample injection valves; the other capillary end may be any of the above standards.

3.5 Column Thermostat

Column temperature is an important separation parameter in view of analysis precision and speed, detection limit and, in many cases, separation selectivity.

Therefore:

● column temperature should be selectable between room temperature and about 100 °C;
● column temperature must be kept constant within $+/-$ 0.1 to 0.2 degrees;
● temperature distribution in the column must be homogeneous (no axial and radial temperature gradients);
● the column compartment should allow easy installation of columns of various dimensions and a column switching valve.

In addition to the information in Chapter 2, some practical hints on the role of column temperature in optimizing LC analyses are given below (Section 3.5.1 to 3.5.3).

3.5.1 Column Temperature Stability and Retention Time Precision

In normal phase chromatography, changes of the capacity factor k of up to 10% per degree of temperature change are reported [18]. Particularly when a poorly soluble modifier (like water) is used, partition equilibrium of the modifier between stationary and mobile phase is only reached when the column temperature is well controlled. In reverse phase chromatography temperature influence is less dramatic. It reaches 2 to 3% change of k per degree temperature change, with increasing tendency for later eluting substances [19, 20, 21].

3.5.2 Column Temperature and Analysis Speed

In many separations change of column temperature can successfully be used as a means to speed up analysis. A temperature increase will in most cases – however not always – cause a decrease in k values of the separated substances. In addition column efficiency may also increase with temperature [22, 23], together with a shift of the efficiency optimum to higher mobile phase velocities (this shift will only be of practical interest when column packings with particle diameters <10 µm are used). Efficiency gains can be as high as 20 to 40% when temperature is raised from ambient to 70 °C. The combination of decreased k and increased column efficiency leads to a marked increase of peak height.

The increase of column temperature will cause the mobile phase viscosity to decrease. Therefore, if excess resolution is available, the analysis can be speeded up by increasing the flow (with a larger margin to the upper pressure limit of the instrument).

3.5.3 Column Temperature and Selectivity

The magnitude of column temperature influence on k may differ significantly for particular components of a sample. This effect can successfully be exploited to enhance separation selectivity. Impressive examples of this demonstrating even reversal of elution order for moderate temperature changes are given in [19].

3.5.4 Column Thermostat Embodiments

Heat transfer from a heating element to the column can be achieved through air, a liquid or direct metallic contact. Either method has advantages and drawbacks:

a) Most widely used are air bath thermostats in which the air temperature is controlled. The actual column bed and mobile phase temperature depend on the heat transfer from the circulated air to and through the column walls and finally into the column bed and mobile phase. Air velocity as well as nature and flow-rate of the mobile phase will thus have some influence on the mean effective column bed temperature.

With this thermostat type, safety aspects need particular attention. Some solvent vapor/air mixtures are ignitable in a wide concentration range and have low spontaneous ignition temperatures (e. g. diethylether 186 °C, n-hexane 261 °C [24]. No part inside the column compartment which could come in contact with solvent vapors of ignitable concentration should ever reach the ignition temperature of any of the solvents used. Low surface temperature heaters or other suitable safety devices are strongly recommended.

The advantage of an air thermostat is that it offers maximum flexibility with regard to the use of various column sizes/column combinations and installation of column switching valves and even detectors in the thermostated zone.

b) The column is surrounded by a water jacket through which thermostated water or other suitable liquid is circulated. This solution will probably result in the best heat transfer to the column walls. The mean effective column bed temperature will, however, still be influenced by the heat transfer through the column walls and into the bed and mobile phase. It does not raise any questions with regard to safety, but is cumbersome to use and offers little flexibility.

c) The column is embedded in a split aluminum block which is thermally insulated. Temperature depends on the heat transfer from the aluminum block to and through the column wall into column bed and mobile phase.

The quality of the thermal contact between aluminum block and column, and nature and flow-rate of mobile phase will influence the mean effective column bed temperature. The use of this thermostat design is usually limited to certain column dimensions and hardly allows to efficiently thermostat column switching arrangements including the switching valves.

3.5.4.1 Mobile Phase Pre-Heating

It was mentioned above that in all common column thermostats a certain dependence of the mean effective column bed temperature on the kind and flow-rate of the mobile phase must be anticipated. In [25] and [26] some experimental data on the consequences and magnitude of such effects can be found. If mobile phase at room temperature enters a column thermostated at elevated temperature, then axial and radial temperature gradients will occur in the column bed, resulting in a loss of column efficiency and in some dependence of k on mobile phase flow-rate. Also the mean bed temperature will be lower than the thermostat temperature, impairing the comparability of k-data measured on instruments with different thermostat designs. The use of a suitable mobile phase pre-heater as suggested in [26] will completely avoid these problems.

3.6 Detectors

Detection is still widely regarded as the weak point in practical HPLC. Although much progress has been made in the design of sensitive specific detectors, a general purpose (i. e. non specific) detector with satisfactory lower limit of detection is still felt to be missing. The problem is the similarity of many physical and chemical properties of the mobile phase and impurities in the mobile phase compared to the samples to be detected. In this chapter those detectors most commonly used in practice will be dealt with.

3.6.1 Some general Terms

3.6.1.1 Specific − Non Specific Detectors

A detector is called *specific* (or solute detector) if it selectively responds to certain types of substances which have one typical property in common, not found in other (concomitant) substances. An example for this detector type is the UV-absorbance detector. Correspondingly a *non specific* (or bulk property) detector responds to all (or at least to most) of the substances present in the column eluate, including the mobile phase. A typical representative of this group is the refractive index detector.

3.6.1.2 Response Factor, LLD and Linear Range

When the column eluate passing through a detector changes the property, which is measured by this detector (e. g. UV absorbance at 254 nm), by a certain amount ΔA, then the detector output signal changes by ΔS. The *response factor* (or sensitivity), R_D, is then defined as

$$R_D = \frac{\Delta S}{\Delta A} \ .$$

The *lower limit of detection (LLD)* is regarded as the smallest change of the measured property which would result in a change of output signal which can just be reliably distinguished from the output signal noise. The LLD with regard to injected sample can only be given for an entire chromatographic system (including column); LLD is the minimum amount of a substance injected into the column, which produces a peak just distinguishable from the noise level, commonly with a peak height twice the noise level.

LLD, given as a property for the detector alone, is therefore only useful as a quality criterion for this detector. In the literature the terms sensitivity and LLD are often mixed up.

The *linear range* (also sometimes referred to as "linear dynamic range" or "dynamic range") is the ratio between the upper limit value of the measured property for which the output signal is linear within a given limit (e. g. 1%), and the LLD as defined above. In other words: The linear range of a detector reaches over that range of the measured property for which the response factor R_D is constant within a given limit. A specification of a dynamic range is therefore only complete if the allowed limit of deviation from the average response factor is also given.

3.6.1.3 Quantitative and Qualitative Detector Response

One purpose of the detector is to *quantify* certain or all constituents of a separated sample. It can also yield *qualitative* information on the sample constituents. This is usually the case if a detector parameter, which selectively influences the response factor for certain constituents, can be modified, e. g. the detection wavelength in an absorbance detector, the electrode potential in an electrochemical detector or the mass filter setting of a mass spectrometer. In the case of the (UV-VIS-) absorbance detector the ratio(s) of the detector response measured at two or more different wavelengths can give an excellent identification aid in addition to the retention time.

3.6.1.4 Impact of Detector on Peak Broadening

There is a more or less empiric rule in LC, sometimes referred to as "the iron rule of chromatography" which says that the extra column peak broadening effects must not contribute more than 10% to the peak width. Two contributors to such external effects are detector volume and detector response time constant; upper limits for these can be estimated from column performance. A substance with a capacity ratio k would elute from a column with n theoretical plates and a total retention volume $V_M \cdot (1 + k)$ with a peak volume (at base) w_b of

$$w_b = \frac{4 \cdot V_M \cdot (1 + k)}{\sqrt{n}} \qquad \text{(if peak shape is Gaussian).}$$

According to a rule of thumb given in [27], contribution of detector volume V_D to band broadening will be insignificant, if

$$V_D < 0.1 \cdot w_b .$$

A similar rule could be applied to determine the upper limit for the detector time constant τ, which should not exceed about one tenth of the peak base width (in time units):

$$\tau \leq \frac{0.4 \cdot V_M (1 + k)}{F \cdot \sqrt{n}} .$$

E. g. for a column of 10 cm length, 4 mm i. d., total porosity 0.8 and 5000 plates, and for $k = 0.5$ and a maximum flow-rate of 4 mL/min the detector volume should not exceed 10 µL and the detector time constant should not exceed 130 ms.

Attention should also be paid to band broadening contributions of fittings and interconnecting capillaries. Tubing with 0.1 to 0.15 mm i. d. is preferable (to 0.25 mm) when working with high efficiency columns.

3.6.2 Refractive Index Detector

3.6.2.1 General Application Guidelines

The refractive index (RI) of dilute solutions changes proportionally with solute concentration, which effect can be used for quantitative detection of solutes in the column eluate. The relationship between change of RI and solute concentration is only moderately dependent on the type of solute, making this a quite universal, yet not very sensitive detection principle. E. g. the RI of a 0.1% aqueous sugar solution (a popular example) is 1.3331 compared to 1.3330 for pure water (at 20 °C and 589.3 nm). The LLD (as defined in 3.6.1.2) of a modern RI detector is in the order of $1 \cdot 10^{-8} \Delta$ RI units.

As usual with non-specific (universal) detection methods, the theoretical LLD of an RI-detector can be impaired by a number of side effects. Temperature influence on the RI of solvents is in the order of 2 to $4 \cdot 10^{-4} \Delta$ RI units/°C. Pressure influence is about $5 \cdot 10^{-5}$ Δ RI/bar [28]. The RI of gas (e. g. air) saturated solvent differs by about 10^{-4} to $10^{-5} \Delta$ RI units from that of a totally degassed solvent. Therefore some precautions have to be taken when an LC system is operated with an RI detector and detection is done at the LLD. Short term flow fluctuations (flow ripple or pulsation and flow wander) should be smaller than about 0.01 mL/min at column outlet, any flow restrictors downstream of the detector must be avoided. The column should be operated in a temperature controlled environment. Connection capillaries between column and detector, and the detector itself must be protected from air drafts and direct heat radiation. The detector reference cell (if operated "static") must not be closed by an external loop but connected to an open "expansion vessel" filled with solvent. The eluent should be kept saturated with e. g. Helium at constant temperature. RI detection and gradient elution exclude each other.

3.6.2.2 Common Operating Principles of RI Detectors

RI detectors marketed at present are based on one of the following three operating principles:

1. Measurement of RI by measurement of *beam deflection* (Figure 3-16): a beam of collimated light passes a "null glass" (used for optical balancing of the detector) and two parallel prismatic cavities in a glass block, forming sample and reference cell. If both cells are filled with the same liquid, i.e. $n_S = n_R$, then the light beam leaving the cells is slightly shifted, parallel to the incident beam. Should be RI in the sample cell n_S, change then the beam will also change its direction as indicated in Figure 3-16. The position of the beam is measured by a differential photodiode and is adjusted (by means of the null glass) such that the signal is balanced when $n_S = n_R$. The output signal can be positive or negative depending on whether n_S is larger or smaller than n_R. Good detectors of this type have a noise level corresponding to $5 \cdot 10^{-9} \, \Delta$ RI units.

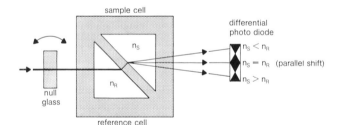

Figure 3-16. Operating schematics of a beam deflection type RI-Detector.

2. RI measurement using *Fresnel's law* (Figure 3-17): A light beam incidenting upon the boundary surface between two optical media (e. g. glass and a liquid) is split into a reflected beam and a beam penetrating into the second medium (the liquid). If the angle of incidence is adjusted so that the penetration angle is near 90° (close to total reflection) then a small change of the refractive index of the liquid will result in a significant change in the intensity of the penetrating beam (see Figure 3-17). This behaviour (more completely described in the Fresnel equations) is utilized in an RI detector, as shown schematically in Figure 3-18. Two such light paths are used in parallel, one being the sample light path (penetrating the sample cell) and the other being the reference light path (penetrating the reference cell). Small differences between the RI of sample and reference liquid will cause a corresponding difference of light intensity backscattered from the two cells. This intensity difference is measured and converted into the output signal, proportional to RI. The noise level of this detector type is comparable to that of the deflection type. When eluents with a wide range of RI's are used, then a change of the prism may be necessary, limiting the flexibility of this detector type.

Figure 3-17. Measurement principle of a fresnel type RI-Detector:

Φ_0 intensity of incident light

Φ_1 intensity of light penetrating boundary surface between glass and liquid (into liquid)

Φ_2 intensity of reflected light.

A small change of n_{liquid} *changes* α *and therefore* Φ_1/Φ_0.

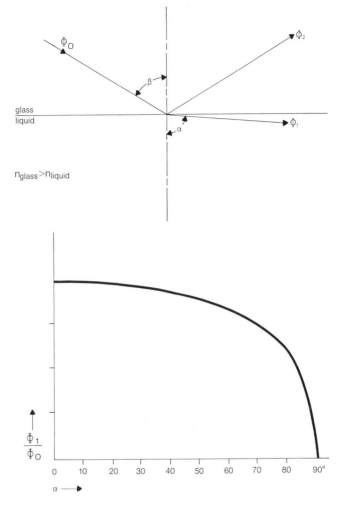

Figure 3-18. Operating schematics of a fresnel type RI-Detector: B light source, P glass prism, S steel plate, M PTFE gasket with cutouts for cell cavities, G light penetrating into sample (or reference) cell and backscattered by steel surface to photodetector D, R reflected light (not used), K inlet and outlet capillaries.

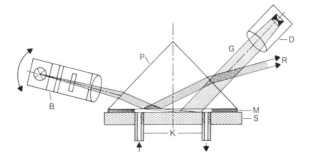

3. RI measurement by *light interference* (Figure 3-19): The optical path length of a light path δ is defined as the product of geometric path length l and refractive index of the optical medium

n_S: $\delta = l \cdot n_S$; i.e. a change of RI will cause a change in optical path length. This effect is used in the RI detector shown schematically in Figure 3-19. One of two coherent wavetrains passes a sample cell, the other one a reference cell; both wavetrains are then superimposed and the light intensity measured by a photodiode. If the RI in sample and reference cell are equal, there is no phase difference between the interfering wavetrains, the light intensity at the photodiode is maximum. If sample and reference RI differ by Δn, the two wavetrains interfere at a phase-difference of $\Delta\delta = l \cdot \Delta n$; this results in a decrease of light intensity to the minimum at $\Delta\delta = 0.5\ \lambda$ (λ wavelength of interfering light). E. g. for $l = 1$ cm and $\lambda = 600$ nm, an intensity change from maximum to minimum is caused by a change of n_S from 0 to $3 \cdot 10^{-5} \Delta$ RI units. This is the RI detector type with, currently, the best LLD, reaching noise levels corresponding to $1 \cdot 10^{-9}$ Δ RI units. Its directly usable dynamic range is limited since if $\Delta\delta$ exceeds $0.5\ \lambda$, then light intensity increases again, until $\Delta\delta = \lambda$ etc., making the output signal ambiguous.

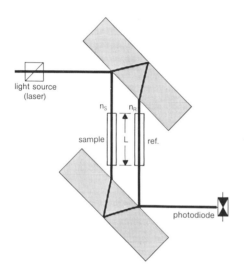

light source
(laser)

n_S n_R

sample   L   ref.

photodiode

Figure 3-19. Operating schematics of an interference type RI-Detector (Jamin refractometer): L geometrical path length of sample and reference cell, n_S RI of sample solution, n_R RI of reference; optical path length difference = phase difference of both wavetrains $\Delta\delta = $ L ($n_S - n_R$); light intensity on photodiode changes from maximum to minimum when $\Delta\delta$ changes from 0 to $0.5 \cdot \lambda$.

3.6.3 UV-VIS-Absorption Detectors

3.6.3.1 Application Guidelines

The basis of quantitative absorption photometry is *Lambert-Beer's Law:* the absorbance A (the logarithmic ratio of the light intensities before and after passing the absorbing medium) of a solution is proportional to the concentration c_S of the absorbing solute, the light path length l and the coefficient of absorbance ε.

$$A = \varepsilon \cdot c_S \cdot l.$$

The applicability of this law is tied to the observance of some boundary conditions:

a) Within measurement error, ε can only be considered a constant for solute concentrations up to $c_S = 0.1$ mol/L.

b) "Apparent deviations" from the law occur if the light used to measure the absorbance is not monochromatic (too large a band pass of monochromator, or too much stray light) and the spectrum of the absorbant solute shows large change of ε vs λ at or near the nominal measurement wavelength. For LC detection a bandwidth of 2 to 4 nm (or smaller) will usually result in acceptable (i. e. $\leq 1\%$) linearity up to 0.5 (to 1) absorbance units. If larger bandwidths are to be used for sensitivity enhancement (increased light througput) then linearity should be checked at least for those sample components producing larger absorbance signals.

c) "True deviations" from the law, i. e. changes of ε of a solution, can be caused by changes of chemical equilibriums or intermolecular forces. This concerns, for example, dissociation or association processes and also the state of solvation. In LC the effect will mainly occur in unbuffered aqueous solutions and/or at high sample concentration. When such mobile phases are used, all calibrations and sample analyses must be carried out with the same mobile phase pH and ionic strength and if applicable with the same mobile phase gradients.

Other secondary effects which can impair quantitative precision when working close to the LLD, are mainly caused by the flow-through operation mode of the detector cell.

Since the mobile phase solvent in the cell is part of the entire optical system of the detector, change of its refractive index (RI) can change light throughput and thus "simulate" absorbance changes which result in baseline wander and peak quantitation errors. RI changes of the mobile phase do occur in gradient elution and as a result of temperature fluctuations. Also, flow-rate changes cause baseline perturbations. It is likely that local flow turbulences with flow dependent frequency and distribution in the cell will cause "Schlieren" (irregular layers of different RI), seen by the detector as absorbance. Good UV-VIS detectors show flow dependence smaller than $1 \cdot 10^{-3}$ AU/mL/min. The influence of air (oxygen) dissolved in the mobile phase on the signal of UV-detectors is mentioned in section 3.2.1.

A particular problem in gradient elution, mainly with aqueous solvents, is the enrichment of solvent impurities on the column at lower mobile phase strength. These elute (together with the sample components) at higher solvent strength. Water purified by distillation or reverse osmosis is better than deionised water, additional purification by a (large volume) reverse phase column is recommended when high detector sensitivity is needed [29].

High "background" absorption (i. e. absorption at the detection wavelength by the mobile phase) will in addition to increasing baseline noise, result in a reduction of the detector's usable linear range. Although the detector electronics may be able to "balance" the signal to seemingly zero absorbance, the detector still "sees" the combined (i. e. total) absorbance of mobile phase and solute. Some detectors will warn the operator of high background absorbance.

3.6.3.2 Types of UV-VIS-Detectors

The main components of any absorbance detector are light source, collimating optics, optical filter, flow-through cuvette(s), image forming optics, photodetector(s) and signal electronics. A classification of detectors can be made according to certain characteristics of these elements and their optical arrangement.

Fixed Wavelength Detectors utilize so called line sources, i. e. lamps which are emitting at a few discrete wavelengths (lines). The most common of these lamps is the low pressure mercury lamp emitting over 90% of its light at 254 nm (other emission lines are 313, 365, 405, 436, 546 and 579 nm). Lower wavelengths (than 254 nm) are available from zinc lamps (214 nm) and from cadmium lamps (229 and 326 nm). The combination of the lamp and a (band- or cut-off) filter determines the fixed operating wavelength of the detector. Most detector types allow exchange of filter and light source. A typical optical scheme of such a detector is shown in Figure 3-20.

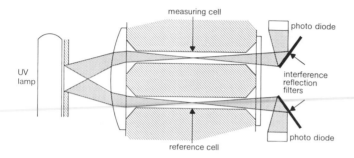

Figure 3-20. Optical schematics of a fixed wavelength UV-Detector. (Published with permission of Hewlett-Packard GmbH, Waldbronn, W-Germany).

The advantages of fixed wavelength detectors are low noise level because of high light intensity (at the major emission line of the lamp), low investment and operating cost, reliability and simplicity of operation. The 254 nm detector with a mercury lamp can particularly be considered a "workhorse" in routine HPLC. Typical noise level of this detector corresponds to $1 \cdot 10^{-5}$ absorbance units; typical replacement cost of the lamp is 100 to 200 US $, average lamp lifetime is 5000 operating hours.

Variable Wavelength (VW) Detectors use a light source with a continuous emission spectrum and a continuously adjustable (narrow) band filter, called monochromator. The most common source for this purpose is the deuterium lamp whose usable emission spectrum reaches from about 190 nm to about 600 nm, with an intensity maximum between 220 and 240 nm. Above 300 nm the output intensity is low, therefore relatively large filter bandwidths must be used to maintain good detector sensitivity. Typical lifetime of the D2 lamp is only of the order of 500 to 800 operating hours. An alternative to the D2 lamp, with higher available output intensity, is the xenon lamp which has not found wide use.

Some VW detectors have an additional or optional tungsten lamp, which can be used at wavelength settings above 350 nm.

The traditional VW detectors were suitably modified versions of general purpose UV-VIS spectrophotometers with manual micrometer adjustment of the monochromator. With this detector type, a compromise wavelength has to be selected for all components of interest in a sample, change of the wavelength setting during sample elution is hardly possible (under normal conditions of quantitative analysis).

Within recent years, specially designed VW detectors for HPLC were introduced which allow automatic rapid change of wavelength setting within 1 to 2 s or less across their entire wavelength setting range, which typically reaches from about 190 nm to about 600 nm. Examples for optical schemes of two such VW detectors with rapid automatic wavelength setting are shown in Figures 3 – 21 and 3 – 22. These detector types allow the operator to time-program several wavelength changes to occur during the chromatographic run (preferably between eluting peaks). This means that wavelength setting can be optimized individually for either selectivity of detectibility (or both) for several or all components of interest. Ideally the automatic wavelength setting and autobalance operation of the detector is coupled with the instrument integrator such that the detector would wait to follow up a time programmed wavelength change while a peak is eluting, until the integrator recognices the end of this peak. With this wavelength programming can be used also with, densely populated chromatograms without the danger of losing any significant quantitative information.

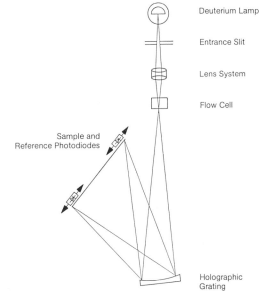

Figure 3-21. Optical schematics of a variable wavelength detector with rapid automatic wavelength setting. The two photodiodes are independently moved by stepping motors across the (spherical) image of the spectrum for wavelength setting.
(Published with permission of Hewlett-Packard GmbH, Waldbronn, W-Germany).

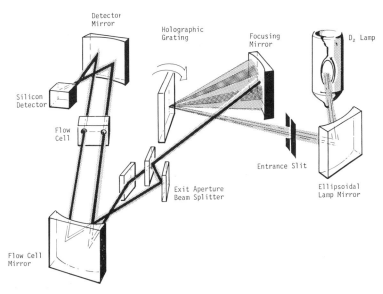

Figure 3-22. Optical schematics of a variable wavelength detector with rapid automatic wavelength setting. The grating is rapidly moved by servo mechanism for wavelength setting. (Published with permission of Beckman Instruments Co.).

Further possible applications of programmable VW detectors include taking UV spectra of selected eluting substances and/or measuring absorbance ratios (i. e. the ratio of absorbance of an eluting substance at different wavelengths). This information can be extremely useful in confirming peak identity. Examples of how these features can be used in practical HPLC are discussed in [30].

The latest development in this field is the Diode Array Detector (DAD). A linear photo diode array is a silicon substrate on which, by semiconductor process technology, a large number (200 to 1000) of tiny photodiodes is applied in a single row of about 2 cm length. Assigned to each of the diodes is an integrated readout device, basically consisting of a capacitor which is charged to a certain voltage and discharged via the photodiode during the time between charge and readout. The discharge voltages (currents) are periodically measured (and the capacitor recharged) in time intervals of, for example 10 ms, yielding almost simultaneous information on the light intensities to which each photodiode was exposed over this time interval.

As shown in the optical scheme of such a detector in Figure 3-23 the image of the absorbance spectrum of the eluate in the detector cuvette is formed on the diode array. Thus within every readout interval the complete spectrum is transferred to the signal electronics with a resolution determined by the spectral range (and entrance slit width) of the dispersing element over the width of the array (e. g. 200 to 600 nm) and the number of diodes available on the array (e. g. 200). More detailed information on the operating principles of a linear diode array spectrometer can be found in [31].

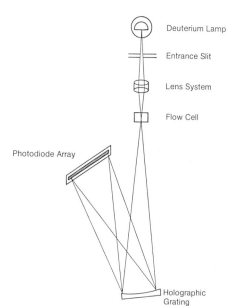

Deuterium Lamp

Entrance Slit

Lens System

Flow Cell

Photodiode Array

Holographic Grating

Figure 3-23. Optical schematics of a photo diode array detector (DAD).
(Published with permission of Hewlett-Packard GmbH, Waldbronn, W-Germany).

The very fast, quasiparallel and quasicontinous availability of the entire UV/VIS absorbance spectrum of the sample will (if the detector has accordingly powerful signal electronics) yield significant additional information on the column eluate which would be difficult and time consuming to obtain with a conventional UV detector. With a suitable graphics screen, three dimensional chromatogram records at different monitoring wavelengths can give a quick overall impression of optimum monitoring wavelengths for every peak in the chromatogram. "On the fly" records of spectra at different positions of a single peak can indicate whether or not this peak represents a pure sample component. Similar information can be obtained for the entire chromatogram through continuous records of absorbance ratios. Spectra taken routinely, of certain or all peaks of interest, in addition to the sample chromatogram(s) will support component identification and identity confirmation of sample constituents. By selecting larger monitoring bandwidths (averaging the signal of several photodiodes), signal-to-noise ratio can be enhanced, sacrificing, however, linearity as mentioned in section 3.6.3.1 b. Another way of signal-to-noise enhancement is averaging signals from several to many reading intervals; this would accordingly increase detector time constant with possible consequences on chromatogram resolution (see Section 3.6.1.4).

3.6.4 Fluorescence Detector

Fluorescence detection, although offering distinct advantages (over UV-VIS absorbance detection) with regard to detection limit and specificity in many LC applications, has not yet found as wide a use as it deserves. Consideration of this detector type is therefore expressly encouraged here.

3.6.4.1 Some General Application Guidelines

The quantity of fluorescent light emitted from excited molecules in dilute solution is proportional to:

- intensity of excitation source;
- illuminated volume of the sample solution (in contrast to absorbance measurement light path should be as short as possible, requiring quite a different cell geometry);
- quantum efficiency of fluorescence of sample (ratio of radiating to non radiating transfer energy from excited to ground state) can be optimized by selection of proper excitation conditions);
- Concentration of solute to be detected.

Fluorescence (and phosphorescence) radiation is emitted from the (illuminated) sample in all directions. Ideally this radiation is collected by a spherical mirror around the sample cell. However this mirror must not collect light coming directly from the excitation source.

Some factors which can impair fluorescence detection are:

- Dissolved oxygen (see also Section 3.2.1) or other impurities in the eluent which can cause fluorescence quenching.
- Stray light (from the excitation source) caused by large molecules or other scattering material in the eluate, or by stains etc. on the surface of sample cell or other parts in the light path; stray light is recognized through increased noise level and may result in decreasing linearity of response characteristics.

Some possibilities for enhancing fluorescence or phosphorescence yield are:

- selection of excitation wavelength to yield a maximum of excited states (triplett) with a favourite ratio of radiant to non radiant transfer energy to ground state;
- use of micellar solutions to induce (room temperature) phosphorescence [32];
- adding a substance (e. g. biacetyl) to the eluate whose molecules are transferred to the triplett state by (non radiant) transfer energy from excited sample molecules; the phosphorescence radiation resulting from the spontaneous retransfer of these "acceptor" molecules to the ground state, is then measured [33].

3.6.4.2 Excitation Sources

In principle any light-source/filter (or monochromator) combination suitable for UV-VIS absorption photometry could be used as an excitation source in fluorescence detection: Collimating optics however must be adapted to the geometry requirements of a fluorescence detector cell. This means illuminating a given sample volume (limited by considerations of elution band broadening) across the shortest possible light path length. If best achievable LLD is a requirement then the excitation source filter should be selected for maximum light throughput at the desired excitation band (not for the narrowest possible band pass) and for as large as possible attenuation at longer wavelengths, particularly near the emission filter band pass. High intensity sources like xenon lamps offer good conditions for fluorescence measurements since the shot noise problem mentioned in Section 3.6.3.2 does not apply. Also the use of lasers [34] and ^{63}Ni-sources [35] as excitation sources in fluorescence detection have been reported.

3.6.4.3 Measurement of Emission

Ideally, fluorescence radiation, as a result of suitable excitation of the sample molecules, is measured against a dark background. Therefore the main source of detector noise is dark current noise of the photo detector, which is mainly determined by temperature. As a rule of thumb, every $10\,^{\circ}C$ increase in temperature of a photodiode would double its darkcurrent noise. Shot noise (proportional to the square root of light intensity) being a dominant factor in absorbance detection, can almost be ignored in fluorescence detection. For sample components with high quantum efficiency of fluorescence, LLD can thus be expected to be up to ten fold better in fluorescence than in absorbance detection.

As in absorbance measurement, imaging detectors like linear photodiode arrays (see also Section 3.6.3.2) and silicon target vidicons found their way into fluorescence spectroscopy and lately into LC detection [36, 37, 38].

3.6.5 Electrochemical Detectors

The use of detectors based upon electroanalytical methods has become very popular in recent years. This is not without reason (see below). In fact, they are the detectors most often preferred in certain applications, in particular in trace analysis and in ion chromatography.

Since electroanalysis is a broad discipline a classification of the methods used in HPLC detectors is necessary. We distinguish between:

a) bulk property electrochemical detectors;
b) solute property electrochemical detectors.

a) Bulk property electrochemical detectors respond to a change in an electrochemical property of the bulk liquid flowing through the measuring cell. Changes of electrical conductivity of the mobile phase – measured as a change in cell resistance – and of the dielectric constant (permittivity) of the flowing liquid [39, 40, 41] – measured as capacity change of the cell – are two electroanalytical methods which have been used for bulk property electrochemical detection. In particular, the conductivity detector has become very important recently. In combination with so called suppressor columns they have been shown to be very versatile in ion chromatography.

b) Solute property electrochemical detectors respond to a change in voltage (potentiometry) or current (voltammetry or coulometry) as the analyte is passing through the cell. Potentiometry has not yet found widespread use as a detection principle for HPLC [42, 43], because it has a high LLD. On the other hand, by careful design of the electrode, a very selective detection device can be obtained.

The major part of all electrochemical detectors are using voltammetric or coulometric methods for monitoring the analyte concentration in flowing liquids. The basic requirement for response is the presence of an electrophor (analog to a chromophor in photometric detection) in the molecule of interest. An electrophor is a (sub)structure in the molecule which easily accepts (reduction) or releases electrons (oxidation) under suitable conditions (potential). Therefore basically, in voltammetric and coulometric methods for HPLC detection a change in cell current in response to a change in analyte concentration is observed.

Potentiometric detectors have not been commercialized. Voltammetric and coulometric detectors on the contrary are offered by various manufacturers. Therefore, these detectors as well as the conductivity detector will be discussed in greater detail.

3.6.5.1 Conductivity Detectors

3.6.5.1.1 Basic Considerations

Upon application of a potential, ions in a solution are forced to move towards the electrode of opposite charge. The conductance, which is the reciprocal of the electrical resistance, depends directly on the number of charged particles in the solution. This dependence is the basis of quantitation by conductivity measurements. However it must be realized, that the method has its intrinsic limitations. In order to elucidate these, a few basic relations will be discussed.

The conductance of a solution (G) is the reciprocal of the electrical resistance that is,

$$G = \frac{1}{R_E} \, .$$

In analogy to the resistance in electrical conductors, the specific conductance can be defined by:

$$G = \kappa \frac{A}{l} = \kappa \cdot \text{cell constant}$$

in which A is the cross sectional area of the electrodes and l the distance between these electrodes. So it is κ, the specific conductance which is, in fact, the concentration dependent parameter. The term A/l is the so called cell constant, depending alone on the geometry of the cell. If absolute values of the conductivity are required the cell constant can be established from the known values of κ of standard solutions. In applications as HPLC detector, absolute conductivity data are not required.

The mobility of the ions will differ depending on their size, charge and polarizability. The molar conductivity (Λ) defined as the conductance of one gram-equivalent of solute contained between two electrodes spaced one cm apart, accounts for this. After matching the dimensions:

$$\Lambda = \frac{1000 \cdot \kappa}{c}$$

is obtained. Combining the expression for G and Λ gives:

$$G = \frac{\text{cell constant} \cdot \Lambda \cdot c}{1000} \, .$$

For detection and quantitation with HPLC detectors based upon conductivity therefore, the molar conductivity has to be constant. This is true in very dilute solutions. Only then is the mobility of the ions governed by the electrical field and by counteracting frictional forces. The molar conductivity at infinite dilution (Λ_0) is a species characteristic parameter. At finite concentrations, however, electrophoretic flow, in the opposite direction, and relaxation become important and Λ will be dependent on concentration. In the presence of buffer ions, the change in conductance caused by the analyte of interest, can therefore become largely masked.

This has important consequences for the chromatography. Because we want to register the concentration profile of the eluting component accurately, the detector must show a constant, concentration independent, sensitivity. Fortunately, the concentration in the sample usually will be well below 10^{-3} mol/L. Because in addition the column will dilute the sample components, depending on column dimensions, capacity factor and plate number, with a factor of 5 to 50, it can be reasoned that the molar conductivity for the ions of interest will be constant.

The effect of buffer ions in the mobile phase must be suppressed as far as possible. Because plain water is in most cases not an adequate mobile phase for the separation of ions, the use of buffers in the mobile phase cannot be avoided. Therefore, the concentration of mobile phase buffers must be kept as low as possible. A very elegant solution for this dilemma has been described by Small et al. [45]: By ingenious combination of mobile phase buffers and a so-called suppressor column, buffer ions are virtually eliminated after separation by the serially connected suppressor column.

3.6.5.1.2 Measurement Principle

In contrast to the electrochemical detectors which are described in the next section, the occurence of so called galvanic processes at the electrode surfaces, i. e. electrochemical reactions, are to be avoided. Therefore alternating current sources with frequencies between 50 and 1000 Hz and voltage outputs between 5 and 10 V are used. Moreover, the electrodes are platinized to increase their surface area and thereby increase their polarizability and thus their capacitance which minimizes faradayic current.

The mobility of the ions is strongly influenced by temperature. A temperature coefficient of 2%/°C has been reported. The high demands for precision and repeatability in HPLC detectors can be fulfilled by the use of a reference cell in the measuring chain. This cell can be filled with mobile phase and sealed or continuously purged with mobile phase. The signal obtained from sample cell and reference cell can be used to balance the two transducers.

A basis for measurement is the Wheatstone resistance bridge or simply Ohm's law. A diagram of this last principle is shown in Figure 3-24.

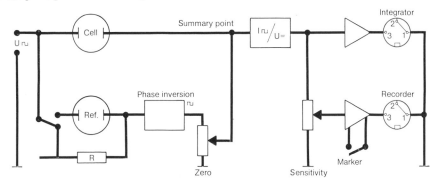

Figure 3-24. Block diagram of a modern conductivity detector for HPLC. (Courtesy of Dr. H. Knauer, Berlin/FRG).

3.6.5.1.3 Application Guidelines

It will be evident that this detector is best used for detection of charged species in column effluents. Although many of these species, organic and inorganic ions, often show absorption of light in the UV-region of the spectrum, there are intrinsic disadvantages to working with spectrophotometric detectors at very low wavelengths. The conductivity HPLC detector provides an excellent, and economic, detection alternative which is preferable in particular for detection of minute ion concentrations.

The techniques described by Small et al. [45] for removing mobile phase buffer ions has driven development in this area. At present even dedicated systems for ion analysis are commercially available (Dionex) which were specially developed to meet the demands of ion analysis.

3.6.5.2 Voltammetric and Coulometric Detectors

3.6.5.2.1 Basic Considerations

In order to explain the working principle of these detectors Figure 3-25 shows a typical response curve (current vs voltage) of an electroactive substance under static (= batch) conditions. This curve is called a voltammogram (or polarogram when it is measured with a dropping mercury electrode). The picture does not change if the solvent is moving as is the case in HPLC. The curve is then called a hydrodynamic voltammogram and only differs from a voltammogram in that it cannot be measured continuously.

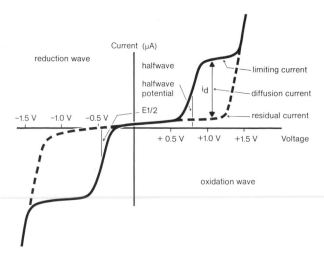

Figure 3-25. Voltammogram of an electroactive substance showing a reduction wave as well as an oxidation wave. The --- curve shows the current when no electroactive analyte is present.

A characteristic feature of the voltammogram is the region in which the current, after a sharp increase, does not change much with increase in the applied voltage. This current is called the limiting current. Because electrochemical conversion is instantaneous in the interface electrode solution, a concentration gradient is built up, which is counteracted by diffusion of unreacted analyte molecules to the interface. However, diffusion is a relative slow process and therefore a steady state situation will be built up in which the current is limited by the transport of electroactive compounds to the electrode. This diffusion current is directly proportional to the concentration of the analyte and to geometrical parameters of the cell. These are quantifiable when the transport equations for the cell are solved. Ilkovic type of equations for several types of voltammetric detectors have been discussed by Hanekamp et al. [46].

Figure 3-25 also shows that the limiting current also contains a contribution from the supporting electrolyte solution (residual or background current). The diffusion current is the difference between the limiting current and the residual current. Quantitative determinations with voltammetry will therefore depend on the degree in which the diffusion current can be detected in the presence of residual or background current. It must be realized that the background currents in HPLC-EC detection are in many cases more than 1000 times higher than the diffusion currents (see paragraph on drift and noise).

Another characteristic feature of the voltammogram is the so-called half wave potential. This is the potential at which the current equals half of the diffusion current, under these particular experimental conditions, and can be used for qualitative information.

The term amperometry in HPLC-EC detection or in electroanalysis means that the voltage is set to a fixed value, at which the limiting current for a particular – or class of – analytes is reached. Amperometric detectors which use dropping mercury as the electrode, are called polarographic detectors.

The electrochemical conversion in a voltammetric method is minimal. Only a 1 to 3% conversion yield is reached. However the cell can also be configured so that a 100% yield is achieved. In this case the detector is called a coulometric detector. The limitations caused by restrictive mass transport are overcome by reducing the lengths of the diffusion paths, e. g. a porous electrode or a big surface covered by a very thin liquid film ($< 50 \mu m$) [47].

Provided that the coulometric yield is constant, preferably quantitative, the registered current is now directly proportional to the mass flow (mol/s) of the analyte. The detector is therefore a mass sensitive detector, in contrast to the voltametric mode in which the detector is of a concentration sensitive type.

It is appropriate now to oppose amperometric and coulometric type HPLC detectors. This is summarized in Table 3-2. In this table the amperometric detectors are limited to those with solid electrodes.

Table 3-2. Features of Amperometric (with Solid Electrodes) and Coulometric HPLC Detectors.

Amperometric Detectors	Coulometric Detectors
Respond to concentration (mol/L)	Respond to mass (mol)
Flow variations will affect peak areas	Flow variations will not affect peak areas
Response increases with flow-rate increase	Response decreases with flow-rate increase
Passivation of electrode surface quickly decreases response	Passivation of electrode surface gradually influences response
Noise <10 pA	Noise ca. 1 nA
Background current 10 to 100 nA	Background current 1 to 10 μA

Because amperometric detectors are concentration sensitive devices, peak areas will fluctuate with flow-rate fluctuations. Highly constant flow-rate is thus of prime importance to achieve precision with these detectors. In addition, the response of an amperometric detector, i. e. peak height, will increase when the flow-rate increases. This can be understood because the thickness of the diffusion layer, which is built up in milliseconds when the analyte flows over the electrode surface, is reduced, when the flow-rate is increased. Depletion of electroactive material is replenished faster. Therefore more material arrives at the electrode/liquid interface and can be converted (Figure 3-26). An example of this is given in [48].

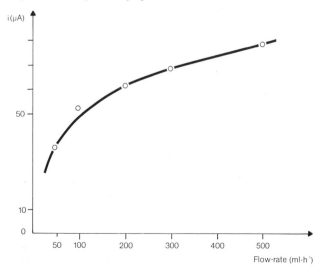

Figure 3-26. Response of an amperometric detector versus flow rate [48]. (Published with permission of Elsevier Scientific Publishers, Amsterdam).

In practice this effect will be obscured by the dependence of peak width on flow-rate and by the combined effect of external band broadening and finite response time of electrochemistry and electronics.

In coulometric detectors, however, response decreases with flow-rate increase because the coulometric yield will decrease. This is caused by the reduced residence time in the electrochemical detection cell. This is illustrated by Figure 3-27 [47].

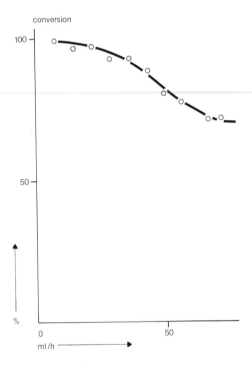

Figure 3-27. Coulometric yield versus flow-rate [47]. (Published with permission of Elsevier Scientific Publishers, Amsterdam).

Passivation of the electrode surface by irreversible adsorption of mobile phase constituents or of the debris of the electrochemical reaction will cause decrease of response of the amperometric detectors. This is inconvenient for quantitation because calibration with internal standards becomes inevitable. Internal standards do have advantages, e.g. monitoring of extraction efficiency from biological samples or accounting for poor precision of sample introduction, but they do also have serious limitations. In addition, electrode-passivation will cause a gradual baseline drift. Cumbersome cleaning (= polishing) of the electrode surfaces is effective in restoring the original detector response and provides a flat baseline again. This is a requirement incompatible with routine analysis. Therefore creative solutions to beat electrode passivation have been suggested [49]. Because of their larger electrode surface, coulometric detectors are not so sensitive to electrode passivation.

The last two features from Table 3-2 will be discussed in Section 3.6.5.2.3.

3.6.5.2.2 Cell Design and Electrode Materials

The minimum requirement for a transducer to be called an electrochemical measuring device are two electrodes between which a voltage is applied. In amperometry and coulometry this voltage is fixed at a constant level. The electrode at which the reaction of interest takes place is called the working electrode (w. e.), the other is called the reference electrode (r. e.). One of these will function as a cathode, i. e. a reduction takes place at the electrode. An oxidation will inevitably take place at the other electrode (anode).

By definition, the cell potential is given by the potential difference between the cathode and anode:

$$E_{cell} = E_{cathode} - E_{anode} \ .$$

If this difference is positive, the reaction – with some restriction – can take place and the cell will function as a galvanic (current delivering) cell. If this potential difference is negative the applied potential, E_{appl} has to be larger or equal to E_{cell} for the desired reaction to take place. The cell is an electrolytical cell. An example will clarify this.

Suppose we want to detect hydroquinone by electrochemical oxidation. Now the w. e. must function as the anode and the r. e. as the cathode. From the known data on the standard potential of the half reaction:

$$quinone \ + \ 2e^- \ + \ 2H^+ \ \rightarrow \ hydroquinone \qquad E = 0.7 \ V$$

and Nernst's law, the anode potential, can be calculated. Because the cathode is now the reference electrode, its potential is known. Only a few, well characterized reference electrodes are used in practice (in this example Ag/AgCl).

Now the cell potential can be calculated, e. g.,

$$E_{cell} = E_{cathode} - E_{anode} = E_{r.e.} - E_{w.e.} = -0.47 \ V$$
$$So \ E_{appl} \geqslant - (E_{cathode} - E_{anode}) = 0.47 \ V \ .$$

However, because of the electrochemical reactions that take place, a current flows through the cell. This current ist carried through the cell by movement of ions as was discussed under Section 3.6.5.1. There will be a resistance to this movement which will increase the actual cell potential:

$$E_{cell} = E_{r.e.} - E_{w.e.} - iR$$
and $\qquad E_{appl} \geqslant - (E_{r.e.} - E_{w.e.} - iR)$

where i is the current through the cell and R its internal resistance.

The iR-drop should preferably be kept as low as possible. This can be achieved by the use of conducting eluents. Therefore it is not surprising that HPLC with electrochemical detection became increasingly popular with growing application of reversed phase chromatography.

So far, we have supposed that the r. e. functiones as the cathode in order to provide a return path for the current through the cell. The electrochemical reactions that take place at the r. e. will change it. As its function is to be a reference for the w. e. it will become difficult to maintain that w. e. at a constant voltage. Therefore in most electrochemical detectors a third electrode is present, the auxiliary (a. e.) electrode, which carries the major part of the current. The r. e. carrying virtually no current can be of high impedance and of small dimensions. The voltage difference between w. e. and r. e. can be kept constant more easily, because the voltage of the r. e. is now constant.

Apart from basic electrochemical considerations, cell design is governed by chromatography and by the column. In particular the cell dimensions and the response times of electrodes and attached elctronics have to match the demands for registering small volume and fast concentration profiles which are generated by modern, highly efficient columns.

Therefore small volume cells ($<5\mu l$) are a prerequisite, although this does not neccessarily mean a small geometrical volume as in spectrophotometric detectors. The volume in which detection takes place, the response volume, should be very small. It is obvious that small cells are more easily constructed with solid electrode materials than with liquid (mercury) electrode material. Time constants of voltametric cells are relatively high ($> 0,5$ s). Moreover, in order to reduce high frequency noise, analog filters in the detector electronics are necessary. This inevitably means further increase of detector time constants (up to 5 s).

Metals, platinum and gold, and carbon based materials such as glassy carbon, carbon paste and graphite are most frequently used, both for working electrodes and for auxiliary electrode.

The electrode material is of decisive importance for the versatility of the electrochemical detector. Each material has its own characteristic overvoltage for the electrochemical breakdown of the supporting liquid (eluent). Therefore the voltage range within which detection of analytes can take place will depend strongly on the electrode material. For glassy carbon this range is approximately $-1,0$ to $1,3$ V and for mercury $-2,0$ to $0,3$ V. These figures are of no value without referring to the reference electrode, in this case saturated calomel (SCE). Most used reference electrodes are the Ag/AgCl couple and the Hg/HgCl couple (SCE). They are very well characterized (temperature coefficient) and easily miniaturized, which is very important in this application.

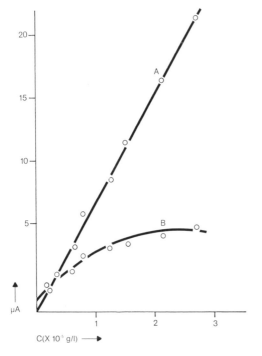

Figure 3-28. Linearity of detector signal for two electrode arrangements [47].
A: w. e. and a. e. opposite to each other,
B: a. e. downstream of w. e.
(Published with permission of Elsevier Scientific Publishers, Amsterdam).

A small cell volume alone is not sufficient for a transducer to function as a detector cell. The mutual arrangements of w. e., r. e. and a. e. are of prime importance. In particular the position of the current carrying electrodes is critical because the magnitude of the iR-drop directly depends on the distance between them.

A too high value of the iR-drop will have a great impact on the detector performance, in particular on linearity (Figure 3-28). This has been shown by Lanklema and Poppe [47] for the coulometric detector they described.

The implementation of these design demands has been solved in several ways (table 3-3).

Table 3-3. Cell Design for Amperometric and Coulometric Detectors.

Detector	Cell Design	Reference
Amperometric Type	1) Thin layer cell, 3 electrodes, 0.5 μL	[50]
	2) Wall jet cell, 3 electrodes, 4 μL	[51]
	3) Tubular	[52]
Coulometric Type	4) Planar cell, 3 electrodes, geom. vol. = 28 μL, response time	
	0.6 s	[47]
	5) Porous disc	[53]

All of these designs are applied commercially by several different manufacturers.

The use of mercury as electrode material for an HPLC-EC detector, very attractive in view of the large cathodic (reduction) range, has been hampered by difficulties in the realization of a low volume transducer in which mercury freely drops and in solving the problems of the gigantic capacitance currents — caused by changing drop diameter — without high filter time constants.

A very elegant solution has been described by Frei and Hanekamp [54] (Figure 3-29).

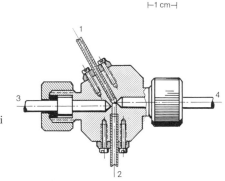

⊢1 cm⊣

Figure 3-29. Polarographic detector according to Frei and Hanekamp [54]. 1 inlet, 2 outlet (auxiliary electrode), 3 reference electrode, 4 dropping mercury electrode.

The horizontal mercury capillary is chosen deliberately to garantee very fast drop times (ms) which substantially reduces the problem of the capacitance currents. Because of the very small drops the response volume, i. e. the volume in which detection takes place is also very small (<10 μl).

3.6.5.2.3 *Drift and Noise*

The intrinsic difficulty in detection in HPLC, i. e. the registration of small changes, induced by concentration changes, superimposed on a much bigger − 10 to 1000 times − standing background signal is very pronounced in electrochemical detection. This will become obvious to the user by the wide range of the "offset" knob on these detectors, necessary for "zeroing" the signal. But because zeroing the signal does not mean eliminating the high background, the disadvantages of working on high background will be clearly manifested in such detector parameters as drift, wander and noise.

Because the basis of the background signal is electrochemical, drift and wander will be strongly influenced by environmental factors (temperature, humidity). Careful design of the cell compartment in the detector housing in order to isolate the cell from these environmental factors is a prime prerequisite for controlling drift and wander. In the authors opinion this has not been satisfactorily solved in most of the commercial instruments presently in use.

Moreover it must be realized that currents in the picoampere range are generated and must be processed. Therefore electrical insulation of the cell compartment (Faraday-cage) and of the leads from the environment must also be done carefully. In addition appropriate design of power supplies and wiring to avoid frequency pick-up is evident.

The intrinsic noise of the detector is of electrical and electrochemical origin. Voltage noise present at the reference electrode connection, generated by potentiostate and r. e. will cause charging effects at the surface of the working electrode resulting in current noise which is converted to voltage output noise. The magnitude of the w. e. surface area will therefore have a great influence on the noise of the detector [49].

A proper design and use of high quality electrical parts is therefore of paramount importance.

However, the electrochemically based noise, i. e. oxidation/reduction of oxidizable/reducible impurities in the mobile phase is often much higher than the electrical noise, especially at the end of the voltage range of the cell. In the reduction mode in particular, the presence of metal ions, leached out of the steel capillaries and of dissolved oxygen can cause high background currents on which the noise will be proportionally higher.

To overcome this last problem, Frei et al. [55] have suggested use of an electrochemical mobile phase scrubber. This scrubber, which is a high capacity electrochemical cell, is placed in the solvent line between pump and injection point. Its potential is set so that is oxidizes/reduces all interfering substances before the sample is introduced.

3.6.5.2.4 *Developments*

Electroanalytical chemistry, being a mature method in analytical chemistry, has seen a lot of enhancements since the first methods were introduced. The application of pulsed voltages, formation of differential signals, the usage of scan modes made voltammetry a powerful analytical method. The implementation of these techniques will increase its potentiality as a detection method in HPLC.

The authors anticipate a gradual introduction of these techniques in the coming years. This will not facilitate the use of these detectors. However it is to be expected that these developments will provide electrochemical detectors which can be easily used as routine monitors combining the ruggedness of UV detectors with the selectivity, sensitivity and LLD of EC detectors.

As mentioned before, the basic requirement for an analyte to be detectable, with voltammetric or coulometric detection devices, is the presence of the so called electrophor. But in addition, the voltage at which the electrochemical reaction takes place must fall within the limits set by the electrode materials which make up the cell. For these reasons the number of substance classes which are detectable is limited.

Moreover, because the detection principle requires conducting liquids, chromatography is limited to those techniques which use aqueous, buffered mobile phases.

In Tabel 3-4 the most important substance classes and their voltage range for oxidation/reduction are outlined. Detailed literature references about particular applications are amply given by most instrument manufacturers (Bioanalytical Systems, Methrom).

Table 3-4. Survey of Electroactive Analytes for HPLC-EC.

Analyses	Voltage				
	− 2 V	− 1 V	0 V	+ 1 V	+ 2 V
Phenols		------			
Catechols/Dihydroxyindoles		----			
Aromatic Amines		-----			
Mercaptanes/Sulfides			-----		
Purines				----	
Phenothiazines				---	
Nitrocompounds		-------			
Nitrosocompounds		------			
Quinones		----			
Imines, Semicarbazides		----			

One general application guideline can be formulated: although the versatility is limited, amperometric and coulometric detectors are the preferred detectors, when the substance class is responsive to electrochemical conversion, because of their selectivity, sensitivity and their potential to detect even minute amounts of substances.

3.6.6 Detection with Chemical Reactions

3.6.6.1 Introduction

It was demonstrated in previous sections that detection of the eluting sample components will be possible when the solutes posses a specific property to distinguish them from the mobile phase molecules or when the mobile phase bulk changes a particular property because of the presence of the analytes. However these requirements limit solute detection as well. Bulk property detectors have limited detectability (e. g. RI-Detection) while solute property detectors only respond when a chromophor or electrophor is present.

This becomes a detection problem when analytes carrying no chromophores or electrophores have to be detected at low concentration levels.

Detection of light absorbing analytes can be cumbersome, when the sample matrix is complex e. g. samples of biological or medical origin. In this case, selectivity in detection is required.

Chemical reaction detection provides a viable possibility to detect under these conditions. The basis of the method is the introduction of chromophores or electrophores by chemical reaction (derivatization). Of course, this derivatization can be done before column chromatography takes place. This is then called "precolumn derivatization". In post column derivatization, the column eluate is mixed with a reagent stream. The dissolved solutes are derivatized to a light absorbing or fluorescent molecule. If required, reagent stream and mobile phase stream are intensively mixed, heated and/or delayed in a volume, to allow slower reactions to take place.

Directly after reaction, the reaction mixture enters the detector as normal. This detector will be an optical (fluorometric) detector in most cases.

Opposing pre- to post-column derivatization (Table 3-5) shows the advantages and disadvantages of both derivatization methods. The selection of pre-column derivatization or post-column derivatization will depend on the particular application.

Table 3-5. Features of Pre- and Post-Column Derivatization.

	Pre-Column Derivatization	Post-Column Derivatization
Reaction Conditions	Can be selected optimal for the chemical reaction	Reagent and reaction must be compatible with the mobile phase
	Reaction time is not limiting	Reaction time is governed by the achieved separation
	Conversion must be 100%	Conversion must be reproducible
Derivatives	Chromatographic separation is hampered because the derivatives are "more" identical	Chromatography is not impaired by derivatization
	Formation of artefacts and diastereo-isomers possible. Will elute separately	Artefacts and isomers coelute
	Simple procedure	Not easy for routine analysis

3.6.6.2 General Considerations

After leaving the column (c), the analyte (j) is contained in a volume (V) characterized by its volume variance ($\sigma^2_{V,j(c)}$):

$$\sigma^2_{V,j(c)} = V^2_{R,j}/n$$

$V_{R,j}$ is the retention volume of analyte j and n is the plate number of the column. In this discussion the contribution of external bandspreading other than that of the reactor to this volume variance will be ignored.

When the column eluate is mixed with the reagent stream (r), this band is further dispersed according to:

$$\sigma^2_{V,j(c+r)} = ((F_c + F_r)/F_c)^2 \cdot \sigma^2_{V,j(c)} = F^2_S \cdot \sigma^2_{V,j(c)} \ .$$

In this equation, F_c is the flow-rate through the column and F_r is the reagent flow-rate. F_S is then the flow ratio.

The reactor itself will contribute to the overall bandwidth as well. This contribution is characterized by the variance $\sigma^2_{V,R}$. So the total bandwidth after reaction is given by

$$\sigma^2_{V,j(c+r+R)} = F^2_S \cdot \sigma^2_{V,j(c)} + \sigma^2_{V,R} .$$

The chromatographic resolution, which is the maximum attainable, is given by

$$R^{max} = \Delta V_{Rji}/4 \, \sigma_{V,j(c)} .$$

In this equation ΔV_{Rji} is the difference in retention volume between two consecutive eluting peaks i and j. On mixing with the reagent stream and reaction in the reactor, this difference will become: $F_S \cdot \Delta V_{Rji}$.

So, resolution after chemical reaction will be

$$R = F_S \cdot \Delta V_{Rji}/4 \, \sigma_{V,j(c+r+R)} .$$

Combining the last two equations, gives

$$R = \left(1 + \frac{1}{F^2_s} \cdot \frac{\sigma^2_{V,R}}{\sigma^2_{V,j(c)}} \right)^{-1/2} \cdot R^{max} .$$

As $\sigma_{V,j(c)}$ is fixed by the column, the loss in resolution by bandspreading in the reactor is determined by the flow ratio F_S and the selected reactor type and its $\sigma_{V,R}$. If the maximum tolerable resolution loss is defined, the maximum allowable bandspreading in the reactor can be calculated from the chromatographic bandwidth.

E. g. inserting $R/R^{max} = 0.8$, i. e. tolerating a 20% loss in resolution caused by the reactor yields:

$$\sigma_{V,R} \leqslant 0.75 \, \sigma_{V,j(c)} \cdot F_S$$

or in time units

$$\sigma_{t,R} \leqslant 0.75 \, \sigma_{t,j(c)} .$$

These demands can become very forceful when the column volume is reduced.

3.6.6.3 Reactor Types

The fundamental consideration for a post-column reactor design is to match the required reaction time with minimal dispersion in the reactor. It is obvious that the bandspreading in the reactor will increase with time.

In addition it must be realized that although bandspreading in longitudinal (flow) direction has to be limited, on combining of reactant and eluent, a thorough mixing in radial (cross sectional) direction is required, to assure that all analyte molecules "see" a reagent molecule. These somewhat contradictionary demands can be solved in a number of ways.

3.6.6.3.1 Packed Bed Reactors

Design and evaluation of packed bed reactors have been reported by Jonker and van den Berg [56, 57]. In most cases, packed bed reactors are made from standard LC-column hardware filled with inert, nonpermeable particles of 5 to 35 μm. Longitudinal dispersion in these reactors is controlled by appropriate selection of particle size. The reaction time can be manipulated with the reactor length.

The nomogram of Figure 3-30 is a useful aid for selecting the optimal conditions. From the required reaction time (t_r) and the allowable bandwidth (σ_t), particle size and pressure drop over the packed bed can be found. The diameter of the reactor can be calculated from reaction time and pressure drop.

Packed bed reactors should be selected when the demands of band spreading in the reactor are forceful (very small broadening in the reactor). Unfortunately, in a reactor packed with small particles, mixing in a radial direction is poor [58]. It is therefore neccesary to use an additional mixing device.

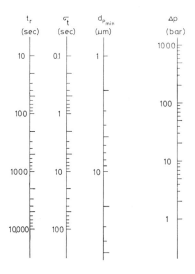

Figure 3-30. Nomogram representing graphically the relationship between the design parameters for a packed-bed flow reactor [56].

Several ingenious T-pieces have been suggested [56, 59, 60]. A low volume mixing column (e. g. 100 × 1 mm) packed with big particles (100 μm) is, according to the authors own experiences, a very practical and efficient solution [56].

3.6.6.3.2 Tubular Reactors

Flow through straight pipes (capillaries) in relation to band spreading in chromatographic systems has been amply reported in the literature [61, 62, 63, 64]. The results of this work and the results of Jonker [56] and van den Berg [57] show that capillaries are not applicable as reactors, unless band spreading is reduced below what theory predicts for straight capillaries. This is achieved by the so-called "secondary flow effect".

It is obvious that with "primary" flow the flow (direction) caused by an external force (pump) is meant. Secondary flow is caused by centrifugal forces which operate in a perpendicular direction to the direction of the primary flow.

As, for practical reasons, capillaries are coiled, it is very important to consider this coiling as an experimental parameter, which can manipulate the bandspreading in a tubular reactor. Figure 3-31 shows the effect of coil diameter on bandwith in a tubular reactor.

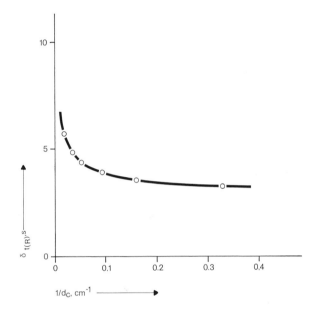

Figure 3-31. Influence of tube coiling on band spreading [57].

The quantitative relationship between the secondary flow effect and the coil diameter has been described [57, 62]. The effect becomes noticable for coil diameter/tube diameter ratios smaller than 25 to 50.

Figure 3-32. Knitted tube reactor (Courtesy of Prof. Dr. H. Engelhardt [60]).

Squeezing capillaries has been also demonstrated to reduce band spreading in tubular reactors [63].

A very elegant way to introduce secondary flow in a tube has been described by Engelhardt et al. [60]. Long lenths of flexible teflon tubing were knitted into a compact cord (Figure 3-32). These tubular reactors show a remarkable flow independence of the band spreading in contrast to the theoretical flow dependence of the band spreading in straight tubes

The secondary flow effect will also cause good radial mixing. External mixing devices can thus be abandoned if secondary flow is present.

3.6.6.3.3 Segmented Flow Reactors

These reactors are also tubular reactors. They are an application of the well known continuous flow analyzers (Technicon) for chemical reaction detection. In this reactor type, the streaming liquids are segmented by a non miscible phase (gas or liquid). Air is most commonly used for segmentation (Figure 3-33).

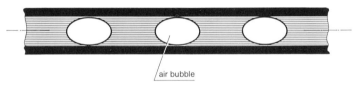

air bubble

Figure 3-33. Flow segmentation with air.

The theoratical basis of band spreading in such reactor types has been dealt with by Snyder [65] and Deelder [66].

Segmented flow reactors have found wide spread use as post column reaction detectors. However they are not easily adapted to the demands of HPLC, although some progress has been made [67]. By the nature of this reactor only moderate temperature levels can be applied, so long reaction times are often required.

3.6.6.4 Selection of Reactors; Reaction Detector Systems

It was argued in Section 3.6.6.2 that the selection of a reactor should be governed by the quality of the separation achieved on the column. Relating this to reactor type selection will be the responsibility of the chromatographer. However a few general guidelines can be given: When the demand is for the lowest band spreading in the reactor, packed bed reactors should be selected. Coiled, squeezed or knitted tubes are very attractive as reactors because the hardware is readily available and they are simple to use. Moreover plugging occurs less easily in tubular reactors than in packed bed reactors. However despite the secondary flow effects, band spreading in these reactors is more severe, which limits their application.

Segmented flow reactors should be selected when long reaction times are neccesary. Their advantage is the commercial availability of the system parts. (De)bubblers, phase separators, reaction coils, reagent pumps and fittings are being used in continuous flow analyzers as well.

Only limited, dedicated hardware for post column chemical reaction detection with tubular/packed bed reactors is offered commercially. Most system parts, i.e. reactor, thermostated oven, reagent pumps (low pressure constant volume pumps) connecting tees, mixing devices and backpressure regulators, the chromatographer has to assemble himself.

3.6.6.5 Application Guidelines

The wide spread application of post column chemical reaction detection clearly demonstrates the versatility of the method. Two excellent reviews by Frei and Lawrence [68, 69] have appeared which cover in detail the most important application areas.

It is beyond the scope of this book to discuss these here. But it has to be pointed out that in this application field there is as wide a domain for chemical reaction detection as there are specific reactions in organic analysis [70, 71]. The detection problem in organic analysis is the same as in HPLC detection: to distinguish the analyte molecules from their matrix. The countless number of reactions which have been developed for organic analysis call for their application in chemical reaction detection.

3.7 Preparative Separations

3.7.1 Introduction

Als already mentioned in the introduction of this book, liquid chromatography originally and for a long time was used as a preparative method. Since the early 60 s, and with the advent of suitable detectors, which could be coupled and operated on-line with the separation column the method has been employed for analytical purposes too.

In a recent market survey among analysts the question was asked: "If you intend to perform preparative LC separations, then how much pure sample do you want to isolate?" The result is shown in Figure 3-34 with the percentage of all answers over the amount of sample which would be isolated. According to this, for 40% of all purposes, amounts of less than 100 mg seem to be sufficient. Most applications require amounts of a few hundred mg.

For preparative work, chromatography, compared to other separation techniques, has the unsurpassed advantage of high selectivity and separation efficiency, so that extremely complex mixtures can be separated in a very short time. For this reason it is the preferred technique if pure compounds have to be isolated in quantities which lie in the range indiciated in Figure 3-34.

The disadvantage of the method, if employed for preparative separations, is that the loadability of chromatographic columns is very limited. Depending on the solubility of the sample molecules in the mobile phase and the characteristic of the distribution isotherm, the amount of substance which can be put on a column lies between 0.01 and 10 mg/g of stationary phase. If this value is exceeded a very steep decline of column efficiency in terms of theoretical plates will be noticed, as shown qualitatively in Figure 3-35. This effect can only be compensated by either enlarging the column dimensions [72] or by repeating the injection of a small quantity of the sample as often as necessary to obtain the desired amount of pure substance [73].

Scaling-up of liquid chromatographic columns unlike that of gas chromatographic columns, can be accomplished without loss in separation efficiency.

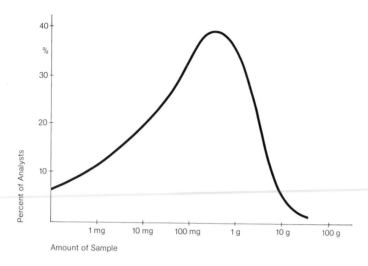

Figure 3-34. Result of an Opinion Poll:
Percentage of analysts who want to separate a certain amount of sample.

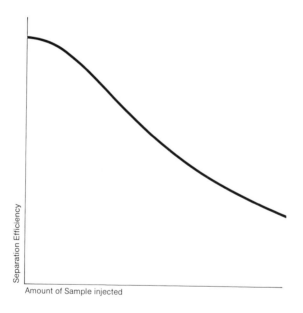

Figure 3-35. Separation efficiency in dependance of the injected amount of sample.

3.7.2 Working Areas and Conditions

The practical development of preparative liquid chromatography has recognized the fact
described above and led to a number of different systems each of which offers a specific set of

conditions as far as sample through-put and separation efficiency are concerned. A graph similar to Figure 3-35 is well suited to demonstrate this situation: In Figure 3-36, which again is a plot of separation efficiency (illustrated by chromatograms) over sample throughput, three areas can be recognized:

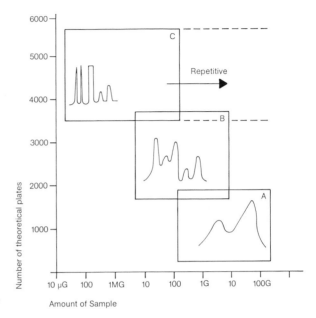

Figure 3-36. The working areas of preparative liquid chromatography.

A is the area of classical column chromatography. The separation problem is usually easy. The sample amounts to be separated lie between 100 mg and a few grams, which normally are separated in one run. Typical applications are purification of synthesized compounds from unwanted by-products or a rough fractionation of groups of compounds for instance from a plant extract. Columns are normally glass with inside diameters between 2 and 10 cm filled with Sephadex or silica gel as the stationary phase. The mobile phase percolates the column by gravity or aided by a low pressure pump. There is no automatic control system, the effluent is collected blind by a fraction collector and the fractions are later inspected by thin-layer chromatography, spectroscopy or visually. Such a system has the advantage of being simple, cheap and easy to survey. Its capabilities with respect to separation efficiency, however, are limited.

An interesting approach to improve the performance of this type of columns is offered by Jobin Yvon Co. in its Chromatospac Prep 100-system [74]. As shown in Figure 3-37 the bottom of the column is a piston which can be moved upward by the aid of compressed air. The stationary phase is filled into the column as a slurry with the piston in its down-stroke position. The column top is then closed and the piston pushed upward, compressing the packing and simultaneously removing excess solvent. The sample is then put onto the column and the separation performed. Beside a dense and more homogenious column packing the system offers the advantage that the separated fractions not necessarily need to be completely eluted from the column. As soon as the first fraction appears at the end of the column, the elution process is stopped and with the top terminator removed the packing is pushed out of the column. The fractions contained in the packing can easily be detected with an UV-lamp and those of interest removed and extracted. This technique, which has similarities to the way in which M. S. Tswett performed chromatography, can save solvent and operation time. The system typically works with columns of 10 by 100 cm, flow-rates between 20 and 100 mL/min and sample sizes of 1 to 100 grams per injection.

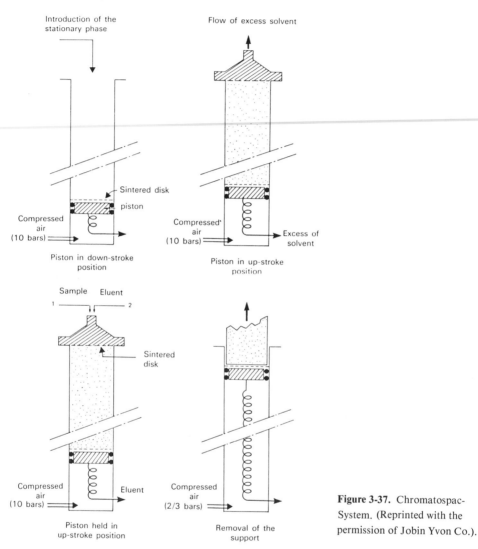

Figure 3-37. Chromatospac-System. (Reprinted with the permission of Jobin Yvon Co.).

B in Figure 3-36 is the applications area where very pure substances are required for example for synthetic purposes or biological tests. Stationary phases with higher performance and smaller particles have to be used and we are in a transition region with high-performance liquid chromatography. The price of the stationary phases and the solvents limits the column dimensions. Typical parameters are: column diameter: 2.5 cm, column length: 50 cm, flow-rate: 50 to 250 mL/min, injected sample size: 50 mg per cycle. These systems when commercially manufactured are sometimes automated for repetitive injection, continuous effluent monitoring and sample collection.

An example of an instrument falling in this working range is the Waters Prep LC/System 500, the flow diagram of which is shown in Figure 3-38. The stationary phase is contained in a prepacked polyethylene cartridge which is arranged in a chamber and radially compressed by the pressure of the mobile phase, so as to obtain a dense and homogenious packing structure. A refractometer is used as the effluent monitor to assure detection of all compounds leaving the column.

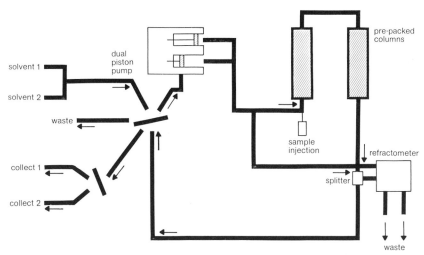

Figure 3-38. Flow diagram of a Prep LC/System 500. (Reprinted with the permission of Waters Ass. Co.).

C in Figure 3-36 is the area of semi-preparative liquid chromatography where analytical separations are scaled up in such a way that:

● the analytical instrument may be used for the preparative separation,
● the separation efficiency of the analytical column is fully maintained,
● a sufficient amount of substance of adequate purity is obtained to conduct all kinds of compound identification and structure elucidation, as indicated in Figure 3-39.

Figure 3-40 shows the flow scheme of a Hewlett-Packard 1084 B Analytical High Pressure Liquid Chromatograph to which, in order to perform preparative separations, the following components have been added: preparative injection system, preparative column, fraction collector and a system for the automatic control of the injection system and fraction collector.

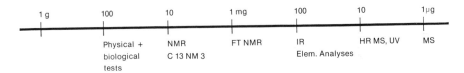

Figure 3-39. Sample amounts necessary for compound identification.

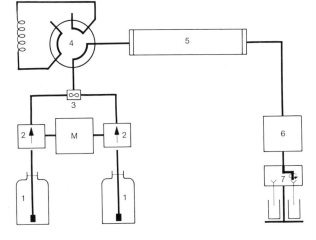

Figure 3-40. Flow scheme of an analytical liquid chromatograph equipped with components for preparative separations: 1 Solvent Reservoir, 2 Pump, 3 Mixing Chamber, 4 Injection System, 5 Column 6 Detector, 7 Fraction Collector. (Reprinted with the permission of Hewlett-Packard Company).

The injection system is a 6-port-valve to which a sample storage capillary is connected (Figure 3-41). In the position shown (full lines) the capillary, which may have a volume of up to 50 mL, can be filled with a syringe. In this position the solvent delivered by the pump is led directly into the column. If the valve is switched (dotted lines) the pump displaces a corresponding sample volume from the storage capillary onto the column. The switching time which can be set via the key board of the instrument controller and the flow-rate delivered by the pump determine the injected volume. With a flow-rate of 5 mL/min and a switching time of 0.1 min the injected sample volume amounts to 500 µL. Hence a storage capillary with a volume of 25 mL would allow 50 repetitive injections.

Figures 3-42 and 3-43 show the fraction collector. The effluent having passed the detector is fed to a glass-walled cylindrical space. The end of the capillary can be turned through 360°. The circle is divided in either 6 or 12 segments connected to outlets which directly lead into small fraction vials as shown in Figure 3-43 or which can be connected to bigger vessels via adequate hoses.

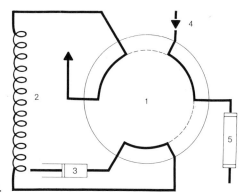

Figure 3-41. Injection System for preparative
separations: 1 6-Port Valve, 2 sample storage
capillary, 3 filling syringe, 4 from pump, 5 column.

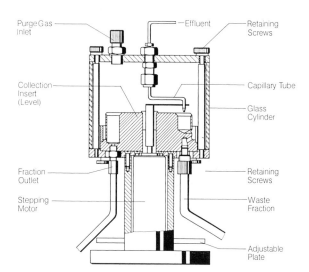

Figure 3-42. Fraction Collector.
(Reprinted with the permission of
Hewlett-Packard Company).

The injection system and fraction collector are controlled by the instrument microprocessor.
As the example in Figure 3-44 shows, the following functions can be preprogrammed: time of
injection, number of injections, injection volume, switching points of fraction collector and
duration of separation cycle. Figure 3-44 shows how the preparative time table becomes part of
the overall time table with control functions such as gradient forming.

An instrument like the one described, with its capabilities for automatic control and repeated
injection, can generate very pure substances in large amounts. With sufficient solvent in the
reservoirs and anough sample in the storage capillary, overnight operation is possible.

Generally speaking, choosing under which conditions to work will depend on the problem at
hand: If a phase system with high selectivity factor is available, high amounts of sample can be
injected and the requirements for the separation efficiency with respect to column plate number

are low, so that columns with coarse particles may be used. The opposite is true for problems where the separation of the idividual components is difficult (small-α-values) and the demands for purity of the collected compounds are high (high resolution necessary). Sometimes it may be advisable to do the separation in two steps: a rough separation on a column with lower efficiency and a final separation under high efficiency conditions.

Figure 3-43. Fraction Collector. (Reprinted with the permission of Hewlett-Packard Company).

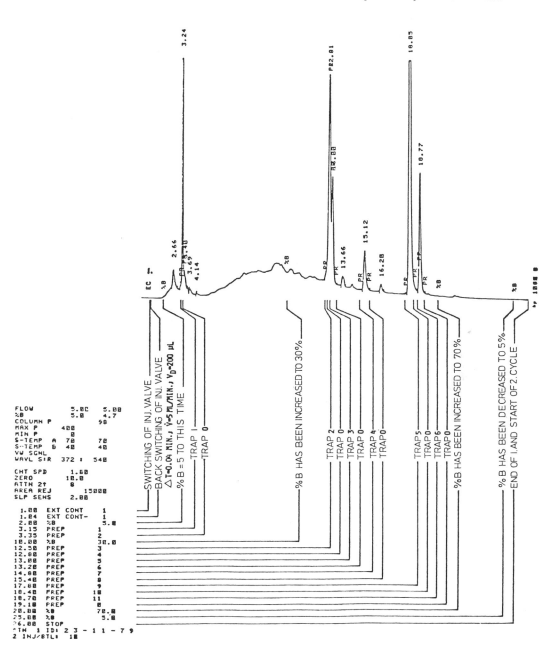

Figure 3-44. Preparative separation of radix gentianae. Column: RP 8 (7 μm) 250 × 8 mm, flow-rate: 5 mL/min; injection volume: 200 μL; temperature: ambient; mobile phase: gradient water-acetonitril 5 – 70% (v/v). Timetable shows automatic control functions.

3.8 References

[1] *Handbook of Chemistry and Physis,* 57th Ed., D 108 – D 112. Chemical Rubber Co., Cleveland.

[2] Roth Daunderer: *Giftliste 2, Toxicologische Enzyklopaedie.* ecomed.

[3] S. R. Bakalyar, M. P. T. Bradley, and R. Honganen, *J. Chromatogr.* 158, 277 (1978).

[4] J. N. Brown, M. Hewins, J. H. M. van der Linden, and R. J. Lynch, Publ. No. 7042.36.3877.11. Pye Unicam Cambridge.

[5] H. Schrenker, *CZ-Chemie-Technik* **1,** 73 (1972).

[6] H. Schrenker, *Am. Lab.,* March 1978.

[7] H. Schrenker, *Simulations of Effects of Flow-rate Instabilities in Isocratic and Gradient* LC (not yet published).

[8] P. J. Schoenmakers, H. A. H. Billiet, and L. de Galan, *J. Chromatogr.* **185,** 179 (1979).

[9] L. R. Snyder, and van der Wal, S., *Anal. Chem.* **53,** 877 (1981).

[10] A. Schmid, *Chromatographia* **12,** 825 (1979).

[11] H. Loreny, *Chemie-Technik* **6,** 233 (1977).

[12] G. Plein, *Labor Praxis* **3,** 112 (1979).

[13] Product Bulletin "Compact Glas Columns", E. Merck, Darmstadt.

[14] *Techn. Bull.* No. **IM 182 913** (1979). Waters Associates Inc.

[15] J. H. Knox, G. R. Laird, and P. A. Raven; *J. Chromatogr.* **122,** 129 (1976).

[16] M. J. E. Golay, *J. Chromatogr.* **240,** 180 (1982).

[17] T. Tweeten, Personal Communication.

[18] W. R. Sisco, and R. K. Gilpin, *J. Chromatogr. Sci.* **18,** 41 (1980).

[19] J. Chmielowiec, and H. Sawatzky, *J. Chromatogr. Sci.* **17,** 245 (1979).

[20] J. R. Gant, J. W. Dolan, and L. R. Snyder, *J. Chromatogr.* **185,** 153 (1979).

[21] W. R. Melander, A. Nahum, and C. Horvath, *J. Chromatogr.* **185,** 129 (1979).

[22] G. Herbut, and J. S. Kowalczuk; *J. H. R. C. & CC* **4,** 27 (1981).

[23] W. R. Melander, and C. Horvath, in: C. Horvath (ed.): *High Performance Liquid Chromatography: Advances and Perspectives, Vol.* **2,** p. 192. Academic Press, New York 1980.

[24] J. Perry (ed.), in: *Chemical Engineers Handbook,* 4th Ed. McGraw Hill (1963).

[25] R. J. Perdalski, and B. J. Wilder *Anal. Chem.* **51,** 744 (1979).

[26] H. Schrenker, *J. Chromatogr.* **213,** 243 (1981).

[27] J. J. Kirkland, W. W. Yau, H. J. Stoklosa, and C. H. Dilks, *J. Chromatogr. Sci.* **15,** 303 (1977).

[28] H. Colin, A. Jaulmes, A. Guiochon, J. Corno, and J. Simon, *J. Chromatogr. Sci.* **17,** 485 (1979).

[29] J. Ripphahn, *Kontakte* **3,** 28 (1978). Publication of E. Merck, Darmstadt.

[30] H. Schrenker, "Run Programming and Wavelength Programming Significantly Improve HPLC Lab Efficiency", *Hewlett-Packard Publication* No **5935-0025.**

[31] R. E. Dessy, W. D. Reynolds, W. G. Nunn, C. A. Titus, and G. F. Moler, *J. Chromatogr.* **126,** 347 (1976).

[32] L. J. Cline-Love, and M. Skrilec, *Int. Lab.* (Apr. 1981) 50.

[33] L. Gooyer, "Sensitized Room Temperature Phosphorescense", Paper presented at the: *Symposium on Detection in HPLC Jan 19 – 20. 1982 at the Free University of Amsterdam.*

[34] H. Todoriki, and A. Y. Hirokawa, *Chem. Pharm. Bull.* **28,** 1337 (1980).

[35] D. J. Malcolm-Lawes, P. Warwick, and L. A. Gifford, *J. Chromatogr.* **176,** 157 (1979) and *J. Chromatogr.* **200,** 47 (1980).

[36] J. R. Jadamec, W. A. Sauer, and J. Tolmi, *Anal. Chem.* **49,** 1316 (1977).

[37] L. W. Hershberger, J. B. Callis, and G. D. Christian, *Anal. Chem.* **53,** 971 (1981).

[38] M. P. Fogarty, D. C. Shelly, and I. M. Warner, *J. HRC & CC* **11,** 561 (1981).

[39] S. Haderka, *J. Chromatogr.* **54,** 357 (1971); **57,** 181 (1971); **62,** 53 (1972).

[40] R. Vespalec, *J. Chromatogr.* **108,** 243 (1975).

[41] H. Poppe, and J. Kuysten, *J. Chromatogr.* **132,** 369 (1977).

[42] E. A. Schultz, and D. E. Mathis, *Anal. Chem.* **46,** 2253, (1976).

[43] R. S. Deelder, H. A. J. Linssen, J. G. Koen, and A. J. B. Beeren, *J. Chromatogr.* **203,** 153 (1981).

[44] C. R. Loscombe, C. B. Cox, and J. W. Dalziel, *J. Chromatogr.* **166,** 403 (1978).

[45] H. Small. T. S. Stevens, and W. C. Bauman, *Anal. Chem.* **47,** 1801 (1975).

[46] H. B. Hanekamp, Thesis 1981, Free University of Amsterdam; H. B. Hanekamp, and H. J. van Nieuwkerk, *Anal. Chim. Acta* **121**, 13 (1980).

[47] J. Lanklema, Thesis 1976, Municipal University of Amsterdam; J. Lanklema, and H. Poppe, *J. Chromatogr.* **125**, 375 (1976).

[48] C. Bollet, P. Oliva, and M. Caude, *J. Chromatogr.* **149**, 625 (1977).

[49] H. W. van Rooyen, Thesis 1981, Municipal University of Amsterdam.

[50] P. T. Kissinger, C. Refshauge, R. Dreiling, and R. N. Adams, *Anal. Lett.* **6**, 465 (1973).

[51] B. Fleet, and C. J. Little, *J.Chromatogr. Sci.* **12**, 747 (1973).

[52] D. N. Armentrout, J. D. McLean, and M. W. Long, *Anal. Chem.* **51**, 1039 (1979).

[53] *Product Bulletin ESA Coulochem,* Bedford, Massachusetts.

[54] H. B. Hanekamp, W. H. Voogt, P. Bos, and R. W. Frei, *Anal. Lett.* **12**, 175 (1979).

[55] H. B. Hanekamp, W. H. Voogt, P. Bos, and R. W. Frei, *Anal. Chim. Acta* **118**, 81 (1980).

[56] J. F. K. Huber, K. M. Jonker, and H. Poppe, *Anal. Chem.* **52**, 2 (1980).

[57] J. H. M. van den Berg, Thesis 1979, Technical University of Eindhoven.

[58] H. Knox, and J. F. Parcher, *Anal. Chem.* **41**, 1599 (1969).

[59] R. W. Frei, L. Michel, and W. Santi, *J. Chromatogr.* **126**, 261 (1977).

[60] H. Engelhardt, and U. D. Neue, *Chromatographia* **15**, 403 (1982).

[61] G. T. Taylor, *Proc. Roy. Soc.* **A 219**, 186 (1958); A. Aris, *Proc. Roy. Soc.* **A 235**, 67 (1956).

[62] R. Tijssen, Thesis 1979, Technical University of Delft.

[63] K. Hofmann, and I. Halasz; *J. Chromatogr.* **149**, 3 (1980).

[64] J. G. Atwood, and M. J. E. Golay, *J. Chromatogr.* **218**, 97 (1981).

[65] L. R. Snyder, *J. Chromatogr.* **125**, 287 (1976).

[66] R. W. Deelder, and P. H. J. Hendricks, *J. Chromatogr.* **83**, 343 (1973).

[67] A. H. T. M. Scholten, U. A. Th. Brinkmann, and R. W. Frei, *Anal. Chim. Acta* **114**, 137 (1980).

[68] J. F. Lawrence, and R. W. Frei: *Chemical Derivatization in Liquid Chromatography.* Elsevier, Amsterdam 1976.

[69] R. W. Frei, and J. F. Lawrence: *Chemical Derivatization in Analytical Chromatography.* Plessum Press, New York 1981.

[70] D. R. Knapp: *Handbook of Analytical Derivatization Reactions.* Wiley, New York 1979.

[71] G. Zweig, and J. Sherna (eds.): *CRC and Book of Chromatography.* Chemical Rubber Company.

[72] K.-P. Hupe, and H. H. Lauer, *J. Chromatogr.* **203**, 41 (1981).

[73] K.-P. Hupe, H. H. Lauer, and K. Zech, *Chromatogr.* **12**, 1 (1980).

[74] Publications No. Imprex **833 7662**. ISA Jobin Yvon.

4 Amino Acids, Peptides, Proteins

by *Friedrich Lottspeich* and *Agnes Henschen*

4 Amino Acids, Peptides, Proteins

4.1 Amino Acids

4.1.1 Introduction

Amino acids are small, amphoteric compounds with a molecular mass of 75 to 200. They occur in a multitude of biologically important forms in nature, either as free amino acids, or as conjugates of various unrelated compounds, or as the building blocks of peptides and proteins. The general structure of an amino acid is given in the formula below, the various amino acids (except those of the proline-type; see below) differing only in the side chain R.

Only 20 different amino acids are used by nature during ordinary biosynthesis of peptides and proteins, as only 20 amino acids are coded for by the nucleic acids of the genes. These amino acids and some of their properties are listed in Table 4-1.

Table 4-1. Structure of Common Amino Acids.

Name	Structure	Values of pK_a	pI
I. Aliphatic amino acids			
Glycine (Gly)	$H_2N-CH_2-CO_2H$	2.34; 9.6	5.97
Alanine (Ala)	$\overset{CH_3}{\underset{H_2N-CH-CO_2H}{\mid}}$	2.35; 9.69	6.02
Valine (Val)	$\overset{CH_3 \quad CH_3}{\underset{H_2N-CH-CO_2H}{\diagdown CH \diagup}}$	2.32; 9.62	5.97
Leucine (Leu)	$\overset{CH_3 \quad CH_3}{\underset{H_2N-CH-CO_2H}{\underset{CH_2}{\underset{CH}{\diagdown \diagup}}}}$	2.36; 9.60	5.98
Isoleucine (Ile)	$\overset{CH_3}{\underset{H_2N-CH-CO_2H}{\underset{CH-CH_3}{\underset{CH_2}{\mid}}}}$	2.36; 9.68	6.02
II. Hydroxyamino acids			
Serine (Ser)	$\overset{CH_2OH}{\underset{H_2N-CH-CO_2H}{\mid}}$	2.21; 9.15	5.68

Table 4-1. (Continued).

Name	Structure	Values of pK_a	pI
Threonine (Thr)	CH_3 $CH–OH$ $H_2N–CH–CO_2H$	2.63; 10.43	6.53

III. Dicarboxylic amino acids
   and their amides

Aspartic acid (Asp)	CO_2H CH_2 $H_2N–CH–CO_2H$	2.09 (α-carboxyl); 3.86 (β-carboxyl); 9.82	2.87
Asparagine (AspNH$_2$) (or Asn)	$CONH_2$ CH_2 $H_2N–CH–CO_2H$	2.02; 8.8	5.41
Glutamic acid (Glu)	CO_2H CH_2 CH_2 $H_2N–CH–CO_2H$	2.19 (α-carboxyl); 4.25 (γ-carboxyl); 9.67	3.22
Glutamine (GluNH$_2$) (or Gln)	$CONH_2$ CH_2 CH_2 $H_2N–CH–CO_2H$	2.17; 9.13	5.65

IV. Amino acids having
   basic functions

Lysine (Lys)	$(CH_2)_4–NH_2$ $H_2N–CH–CO_2H$	2.18; 8.95 (α-amino); 10.53 (ε-amino)	9.74
Histidine (His)	$HC–N$ $HC–N$ $\quad H$ CH_2 $NH_2–CH–CO_2H$	1.82; 6.0 (imidazole); 9.17	7.58
Arginine (Arg)	$\quad\quad H\ NH$ $(CH_2)_3–N–C–NH_2$ $NH_2–CH–CO_2H$	2.17; 9.04 (α-amino); 12.48 (guanidino)	10.76

V. Aromatic amino acids
(histidine included in category IV)

Phenylalanine (Phe)	CH_2 $NH_2–CH–CO_2H$	1.83; 9.13	5.98
Tyrosine (Tyr)	OH CH_2 $NH_2–CH–CO_2H$	2.20; 9.11 (α-amino); 10.07 (phenolic hydroxyl)	5.65

Table 4-1. (Continued).

Name	Structure	Values of pK_a	pI
Tryptophan (Trp)		2.38; 9.39	5.88
VI. Sulfur-containing amino acids			
Cystine (Cys)	CH_2-SH $NH_2-CH-CO_2H$	1.71; 8.33 (sulfhydryl); 10.78 (α-amino)	5.02
Cystine	$(CH_2-S-$ $NH_2-CH-CO_2H)_2$	1.65; 2.26 (carboxyls) 7.85; 9.85 aminos)	5.06
Methionine (Met)	$(CH_2)_2-SCH_3$ $NH_2-CH-CO_2H$	2.28; 9.21	5.75
VII. Imino acids			
Proline (Pro)		1.99; 10.60	6.10

However, a much greater number of different amino acids are found outside the peptides and proteins [1] and even in the peptides and proteins many post-translational modifications have been recognised [2]. This review will be restricted primarily to the 20 amino acids found in peptides and proteins and some of their derivatives which are common in protein chemical research.

Two main problems are encountered in HPLC-separations of amino acids. One is caused by the pronounced differences in polarity between the various amino acids, the difficulties primarily being due to the high polarity of amino acids carrying side chain charges. Another problem is caused by the low UV extinction coefficients of most amino acids. The UV absorption at very low wavelength, i. e. 200 nm, can be used for the detection of free amino acids, but the low extinction coefficient of the carboxylic group necessitates the use of very pure solvents. To circumvent these difficulties, pre- or post-column derivatizations of the amino acids have been used. Pre-column derivatization can be employed to make the amino acids more hydrophobic and thereby easier to handle by HPLC. Furthermore, derivatizing reagents can be selected which give the amino acids considerably higher extinction coefficients. Post-column derivatization is used as a detection method in a similar way as in a classical amino acid analyser. Disadvantages with post-column derivatization are the requirement for additional, often not commercially available equipment and peak broadening.

4.1.2 Free Amino Acids

During the last 15 years, the standard technique for the separation of free amino acids has been ion-exchange chromatography, as described by Spackman et al. [3] using post-column derivatization with ninhydrin, fluorescamine or o-phthalaldehyde for detection. Recently some attempts have been made to introduce HPLC for amino acid analysis. So far free amino acids have been successfully separated by chromatography on bonded phases, i. e. reversed-phase and NH_2-phase, ion-pair chromatography, ligand-exchange chromatography and by ion-exchange chromatography.

4.1.2.1 Bonded Phase Chromatography

Fundamental investigations into the separation of amino acids on non-polar stationary phases have been published by Molnar and Horvath [4]. They described separations of non-polar amino acids on reversed-phase material, under isocratic conditions. Aqueous buffers with a pH of 0.2 to 2.0 were used as eluents. In such buffers the carboxylic groups of the amino acids are mainly undissociated, and thus the retention times can be increased. Detection was performed at 200 nm. A linear relationship between the logarithm of the capacity factor and the number of carbon atoms in the side chain of simple alkyl amino acids was observed, as shown in Figure 4-1.

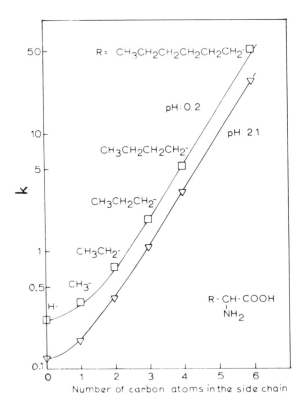

Figure 4-1. Plots of the logarithm of the capacity factor against the number of side chain carbon atoms of n-alkyl-amino acids [4]. Column: LiChrosorb RP-18 (5 μ); solvent system: 0.5 mol/L perchloric acid or 0.1 mol/L phosphate buffer, pH 2.1; temperature: 70 °C.

Because of their high degree of polarity, the hydrophilic amino acids are only weakly retarded on the hydrophobic stationary phases, but a separation can be achieved by including an ionic surfactant, such as decyl sulfate, in the mobile phase. In this so-called ion-pair chromatography the hydrophobic, but charged ion-pairing reagent associates with the oppositely charged group of the amino acid, this leads to a higher capacity factor for the resulting ion-pair complex than for the free amino acid.

Another example of ion-pair chromatography of amino acids is given in the work of Radjai and Hatch [5]. The separation of all the amino acids obtained from protein hydrolysates, except for the pair Glu/Gly, is shown in Figure 4-2.

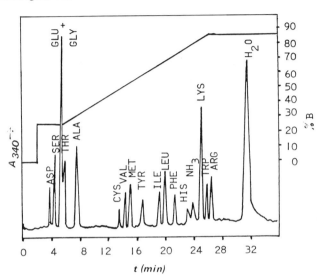

Figure 4-2. Separation by ion-pair chromatography of a standard mixture of free amino acids (3 nmol) [5].
Column: μ-Bondapak C-18; solvent system: step gradient, A: pH 2.85, 0.07% sodium decylsulfate, 0.5% acetic acid, B: 0.12% heptane sulfonate, 0.25% acetic acid, 20% aceto-nitrile, 10% methanol; post column derivatisation with o-phthalaldehyde/2-mercapto-ethanol.

The detectability of about 3 nmol amino acid is achieved by on-line post-column derivatization of the amino acids by o-phthalaldehyde/mercaptoethanol. The instrumentation, as outlined in Figure 4-3, is an example of the extra equipment required in connection with post-column derivatization.

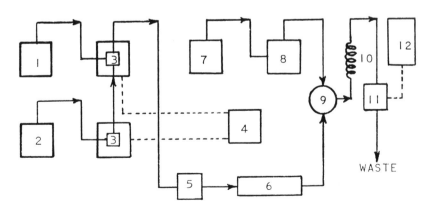

Figure 4-3. Schematic diagram of the equipment for post-column derivatisation [5].
1,2 reservoirs of eluents; 3 pump; 4 solvent programmer; 5 injector; 6 column; 7 post column derivatiser reservoir; 8 pump; 9 three-way tee; 10 tube; 11 UV detector; 12 recorder.

146   4 Amino Acids, Peptides, Proteins

A somewhat different approach to the separation of the hydrophilic amino acids is to employ a more polar stationary phase. Schuster [6] described the separation of free amino acids on a NH$_2$-column. All the amino acids present in protein hydrolysates are separated within 30 min by an acetonitrile/phosphate buffer gradient at 35 °C, and detected at 200 nm. The objective of the system described was the determination of free amino acids in solutions for intravenous administration and in pharmaceutical preparations. It was found that in protein hydrolysates, UV absorbing contaminants may interfere with the interpretation of the chromatogram, especially at lower levels of detection.

4.1.2.2 Ligand-Exchange Chromatography

Ligand-exchange chromatography is based on the formation of a labile complex between the compound to be analysed and a complex-forming ion, which is usually attached to the stationary phase by ionic, covalent or coordinational bonds. A separation of the 20 common amino acids by means of two different isocratic runs was described by Foucault et al. [7] and is shown in

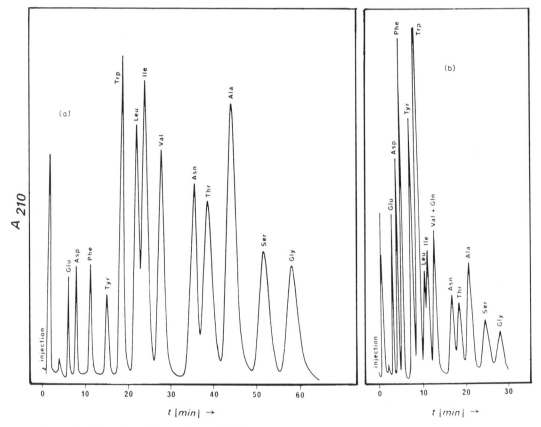

Figure 4-4. Separation of free amino acids [7].
Column: a) Cu(II) modified Partisil 5, b) Cu(II) modified Spherosil XOA 600; solvent system: a) water/acetonitrile (52:48)/0.15 mol/L ammonia, b) water/acetonitrile (50:50)/0.17 mol/L ammonia.

Figure 4-4. The chromatography, a combination of ligand-exchange chromatography and normal phase partition, is performed on unmodified silica gel treated with copper (II)-sulfate/ammonia. The copper ions become strongly fixed to the silica matrix. The columns are not stable over longer periods, but inexpensive and easy to prepare. Detection was carried out at 210 nm.

4.1.2.3 Ion-Exchange Chromatography

In the standard procedure, amino acids are separated on crosslinked sulfonated polystyrene resins, using citrate buffers as eluants and a post-column derivatization reaction with ninhydrin, fluorescamine or o-phthalaldehyde for detection (structures given in formula below).

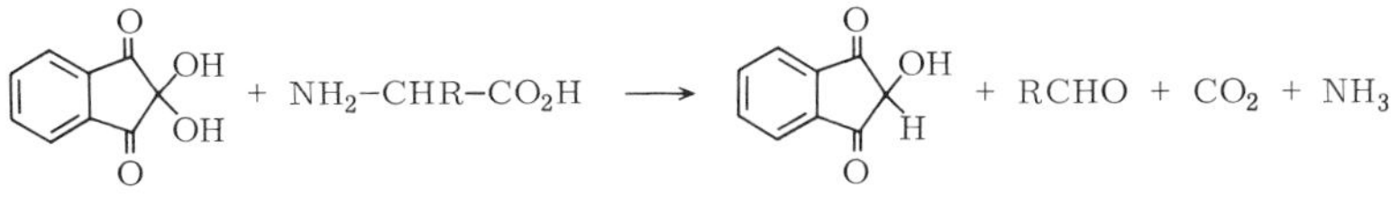

ninhydrin hydrindantin

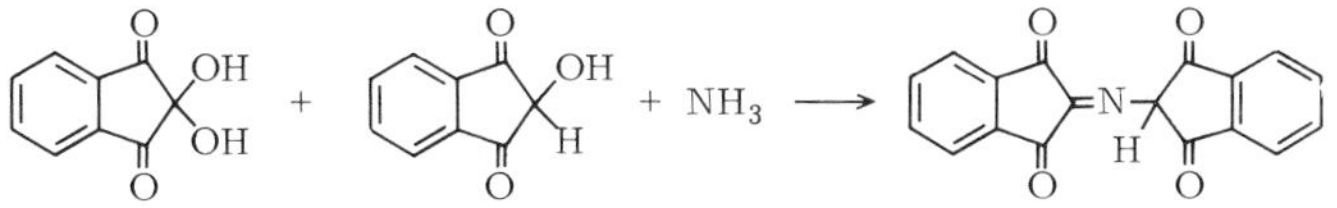

purple

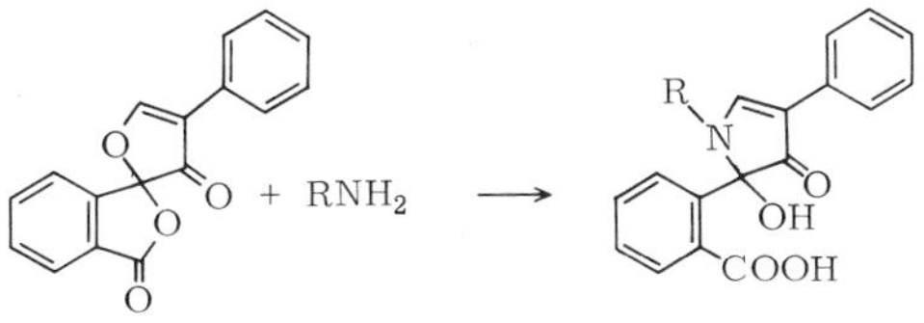

fluorescamine

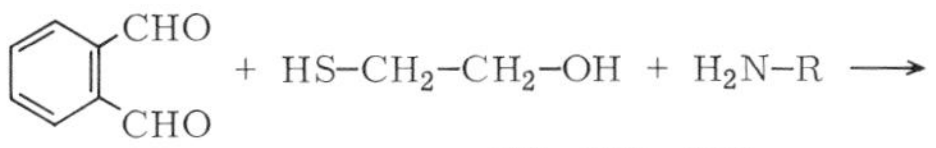

orthophthalaldehyde
(OPA)

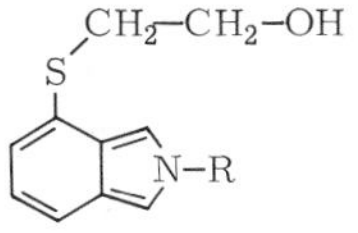

Fluorescamine and o-phthalaldehyde are non-fluorescent reagents which react with primary amines in alkaline medium, forming fluorescent compounds. O-phthalaldehyde has been claimed to exhibit higher fluorescence intensity than fluorescamine and has the additional advantage of water solubility. Neither reagent will react with secondary amines, and proline can therefore not be detected. This disadvantage may be partly overcome by oxidizing proline in the column effluent with sodium hypochlorite [8, 9] or with sodium N-chloro-p-toluenesulfonamide (Chloramine-T) [10]. It is, however, critical that the oxidizing agent only is delivered at the appropriate time, as it will cause destruction of other amino acids.

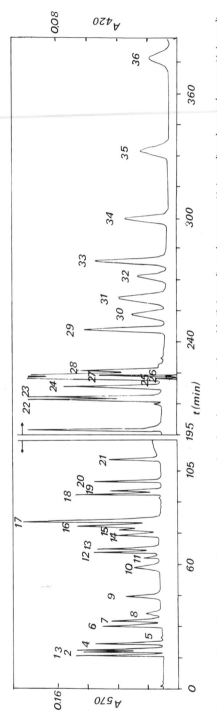

Figure 4-5. Separation by ion-exchange chromatography of a mixture of amino acids (2.5 nmol), amino sugars (4.4 nmol) and neutral sugars (4.4 nmol) [11].

Columns: DC-8-9 resin for amino acids and amino sugars, DA-X-8-8 resin for neutral sugars; solvent system: sodium citrate and borate buffers, solvent and temperature gradients; peaks: 1 Asp, 2 Thr, 3 Ser, 4 Glu, 5 Pro, 6 Gly, 7 Ala, 8 Cys, 9 Val, 10 Met, 11 ?, 12 Ile, 13 Leu, 14 Tyr, 15 Phe, 16 galactosamine, 17 glucosamine, 18 Lys, 19 ammonia, 20 His, 21 Arg, 22 sucrose, 23 trehalose, 24 cellobiose, 25 maltose, 26 rhamnose, 27 lactose, 28 ribose, 29 mannose, 30 fructose, 31 arabinose, 32 galactose, 33 xylose, 34 glucose, 35 gentobiose, 36 melibiose, 37 fucose.

Using small particle size resins (5μ) and the sensitive fluorescence detection, the identification and quantification on the subpicomolar level is possible.

A method for the simultaneous detection of amino acids, amino sugars and neutral sugars is described by Tikhomirov et al. [11]. The chromatogram is shown in Figure 4-5. The detection in this system was carried out with ninhydrin for the amino acids and with orcinol-sulfuric acid for the sugars.

Drescher and Lee [10] have published a method for amino acid analysis of proteins eluted from polyacrylamide gels. After extraction of the stained protein band from the gel with sodium dodecyl sulfate and subsequent hydrolysis with methane sulfonic acid, the analysis was performed on a cation-exchange column. For detection the post-column reaction with o-phthalaldehyde was used, the proline-containing part of the effluent having been oxidized with Chloramine-T prior to the derivatization reaction. The chromatogram is given in Figure 4-6.

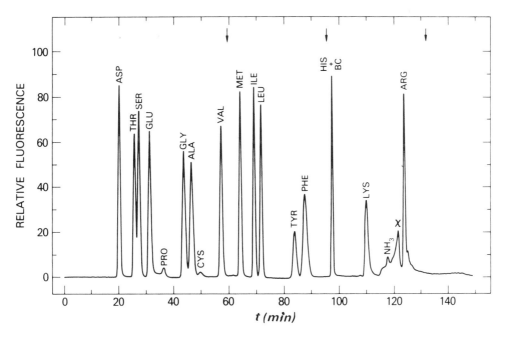

Figure 4-6. Separation of amino acids (300 pmol) [10].
Column: Aminco J5-7409 cation-exchanger; solvent system: sodium formate and borate buffers, pH 3.25 to 10.8, solvent gradients; temperature: 51 °C; BC buffer change peak.

Later, Drescher et al. [12] described an HPLC system for the analysis of the larger number of amino acids and related compounds which are present in physiological fluids. The separation was performed on a cation-exchange column (which 5μ beads), in lithium citrate buffers, with a change in column temperature and fluorometric detection of the o-phthalaldehyde derivatives of the amino acids. The detection limit is about 0.5 pmol, and the analysis time 5 hours. The chromatogram is shown in Figure 4-7.

Hughes et al. reported 1982 the separation of amino acids normally found in protein hydrolysates in 45 min with HPLC equipment normally used for peptide and protein separation

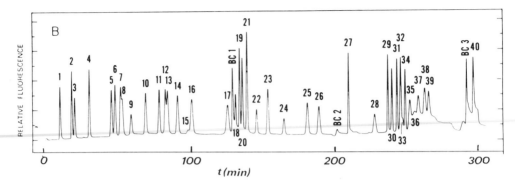

Figure 4-7. Separation by ion-exchange chromatography of amino acids and related compounds (100 pmol) [12].
Column: Aminco J5-7409; solvent system: lithium citrate buffers, pH 3.2 to 7.7; temperature: 37 to 62 °C; peaks: 1 phospho-Ser, 2 taurine, 3 phospho-ethanolamine, 4 Asp, 5 Thr, 6 Ser, 7 Glu, 8 Asn, 9 Gln, 10 α-amino-acid, 11 Gly, 12 Ala, 13 citrullin, 14 Abu, 15 Cys, 16 Val, 17 Met, 18 ?, 19 Ile, 20 Leu, 21 Nle, 22 Tyr, 23 Phe, 24 homocystine, 25 β-Ala, 26 β-Aib, 27 γ-Aib, 28 Trp, 29 His, 30 His(3-Me), 31 His(1-Me), 32 carnosine, 33 Hyl, 34 anserine, 35 ethanolamine, 36 ammonia, 37 Orn, 38 Lys, 39 α-amino-β-guanidinopropionic acid, 40 Arg, BC buffer change peak.

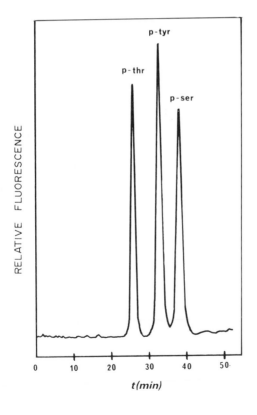

Figure 4-8. Separation by ion-exchange chromatography of phosphohydroxyamino acids [16].
Column: Partisil 10 SAX; solvent system: 10 mmol/L potassium phosphate, pH 3/12.5% methanol (v/v).

[13]. Analysis is performed on a cation-exchange column, eluted with formate buffers. The detection limit lies in the low nanomole level when ninhydrin is used and in the low picomole level when o-phthalaldehyde is used.

Kraak et al. [14] have employed a solvent-generated (dynamic) ion-exchange system for the separation of amino acids. The system consists of a hydrophobic stationary phase (RP C-8) and a water-organic solvent mixture containing a small amount of an anionic detergent. The hydrophobic part of the detergent binds via hydrophobic interaction to the reversed-phase column and the free, charged, hydrophilic part can act as an ion-exchanger. The ninhydrin reaction was used for detection. The influence of the various chromatographic parameters was extensively discussed. The selectivity of such solvent generated ion-exchange systems seems to be higher than that of conventional ion-exchange systems.

The phosphohydroxyamino acids (phoshoserine, phosphothreonine and phosphotyrosine) can be analysed by HPLC. Two methods have been described, one by Swarup et al. [15] and the other by Yang et al [16]. Swarup et al. separated the phosphohydroxy amino acids on an Ultrasil Ax anion-exchange column in phosphate buffer, pH 7.8. The detection was performed in UV at 206 nm. More recently Yang et al. decribed a method for baseline separation on a Partisil anion-exchange resin using a mobile phase with phosphate buffer, pH 3, in methanol. The detection was performed by post-column reaction of the effluent with o-phthalaldehyde. The detection limit was 10 pmol. The chromatogram is given in Figure 4-8.

4.1.3 Derivatized Amino Acids

The separation of derivatized amino acids plays an important role in many protein-chemical procedures. As already mentioned above, derivatization may be used both to improve the chromatographic behaviour, i. e. separability, and to increase the extinction coefficient, i. e. detectability and wavelength. Derivatization is also used to label amino acid residues of peptides and proteins, especially the N-terminal amino acid, i. e. the residue which has a free α-amino group. The labeled residue is, depending on the nature of the label, released by hydrolysis with strong acid or by intramolecular rearrangement induced by the label. The amino acid derivatives released from peptide chains may be the same as those employed with free amino acids.

All derivatization reactions primarily modify the α-amino group and, if present, the ε-amino group of the amino acids. In several instances other reactive side chains, such as the imidazol group, phenolic hydroxyl group, and sulfhydryl group are also modified. In other instances, the end stage of the modification reaction will also engage the α-carboxyl group of the amino acids.

The more common reagents are aryl fluorides or chlorides (Sanger-type reagents), aldehydes and isothiocyanates (Edman-type reagents). All these reagents may be employed to modify free amino acids, and all, except the aldehyde, are useful as labels in N-terminal amino acid determination. Only isothiocyanates produce derivatives of peptides and proteins which can be selectively released for identification without the destruction of the remaining peptide chain. Direct sequence analysis is thus exclusively achieved with these reagents.

4.1.3.1 Dinitrophenyl (DNP) Amino Acids

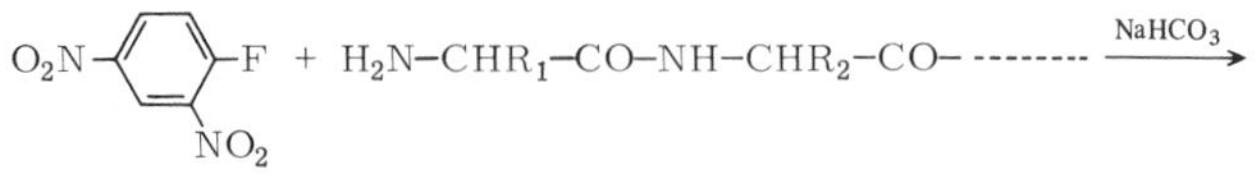

$$O_2N-\!\!\!\bigcirc\!\!\!-F \; + \; H_2N-CHR_1-CO-NH-CHR_2-CO-\; \cdots\cdots \xrightarrow{\text{NaHCO}_3}$$

fluorodinitrobenzene

$$O_2N-\!\!\!\bigcirc\!\!\!-NH-CHR_1-CO-NH-CHR_2-CO-\; \cdots\cdots \xrightarrow{\text{H}_2\text{O}}$$

$$O_2N-\!\!\!\bigcirc\!\!\!-NH-CHR_1-COOH \; + \; NH_2-CHR_2-COOH \; + \cdots\cdots$$

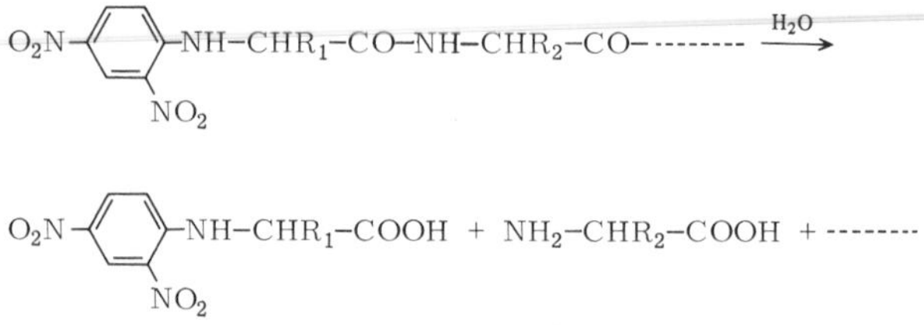

DNP amino acid

One of the first reagents used for the labeling of amino groups in amino acids and peptides was fluorodinitrobenzene, i.e. Sanger's reagent [17]. Reactive amino acid side-chains are also modified and acid hydrolysis is needed for the release from peptide chains. The yellow DNP amino acids may be identified by paper or thin-layer chromatography or by HPLC. DNP amino acid analysis by HPLC with gradient elution is described by Zimmerman and Pisano [18].

4.1.3.2 Dimethylaminonaphthalene-sulfonyl (dansyl) Amino Acids

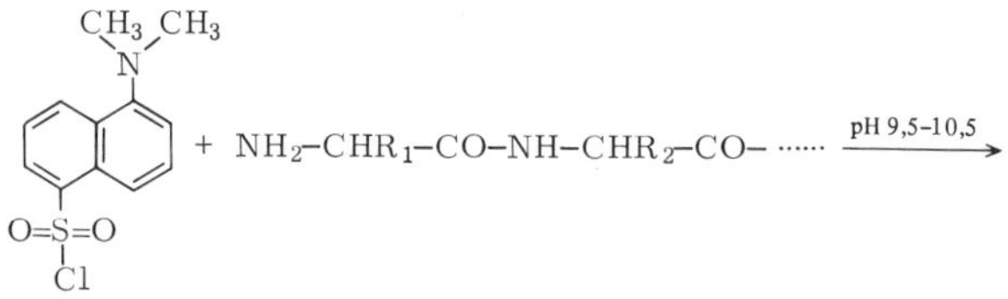

$$\text{dansyl chloride} \; + \; NH_2-CHR_1-CO-NH-CHR_2-CO-\; \cdots \xrightarrow{\text{pH 9,5--10,5}}$$

dansyl chloride

$$\cdots \xrightarrow{\text{H}_2\text{O}}$$

$$+ \; NH_2-CHR_2-COOH \; + \cdots$$

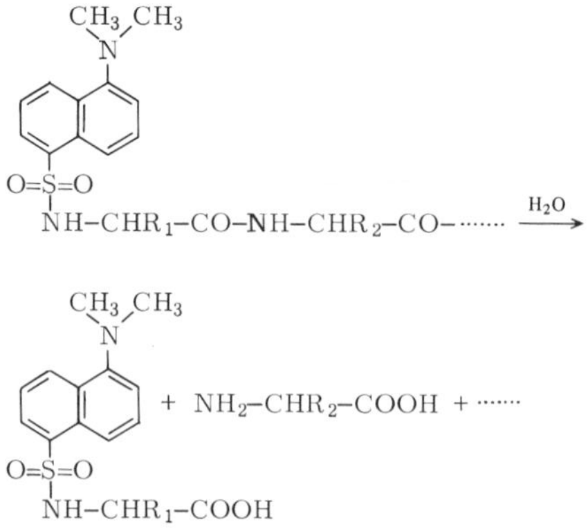

dansyl amino acid

When primary and secondary amino acids are reacted with dansyl chloride, i. e. a Sanger-type reagent, strongly fluorescent compounds, the dansyl amino acids are generated. Dansyl chloride does, however, not only react with the α-amino and -imino groups of the amino acids, but also with some reactive side chains, i. e. the ϵ-amino group of Lys, the imidazol ring of His and the hydroxyl group of Tyr. Dansyl amino acids are also obtained when peptides or proteins are reacted with dansyl chloride and the product hydrolysed by hydrochloric acid. The dansyl label is then only attached to the α-amino group of the originally N-terminal amino acid (and to some reactive side chains), which can then be identified by thin-layer chromatography or HPLC. This procedure is widely used as an indirect method of amino acid sequence determination method, i. e. the so called dansyl-Edman method, developed by Gray and Hartley [19]. It should be noticed that in this type of sequence analysis, several amino acids are modified or destroyed by the acid hydrolysis involved, i. e. asparagine and glutamine are desamidated, tryptophan is destroyed, and many modifications of amino acids are lost. However, dansyl amino acids are suitable derivatives for amino acid analysis, as they can be detected at the femtomole level, provided nonaqueous buffers are used in order to avoid fluorescence quenching.

Bayer et al. first reported an HPLC separation of dansyl amino acids with a two-column system on LiChrosorb Si 60 (5μ) in 30 min [20]. The separation is performed at a temperature of 65 °C with a gradient of benzene-pyridine-acetic acid/pyridine-acetic acid. Using a fluorescence

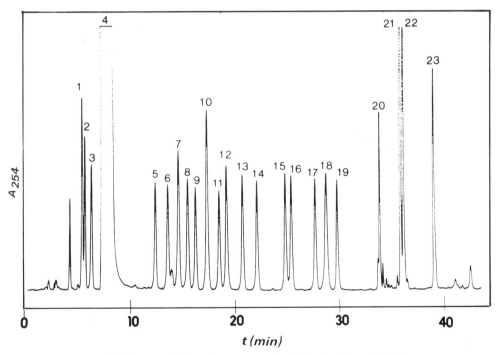

Figure 4-9. Separation by reversed-phase chromatography of dansyl amino acids [24].
Column: Spherisorb hexyl (5μ); solvent system: gradient, phosphate, pH 6/acetonitrile; temperature: 34 °C; peaks: 1 cysteic acid, 2 Asp, 3 Glu, 4 dansyl sulfonic acid, 5 Ser, 6 Thr, 7 Gly, 8 Ala, 9 Met(O), 10 Abu, 11 Arg, 12 Pro, 13 Val, 14 Met, 15 Ile, 16 Leu, 17 Phe, 18 dansyl chloride, 19 cystine, 20 dansyl amide, 21 Lys, 22 His, 23 Tyr.

detector (excitation at 340 nm, emmission at 510 nm) a detection limit in the femtomole range could be obtained. In the same publication, a reversed-phase system is described by which most of the common dansyl amino acids are resolved.

Several useful separations of all amino acids obtained from proteins by acidic or enzymatic hydrolysis have been described in the literature [21 to 24, 405], the chromatography of Mackey and Beck may serve as an example, (see Figure 4-9) [24]. A procedure for the reproducible high-yield derivatization of amino acids has been given by Tapuhi et al. [25].

An increase in detectability can be obtained, if the dansyl amino acids are excited by a chemical reaction and not by UV irradiation [26]. Chemiluminescence of the dansyl amino acids can be generated by bis(2,4,6-trichlorophenyl)oxalate and hydrogen peroxide. The proposed reaction mechanism is given in the scheme below. In this way a detection of dansyl amino acids in the low femtomole range is possible.

$$Ar-\overset{\overset{O}{\parallel}}{C}-\overset{\overset{O}{\parallel}}{C}-Ar \; + \; H_2O_2 \longrightarrow \; \underset{\underset{O-O}{|\quad|}}{\overset{\overset{O}{\parallel}}{C}-\overset{\overset{O}{\parallel}}{C}} \; + \; 2 \; ArOH$$

oxalic ester

1,2-dioxethane dione

$$\underset{\underset{O-O}{|\quad|}}{\overset{\overset{O}{\parallel}}{C}-\overset{\overset{O}{\parallel}}{C}} \; + \; fluorophor \longrightarrow \; fluorophor^* + \; 2 \; CO_2$$

(exited state)

$$fluorophor^* \longrightarrow light \; + \; fluorophor$$

4.1.3.3 Dimethylaminoazobenzenesulfonyl (DABS) Amino Acids

DABS-Cl

DABS amino acid

Chang et al. described a system for amino acid analysis at the low picomole level by pre-column reaction of free amino acids with DABS chloride, i. e. another Sanger-type reagent, [27]. Under carefully selected conditions this reaction is reproducible. The DABS amino acids are separated by reversed-phase chromatography with two different gradient systems. As the derivatives are strongly coloured, the detection is performed in the visible region at 436 nm, the detection limit being 3 to 5 pmol of DABS amino acid. All the common amino acids present in protein hydrolysates, except for Asp and Ser, are separated with a gradient of 50 mmol/L sodium acetate, pH 4.13/acetonitrile. The non-resolved amino acids may be separated with a second gradient system, containing 28 mmol/L phosphate buffer, pH 7.2/acetonitrile, but, in this system, the resolution of the other DABS amino acids is inferior to that obtained with the first system.

4.1.3.4 Nitrobenzoxadiazole (NBD) Derivatives

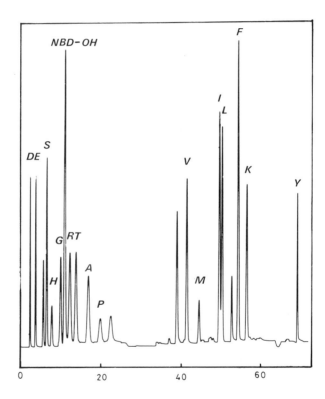

7 fluoro-4-nitrobenzo-
2 oxa-1,3-diazole

NBD-derivative of
amino acid

Watanabe and Imai used NBD-F as a pre-column fluorescent labeling reagent for the HPLC of amino acids, including Pro and Hyp [28]. The reaction is performed at pH 8.0 at 60 °C for 1 min. The derivatives of 18 amino acids were separated on a reversed-phase column and it was possible to detect them at a level of 10 fmol with excitation at 470 nm and emmission at 530 nm (see Figure 4-10).

Figure 4-10. Separation by reversed-phase chromatography of NBD-derivatives of amino acids (10 pmol) [28]. Column: μ-Bondapak C-18 (10μ); solvent system: gradient, 0.1 mol/L phosphate, pH 6/methanol/tetrahydrofurane (THF).

4.1.3.5 Orthophthalaldehyde (OPA) Derivatives

orthophthalaldehyde

Pre-column derivatization with OPA is frequently used for the determination of amino acids in biological fluids and protein hydrolysates. The non-fluorescent reagent reacts in the presence of a reducing agent, such as mercaptoethanol, with a primary amino group forming a fluorescent compound. With this method proline is not detectable and cystine gives a low fluorescence response. Pretreatment of the sample with iodoacetic acid results in good fluorescence of the cysteine derivative [29]. The separation of the OPA amino acids is usually performed on reversed-phase materials in about 30 to 50 min using multistep gradient elution and fluorescence detection (excitation around 330 nm, emmission around 460 nm). Detection in the low picomole range is possible as demonstrated by Umgat et al. [30] and shown in Figure 4-11. Other excellent separation systems have been described by Kabus and Koch [31] and Turnell and Cooper [32].

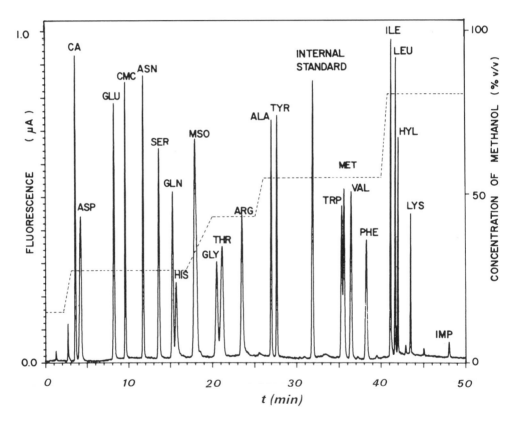

Figure 4-11. Separation by reversed-phase chromatography of OPA-amino acids [30].
Column: Ultrasphere ODS (5 μ); solvent system: linear step gradient, THF/0.05 mol/L sodium acetate, pH 6.6/methanol.

Hill et al. performed the derivatization of the amino acids with OPA/ethanediol, generating derivatives with stronger fluorescence [33].

4.1.3.6 Phenylthiohydantoin (PTH) Amino Acids

The original reagent used in direct amino acid sequence analysis is phenylisothiocyanate (PITC), i. e. Edman's reagent, first described over 30 years ago [34] and the principal reagent in the great majority of protein structure elucidations carried out so far. The following series of reactions form the basis of the sequencial degradation [35]:

I   ⟨◯⟩–N=C=S + NH₂–CH(R)–C(=O)–NHX ⟶ ⟨◯⟩–NH–C(=S)–NH–CH(R)–C(=O)–NHX

   phenyl-   peptide   PTC peptide
   isothiocyanate

II   ⟨◯⟩–NH–C(=S)–NH–CH(R)–C(=O)–NHX $\xrightarrow{H^+}$ ⟨◯⟩–NH–C(S···C(=O)CHR)=NH⁺ + NH₃⁺X

                                                      ATZ amino acid

III   ⟨◯⟩–NH–C(S···C(=O)CHR)=NH⁺ + H₂O ⟶ ⟨◯⟩–NH–C(=S)–NH–CHR–COOH + H⁺

       ⟨◯⟩–NH–C(=S)–NH–CHR–COOH $\xrightarrow{H^+}$ ⟨◯⟩–N–C(=O)–CH(R)–N(H)–C(=S) (ring)

                                                      PTH amino acid

The reactions I, II and III are referred to as coupling, cleavage and conversion, respectively. The products are termed phenylthiocarbamyl (PTC) derivative of the peptide or amino acid, anilinothiazolinone (ATZ) derivative of the amino acid and phenylthiohydantoin (PTH) derivate of the amino acid, respectively. The reactions are often carried out automatically in a protein-peptide sequenator [36]. The reaction end products, the PTH derivatives, may be identified by paper, thin-layer or gas chromatography [35], by amino acid analysis after hydrolysis, by mass spectrometry or, more recently, by HPLC . The introduction of HPLC analysis [37] has revolutionised structure elucidation with regard to the amount of material needed, as HPLC detection is three orders of magnitude more sensitive than, for example, thin-layer chromatography and allows quantification. A detection limit of down to 5 pmol using simple UV detection at 254 to 269 nm is reached in many laboratories.

The task of separating the PTH derivatives of all common amino acids is a complex one, because of the great difference in polarity. In an early communication Frank and Strubert [38] solved the problem by using different columns for hydrophobic and hydrophilic amino acid derivatives, the elution being isocratic. The system is still useful as only simple equipment is needed and the separation time is short. Some years later Zimmerman et al. [37] succeded for the first time in separating the derivatives of all common amino acids by means of gradient elution. The chromatogram is shown in Figure 4-12.

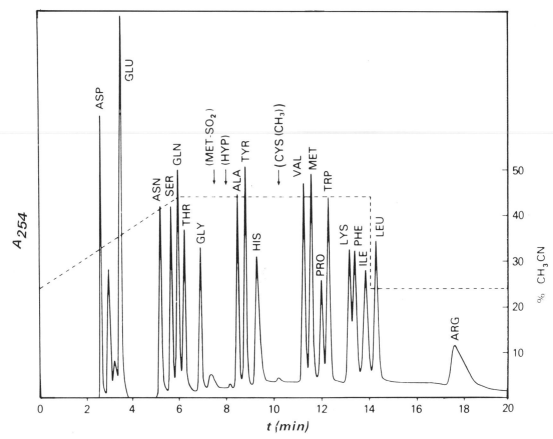

Figure 4-12. Separation by reversed-phase chromatography of PTH-amino acids [37]. Column: Zorbax ODS; solvent system: gradient, 0.01 mol/L sodium acetate, pH 4.5/acetonitrile; temperature: 62 °C.

Since then a very large number of separation systems have been developed, several of the most useful systems being listed in Table 4-2.

Many systems are in principle based on the original gradient system of Zimmerman et al. An example is given in Figure 4-13.

There are, however, certain disadvantages inherent in gradient elution, and therefore many isocratic separation conditions have also been worked out. These are listed in the later part of Table 4-2 and an example is shown in Figure 4-14.

Isocratic elution of PTH amino acids may be superior to gradient elution with regard to:

● the reproducibility of these highly complex patterns, especially after a column change;
● the number of injections giving acceptable separations;
● and, most importantly, the baseline stability at high detection sensitivity.

Furthermore, a simpler HPLC apparatus may be employed.

Table 4-2. Separation Systems for Phenylthiohydantoin (PTH) Amino Acids.

Column	g/i	Analysis Time (min)	Temp. °C	Nonseparated Common Amino Acids	Additionally Separated Amino Acids or Derivatives	Ref.
Zorbax ODS	g	20	62	Val/Met,Arg?,His?	Met(O_2), Hyp, Cys(Me)	[37]
Zorbax ODS	g	48	rt		Hyp	[39]
Spherisorb S5-ODS	g	23	37	(Val/Met), (Ile/Trp/Phe/Leu)	Cys(CH_2CONH_2), Hyp	[40]
Zorbax CN	g	28	31			[41]
μ-Bondapak Phenyl	g	60	?			[42]
Ultrasphere ODS	g	37	45		Met(O_2), Hyp, Cys(Me), Nle	[43]
μ-Bondapak C-18	g	30	37		Nva	[44]
Zorbax ODS	g	26	55	Arg?,His?		[45]
Zorbax CN	g	36	31	Asp?,Glu?	Asp(OMe), Glu(OMe)	[46]
Ultrasphere ODS	g	13	50	Glu/Asn	Met(O), Asp(OMe), Glu(OMe), Cys(CH_2COOMe), Nle, PTC-Gly(OMe), PTC-P(OMe), PTU, DPTU	[47]
Zorbax ODS	g	19	62	Pro/Trp	side chain protected amino acids	[48]
Si 60	i	2 x 5	rt	Arg?,His?	Asp(OMe), Glu(OMe)	[38]
Zorbax ODS	i	14	55	Ser/Gln	Hyp, succinyl-Lys, Nle	[49]
R-Sil C-18	i	23	64	(Gln/Ser)		[50]
Zorbax ODS + LiChrosorb RP-18	i	35	52	Ser?	Nle	[51]
Zorbax ODS	i/g	20	60		Nle	[52]
LiChrosorb RP-18	i	14	62	(Gln/Ser)	Met(O_2), Hyp, Asp(OMe), Glu(OMe), Aib, Abu, Cys(Me), Cys(CH_2COOMe), Hyl, Nva, Cys(PTCAet), Nle, PTU, DPTU	[53]
Ultrasphere ODS	i	9	55		Asp(OMe), Glu(OMe), Abu, Cys(Me), Cys(CH_2COOMe), Cys(pyridylethyl), Cys(sulfopropyl), acetyl-Lys, succinyl-Lys(OMe), Nle, PTC-Gly(OMe), PTC-Pro(OMe), PTU, DPTU	[54]
Ultrasphere ODS	i	20	55	(His/Ala)		[55]

g/i gradient or isocratic conditions, amino acid pairs in parenthesis are not well resolved.

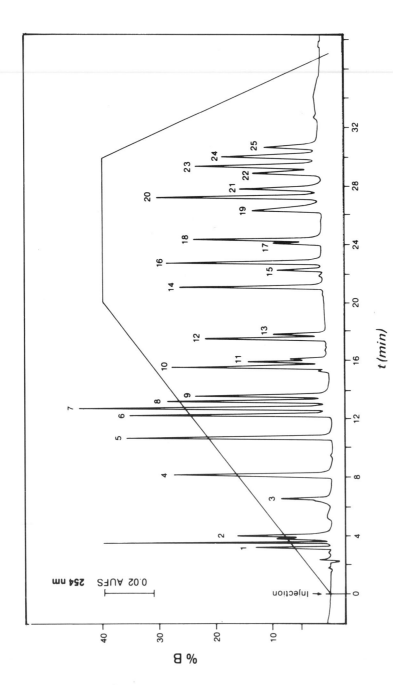

Figure 4-13. Separation by reversed-phase chromatography of PTH-amino acids [43]. Column: Ultrasphere ODS; solvent system: 5% THF in 0.042 mol/L sodium acetate, pH 5.16/10% THF in acetonitrile; temperature: 45 °C; peaks: 1 cysteic acid, 2 Asp, 3 Cys(CM), 4 Glu, 5 Asn, 6 Ser, 7 Gln, 8 Thr, 9 Gly, 10 His, 11 Met(O$_2$), 12 Ala, 13 Hyp, 14 Tyr, 15 Cys(Me), 16 Pro, 17 Met, 18 Val, 19 Arg, 20 Trp, 21 Phe, 22 Ile, 23 Lys, 24 Leu, 25 Nle.

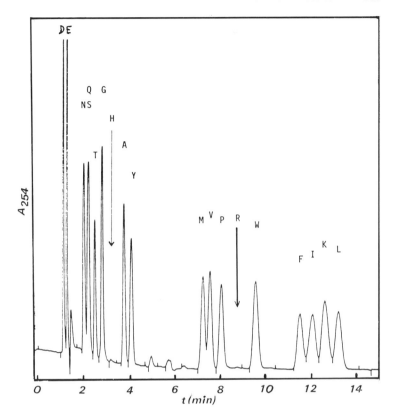

Figure 4-14. Separation by reversed-phase chromatography of PTH-amino acids [53]. Column: LiChrosorb RP-18 (5 μ); solvent system: isocratic, 68.5% sodium acetate, pH 5.2/31.5% acetonitrile/0.5% dichloroethane; temperature: 62 °C.

As is obvious from Table 4-2 there is an abundance of conditions which will separate all the common amino acids and, in addition will separate many of them in a modified form. Separation problems occur within the groups Ser/Gln, Met/Val/Pro and Phe/Ile/Lys/Leu. The conditions have to be optimised carefully, as temperature, pH, shape of gradient or solvent composition are all of critical importance. It has been observed that the retention times of Arg and His shift during column life, but that the shifts can be completely corrected by changes in the buffer concentrations [53].

4.1.3.7 Dimethylaminoazobenzenethiohydantoin (DABTH) Amino Acids

In amino acid sequence analysis of peptides, the classical phenylisothiocyanate may be exchanged against diaminoazobenzeneisothiocyanate (DABITC), the resulting amino acid derivatives being the colored DABTH amino acids. They can be detected in the visible region at 436 nm with a detection limit of 1 to 5 pmol. Chang published the separation of DABTH amino acids by an HPLC system on a reversed-phase column (see Figure 4-15) [56].

$$H_3C \diagdown N - \!\!\bigcirc\!\!\!- N\!=\!N\!-\!\!\bigcirc\!\!\!- N\!=\!C\!=\!S \; + \; NH_2\!-\!\overset{R}{\underset{}{CH}}\!-\!\overset{}{\underset{O}{C}}\!-\!NH\!-\!X$$

DABITC   peptide

$\Big\downarrow$ pH 8–10

$$H_3C \diagdown N - \!\!\bigcirc\!\!\!- N\!=\!N\!-\!\!\bigcirc\!\!\!- NH\!-\!\overset{}{\underset{S}{C}}\!-\!NH\!-\!\overset{R}{\underset{}{CH}}\!-\!\overset{}{\underset{O}{C}}\!-\!NH\!-\!X$$

DABTC peptide

$\Big\downarrow$ H$^+$

$$H_3C \diagdown N - \!\!\bigcirc\!\!\!- N\!=\!N\!-\!\!\bigcirc\!\!\!- N\diagup$$

DABTH amino acid

One pair of DABTH amino acids, i.e. Leu/Ile, is not resolved. It should, however, be mentioned that all the common DABTH amino acids may be resolved by thin-layer chromatography with about the same detectability and that thin-layer chromatography offers the possibility of discriminating between the DABTH derivative and the dimethylaminoazo-benzenethiocarbamyl (DABTC) derivative, i.e. between various derivatives formed in the course of sequencial peptide degradation, that differ in color. The main advantage of HPLC analysis lies in the quantification of the DABTH amino acid. However, it should be kept in mind that the coupling yield with DABITC, i.e. its reaction with the peptide amino group, is not quantitative.

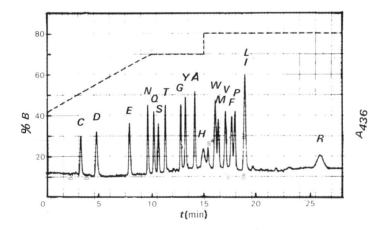

Figure 4-15. Separation by reversed-phase chromatography of DABTH-amino acids [56]. Column: Zorbax ODS; solvent system: gradient, 0.035 mol/L acetate, pH 5.0/acetonitrile; temperature: 22 °C.

4.1.3.8 Methylthiohydantoin (MTH) Amino Acids

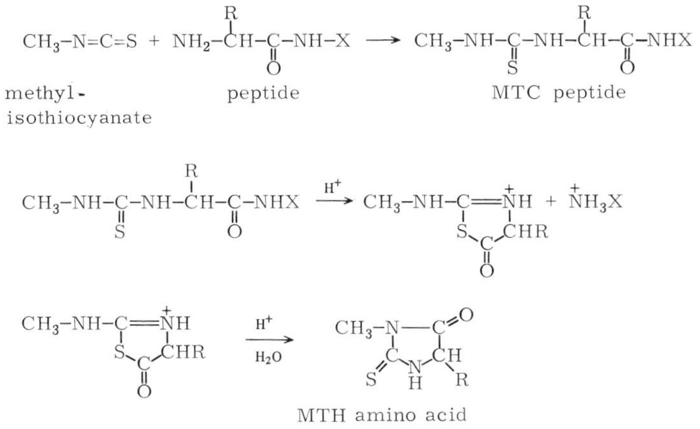

$$CH_3-N{=}C{=}S \ + \ NH_2-\underset{\underset{O}{\|}}{\overset{\overset{R}{|}}{C}}H-C-NH-X \ \longrightarrow \ CH_3-NH-\underset{\underset{S}{\|}}{C}-NH-\underset{\overset{R}{|}}{C}H-\underset{\underset{O}{\|}}{C}-NHX$$

methyl-   peptide   MTC peptide
isothiocyanate

$$CH_3-NH-\underset{\underset{S}{\|}}{C}-NH-\underset{\overset{R}{|}}{C}H-\underset{\underset{O}{\|}}{C}-NHX \ \xrightarrow{H^+} \ CH_3-NH-C{=}\overset{+}{N}H \ + \ \overset{+}{N}H_3X$$

$$CH_3-NH-C{=}\overset{+}{N}H \ \xrightarrow[H_2O]{H^+} \ \text{(MTH amino acid ring structure)}$$

MTH amino acid

Sequential degradation of peptides and proteins may be carried out with methylisothiocyanate (Edman-type reagent). The end products, i. e. the MTH derivatives of the amino acids, have already been identified by thin-layer and gas chromatography and by mass spectrometry. A recent communication by Hearn et al. [57] describes HPLC analysis of the MTH amino acids on a reversed-phase column using gradient elution. Most of the common 20 amino acids were resolved.

4.1.3.9 Diphenylindenonylthiohydantoin (ITH) Amino Acids

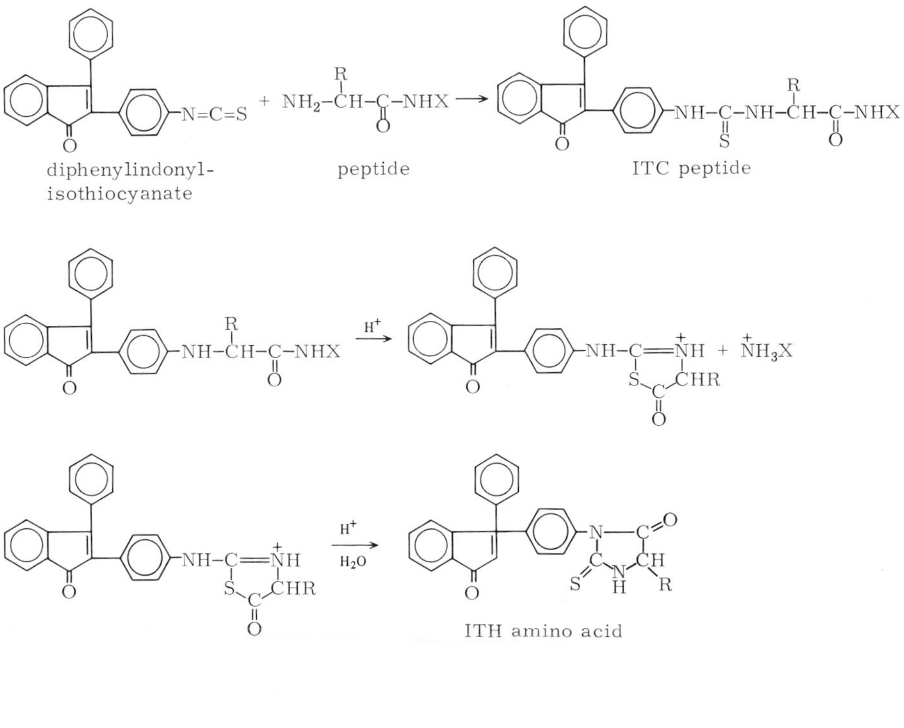

$$\text{(diphenylindonyl-isothiocyanate)}{-}N{=}C{=}S \ + \ NH_2-\underset{\underset{O}{\|}}{\overset{\overset{R}{|}}{C}}H-C-NHX \ \longrightarrow \ \text{ITC peptide}$$

diphenylindonyl- peptide   ITC peptide
isothiocyanate

$$\text{(...)}{-}NH-\underset{\overset{R}{|}}{C}H-\underset{\underset{O}{\|}}{C}-NHX \ \xrightarrow{H^+} \ \text{(...)}{-}NH-C{=}\overset{+}{N}H \ + \ \overset{+}{N}H_3X$$

$$\text{(...)}{-}NH-C{=}\overset{+}{N}H \ \xrightarrow[H_2O]{H^+} \ \text{ITH amino acid}$$

ITH amino acid

A coloured, alternative reagent for peptide sequence analysis is diphenylindenonylisothiocyanate. The amino acid derivatives forming the ITH amino acids have only been identified up to now by thin-layer chromatography. Recently Mancheva et al. [58] reported on the HPLC analysis of these derivatives. By means of three different elution systems, nearly all ITH amino acids could be separated.

4.1.4 Enantiomeric Amino Acids

Methods for resolving the enantiomeric pairs of the amino acids, i. e. their L- and D-forms, are gradually increasing in importance. Both analytical and preparative separation methods are needed for biochemical research and for pharmaceutical and alimentary purposes, because D- and L-amino acids differ in their biological as well as their physico-chemical properties. Earlier the enantiomeric form of an amino acid was determined by selective crystallization, by selective destruction with amino acid oxidases or, after conversion to a diastereoisomeric dipeptide, by gas chromatography or amino acid analysis. More recently, chiral supports were developed for the separation of underivatized amino acid enantiomers, both by gas and by liquid chromatography [59].

Amino acid enantiomer separation by HPLC has been performed by several different procedures. One possibility for this type of separation involves the conversion of the amino acid to a diastereoisomeric peptide by reaction with an N-carboxy-anhydride and subsequent chromatography on a reversed-phase column, as demonstrated by Takaya et al. [59]. The optical purity of most common amino acids could be determined, as little as 0.01% optical antipode being measurable. Allo-forms of Thr and Ile were also resolved, as shown in Figure 4-16.

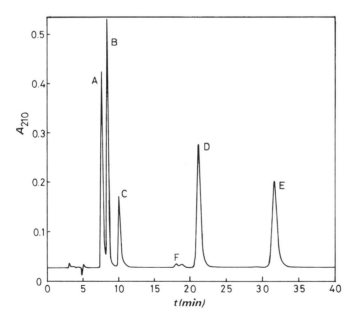

Figure 4-16. Separation by reversed-phase chromatography of a reaction mixture of L-Thr, L-allo-Thr, D-Thr and D-allo-Thr with L-Phe-N-Carboxy-anhydride [59]. Column: Nucleosil 5 C-18; solvent system: 0.1 mol/L phosphoric acid-potassium hydrogen-phosphate, pH 4.5/ acetonitrile (97/3); peaks: A L-Phe-L-Thr, B L-Phe-L-allo-Thr, C Phe, D L-Phe-D-allo-Thr, E L-Phe-D-Thr, F (L-L)hydantoic acid?

Another type of procedure for HPLC separation of amino acid enantiomers is based on the use of a chiral mobile phase. The underivatized amino acids were chromatographed on reversed-phase columns with a solvent containing the cupric complex of L-Pro, that of L-Asp-cyclohexylamide, that of N-(p-toluenesulfonyl)-L-Phe or -D-PheGly or that of N, N-di-n-propyl-L-Ala, according to Gil-Av et al. [60]. Gilon et al. [61], Nimura et al. [62] and Weinstein et al. [63], respectively. The effluents were in most cases analyzed by post-column derivatization. In the report of Nimura et al. a dynamic ligand-exchange mechanism between the two forms of the amino acid and the tosyl-amino acid-cupric ion-bonded phase complex is outlined. The resolution of the enantiomers of a very wide range of amino acids is described in the reports. An example from the work of Weinstein et al. is shown in Figure 4-17.

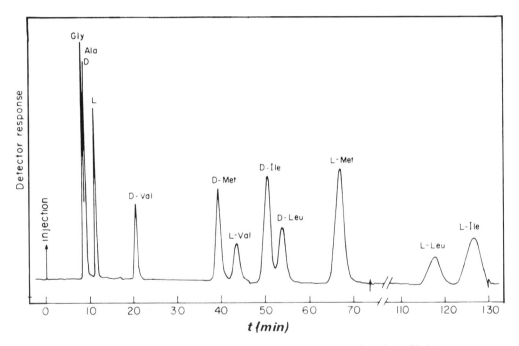

Figure 4-17. Separation by reversed-phase chromatography of enantiomeric amino acids [63]. Column: Spherisorb LC 18 (5 μ); solvent system: 0.008 mol/L N,N-di-n-propyl-L-alanine and 0.004 mol/L cupric acetate, pH 5.5, 1% acetonitrile.

A third way to achieve HPLC separation of amino acid enantiomers is the principle of chiral stationary phases, a number of which have been reported in the literature. The complex formation with cupric ions has also here usually been employed. Davankov et al. describe the separation of many enantiomeric pairs on the cupric complex of (R)-N,N-dibenzyl-propandiamine linked to a polystyrene resin [64] and on the cupric complex of N-alkyl-L-hydroxyproline coated on a reversed-phase packing [65]. Lindner showed that the cupric or cadmium ion complex of L-Pro-amide linked to silica gel would resolve a large number of enantiomeric pairs [66]. Watanabe et al. use cupric ion loaded and L-Phe-, L-Trp- or L-His bonded hydrophilic gel of the TSK 2000 PW-type for the successful separation of many pairs [67]. Most of these authors employ UV detection.

It should also be mentioned that the optical isomers of dansyl amino acids and of N-acetyl amino acid esters have been separated by HPLC using chiral mobile and chiral stationary phases, respectively [68, 70].

4.2 Peptides

4.2.1 Introduction

Peptides are defined as the covalent linkage products of two or more amino acids according to the following general formula:

$$NH_2-\overset{\overset{\displaystyle H}{|}}{\underset{\underset{\displaystyle R}{|}}{C}}-C\overset{\displaystyle O}{\diagup}\quad \overset{\overset{\displaystyle H}{|}}{\underset{\underset{\displaystyle R'}{|}}{NH-C}}-C\overset{\displaystyle O}{\diagup}\quad \overset{\overset{\displaystyle H}{|}}{\underset{\underset{\displaystyle R''}{|}}{NH-C}}-C\overset{\displaystyle O}{\diagup}\quad \overset{\overset{\displaystyle H}{|}}{\underset{\underset{\displaystyle R'''}{|}}{NH-C}}-C\overset{\displaystyle O}{\underset{\displaystyle OH}{\diagup}}$$

The upper limit for peptide size remains arbitrary because some protein cleavage products, traditionally referred to as peptides, can be larger than the smallest of the naturally occurring proteins. For practical purposes the size corresponding to 100 amino acids may be considered as an upper limit. Larger molecules will normally require the methodological approaches employed for proteins (see Section 4.3).

Peptides can be substances of great biological importance. Those encountered in biochemical research may have widely different origins.

A large part of the peptides studied belongs to the group of the naturally occurring peptides. These peptides are often biologically active and may be involved in a very wide range of biochemical reactions and functions. They are common in regulatory processes as hormones and cofactors of enzymes. Large numbers of peptides arise as breakdown products in the biological turnover of proteins. Whenever peptides have to be purified from biological sources great difficulties may be expected, as the peptides occur in extremely complex mixtures together with other peptides, proteins, amino acids and a multitude of peptide-unrelated substances, and as the relevant peptides are often present only in minute amounts.

Probably the largest group of peptides studied at present are those produced during the structural elucidation and characterization of large proteins. The long protein chain usually has to be cleaved by chemical or enzymatic methods to yield smaller fragments suitable for further structural analysis. Only a limited number of selective and quantitative cleavage methods are availabel which produce few and well defined fragments. The usual situation is that very complex peptide mixtures have to be processed, and it is often difficult to obtain the relevant peptides in sufficiently pure form and adequate amount for sequence analysis. The task of structural elucidation is made even more formidable when only small amounts of a biologically interesting protein are available.

Another source of peptides of biochemical interest are the synthetic analogues or derivatives of natural peptides. These provide a useful means for studying structure-function relationships and may be of pharmaceutical importance. In peptide synthesis, the desired product is normally contaminated by peptides with highly similar amino acid sequence or conformational structure, arising from incomplete reactions and racemisation, respectively. A purity check of all the intermediate peptides formed during a synthesis and the final purification of the synthesised peptide requires very precise analytical methods.

Even though the origins of the peptides may vary, the problems encountered during the isolation or purification of these peptides are in many cases similar. Peptides contain hydrophilic as well as hydrophobic amino acids. In general they may be considered to be polar molecules and water soluble. Traditionally the separation of peptides has been carried out by a wide range of well established techniques, such as precipitation procedures, gel chromatography, counter-current distribution, absorption and affinity chromatography, chromatography and electrophoresis on paper or thin-layer supports. Although these elaborate methods are still frequently and successfully employed, each has certain disadvantages or limitations e. g. poor resolution, low recovery and long separation time.

In recent years HPLC has steadily gained in importance as a method for peptide purification and even peptide identification. It is obvious that HPLC has gradually replaced many of the classical methods, particularly for the final stages of purification procedures, because it is often superior to older methods in separation power, yield, speed and lower level of detectability. Sometimes HPLC versions of the classical chromatography methods have been developed. It is, however, often found that HPLC will act as a combination of two or more classical purification methods, as the HPLC-separations more obviously are governed simultaneously by several different properties of the peptides, e. g. both charge and polarity. The unprecedented degrees of resolution which may be obtained with HPLC make it particularly suitable for purity control [70, 71], peptide mapping [72 to 87] or searches for a genetic abnormality [83 to 86, 88, 89] in a protein. In the last mentioned case the HPLC of peptides in the tryptic digest of an abnormal protein has to be compared with that of the corresponding normal protein and the single or the few differing peptides identified, i. e. an updated version of the classical fingerprint-analysis. An example of HPLC-based analysis of genetically abnormal proteins is given in Figure 4-18. The peptides released by thrombin from abnormal fibrinogen variants which differ in a single amino acid residue are compared [89].

HPLC has, for several reasons, proved to be of special importance when handling minute amounts of peptide material. Thus, fewer purification steps are needed and the losses are accordingly reduced. The yields in the HPLC steps are also often higher than in classical purification steps. In addition, non-destructive peptide detection methods are available. Highly sensitive detection by UV absorption at 200 to 220 nm is routinely employed. However, when the solvent system selected makes UV detection at low wavelength impracticable, equivalent detection sensitivity can be obtained by post-column derivatization with ninhydrin, fluorescamine or o-phthalaldehyde, although part of the peptide material is sacrificed for the analysis. The collection of peptides in small volumes of volatile solvents is an additional advantage of HPLC for microscale peptide preparation and analysis.

It is worthwhile considering that the speed of separation which can be achieved with the help of HPLC is important when there is a risk that the peptides in the sample will be altered by the chromatographic conditions. Thus, solvent constituents, such as acids or urea, may gradually modify peptides and cause loss of biological activity, increase the heterogeneity of the peptide mixture, decrease the yield of the relevant peptides and, quite generally, affect the interpretation of the results.

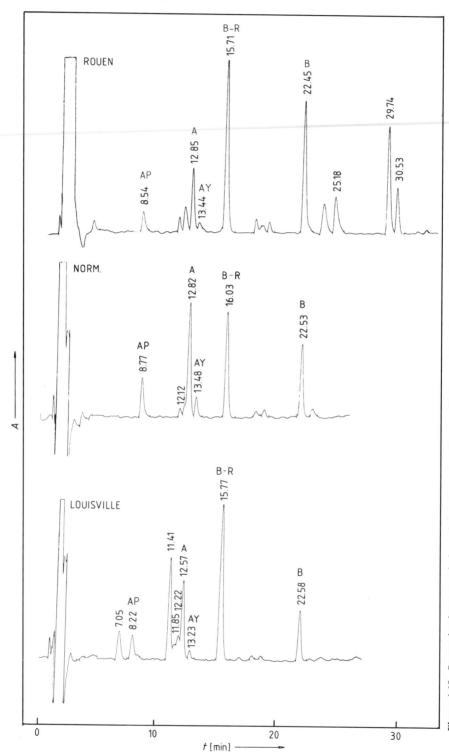

Figure 4-18. Separation by reversed-phase chromatography of human fibrinopeptides of normal and abnormal fibrinogens (Fibrinogen Rouen and Louisville) released by thrombin [89].

Column: LiChrosorb RP-18; solvent system: 0.025 mol/L ammonium acetate, pH 6.0/acetonitrile, gradient from 6 to 17% in 40 min; room temperature.

The number of publications dealing with HPLC-separation of peptides and proteins, so soon after the introduction of the procedure, is already impressive. Because of the great variety of peptides and proteins, stationary and mobile phases, detection methods and other principals described, it seems meaningful to make a survey of the present state of the art in the form of a table, listing peptides and proteins already subjected to HPLC, (Table 4-3). However, many examples of the various separation principles involved and of especially instructive chromato- graphy results will be presented in the relevant context.

Table 4-3. Peptides and Proteins Analysed by HPLC.

Peptide/Protein	Reference
N-Acetylated-permethylated peptides	[167]
Acetylcholin esterase	[390]
α-1-Acid glycoprotein	[280, 323]
Acidic proteins f. mineralised tissues	[369]
ACTH-related peptides	[93, 94, 96, 97, 104, 106, 109, 111, 112, 114, 118, 120, 123, 148, 180, 183, 195, 199, 208, 234, 301, 371, 378, 399]
Actinidine	[72]
Acyl carrier protein	[72, 105]
Adenovirus-encoded protein	[253]
Adenylosuccinate synthetase	[298]
Albumin	[87, 143, 212, 234, 239, 242, 245, 247, 252, 257, 263, 270, 277, 278, 280, 283, 290, 293, 301, 306, 307, 309, 315, 317, 320, 321, 327, 329, 330, 332, 336, 341, 346 – 348, 351 – 353, 356 – 358, 360, 362 – 364, 368, 370, 389, 390, 391, 400, 401, 403, 404, 406, 416]
Alcohol dehydrogenase	[143, 290, 364]
Aldehyde dehydrogenase	[305, 345, 364, 369]
Aldolase	[239, 301, 306, 313, 327, 351, 358, 362, 363, 370]
Allergens	[308]
D-Amino acid oxidase	[337]
Aminopeptidase Aeromonas proteolytica	[137]
Amylase	[277, 323, 394]
Amyloglucosidase	[358]
Amyloid proteins	[82, 159]
Angiotensin	[4, 70, 90, 91, 93, 96, 101, 103, 114, 129, 145, 148, 152, 180, 199, 301, 378]
Antigens, murine 1a tumor associated	[218, 264, 356]
Apolipoprotein	[76, 115, 207, 218, 223, 256, 279, 323]

Table 4-3. (Continued).

Peptide/Protein	Reference
Aprotinin	[148, 327, 353, 371, 407]
Arylsulfatase	[291]
Avidin	[353]
Bacteriorhodopsin	[188, 330, 333, 334]
Bence Jones protein	[128, 154, 159]
Bombesin	[93, 96, 105, 106]
Bradykinin	[90, 91, 114, 148, 199, 263]
Brain protein	
S 100	[155, 159]
14-3-2	[159]
Caerulein	[90, 91]
Calcineurin	[255]
Calcitonin	[93, 96, 118, 122, 227, 376]
Calcium-binding protein	[73, 78, 255, 260]
Calmodulin	[158, 159, 255]
Carbonic anhydrase	[143, 257, 281, 329, 360, 370, 401, 407, 409]
Carboxypeptidase	[323]
Casein	[75, 307]
β-Casomorphin	[148, 300]
Catalase	[239, 301, 306, 313, 327, 329, 351, 353, 362]
Cellulase	[292]
Cholecytokinin	[91]
Chymotrypsin(ogen)	[148, 239, 263, 270, 277, 283, 301, 306, 309, 313, 317, 320, 321, 327, 329, 346, 351, 353, 358, 362, 363, 391, 404, 411]
Chorionic gonadothrophic hormon (HCG)	[308]
Clupein	[321]
Collagen	[98, 142, 156, 244, 247, 252, 254, 416]
Conalbumin	[401]
Corticotropin releasing factor (CRF)	[121, 176, 181, 189, 398]
Creatine kinase	[143, 197, 273, 274, 288, 289]
Creatine phosphokinase	[270, 271, 290]
Cross-reacting protein	[140]
Cytochrome b 5	[205, 207]
Cytochrome b 561	[344]
Cytochrome c	[91, 93, 109, 118, 143, 148, 234, 238, 239, 245, 247, 252, 277, 282, 301, 307, 313, 315, 317, 320, 327, 329, 330, 346, 348, 351 − 354, 357, 358, 363, 370, 380, 390, 391, 401, 403, 404, 407]

Table 4-3. (Continued).

Peptide/Protein	Reference
Cytochrome P 450	[205, 238, 294]
DABTC peptides	[165]
Dansyl peptides	[166]
Delta sleep peptide	[91]
Dermorphin	[217, 299]
DNA-binding protein	[79]
Dynorphin	[91, 216]
Eledoisin	[90, 91, 114, 157]
Elongation factor Tu	[108]
Embryonic inducing factor	[360]
Encephalitogenic peptide	[221]
Endorphin	[90, 94, 96, 97, 103, 105, 106, 109, 112, 114, 118 – 120, 127, 130, 133, 134, 140, 145, 148, 149, 171, 179, 180, 182, 183, 186, 190, 199, 202, 211, 212, 215, 227, 235, 236]
Enkephalin	[90, 91, 93, 96, 97, 103, 105, 112, 114, 118, 122, 123, 127, 130, 133, 134, 144, 148, 153, 198, 199, 203, 212, 216, 219, 227, 234 – 236, 243, 376]
Erabutoxin	[321]
Felypressin	[95, 175]
Ferritin	[148, 266, 301, 306, 313, 317, 351 – 353, 357, 358, 362, 370, 400, 403]
Fetuin	[323]
Fibrinogen	[246, 309, 315, 325, 346, 408]
Fibrinopeptide	[89, 100, 187, 226]
Fibronectin	[126, 238]
Follicel stimulating hormone (FSH)	[157, 308]
β-Galactosidase	[268, 303, 363, 370]
Gastrin	[93, 96]
Glucanase	[292]
Glucose oxidase	[284, 411]
Glucose 6-phosphate dehydrogenase	[306]
Glucuronidase	[363]
Glucagon	[90, 91, 93, 96, 101, 105, 148, 176, 180, 190, 222, 320, 378]
ε-(γ-Glutamyl)lysine	[412]
Glycoprotein,	
surface coat, Trypanosoma rhodiense	[81]
influenca A hemagglutinin	[229]
Growth hormone	[145, 186, 221, 260, 301, 308]

172   4   Amino Acids, Peptides, Proteins

Table 4-3. (Continued).

Peptide/Protein	Reference
Hemocyanin	[233]
Hemoglobin	[74, 83 – 86, 88, 131, 132, 135, 137, 191, 221, 240, 241, 249, 257, 259, 270, 271, 275, 276, 278, 280, 286, 295, 301, 315, 343, 346, 363, 370, 374, 379, 384, 387, 388, 400, 403, 413, 418]
Hexokinase	[306]
High tyrosine component 0.62 from wool	[391]
Histone	[261, 321]
Homocarnosine	[212]
Hyaluronidase	[353]
Immunoglobulin	[124, 166, 218, 280, 306, 307, 309, 315, 317, 321, 323, 329, 346, 348, 360, 363, 403]
Insulin	[93, 96, 101, 103, 105, 109, 118, 120, 145, 148, 176, 189, 190, 212, 221, 224, 239, 242, 243, 245, 263, 281, 283, 301, 313, 320, 321, 327, 329, 356, 371, 378, 391, 397]
Interferon	[251, 253, 262, 397]
Isocitrate dehydrogenase	[353]
Lactalbumin	[255, 307, 329]
Lactate dehydrogenase	[270 – 273, 277, 287, 288, 290, 301, 315, 329, 364, 367, 417, 418]
β-Lactoglobulin	[257, 281, 301, 307, 313, 327, 329, 332, 348, 353, 363, 401, 403, 416]
Lac repressor	[341]
Leucine aminopeptidase	[363]
Lipoamide dehydrogenase	[337]
Lipoprotein	[318, 319, 336, 348 – 350, 392]
β-Lipotropin (LPH)	[93, 96, 97, 111, 112, 123, 127, 149, 171, 182, 192, 208]
Lipoxygenase	[402]
Luteinizing hormone (LH)	[308]
Luteinizing releasing factor (LRF)	[90, 91, 109, 123, 148, 180, 189, 216]
Lysopressin	[95, 103, 175]
Lysozyme	[87, 93, 124, 131, 143, 145, 242, 243, 257, 277, 283, 301, 313, 327, 329, 362, 363, 370, 372, 389, 401, 404]
Maleic dehydrogenase	[143]
α-Melanotrophin (MSH)	[4, 90, 93, 96, 120, 180, 199]
Mellitin	[93, 96, 407]
Membrane proteins	[80, 330, 331, 333, 334, 406]
Milk proteins	[306, 307]

Table 4-3. (Continued).

Peptide/Protein	Reference
Mold proteinase	[285]
Metallothionein	[260, 311, 342]
Mononuclear cell factor	[355]
Motilin	[122]
Mucine, submaxillary	[357]
Murine IA antigen	[218, 264]
Myelin basic protein	[87, 109, 375]
Myoglobin	[87, 93, 143, 234, 270, 290, 301, 309, 313, 315, 317, 327, 346, 347, 352, 353, 357, 358, 363, 370, 391, 401, 403]
Myosin	[306, 310, 391]
Neuropeptide Y	[138]
Neurophysin	[171, 193, 258, 377, 382, 383]
Neurotensin	[90, 91, 93, 96, 106, 148, 180, 396]
Neurotoxin	[170]
Ovalbumin	[87, 140, 143, 148, 239, 242, 243, 245, 263, 277, 278, 301, 306, 307, 309, 313, 315, 317, 320, 321, 323, 327, 329, 332, 346, 351, 353, 358, 363, 370, 389, 391, 401, 403, 404, 409, 415]
Ovoinhibitor	[323]
Ovomucoid	[323]
Ornipressin	[95, 173, 175]
Orosomucoid	[357]
Oxytocin	[90, 91, 93 – 96, 100, 103, 105, 148, 151, 152, 157, 161, 163, 173, 175, 190, 200, 203, 301, 371]
Parathyroid hormone	[152]
Parvalbumin	[143, 255]
Pepsin	[307, 313, 315, 327, 353, 363]
Peroxidase	[346, 353, 411]
Pituitary glycopeptide	[220]
Phosphatase, alkaline	[270, 290]
3-Phosphoglycerate kinase	[143]
Phosphorylase	[321, 329, 370, 416]
Phosphorylated peptides	[232]
Physalaemin	[90, 157]
Poliovirus peptides	[401]
Prealbumin	[280]
Prolyl hydroxylase	[140]
Proopiocortin	[195, 214]

Table 4-3. (Continued).

Peptide/Protein	Reference
Protected peptides	[170, 410]
α1-Proteinase inhibitor	[366]
Proteinase A inhibitor	[113]
Protein kinase, cAMP-depent	[107]
Prothrombin	[414]
Ranatensin	[91, 105]
Ribonuclease (RNAase)	[4, 93, 139, 155, 242, 243, 245, 252, 263, 277, 313, 320, 321, 323, 329, 346, 352, 357, 360, 363, 370, 401, 403, 404, 407, 409]
RNA polymerase	[321]
Secretin	[122, 222, 305]
Serum proteins	[271, 280, 293, 302, 306, 309, 314, 336, 338, 400, 403, 414, 418]
Somatostatin	[90, 91, 93, 96, 103, 105, 106, 109, 114, 118, 120, 123, 148, 176, 180, 185, 194, 196, 206, 212, 216]
Soy protein	[263]
Substance P	[18, 91, 93, 96, 99, 103, 106, 114, 122, 123, 148, 152, 216, 219, 234, 376]
Synacthen	[96, 97, 118, 120, 176, 181]
Synthetic peptides	[70, 71, 100, 116, 120, 130, 157, 160, 164, 169, 172, 174, 184, 186, 199, 211, 221, 234, 237, 378]
Thiamin-binding protein	[386]
Thymopoietin	[116, 148]
Thyroglobulin	[145, 184, 301, 317, 348, 351, 356, 358, 400, 403]
Thyroid-binding protein	[301, 306]
Thyrotrophin	[145, 184, 301]
Thyrotropic releasing hormone (TRF, TRH)	[90, 91, 114, 123, 157, 164, 212, 216, 219]
Transfer factor, human	[385]
Transferrin	[280, 309, 313, 323, 336, 363, 406]
Triosephosphate isomerase	[230]
Tropomyosin	[391]
Troponin c	[255]
Trypsin(ogen)	[265, 270, 290, 301, 313, 353, 363, 389, 411]
Trypsin inhibitor	[137, 143, 270, 306, 313, 320, 321, 329, 356, 359, 360, 401, 403, 407, 411]
Tubulin	[326]
Tubulin-tyrosine ligase	[393]
Tuftsin	[90, 91, 104, 148]

Table 4-3. (Continued).

Peptide/Protein	Reference
Tumor cell growth factor	[125, 281]
Tyrosinase	[247]
Urease	[303, 403]
Urinary proteins	[291, 318, 317]
Urokinase	[304, 339]
Urotensin	[108]
Vasoactive intestinal peptide (VIP)	[91, 106, 122]
Vasopressin	[18, 91, 93, 94, 96, 148, 151, 152, 173, 190, 199, 205, 212, 356]
Vasotocin	[91, 96, 148, 151]
Viral proteins	[80, 229, 242, 243, 253, 305, 401]

4.2.2 Peptides, Underivatized

The great majority of applications described in the literature deal with the separation of underivatized peptides. Two distinct types of separation are used reversed-phase and ion-exchange chromatography. Out of these two the reversed-phase method predominates in the literature.

4.2.2.1 Reversed-Phase Chromatography

Reversed-phase HPLC has become the method of choice for the fractionation of peptide mixtures. In theory, underivatized peptides are very poor candidates for reversed-phase chromatography because of their high polarity. The peptide is unable to interact to a sufficient extent with the hydrophobic surface of the stationary phase, and furthermore it binds strongly to the residual free silanol groups. To overcome these adverse effects, the interaction with the free silanol groups has firstly to be suppressed and, secondly, conditions should be chosen so as to reduce the polar nature of the peptide. The influence of the free silanol groups can be decreased by the addition of salts or strong acids to the solvent system and for this purpose the molarity of the buffer should be about 0.1 mol/L. To reduce the polar character of the peptides the chromatography should be carried out at a low pH (below pH 3), as the carboxylic groups of the aspartic and glutamic acid residue side chains are then in an undissociated form. However, at this pH the side chains of arginine, lysine and histidine residues are charged and therefore a buffer anion should be chosen which is able to form an ion-pair with the basic side chains. By applying these principles HPLC provides a versatile tool with regard to selectivity for the separation and isolation of peptides.

For specified separation conditions, the retention times of peptides shorter than about 25 amino acid residues can, within acceptable limits, be predicted from their amino acid composition [90 to 94]. The retention of the peptide can be considered as a summation of the contributions of the constituent amino acids. Amino acids with aromatic or large, aliphatic side-chains have been shown to make major positive contributions to the retention, those with acidic

applications, it seems to cause problems by corroding even stainless steel and should therefore be avoided.

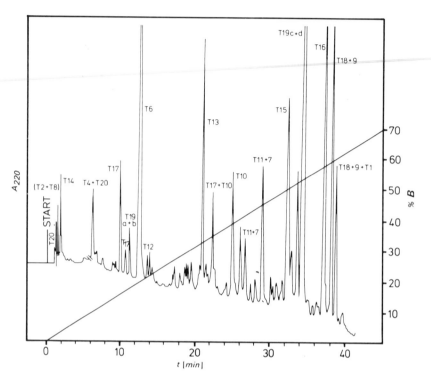

Figure 4-21. Separation by reversed-phase chromatography of a tryptic digest of a Bence Jones protein [128].
Column: Zorbax C-8; solvent system: gradient, A: 0.05 mol/L ammonium acetate, pH 6.0 and B: 0.05 mol/L ammonium acetate, pH 6.0/60% acetonitrile; temperature: 60 °C.

Pyridine acetate and pyridine formate are good solvents for peptides, as is already well known from classical ion-exchange chromatography. These buffers can also be used in reversed-phase HPLC, but show the pronounced disadvantage of high UV absorption, precluding UV detection of the peptides. A reaction detector is therefore necessary [87, 133 to 138].

The elution of peptides from reversed-phase columns is usually accomplished by gradient elution with an organic modifier. Since hydrophobic interaction is the predominant mechanism for the retention of peptides, the retention time is expected to be inversely related to the concentration of the organic modifier in the solvent system. This is, however, only true for an organic modifier concentration up to about 40% [101, 102, 105]. With still higher concentrations of the organic solvent, the retention on the stationary phase increases, as shown in Figure 4-22. This is suggestive of a transition from a reversed-phase separation mode to a polar phase separation mode. It is claimed that this behaviour is caused by the occurrence of different competing sorption mechanisms [101, 102, 105]. At low organic solvent content the hydrophobic adsorption interactions predominate giving rise to the elution behaviour typically observed in reversed-phase chromatography. At higher organic modifier concentration the residual free silanol groups, which are present because of the incomplete surface modification of the silica columns, give rise to silanophilic ionic interactions between charged groups of the peptide and the surface of the stationary phase.

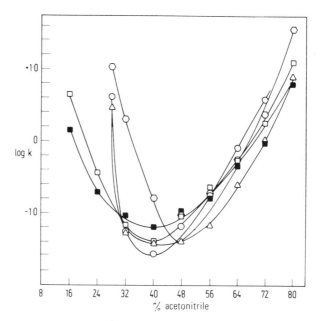

Figure 4-22. Plot log k versus % acetonitrile for several polypeptide hormones [101]. Column: μ-Bondapak C-18; solvent system: isocratic, 0.015 mol/L triethylammonium-phosphate buffer; Glucagon, Insulin, Insulin B-chain, Angiotensin I, Angiotensin II.

The curve in Figure 4-22 suggests a dynamic reorganisation of the interface layer between the hydrophobic surface of the stationary phase and the mobile phase resulting in a stronger interaction of the peptide with the polar groups on the surface of the stationary phase. The shape of the dependency of the retention times on the organic modifier content is different for each peptide and seems to be steeper for larger peptides and proteins. Therefore, for peptides or proteins, optimal elution is only achieved in a relatively narrow zone of organic modifier concentration. This could explain why gradient elution usually gives better results for peptide and protein separations, with regard to resolution and recovery, than isocratic conditions and why peptides elute in relatively narrow peaks. However, it should also be considered in this context that the organic solvent concentration will influence the solubility and the conformation of the peptides, and that a conformational change also may affect the peptide-stationary phase interactions. Clearly, an inadequate choice of gradient conditions could result in loss and/or bad resolution of peptide components. In practice it is advisable to run fairly shallow, linear gradients (not exeeding 1% per minute) and to avoid high concentrations of organic modifier. Care has to be taken that the content of organic modifier in the solvent mixture will not precipitate the buffer salts.

The most commonly used organic modifier is acetonitrile, because of its UV transparency down to 200 nm and excellent selectivity. It is the best organic modifier for peptides, but with hydrophobic proteins, which would elute only with a high concentration of acetonitrile, the danger of precipitation and loss of the protein must be considered.

Isopropanol or n-propanol are occasionally used as organic modifiers especially for larger peptides because of their greater eluotropic power as compared with acetonitrile [139, 140]. Although peak shape and separation are poorer, elution is achieved at a lower organic modifier concentration than with acetonitrile or methanol. Because of the high absorption of propanol at wavelengths below 230 nm the detection of the peptide has either to be carried out at 280 nm, at which wavelength only those peptides which contain tyrosine and/or tryptophan will absorb, or a reaction detector must be used.

The stationary phase offers a range of possibilities to change the selectivity and resolution of a separation. The following factors influence the column surface hydrophobicity:

- silica gel type,
- pore size,
- particle size,
- carbon content,
- type of end capping and
- extent of end capping.

Most commonly used are the reversed-phase materials with C-18 or C-8 carbon spacer arms. In general it can be observed that with higher hydrophobicity of the stationary phase the resolving power increases, but so does the danger of loss of peptide material. Cyanopropyl columns are more polar than those containing C-18 or C-8 packings and therefore better suited to the chromatography of very hydrophobic peptides. Some widely used column packing materials and their properties have been reviewed by Majors [141].

For larger peptides (molecular mass above 4000) the use of reversed-phase material with larger pore size (300 Å) silica gel gives better results than the ordinary reversed-phase columns with a pore size of 60 to 100 Å [142, 143].

In addition to the solvent systems and the stationary phases discussed above, several other parameters which contribute to successful separations of peptides should be mentioned.

The optimal flow-rate is normally between 1 and 2 mL/min.

The effect of temperature has not been extensively investigated, but elevated temperatures seem to be of no advantage. The temperature dependence of the retention time is minimal.

It is important to begin an HPLC program by passing an "empty" gradient through the column, i. e. before the injection of peptide material. There is usually a large amount of UV absorbing material which may be eluted from a column a few hours after the previous elution was discontinued. Furthermore, there are often some spurious peaks caused by contaminantes in the water or the organic modifier and which then later may readily be recognised in the chromatogram of the peptide sample.

The amount of peptide material which can be applied to a normal analytical column (4.6 × 250 mm) can be as high as several mg. For very large sample loadings, radially compressed columns should be considered [144 to 146].

The volume in which the sample is applied should be as small as possible. Larger volumes can be injected, but the peak shape and resolution, especially of the earlier peaks, will deteriorate.

The recovery of peptide material in reversed-phase chromatography is usually very high, i. e. 80 to 100%, even with µg quantities of material, but depends on the nature of the actual peptide. It is difficult to relate the peak size to the amount of material for an unknown peptide, as both the peptide bonds and the various amino acids present in the peptide will contribute to its actual UV absorption. The UV spectra of single amino acids are given in Figure 4-23.

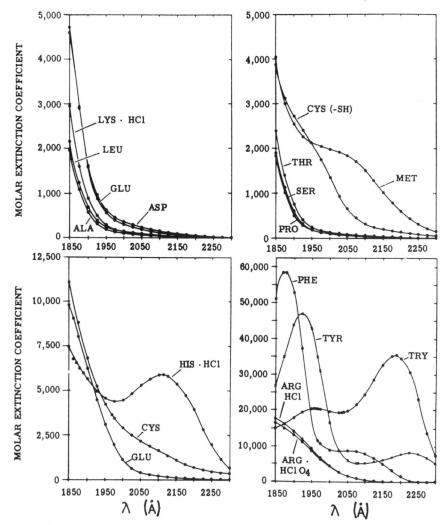

Figure 4-23. UV-spectra of amino acids [147].

4.2.2.2 Ion-Exchange Chromatography

The HPLC version of ion-exchange chromatography for the purpose of peptide purification has, so far, only found limited application. This is probably due to the obvious versatility of reversed-phase HPLC, i. e. there has been little need for ion-exchange methods. There are, however, some advantages connected with ion-exchange HPLC, one being the 10- to 100-fold increase in sample capacity for the same column size, another being the possibility of performing separations under alkaline conditions.

Two types of stationary phase materials have been used, one type being based on silica gel, the other on crosslinked polystyrene. Only the latter type of column material is alkali-resistant.

Table 4-4. Applications of Ion-Exchange Chromatography of Peptides.

Column	s/p	Functional Group	Solvent	Temp. (°C)	Detection	Substance	Ref.
Partisil SCX	s	sulfonyl	pyridine acetate	rt	fluorescamine	angiotensin, immunoglobulin light-chain, insulin, Leu-enkephalin, parathyroid hormone, oxytocin, substance P, vasopressin	[148, 151, 152]
Partisil SCX	s	sulfonyl	pyridine acetate	55	fluorescamine	β-lipotropin	[149]
Partisil SCX	s	sulfonyl	lithium citrate	50	o-phthalaldehyde	His-containing dipeptides	[150]
Dupont SCX	s		sodium phosphate	?	electrochemical	Met-enkephalin	[153]
Hitachi-Gel 3013 C	p		ammonia/acetonitrile/isopropanol/methane-sulfonic acid	70	UV 210 nm	Bence Jones proteins (peptide mapping)	[154]
DC-4 A	p		pyridine acetate	52	ninhydrin	ribonuclease A, brain protein S 100,	[155]
DC-4 A	p		sodium citrate	50 to 75	ninhydrin	collagen (peptide mapping)	[156]
DC-1 A	p		pyridine acetate	43	ninhydrin	thyrotropin releasing hormone	[157]
Hitachi-Gel 3013 N	p		ammonia/acetonitrile/isopropanol/methane-sulfonic acid	20	UV 210 nm	calmodulin (peptide mapping)	[158]
Diajon CDR-10	p		ammonia/methane-sulfonic acid/acetonitrile/isopropanol	22 to 70	UV 210 nm	brain protein 14 – 3 – 2, brain protein S 100 b, calmodulin, Bence Jones protein (peptide mapping)	[159]
Micropak AX-10	s		triethylammonium acetate/acetonitrile	40	UV 220 nm	dipeptides	[160]

s/p spherical or pellicular.

Most of the applications described in the literature deal with the separation of small peptides, i.e. peptides having relative molecular masses below 2000. Some representative and useful separation procedures are summarized in Table 4-4, the upper part showing examples with cation-exchange and the lower part with anion-exchange chromatography.

Acidic peptides are, as would be expected, better separated on anion-exchangers, while neutral and basic peptides are better on cation-exchangers. A chromatogram of a tryptic digest obtained on a polystyrene-based cation exchanger is found in Figure 4-24.

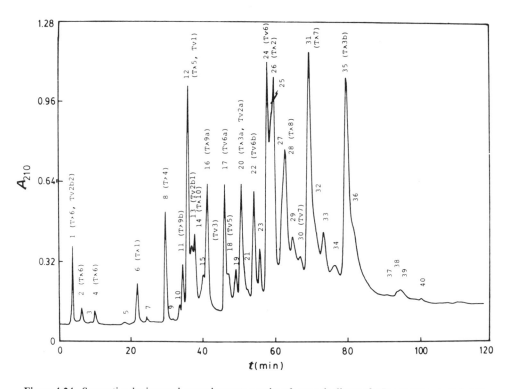

Figure 4-24. Separation by ion-exchange chromatography of a tryptic digest of a Bence Jones protein (50 nmol) [154].
Column: Hitachi-gel 3013 C; solvent system: linear gradient, water to 0.4 mol/L ammonia, pH 6.2 with methanesulfonic acid, 50% acetonitrile, 25% isopropanol; temperature: 70 °C.

Most of the buffers used absorb in the lower UV range. However, detection with good response has been achieved by means of post-column reaction with ninhydrin or fluorescamine, the detection limit being about 10 pmol. Occasionally buffers which permit detection by UV absorption have been described (see Table 4-4). Most buffer systems contain non-volatile components, the pyridine-acetate systems being exceptions. The recoveries of peptide material have been 50 to 80%.

4.2.2.3 Separation of Diastereoisomeric Peptides

A special problem within peptide chromatography is the task of separating diastereoisomeric peptides, i. e. peptides which differ only in the configuration of their amino acid residues. Natural peptides, which are formed by translation of nucleic acids, will only contain L-amino acids, as only L-amino acids are coded for by the genes. However, some examples are known where peptides are formed by other biological mechanisms and here D-amino acids occur. Peptides produced by organic synthesis may contain D-amino acids intentionally, as a means to modify their properties, or unintentionally due to racemization during synthesis.

As diastereoisomeric peptides differ from each other in their chemical, physical and biological properties, it is of importance to anlayse and/or prepare them separately. Prior to the development of HPLC this was achieved by employing the different specificity of proteolytic enzymes or amino acid oxidases towards D- or L-peptides and amino acids or by derivatizing the acid hydrolysates with certain enantiomeric reagents (see enantiomeric amino acids). Diastereoisomers can now be efficiently separated by means of reversed-phase HPLC on C-18 or CN columns [161 to 164] or with ion-exchange HPLC [160].

Detailed experience of diastereoisomer separation has been gained with dipeptides. Thus, DL,DL-dipeptide mixtures may be resolved with HPLC by careful selection of the mobile phase into two peaks, one containing the LL- and DD-isomers and the other the LD- and DL-isomers. The relative order of these two groups depends on the solvent and column conditions. For the nonapeptide oxytocin, conditions were found under which many different diastereomers could be separated [161, 163].

4.2.3 Derivatized Peptides

So far only a few publications have appeared which describe the HPLC behaviour of derivatized peptides. The peptides had been modified for various reasons: pre-column derivatization to increase detection sensitivity; derivatization as a prerequisite for mass spectrometric analysis; and derivatization for peptide synthesis.

Peptide modification by dimethylazobenzene isothiocyanate (DABITC; c. f. under derivatized amino acids) has been recommended by Chang et al. [165, 166] for the purpose of improving the peptide detection limit and to shift the detection wavelength away from the region of solvent interference. The DABTC-peptides formed can be separated by reversed-phase HPLC on a C-18 column with pyridine-acetate/dimethylformamide/acetonitrile solvent. Excellent, so called peptide maps were obtained even with as little as 20 pmol of peptide material, as shown in Figure 4-25, the detection wavelength being 436 nm. The recoveries were reasonably high for most peptides and the chromatography peaks could directly be subjected to sequence analysis, preferably by the DABITC method.

For sequence analysis by direct mass spectrometry N-acetylated-permethylated oligopeptides have often been used, and these derivatized peptides have recently been demonstrated to be separable by HPLC on an octyl-silica bonded phase column using on-line HPLC-mass spectrometry analysis [167]. In these initial experiments peptides with 2 to 5 amino acid residues were separated by a water-acetonitrile system.

In peptide synthesis HPLC has been employed for the purification or quantification of protected peptides [168 to 170]. Various types of protected peptides with over 30 amino acid residues have been chromatographed on various silica and C-18 columns.

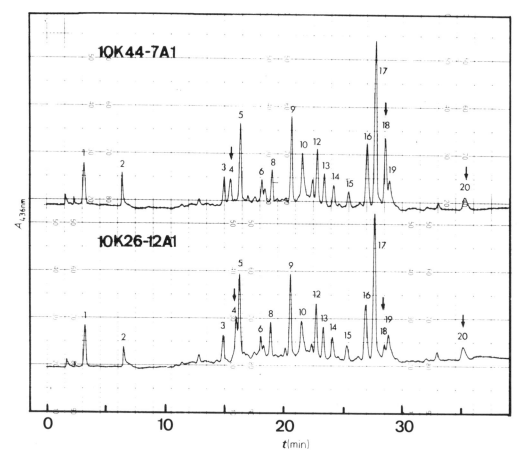

Figure 4-25. Separation by reversed-phase chromatography of DABTC-tryptic peptides (20 pmol) [166]. Column: μ-Bondapak C-18; solvent system: gradient, 0.5% pyridine, pH 7.0 with acetic acid, 2% dimethylformamide, 0.005% mercaptoethanol, 10 to 80% acetonitrile in 40 min; temperature: 22 °C.

4.3 Proteins

4.3.1 Introduction

As already stated there is no fundamental difference between a protein and a large peptide, i. e. one containing over 100 amino acid residues. Many of the above-mentioned facts which apply for peptides will therefore also apply for proteins and these will not be repeated. However, some protein-specific aspects on HPLC will be discussed here separately. Much less experience has been gained with proteins than with peptides and amino acids as regards HPLC. Until recently, useful results were rarely obtained with proteins. Both resolution and recovery were often inferior to those obtained with peptides, the failures mainly being due to unsuitable column materials and solvent systems.

The greater difficulties encountered in HPLC separations of proteins compared to those of lower molecular weight peptides can, to a large extent, be explained by the difference in solubility parameters and by the differential importance of conformational effects. With longer peptide chains the influence of secondary and tertiary structure on such properties as solubility and surface hydrophobicity is much more pronounced, leading to differences in the behaviour of differently folded and of native and denatured forms of the proteins. In HPLC, conditions are often employed which are unfavorable for the solubility of the native protein or which affect protein conformation. Thus, an extreme pH of the buffer and incorporation of an organic solvent are expected to influence both the solubility and the conformational state. Both an increase in organic modifier-concentration and the large contact surface of the stationary phase may cause denaturation during the chromatography. It is, however, well known that proteins vary considerably in their sensitivity to denaturing forces and that some proteins even are able to renature from a denatured state. In HPLC of proteins it is necessary to consider the purpose of the separation, i. e. if biologically active material or material for protein-chemical studies is needed. In the former instance conditions under which the native state is retained or may be re-obtained have to be sought. In the latter instance a much wider range of conditions is available, and it may often be necessary but sometimes even of advantage to perform the separations on denatured material.

Proteins may be chromatographed on several different types of column material. Reversed-phase and ion-exchange columns are available for protein as well as for peptide separations. Columns for size-exclusion chromatography have chiefly been used with proteins. An HPLC version of affinity chromatography of proteins is being developed.

Proteins which have been subjected to HPLC are listed together with the peptides in Table 4-3, Section 4.2.1.

4.3.2 Reversed-Phase-Chromatography

For the first attempts to separate proteins by HPLC the same types of stationary phases were used as were already in use with peptides, i. e. octyl-, octadecyl-, cyanopropyl- or propylphenyl-coated materials having pore sizes of 100 Å or less. In one of the first publications Moench and Dehnen [239] in 1976 describe the successful chromatography of higher molecular mass proteins, such as ovalbumin, (45 000), serum albumin (67 000) and catalase (58 000), using a phosphate buffer, pH 2/isopropanol gradient in the presence of methoxyethanol (Figure 4-26).

Most of the investigations in which 100 Å-material is being used deal mainly with the separations of small and medium-sized proteins, like ribonuclease (14 000) and hemoglobin chains (17 000) [139, 240 to 243], diluted trifluoroacetic acid-acetonitrile being the most common solvent system. A separation of this kind is shown in Figure 4-27. According to Rubinstein [139] RP-8 material is more suited than RP-18 material for protein separations.

The major recent improvement in reversed-phase HPLC of proteins has been the development of stationary phases with large pore size, i. e. greater than 100 Å. These phases give advantages in regard to both higher selectivity and higher yield. Excellent chromatographies on Vydac TP-columns, where the silica has a pore size of 330 Å were published by Lewis et al. [247], van der Rest et al. [244], Pearson et al. [245] and Kehl et al. [246] for such high molecular mass

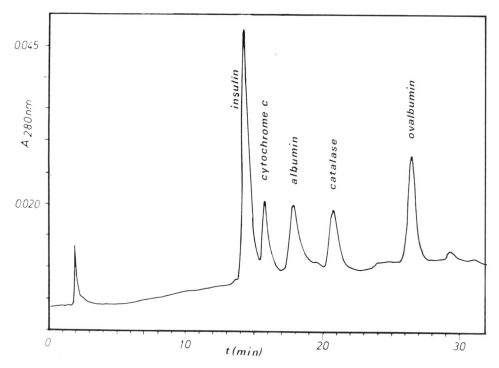

Figure 4-26. Separation by reversed-phase chromatography of proteins [239].
Column: Nucleosil ODS; solvent system: gradient 10 to 50% B in A, A: 0.005 mol/L potassium dihydro-genphosphate-2-methoxyethanol, pH 2 with phosphoric acid, B: isopropanol-2-methoxyethanol, pH 2 with phosphoric acid; temperature: 47 °C.

proteins as collagen and collagen-derived fragments, serum albumin, ovalbumin and fibrinogen chains, most compounds having molecular masses in the range of 40000 to 300000. The last mentioned separation may serve as an example (Figure 4-28). The yields of protein material amounted to over 85% [246, 247].

The larger pore size column material, as such, will not, however, guarantee a good chromatographic result, as the type of silica matrix also seems to play an important role as regards selectivity. When several types of large pore diameter column packings were compared by Pearson et al. [245], the Vydac TP material with 330 Å pores seemed generally most suitable, though LiChrospher Si 1000, which has 1000 Å pores, showed some advantages with the largest proteins [248]. Direct comparisons between a 100 Å and a 330 Å pore octyl support of Bakerbond type and between several bonded phases have also been published by Lewis and DeWald [416].

Pearson et al. [245] and Mahoney [413] tested the influence of column size and found it less important for the resolution, but critically important for the sample capacity. The Vydac TP RP-8 material was shown to bind about 20 mg of a serum albumin-ovalbumin mixture when a 25 × 0.4 cm column was used, excess protein being eluted as a break-through peak due to unavailability of binding sites. The amount of protein which could be loaded was shown to be approximately proportional to the column size. As short columns would separate proteins as efficiently as larger columns it was suggested that the proteins interact with the support by multi-

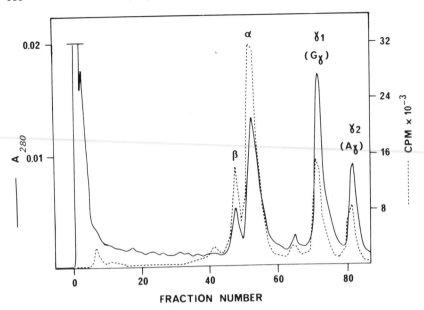

Figure 4-27. Separation by reversed-phase chromatography of globin chains (300 μg) from cord blood ([³H] leucine labelled) [240].
Column: μ-Bondapak C-18; solvent system: gradient, 0.3% trifluoroacetic acid/acetonitrile.

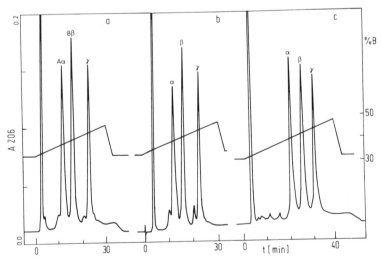

Figure 4-28. Separation by reversed-phase chromatography of S-carboxymethylated fibrinogen- (a), S-carboxymethylated fibrin- (b) and mercaptolysed fibrin-chains (c) [246].
Column: Vydac TP RP-10; solvent system: gradient, 0.1% trifluoroacetic acid/acetonitrile.

site binding [413] and are fractionated by absorption-desorption on the matrix surface [249] rather than by partitioning between the stationary and the mobile phases. This interpretation would also explain why gradient elution is considerably more effective than isocratic elution for protein HPLC.

It should be mentioned that the elution order of the protein components is not correlated to their molecular size, but depends on several other properties of the protein, such as hydrophobicity and charge on the surface of the molecule and conformation of the backbone and side chains. The effective surface hydrophobicity and charge of such large molecules can not easily be calculated from their total amino acid compositions [312] and it is therefore more difficult to predict retention times for proteins than for peptides [93].

In reversed-phase HPLC of proteins volatile organic acids or volatile buffers are most commonly employed. In many publications dilute trifluoroacetic acid [e. g. 241, 242, 245, 246, 250, 413] and, in a few, dilute pentafluoropropionic or heptafluorobutyric acid [244, 413] have been used, the longer carbon chains of the latter acids giving more hydrophobicity to the protein through ion-pairing and thereby increasing the retention time [244, 413] or, alternatively, increasing the hydrophobicity of the solvent and thereby decreasing the retention time. High concentrations of formic acid gave excellent separations and recoveries of many unmodified and modified proteins [401]. For many separations pyridine-formic acid, pH around 4, [139, 247, 251 to 253, 416] and pyridine-acetic acid, pH around 5, [247, 252, 254] have been selected. However, because of the high UV absorption in the lower wavelength range of formic acid, acetic acid as well as pyridine only detection at 280 nm, by post-column derivatization with fluorescamine or similar, or by measuring radioactivity or biological activity is feasible (see also under Peptides). Many publications describe the use of nonvolatile salts, most often phosphate [255 to 259] at pH 6 or pH 2 and sometimes in combination with perchlorate [260, 261]. Other nonvolatile salts employed are tris acetate [260] and sodium acetate [262] at pH 7.5.

The organic modifiers used for protein reversed-phase HPLC are principally the same as those used in peptide separations. However, the difficulty of finding a solvent system sufficiently polar to be a solvent for the protein and sufficiently non-polar to desorb the protein has to be stressed [239]. The most common organic modifiers for protein HPLC are acetonitrile [242, 244, 246, 250, 255], 1-propanol [247, 253, 254, 413, 416], 2-propanol [245, 249, 257, 401, 413] and methanol [256, 258], or occasionally combinations of these [259, 263]. Henderson et al. [242] describe the advantage of acetonitrile or methanol over ethanol and propanols as organic modifiers. Only the former give sharp, well defined peaks with lysozyme (relative molecular mass 15 000) ovalbumin and serum albumin on μ-Bondapak C-18 and phenyl columns. However, with propanol the protein will be desorbed at lower concentration of the modifier which may be beneficial for certain purposes.

Some proteins are incompletely recovered by a single gradient elution. It has been described by Henderson et al. [243] that protein remaining on the column may be eluted by subsequent gradient elutions, as shown in Figure 4-29. These authors have furthermore observed that protein denatured by treatment with guanidine hydrochloride was partly lost on the column. The authors suggest that proteins in a denatured state may be retained by columns due to direct hydrophobic interaction or due to precipitation. The columns could be cleaned and the protein recovered by eluting first with 70% acetic acid satured with guanidine hydrochloride and then with an ordinary acetonitrile gradient, the protein appearing with this gradient as a single peak at its characteristic acetonitrile concentration. The result was interpreted as a refolding of the denatured protein into conformational states which can be eluted.

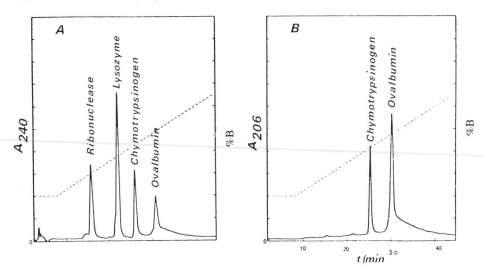

Figure 4-29. Memory effect in reversed-phase chromatography of proteins [243].
Panel A: Separation of a protein mixture (1 mg). Panel B: A blanc gradient (no protein applied) immediately after the separation in panel A.
Column: μ-Bondapak C-18; solvent system: gradient, 0.05% trifluoroacetic acid/0.05% trifluoroacetic acid in acetonitrile.

Similar observations were made by Pearson et al. [245] using a Vydac TP RP-8 type column. In the case of ovalbumin only 60% of the material applied would elute in a first cycle, the remaining 40% being gradually desorbed during the following 11 cycles. This "memory"-effect has also been found with other proteins, though it is more or less pronounced depending on the nature of the protein and the chromatographic conditions.

In order to increase the solubility and improve the purification of some membrane proteins with relativ molecular masses of 28 000 to 33 000 McKeen and Bell [264] included 0.2% of a non-ionic detergent, Triton X-100, in the triethylamine/trifluoroacetic acid, pH 3,/acetonitrile solvent system. When an anionic detergent, sodium dodecylsulfate, was substituted for the non-ionic detergent no protein could be eluted from the column. A certain disadvantage with Triton X-100 is caused by its high UV absorption necessitating other detection methods and, furthermore, the detergent has normally to be removed before the subsequent analyses or chromatographies.

In a few cases proteins have been reported to be recovered from the reversed-phase column with unaltered biological activity. Trypsin and chymotrypsin (relative molecular mass 25 000) were purified according to Strickler et al. [265] or Titani et al. [250] using small pore size C-18 or CN columns and a trifluoroacetic acid/acetonitrile solvent system, the recovered enzymes being employed for protein digestion. A group of calcium-binding proteins, i. e. calmodulin, troponin C, parvalbumin and others, were separated by Klee et al. [255] on a phenyl-coated μ-Bondapak column with the aid of phosphate buffer, pH 6.1/acetonitrile gradient, the biological activity being retained. The authors could show that the presence of calcium ions would decrease the retention times of some of the proteins, indicative of a calcium-induced conformational change. Also several types of interferon relative molecular masses of (about 17 000 to 21 000) have been purified with retained activity by HPLC on various types of reversed-phase columns at neutral or acidic pH [251, 262].

Reversed-phase HPLC has also been employed to assess the binding of a metal derivative, cisplatin, to proteins, UV and atomic absorption being used for the detection [234].

4.3.3 Normal-Phase Chromatography

A special case of partition chromatography was reported by Rubinstein et al. [139, 262, 397]. Using a LiChrosorb Diol-column, serum protein components and interferon could be fractionated by means of a gradient of decreasing concentrations of n-propanol, i. e. from 80 to 50% organic modifier. As all serum protein components eluted with the solvent front when the column had been equilibrated with 50% n-propanol, this result was interpreted as normal-phase chromatography [139]. This type of fractionation can only be used with hydrophobic proteins, i. e. those soluble in high concentrations of organic solvents. The antiviral activity of interferon was not destroyed by the chromatography [262, 397].

4.3.4 Ion-Exchange Chromatography

The HPLC versions of protein ion-exchange chromatography are highly similar to their classical counterparts as regards the functional groups of the columns and the solvent systems employed. However, as the conventional packing materials, based on cellulose, cross-linked dextrane or similar compounds, were insufficiently mechanically stable to allow high flow-rates and high pressures, new solid supports have been developed. With the new types of columns not only much faster separations but also much higher resolutions have been obtained, the improved resolution being due to certain advantageous properties of the particles, including small size, narrow size range, spherical shape, suitable porosity, high ion-exchange capacity and surface hydrophilicity.

Many different approaches have been tried to obtain suitable ion-exchange column material for HPLC. (For reviews see [266 to 268]). Packing materials based both on organic and inorganic supports have been developed. Early successful results were obtained by Mikes et al. [269], using derivatized methacrylate gel, and by Chang et al. [270, 271] and Kudirka et al. [272], using derivatized controlled porosity glass.

The first surface-modified inorganic packings for ion-exchange chromatography were obtained by attaching diethylaminoethyl-(DEAE), methyldiethylaminoethyl-(QAE), carboxymethyl-(CM) or sulfonylpropyl-(SP) side chains to glycerylpropylsilyl-coated controlled porosity glass beads, called Glycophases [270, 271]. As indicated in Table 4-5 several proteins have been chromatographed on these types of supports, which, however, have the disadvantage of not being commercially available.

More recently, an anion-exchanger based on macroporous, spherical silica particles with a thin (pellicular) polyethyleneimine coating, SynChropak AX-300, became commercially available. The pore size of this material is 300 Å. It is a weak anion-exchanger, similar in its ion-exchange properties to DEAE-cellulose. However, as it is silica-based the pH limits are 2 to 8. SynChropak AX-300 has already been used for several different protein separations (see Table 4-5), e. g. for various isoenzymes [273, 274, 298] and hemoglobin types [275, 276], the resolutions being comparable only to those otherwise obtained in gel electrophoresis [277]. A separation of lactate dehydrogenase isoenzymes is shown in Figure 4-30.

Table 4-5. Applications of Ion-Exchange Chromatography of Proteins.

Column	g/s/a	w/s	a/c	Functional Group	Substances	References
DEAE-Glycophase	g	w	a	diethylaminoethyl-	alkaline phosphatase, arylsulfatase, serum proteins, cellulase, creatine kinase, hemoglobin, lactate dehydrogenase, liver homogenate, serum albumin, trypsin	[270 to 273, 287 to 292]
SynChropak AX-300	s	w	a		α-1-acid glycoprotein, adenovirus-encoded protein, adenylosuccinate synthetase, apolipoprotein, creatine kinase, γ-globulin, hemoglobin, hexokinase, lactate dehydrogenase, ovalbumin, prealbumin, serum albumin, transferrin	[253, 270, 273 to 278, 280, 293, 298]
TSK-DEAE	s	w	a	diethylaminoethyl-	aldehyde dehydrogenase, egg proteins, β-lactoglobulin, ovalbumin, serum proteins, serum albumin	[345, 403, 415]
Polyethyleneimine coated large pore silica	s	w	a		lipoxygenase, ovalbumin, serum albumin	[248]
DEAE-Spheron	a	w	a	diethylaminoethyl-	plasma proteins, glucose oxidase, mold protease	[284, 285]
DEAE-Toyopearl or Fractogel	—	w	a	diethylaminoethyl-	egg proteins, ferritin, γ-globulin, hemoglobin, β-lactoglobulin, myoglobin, ovalbumin, ribonuclease, serum proteins, serum albumin, thyroglobulin, trypsin inhibitor, urease	[400, 403]
Anpak			a		cytochrome P-450	[294]
QEAE-Glycophase	g	s	a	methyldiethylamino-ethyl	albumin, chymotrypsinogen, hemoglobin, myoglobin	[270]
TSK-CM	s	w	c	carboxymethyl-	aldehyde dehydrogenase, ribonuclease	[345, 403]
CM-silica	s	w	c	carboxymethyl-	carbonic anhydrase, insulin, β-lactoglobulin	[281]
LiChrosorb KAT	s	w	c		carbonic anhydrase, insulin, β-lactoglobulin	[281]
CM-Glycophase	g	w	c	carboxymethyl-	cytochrome c, soybean trypsin inhibitor	[252, 270]

Table 4-5. (Continued).

Column	g/s/a	w/s	a/c	Functional Group	Substances	References
Bio-Rex 70	a	w	c	carboxyl-	cytochrome c, hemoglobin	[282, 286, 295, 296]
Amberlite CG-50	a	w	c	carboxyl-	cytochrome c	[282]
CM-Spheron	a	w	c	carboxymethyl-	chymotrypsinogen, egg proteins, lysozyme, mold protease, serum albumin and fragments	[283, 285]
Hydroxylapatit			c	phosphate-	cytochrome c	[282]
P-Spheron	a		c	phosphate-	plasma proteins, chymotrypsinogen, lysozyme, serum albumin	[283, 284]
SP-Glycophase	g	s	c	sulfopropyl-	chymotrypsin, trypsin	[270]
S-Spheron	a	s	c	sulfonyl-	glucose oxidase	[284]
Partisil SCX	s	s	c	sulfonyl-	carbonic anhydrase, insulin, interferon, β-lactoglobulin, transforming growth factor	[281, 297]

g/s/a glass-, silica-, acrylic-based; w/s, a/c weak/strong, anion-/cation-exchanger.

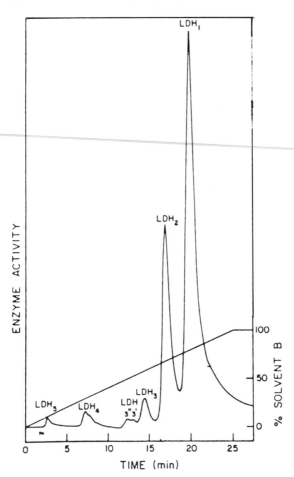

Figure 4-30. Separation by anion-exchange chromatography of lactate dehydrogenase (LDH) isoenzymes [277].
Column:SynChropak AX-300; solvent system: gradient, 0.02 mol/L tris acetate, pH 7.9/0.02 mol/L tris acetate, 0.4 mol/L sodium acetate, pH 7.9.

Vanacek and Regnier found that short columns, i. e. with the dimensions 4 × 50 mm, had a 5- to 10-fold decreased protein loading capacity compared to long columns, i. e. with 4 × 250 mm, but that the shorter columns retained about 75% of the resolution [278]. A maximum of about 10 mg of serum albumin, ovalbumin or apolipoprotein could be chromatographed on a 4 × 250 mm column [278, 279]. The recovery of protein material, even of enzyme activity, was above 85% [266]. However, with small amounts of purified enzymes it was found to be advantageous to dilute with albumin in order to obtain reproducible results [268]. Columns could be used for several hundred separations without deterioration of the performance [276].

The most common buffer systems employed with SynChropak AX-300 is tris acetate, pH about 8, with a sodium acetate concentration gradient [275, 277, 278, 280]. Buffers containing 6 mol/L urea have been sucessfully used for the separation of apolipoproteins [279]. The highest resolutions were obtained with low flow-rates, i. e. 0.25 mL/min for 4 mm inner diameter columns, as shown for the ovalbumin fractionation in Figure 4-31.

Such slow buffer flows necessitate separation times of 2 to 3 hours. Detection of protein in the column effluent is carried out by monitoring the UV absorption at 280 nm or, in the case of

Figure 4-31. Separation by anion-exchange
chromatography of a commercial ovalbumin at different
flow rates [278].
Column: SynChropak AX 300; solvent system:
0.2 mol/L tris acetate, pH 8.0/0.2 mol/L tris acetate,
0.5 mol/L sodium acetate, pH 8.0.

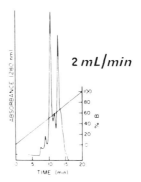

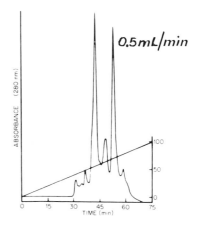

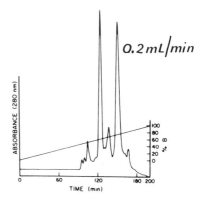

enzymes, by measuring the enzymatic activity, preferably by means of an enzyme-specific
reaction detector [see 268].

Most recently, a new type silica-supported, polyethyleneimine-coated ion-exchanger has been
described by Vanacek and Regnier [248]. Here, even larger pore diameter silicas, i. e. with 1000
and 4000 Å pores, have been employed. Much heavier layers of polyethyleneimine were

crosslinked onto the surfaces, resulting in enhanced ion-exchange capacity and resolution. A pore-size-dependent selectivity was observed. So far, little experience has been gained with this type of material. It is not commercially available.

The silica-based, strong cation-exchanger, Partisil SCX, has recently been employed also for proteins. In the investigations of Frolik et al. the chromatographic behaviour of radio-labelled carbonic anhydrase, β-lactoglobulin and a high-molecular-weight transforming growth factor was studied [281]. Elution was achieved by pyridine-ammonium acetate gradients between pH 2.5 and 6.0, effluent fractions being monitored for radioactivity. Useful separation and good recoveries were obtained especially at elevated temperature.

During the last years several new ion-exchangers on silica supports have become commercially available, i. e. from SynChrom, Pharmacia and Toyo Soda Corporation. So far, however, few publications describing their properties have appeared. The ion-exchangers TSK, DEAE and CM, can be obtained with two different pore sizes, i. e. 130 and 240 Å. The comparisons between the TSK columns and more classical ion-exchange columns carried out by von Bahr-Lindström et al. [345] demonstrate the great advantage of the TSK materials (Figure 4-32). Excellent separations with the TSK ion-exchangers were also obtained by Kato et al. [403, 415].

A quite different type of inorganic material for ion-exchange-like HPLC is hydroxylapatit, i. e. calcium phosphate. With this material, useful separations of cytochrome c-derivatives were obtained by van der Wal and Huber [282].

Several exclusively organic ion-exchangers for HPLC are (meth)acrylate-based. A few different column materials which are commercially available have been tried with proteins, i. e. several substituted Spherons, Bio-Rex 70 and Amberlite CG-50. The carboxymethyl-(CM), phospho-(P), sulpho-(S) and diethylaminoethyl-(DEAE) derivatives of Spheron 300 have been prepared and employed in many different types of separation by Mikes et al. [283 to 285] (see Table 4-5). The Spheron 300 matrix used in this work has an exclusion limit of about 500 000 [283]. A definite advantage of the Spheron ion-exchangers is their high chemical stability at more extreme pH-values. The amounts of protein which were separated on the Spheron ion-exchangers seemed to be somewhat higher than those recommended for, e. g., SynChropak AX-300-columns of comparable size. It was observed by Mikes that proteins eluted in the order of their isoelectric points, indicating ion-exchange to be the main separation principle, even though the Spheron matrix is more hydrophobic than cellulose or polydextran, making a certain hydrophobic interaction with the proteins likely [283]. The Spheron ion-exchanger beads showed excellent stability towards high flow-rates and pressures [283]. Useful separations could often be obtained in one hour, as demonstrated in Figure 4-33. The commercially available material based on Spheron 1000 differs from that employed by Mikes et al. in the way that it has an exclusion limit of 1 000 000, corresponding to a pore diameter of 370 Å [283]. The particle size is rather large, i. e. about 20 μm.

A new promising type of non-silica based ion-exchangers is DEAE-Toyopearl, which is highly stable towards extreme pH-values of the buffer and increased flow-rates or pressure. Very good separations and high yields of a large number of proteins were reported by Kato et al. [400, 403]. The particle size is, however, large, i. e. 20 to 30 μm.

The properties of the non-rigid cation-exchangers Bio-Rex 70 and Amberlite CG-50 were explored by Cole et al. [286] and van der Wal and Huber [282]. For the purposes described, useful separations could be obtained. However, the materials cause problems because they are insufficiently mechanically stable and only commercially available with a too large particle size.

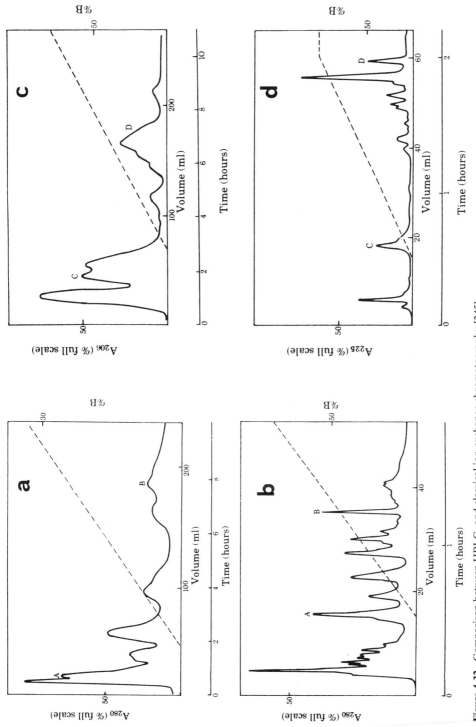

Figure 4-32. Comparison between HPLC- and classical ion-exchange chromatography [345].

Column: a) CM-cellulose (9 × 150 mm); b) Ultropak TSK 535 CM (7.5 × 150 mm); c) DEAE Biogel (10 × 120 mm); d) Ultropak TSK 545 DEAE (7.5 × 15mm); solvent system: a) and b) gradient, 0.02 mol/L ammonium acetate, 8 mol/L urea, pH 5.0/0.02 mol/L ammonium acetate, 8 mol/L urea, pH 5.0, 0.1 mol/L sodium chloride; c) and d) gradient, 0.02 mol/L ammonium bicarbonate/0.2 mol/L ammonium bicarbonate.

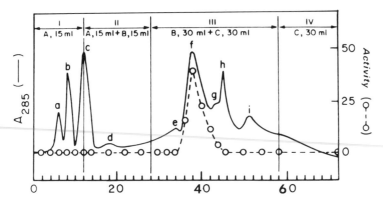

Figure 4-33. Separation by anion-exchange chromatography of technical glucase oxidase [266]. Column: DEAE Spheron; solvent system: A: 0.01 mol/L sodium acetate, pH 6.8, B: 0.3 mol/L sodium acetate, pH 5.5, C: 0.3 mol/L sodium acetate, 1 mol/L sodium chloride, pH 5.5.

4.3.5 Size-Exclusion Chromatography

In ideal size-exclusion or steric-exclusion or gel-permeation chromatography, the protein molecules are separated on the basis of their hydrodynamic volume, the largest molecules being completely excluded from the pores of the support, the smaller having a molecular volume-dependent fraction of the pores available and the smallest being totally included. In practice, however, various interactions between the protein molecules and the surface of the support interfere with an ideal size-exclusion mechanism. Thus, charges on the support surface will, depending on the charge of the protein molecule, gave rise to either ionic sorption or ion exclusion. A hydrophobic surface will cause hydrophobic sorption and often denaturation of the proteins.

The classical column materials for size-exclusion chromatography, like cross-linked dextran, agarose and polyacrylamide, are obviously too soft for HPLC purposes. The first rigid, microparticulate supports tried with proteins were controlled porosity glass and silica, but the negatively charged silanol groups of the supports give rise to deleterious effects. Suitable supports could, however, be obtained by Regnier et al. by derivatizing the glass and silica silanol groups with glycerylpropylsilyl groups, whereby so-called Glycophases or Diolphases are formed [271] and by Engelhardt et al. by derivatizing with N-acetylaminopropyl groups, whereby Amidephases are formed [301].

A large number of packings for aqueous size-exclusion HPLC are nowadays commercially available. The most commonly used materials for this type of protein HPLC are listed together with their fractionation ranges in Table 4-6. Comparisons of the properties of several commercial columns have been published by Pfannkoch et al. [404].

In many reports the properties and the use of the column materials from Toyo Soda Company, called TSK-gels, are described. Three different types of material are available (see Table 4-6), i. e. the SW, PW and HW types. TSK gel of the SW type is silica-based and should therefore only be used in the pH range 2 to 8. The material has a highly hydrophilic surface with hydroxyl groups. It has been widely used with many proteins since 1978 for protein purification

Table 4-6. Column Materials for Size Exclusion Chromatography.

Column Material	Particle Size (μm)	Pore Diameter (Å)	Fractionation Range in Relative Molecular Mass × 10⁻³		
			for Ordinary Buffers	for 6 mol/L Guanidine-HCl	for 0.1 % SDS
TSK 2000 SW or TSK-125	10	130	0.5 to 60	1 to 25	15 to 25
TSK 3000 SW or TSK-250	10	240	1 to 300	2 to 70	10 to 100
TSK 4000 SW or TSK-400	13	450	5 to 1000	3 to 400	15 to 300
TSK 3000 PW or TSK 30	13	200	to 300		
TSK 4000 PW or TSK 40	13		to 1000		
TSK 5000 PW or TSK 50	17		10 to 10000		
TSK 6000 PW	17		to 30000		
Toyopearl or Fractogel HW 40	25 to 40		0.1 to 10		
Toyopearl or Fractogel HW 50	25 to 40		0.5 to 200		
Toyopearl or Fractogel HW 55	25 to 40		1 to 1000		
I – 60	10	60	1 to 20		
I – 125	10	125	2 to 80		
I – 250	10	250	10 to 500		
LiChrosorb Diol	5 or 10		10 to 100		
SynChropak GPC – 100	10	100	5 to 500		
SynChropak GPC – 500	10	500	10 to 3000		

and characterisation purposes [302 to 311]. Excellent recoveries of protein in a biologically active form have been reported.

The TSK SW material is available with several different pore sizes. The corresponding fractionation ranges have repeatedly been tested and the columns employed for molecular size determination. The molecular mass-elution volume calibration curves and the fractionation ranges were found to be different when ordinary buffers were used [302, 303, 306, 307, 313 to 320], than when buffers containing denaturing agents like 6 mol/L guanidine hydrochloride [321 to 324], 0.1% sodium dodecylsulfate [327 to 332] or 1% sodium dodecylsulfate-20% methyl cellosolve [335]. The corresponding approximate fractionation ranges are indicated in Table 4-6. Some representative calibration curves from the work of Kato et al. are shown in Figure 4-34 [314, 322, 328].

The critical importance of the sodium dodecylsulfate concentration in combination with the buffer salt concentration for the elution pattern was pointed out by Imamura et al. [327], Kato et al. [328] and by Takagi et al. [332]. That may be examplified by the following observation: in 8 mmol/L detergent without salts the three proteins serum albumin, ovalbumin and β-lactoglobulin eluted together at the void volume, in 0.74 mmol/L detergent-0.1 mol/L phosphate they all separated from each other and in 0.46 mmol/L detergent-0.2 mol/L phosphate they again eluted together, but with a highly increased retention time [332]. The optimum concentration of a phosphate buffer to be used with 0.1% dodecylsulfate was found to be 0.05 to 0.2 mol/L [328].

The proteins chromatographed in the presence of 6 mol/L guanidine hydrochloride or 0.1% sodium dodecylsulfate have often been mercaptolysed and S-alkylated [321, 322, 328] or only mercaptolysed [327, 329] before analysis.

As a method for molecular mass determination size-exclusion HPLC may be compared with sodium dodecylsulfate-polyacrylamide gelelectrophoresis. The electrophoretic method offers the advantages of a somewhat higher resolving power and the possibility to run several samples in parallel. However, the chromatographic method is superior in the sense that the quantification and recovery of the separated compounds is more easily achieved and that the time required for a single analysis is shorter, especially since no staining-destaining-time is involved. The amounts of material used for analysis are similar for the two methods, but vary considerably in both methods depending on the detection system available. A suitable fractionation range may be selected for the chromatographic method by using the appropriate pore size, similar to the way the gel composition may be varied in the electrophoretic method. The behaviour of carbohydrate-rich polypeptides in this type of HPLC has been specifically analysed by Ui [323].

A "two-dimensional" separation system for the analysis and fractionation of serum proteins has been developed by Kojima et al. [336], the first dimension being isoelectric focusing and the second being size-exclusion HPLC on TSK 3000 SW. More than 70 components could be separated by the system, which, however, is considerably less than described for the two-dimensional O'Farrell-type gel [236].

A few special examples of applications of HPLC on TSK SW-type columns are worth mentioning. Some very complex mixtures like serum or plasma proteins [302, 306, 309, 314, 336, 338], urinary proteins [317] and milk proteins [306, 307] have been fractionated on these columns.

The enzymes β-galactosidase and urease were purified from crude preparations on TSK 3000 SW-column, the recoveries of enzymatic activity being close to quantitative [303]. The different

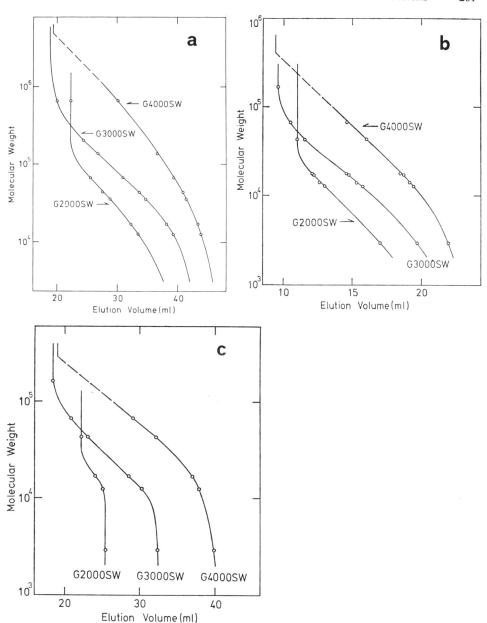

Figure 4-34. Calibration curves for proteins for TSK SW size exclusion columns under different conditions [314, 322, 328].

Column: TSK SW as indicated in the figure; solvent system: a) 0.1 mol/L sodium phosphate, pH 7, 0.3 mol/L sodium chloride; b) 0.1 mol/L sodium phosphate, 6 mol/L guanidine hydrochloride, pH 6; c) 0.1 mol/L sodium phosphate, pH 7, 0.1% sodium dodecylsulfate.

molecular mass forms of urokinase could be quantitated by TSK 3000 SW-analysis, the yield of enzymatic activity being 95 to 100% [304, 339]. The proteolytic activation of prothrombin was studied by means of TSK 3000 SW chromatography; the retention times of calcium-binding fragments were larger in the presence of calcium ions [414]. The complex formation between a plasma proteinase inhibitor and various serine proteinase could be determined by means of TSK 2000 or 3000 SW-chromatography [340].

The heterogeneity of lipoproteins in serum could be evaluated by TSK 3000 or 4000 SW-chromatography after lipoprotein-specific prestaining with a diformazan dye [319] or by selective detection of choline and cholesterol in the effluent [318].

Metalloproteins were identified in extracts of liver, kidney or spleen using TSK 3000 SW columns and metall-specific detection [311, 342].

Membrane proteins from a Halobacterium were purified in a 0.1% sodium dodecylsulfate-containing buffer using TSK 3000 or 4000 SW columns [330, 331]. The membrane protein cytochrome b-561 was analysed in the presence of 0.1% Triton X-100, a nonionic detergent, on a TSK 3000 SW column, in order to evaluate the purity and detergent-binding of the protein [344].

The TSK SW columns give an advantage when used for the separation of large protein fragments. The higher resolution, sensitivity and speed of TSK 2000 SW chromatography, compared to more classical soft-gel chromatography, obtained at the fractionation of cyanogen bromide fragments of hexon viroid capsid protein and tryptic fragments of aldehyde dehydrogenase was demonstrated by von Bahr-Lindström and coworkers. The chromatograms are shown in Figure 4-35. A certain disadvantage of the HPLC version is the low sample capacity. When samples are desalted by size-exclusion HPLC only small volumes can be handled.

The second type of TSK support, designed PW, is a semi-rigid hydrophilic polymer, resistant to solvents in the pH range 2 to 12 and available with several different pore sizes (see Table 4-6). It has not been primarily recommended for protein separations, though protein molecular mass-elution volume calibration curves have been published for the 3000, 4000 and 5000 PW material [346 to 348]. The TSK PW-type columns have mainly been used alone or in combination with TSK SW-type columns for the fractionation and analysis of serum lipoproteins by Okazaki et al. [348 to 350].

A third and newer type of column support from Toyo Soda Company for size exclusion chromatography is designated Toyopearl HW or Fractogel TSK HW. The material is a semi-rigid, hydrophilic polymer, which is available in different pore sizes and can be used over a wide pH range. The particle size is larger than for the SW and PW type material, i. e. 25 to 40 μm or larger. For the Toyopeal HW 55 material, which fractionates in the relative molecular mass range of 10 000 to 1 000 000, a calibration curve has been published and the recoveries of enzymatic activity have been reported to be high [351]. Otherwise little application work has yet appeared.

The Waters I-125 column has been used for similar purposes as the TSK SW columns [352]. Calibration curves for molecular mass estimation are also available for this material, which has a fractionation range of 2 000 to 20 000 [320, 353]. As the material is silica-based it can only be used in the pH range 2 to 8. The inclusion of 20% ethanol in the buffer for the molecular mass analysis was recommended by Hefti [353]. An inclusion of 1% of the detergent desoxycholate in the buffer was used for the purification of the hydrophobic cytochrome c [354]. Good recoveries of biologically active protein were reported [352, 355].

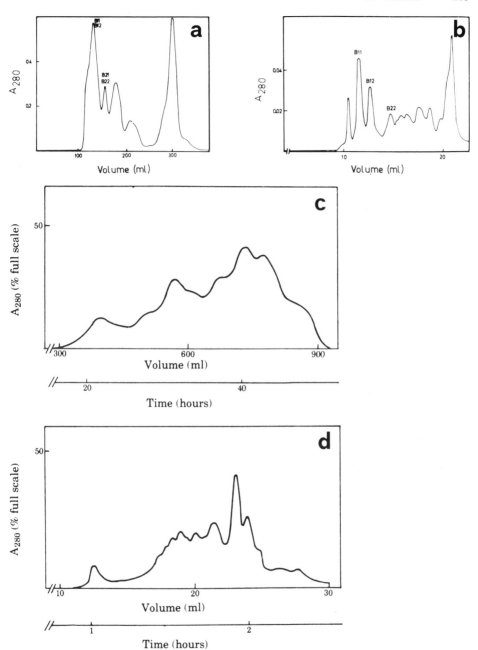

Figure 4-35. Comparison of HPLC and classical size exclusion chromatography [305, 345].
Column: a) and c) Sephadex G-50 fine (15 × 2000 mm); b) TSK G 2000 SW (7.5 × 500 mm); d) TSK G 2000
SW (7.5 × 600 mm); solvent system: a) and c) 30% acetic acid; b) and d) 0.1 mol/L ammonium
bicarbonate; sample: a) and b) cyanogen bromide fragments of a virus protein; c) and d) tryptic digest of
aldehyde dehydrogenase.

A large group of column supports is constituted by the glycerylpropylsilylated porous glass or silica particles. When controlled porosity glass is derivatized, the product is called Glycophase G [271, 361]. When irregular, microparticulate silica, i. e. LiChrosorb, is used the product may be denoted LiChrosorb Diol [362, 363]. When spherical silica, i. e. LiChrospher or Vydac TP Si, is the base material the product is often denoted SynChropak GPC [263, 266, 271, 277, 356, 359, 360]. Many of these supports are commercially available in various pore sizes. So far, the most commonly employed pore size is 100 Å. As for all glass or silica based supports the recommended pH range is limited to 2 to 8.

Commercial Glycophase G has been used in a study of the binding between serum albumin and drugs [361]. The correlation between molecular mass and elution volume for LiChrosorb Diol columns was shown to be linear in the range 10 000 to 100 000 by Roumeliotis and Unger [362] and by Schmidt et al. [363].

Chromatography on SynChropak GPC-100, i. e. with 100 Å pore size, is described in several publications. Linear molecular mass calibration curves in the range 5 000 to 500 000 for ordinary buffers [266, 356] or 1 000 to 70 000 for 1% sodium dodecylsulfate-containing buffer [263] and high protein or biological activity yields were reported [404]. Including 1% sodium dodecyl sulfate or 30% methanol in the buffer increased the recoveries significantly [263]. Similar column materials, based on 300 and 500 Å pore size silica, have also been studied [266, 360]. In most chromatographies Schwarz et al. [360] used 50% formic acid as the eluent without any detrimental effect on the support.

Some general features of size-exclusion HPLC should be considered. The column size is of obvious importance for resolution and sample load capacity. Commercially available columns are 25 to 60 cm long. However, in many publications the use of 120 or 180 cm total column length is described, even for analytical chromatographies. The column diameter should not be too small, as wider columns give higher resolution [266]. Increased sample loads, both with respects to mass and volume, have negative effects on the resolution [266, 277, 362]. On a 7.5 mm-diameter column a few mg of protein can be applied. The sample volume should be below 100 μL, for optimal results. The solubility of the protein and the viscosity of the sample solution have, however, to be considered. Higher viscosities will cause bandspreading [277].

The influence of eluant velocity on resolution has been carefully studied [266, 313]. Even though there is clear evidence that the flow-rate for optimal resolution has to be very low, i. e. 10 to 50 μL/min for a 7.5 mm-diameter column, much higher flow-rates have been specified in most publications, i. e. 0.5 to 1 mL/min. However, the flow-rate will not influence the retention volume and it is therefore often meaningful to compromise between resolution and total chromatography time. The solvent compositions has pronounced effects on the separations obtained, as it will influence the interaction between the protein and the stationary phase [404]. These effects have especially been studied for silica-based supports. The residual free silanol groups act as weak acidic groups with a pK of 3.5 to 4 [359] and give rise to charge effects in the form of ion exclusion at solvent pH-values above the isoelectric point of the protein and ionic sorption at pH-values below the isoelectric point of the protein but above the pK of the silanol group. Ideal size-exclusion is therefore only approached when the protein-support interaction is minimal, i. e. close to the protein isoelectric point [359]. These effects are illustrated in Figure 4-36.

The most pronounced interactions are obtained at low ionic strength, higher salt concentrations give charge shielding [301, 359, 363]. The fact that non-ideal behaviour in size-exclusion chromatography often may be turned to an advantage when solving separation

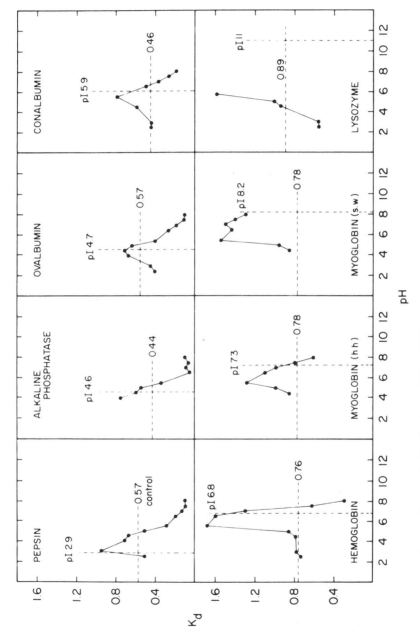

Figure 4-36. Influence of pH on the distribution coefficient [359].
Column: TSK 3000 SW; solvent system: phosphate or acetate buffers with an ionic strength of 0.001.

problems has been clearly stated by Kopaciewicz and Regnier [359]. The need to optimize buffer salt type, concentration and pH has also been exemplified by the observations of Someno et al. [304] for urokinase-types, Okazaki et al. [349] for serum lipoproteins and several research groups for many proteins when using dodecylsulfate-containing buffers [327, 328, 332]. In order to protect the material in the analytical column the inclusion of a small guard column in the flowline between the pump and the main column has often been recommended.

4.3.6 Affinity Chromatography

A few publications dealing with the HPLC-version of bio-affinity chromatography have appeared. In the first report, which was published 1978, Ohlson et al. employ as column support aminohexyl-AMP or antibody against human serum albumin immobilized on glycerylpropylsilylated LiChrosorb Si 60, i. e. silica with 60 Å pore diameter [364]. On the AMP-column alcohol dehydrogenase, lactate dehydrogenase and serum albumin could be separated from each other either by biospecific elution or by elution with high salt concentration. An example is shown in Figure 4-37.

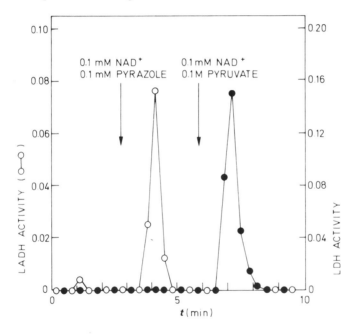

Figure 4-37. Separation by affinity chromatography of lactate dehydrogenase and alcohol dehydrogenase [364].
Column: AMP-silica; solvent system: 0.1 mol/L sodium phosphate, pH 7.5; room temperature.

On the anti-human serum albumin-column bovine and human serum albumin were separated by lowering the pH of the solvent. In a report by Sportsman and Wilson [365] the use of two other immobilized antibodies is described, the antibodies being linked to a similar support, i. e.

glycerylpropylsilylated LiChrospher Si 1000 with 1000 Å pore diameter. An anti-human immunoglobulin G-column was used to evaluate antigen binding, desorption being achieved by a low pH-solvent. A column with attached monoclonal anti-insulin was eluted with dilute acetonitrile. In all experiments close to quantitative specific binding and elution and negligible nonspecific binding was observed [364, 365].

4.4 Conclusion

It is obvious that HPLC methods have already been applied very extensively for the purpose of solving separation problems in protein-, peptide- and amino acid-chemistry and for elucidating the biochemical properties of these compounds. Many of the HPLC methods may primarily be regarded as highly improved versions of classical methods. A few methods, however, have first been conceived as a result of the advent of HPLC. All methods share the advantages of sensitivity, speed and unprecedented resolving power.

4.5 References

[1] H. A. Sober (ed.), in: *Handbook of Biochemistry;* **B 3**. The Chemical Rubber Co. 1970.
[2] F. Wold, *Ann. Rev. Biochem.* 50, 783, (1981).
[3] D. H. Spackman, S. Moore, and W. H. Stein, *Anal. Chem.* **30**, 1190 (1958).
[4] I. Molnar, and C. Horvath, *J. Chromatogr.* **142**, 623 (1977).
[5] M. K. Radjai, and R. T. Hatch, *J. Chromatogr.* **196**, 319 (1980).
[6] R. Schuster, *Anal. Chem.* **52**, 617 (1980).
[7] A. Foucault, M. Caude, and L. Oliveros, *J. Chromatogr.* **185**, 345 (1979).
[8] M. Roth, *Anal. Chem.* **43**, 880 (1971).
[9] Y. Ishida, T. Fujita, and K. Asai, *J. Chromatogr.* **204**, 143 (1981).
[10] D. G. Drescher, and K. S. Lee, *Anal. Biochem.* **84**, 559 (1978).
[11] M. M. Tikhomirov, A. Y. Khorlin, W. Voelter, and H. Bauer, *J. Chromatogr.* **167**, 197 (1978).
[12] M. J. Drescher, J. E. Medina, and D. G. Drescher, *Anal. Biochem.* **116**, 280 (1981).
[13] G. J. Hughes, K. H. Winterhalter, E. Boller, and K. J. Wilson, *J. Chromatogr.* **235**, 417 (1982).
[14] J. C. Kraak, K. M. Jonker, and J. F. K. Huber, *J. Chromatogr.* **142**, 671 (1977).
[15] G. Swarup, S. Cohen, and D. L. Garbers, *J. Biol. Chem.* **256**, 8197 (1981).
[16] J. C. Yang, J. M. Fujitaki, and R. A. Smith, *Anal. Biochem.* **122**, 360 (1982).
[17] F. Sanger, *Biochem. J.* **39**, 507 (1945).
[18] C. L. Zimmerman, and J. J. Pisano, in: C. H. W. Hirs, and S. N. Timasheff (eds.): *Methods in Enzymology* **XLVII**, p. 45. Academic Press, New York — San Francisco — London 1977.
[19] W. R. Gray, In: C. H. W. Hirs, and S. N. Timasheff (eds.): *Methods in Enzymology* **XXV**, p. 121, 333. Academic Press, New York 1972.
[20] E. Bayer, E. Grom, B. Kaltenegger, and R. Uhmann, *Anal. Chem.* **48**, 1106 (1976).
[21] J. M. Wilkinson, *J. Chromatogr. Sci.* **16**, 547 (1978).
[22] Y. Tapuhi, N. Miller, and B. L. Karger, *J. Chromatogr.* **205**, 325 (1981).
[23] C. De Jong, G. J. Hughes, E. van Wieringen, and K. J. Wilson, *J. Chromatogr.* **241**, 345 (1982).
[24] L. N. Mackey, and T. A. Beck, *J. Chromatogr.* **240**, 455 (1982).
[25] Y. Tapuhi, D. E. Schmidt, W. Lindner, and B. L. Karger, *Anal. Biochem.* **115**, 123 (1981).

[26] S. Kobayashi, and K. Imai, *Anal. Chem.* **52**, 424 (1980).

[27] J.-Y. Chang, R. Knecht, and D. G. Braun, *Biochem. J.* **199**, 547 (1981).

[28] Y. Watanabe, and K. Imai, *J. Chromatogr.* **239**, 723 (1982).

[29] J. D. H. Cooper, and D. C. Turnell, *J. Chromatogr.* **227**, 158 (1982).

[30] H. Umagat, P. Kucera, and L.-F. Wen, *J. Chromatogr.* **239**, 463 (1982).

[31] P. Kabus, and G. Koch, *Biochem. Biophys. Res. Comm.* **108**, 783 (1982).

[32] D. C. Turnell, and J. D. H. Cooper, *Clin. Chem.* **28**, 527 (1982).

[33] D. W. Hill, F. H. Walters, T. D. Wilson, and J. D. Stuart, *Anal. Chem.* **51**, 1338 (1979).

[34] P. Edman, *Acta Chem. Scand.* **4**, 283 (1950).

[35] P. Edman, and A. Henschen, in: S. B. Needleman (ed.): *Protein Sequence Determination* 2nd Ed., p. 232. Springer Verlag Berlin 1975.

[36] P. Edman, and G. Begg, *Eur. J. Biochem.* **1**, 80 (1967).

[37] C. L. Zimmerman, E. Appella, and J. J. Pisano, *Anal. Biochem.* **77**, 569 (1977).

[38] G. Frank, and W. Strubert, *Chromatographia,* **6**, 522 (1973).

[39] D. J. Mc Kean, and R. A. Maurer, *Biochemistry,* **17**, 5215 (1978).

[40] P. W. Moser, and E. E. Rickli, *J. Chromatogr.* **176**, 451 (1979).

[41] N. D. Johnson, M. W. Hunkapiller, and L. E. Hood, *Anal. Biochem.* **100**, 335 (1979).

[42] L. E. Henderson, T. D. Copeland, and S. Oroszlan, *Anal. Biochem.* **102**, 1 (1980).

[43] R. Somack, *Anal. Biochem.* **104**, 464 (1980).

[44] J. Fohlman, L. Rask, and P. A. Peterson, *Anal. Biochem.* **106**, 22 (1980).

[45] P. E. Nute, and W. C. Mahoney, *Hemoglobin* **4**, 109 (1980).

[46] S. J. DiMari, J. P. Robinson, and J. H. Hash, *J. Chromatogr.* **213**, 91 (1981).

[47] S. D. Black, and M. J. Coon, *Anal. Biochem.* **121**, 281 (1982).

[48] J. Simmons, and D. H. Schlesinger, *Anal. Biochem.* **104**, 254 (1980).

[49] F. T. Gates, J. E. Coligan, and T. J. Kindt, *Biochemistry* **18**, 2267 (1979).

[50] J. van Beeumen, J. van Damme, P. Tempst, and J. de Loy, in:C. Birr (ed.): *Methods in Peptide and Protein Sequence Analysis,* p. 503. Elsevier, Amsterdam 1980.

[51] S. M. Rose, and B. D. Schwartz, *Anal. Biochem.* **107**, 206 (1980).

[52] C. Zalut, and H. W. Harris, *J. Biochem. Biophys. Meth.* **2**, 155 (1980).

[53] F. Lottspeich, *Hoppe-Seylers's Z. Physiol. Chem.* **361**, 1829 (1980).

[54] G. E. Tarr, *Anal. Biochem.* **111**, 27 (1981).

[55] S. M. Kim, *J. Chromatogr.* **247**, 103 (1982).

[56] J.-Y. Chang, *Biochem. J.* **199**, 557 (1981).

[57] M. J. Horn, P. A. Hargrave, and J. K. Wang, *J. Chromatogr.* **180**, 111 (1979).

[58] I. N. Mancheva, R. N. Nikolov, and J. Pfletschinger, *J. Chromatogr.* **213**, 99 (1981).

[59] T. Takaya, Y. Kishida, and S. Sakakibara, *J. Chromatogr.* **215**, 279 (1981).

[60] E. Gil-Av, A. Tishbee, and P. E. Hare, *J. Am. Chem. Soc.* **102**, 5115 (1980).

[61] C. Gilon, R. Leshem, and E. Grushka, *Anal. Chem.* **52**, 1206 (1980).

[62] N. Nimura, A. Toyama, Y. Kasahara, and T. Kinoshita, *J. Chromatogr.* **239**, 671 (1982).

[63] S. Weinstein, M. H. Engel, and P. E. Hare, *Anal. Biochem.* **121**, 370 (1982).

[64] V. A. Davankov, and A. A. Kurganov, *Chromatographia* **13**, 339 (1980).

[65] V. A. Davankov, A. S. Bochkov, and A. A. Kurganov, *Chromatographia* **13**, 677 (1980).

[66] W. Lindner, *Naturwissenschaften* **67**, 354 (1980).

[67] N. Watanabe, H. Ohzeki, and E. Niki, *J. Chromatogr.* **216**, 406 (1981).

[68] W. Lindner, J. N. Le Page, G. Davies, D. E. Seitz, and B. L. Karger, *J. Chromatogr.* **185**, 323 (1979).

[69] S. Hara, and A. Dobashi, *J. Chromatogr.* **186**, 543 (1979).

[70] M. Takai, S. Kumagae, Y. Kishida, and S. Sakakibara, *Peptide Chemistry, p. 67. Protein Research Foundation, Osaka 1978.*

[71] *C. A. Bishop, D. R. K. Harding, L. J. Meyer, W. S. Hancock, and M. T. W. Hearn, J. Chromatogr.* **192**, 222 (1980).

[72] W. S. Hancock, C. A. Bishop, R. L. Prestidge, and M. T. W. Hearn, *Anal. Biochem.* **89**, 203 (1978).

[73] C. S. Fullmer, and R. H. Wasserman, *J. Biol. Chem.* **254**, 7208 (1979).

[74] C. A. Bishop, W. S. Hancock, S. O. Brennan, R. W. Carrell, and M. T. W. Hearn, *J. Liqu. Chromatogr.* **4**, 599 (1981).

[75] A. A. Hobbs, B. Grego, M. G. Smith, and M.T.W. Hearn, *J. Liqu. Chromatogr.* **4**, 651 (1981).

[76] L. V. Pereira, and P. J. Dolphin, *Can. J. Biochem.* **60**, 790 (1982).

[77] F. S. Heinemann, and J. Ozols, in: M. Elzinga (ed.): *Methods in Protein Sequence Analysis*, p. 435. Humana Press Clifton, New Jersey 1982.

[78] C. S. Fullmer, and R. H. Wasserman, in: M. Elzinga (ed.): *Methods in Protein Sequence Analysis*, p. 489. Humana Press Clifton, New Jersey 1982.

[79] K. R. Williams, J. J. L'Italien, R. A. Guggenheimer, L. Sillerud, E. Spicer, J. Chase, and W. Konigsberg, in: M. Elzinga (ed.): *Methods in Protein Sequence Analysis*, p. 499. Humana Press Clifton, New Jersey 1982.

[80] R. P. Darveau, N. G. Seidah, M. Chrétien, and J. Lecomte, *J. Virol. Meth.* **4**, 77 (1982).

[81] M. P. Strickler, R. W. Travis, and J. G. Olenick, *J. Liqu. Chromatogr.* **5**, 1933 (1982).

[82] J. K. Anderson, and J. E. Mole, *Anal. Biochem.* **123**, 413 (1982).

[83] G. D. Efremov, J. B. Wilson, and T. H. J. Huisman, *Biochem. Biophys. Acta* **579**, 421 (1979).

[84] J. B. Wilson, H. Lam. P. Pravatmuang, and T. H. J. Huisman, *J. Chromatogr.* **179**, 271 (1979).

[85] W. A. Schroeder, J. B. Shelton, and J. R. Shelton, *Hemoglobin* **4**, 551 (1980).

[86] J. - P. Boissel, H. Wajcman, H. Fabritius, R. Cabannes, and D. Labie, *Biochim. Biophys. Acta* **670**, 203 (1981).

[87] P. Böhlen, and G. Kleeman, *J. Chromatogr.* **205**, 65 (1981).

[88] W. A. Schroeder, J. B. Shelton, J. R. Shelton, and D. Powars, *J. Chromatogr.* **174**, 385 (1979).

[89] M. Kehl, F. Lottspeich, und A. Henschen, *Hoppe-Seyler's Z. Physiol. Chem.* **362**, 1661 (1981).

[90] J. L. Meek, *Proc. Natl. Acad. Sci. USA* **77**, 1632 (1980).

[91] J. L. Meek, and Z. L. Rossetti, *J. Chromatogr.* **211**, 15 (1981).

[92] S.-J. Su, B. Grego, B. Niven, and M. T. W. Hearn, *J. Liqu. Chromatogr.* **4**, 1745 (1981).

[93] T. Sasagawa, T. Okuyama, and D. C. Teller, *J. Chromatogr.* **240**, 329 (1982).

[94] C. A. Browne, H. P. J. Bennett, and S. Solomon, *Anal. Biochem.* **124**, 201 (1982).

[95] K. Krummen, and R. W. Frei, *J. Chromatogr.* **132**, 27 (1977).

[96] M. J. O'Hare, and E. C. Nice, *J. Chromatogr.* **171**, 209 (1979).

[97] E. C. Nice, and M. J. O'Hare, *J. Chromatogr.* **162**, 401 (1979).

[98] C. Black, D. M. Douglas, and M. L. Tanzer, *J. Chromatogr.* **190**, 393 (1980).

[99] E. Floor, and S. E. Leeman, *Anal. Biochem.* **101**, 498 (1980).

[100] J. A. Koehn, and R. E. Canfield, *Anal. Biochem.* **116**, 349 (1981).

[101] B. Grego, and M. T. W. Hearn, *Chromatographia* **14**, 589 (1981).

[102] M. T. W. Hearn, and B. Grego, *J. Chromatogr.* **218**, 497 (1981).

[103] M. T. W. Hearn, and B. Grego, *J. Chromatogr.* **203**, 349 (1981).

[104] A. A. Amoscato, G. F. Babcock, and K. Nishioka, *J. Chromatogr.* **205**, 179 (1981).

[105] C. T. Wehr, L. Correia, and S. R. Abbott, *J. Chromatogr. Sci.* **20**, 114 (1982).

[106] T. P. Davis, H. Schoemaker, A. Chen, and H. I. Yamamura, *Life Sci.* **30**, 971 (1982).

[107] S. Taylor, A. Kerlavage, N. Nelson, S. Weldon, and M. Zoller, in: M. Elzinga (ed.): *Methods in Protein Sequence Analysis*, p. 471. Humana Press Clifton, New Jersey 1982.

[108] J. J. L'Italien, and R. A. Laursen, in: M. Elzinga (ed.): *Methods in Protein Sequence Analysis*, p. 383. Humana Press Clifton, New Jersey 1982.

[109] J. E. Rivier, *J. Liqu. Chromatogr.* **1**, 343 (1978).

[110] W. S. Hancock, C. A. Bishop, J. E. Battersby, D. R. K. Harding, and M. T. W. Hearn, *J. Chromatogr.* **168**, 377 (1979).

[111] N. G. Seidah, J. S. D. Chan, G. Mardini, S. Benjannet, M. Chrétien, R. Boucher, and J. Genest, *Biochem. Biophys. Res. Comm.* **86**, 1002 (1979).

[112] N. G. Seidah, R. Routhier, S. Benjannet, N. Larivière, F. Gossard, and M. Chrétien, *J. Chromatogr.* **193**, 291 (1980).

[113] K. Biedermann, U. Montali, B. Martin, I. Svendsen, and M. Ottesen, *Carlsberg Res. Commun.* **45**, 225 (1980).

[114] D. M. Desiderio, J. L. Stein, M. D. Cunningham, and J. Z. Sabbatini, *J. Chromatogr.* **195**, 369 (1980).

[115] W. S. Hancock, and J. T. Sparrow, *J. Chromatogr.* **206**, 71 (1981).

[116] J. P. Tischio, and N. Hetyei, *J. Chromatogr.* **236**, 237 (1982).

[117] H. P. J. Bennett, C. A. Browne, D. Goltzman, and S. Solomon, in: E. Gross, and J. Meienhofer (eds.): *Proceedings of the 6. American Peptide Symposium*, p. 121. Pierce Chemical Company, Rockford, Illinois, USA 1980.

[118] H. P. J. Bennett, C. A. Browne, and S. Solomon, *J. Liqu. Chromatogr.* **3**, 1353 (1980).

[119] C. E. Dunlap, S. Gentleman, and L. I. Lowney, *J. Chromatogr.* **160,** 191 (1978).
[120] H. P. J. Bennett, C. A. Browne, and S. Solomon, *Biochemistry* **20,** 4530 (1981).
[121] W. Vale, J. Spiess, C. Rivier, and J. Rivier, *Science* **213,** 1394 (1981).
[122] D. Voskamp, C. Olieman, and H. C. Beyerman, *J. Royal Netherlands Chem. Soc.* **99,** 105 (1980).
[123] J. R. McDermott, A. I. Smith, J. A. Biggins, M. C. Al-Noaemi, and J. A. Edwardson, *J. Chromatogr.* **222,** 371 (1981).
[124] N. Takahashi, D. Tetaert, and F. W. Putnam, in: M. Elzinga (ed.): *Methods in Protein Sequence Analysis,* p. 463. Humana Press Clifton, New Jersey 1982.
[125] M. Barfod, *J. Chromatogr.* **230,** 289 (1982).
[126] H. Pande, and J. E. Shively, *Arch. Biochem. Biophys.* **213,** 258 (1982).
[127] J. G. Loeber, J. Verhoef, J. P. H. Burbach, and A. Witter, *Biochem. Biophys. Res. Comm.* **86,** 1288 (1979).
[128] H. Kratzin, C.-Y. Yang, J. U. Krusche, and N. Hilschmann, *Hoppe-Seyler's Z. Physiol. Chem.* **361,** 1591 (1980).
[129] J. A. D. M. Tonnaer, J. Verhoef, V. M. Wiegant, and W. de Jong, *J. Chromatogr.* **183,** 303 (1980).
[130] B. L. Currie, J. K. Chang, and R. Cooley, *J. Liqu. Chromatogr.* **3,** 513 (1980).
[131] T. Imoto, and K. Okazaki, *J. Biochem.* **89,** 437 (1981).
[132] J. Sugihara, T. Imamura, T. Imoto, and T. Yanase, *Biochim. Biophys. Acta* **669,** 105 (1981).
[133] M. Rubinstein, S. Stein, and S. Udenfriend, *Proc. Natl. Acad. Sci. USA* **74,** 4969 (1977).
[134] R. V. Lewis, S. Stein, and S. Udenfriend, *Int. J. Pept. Prot. Res.* **13,** 493 (1979).
[135] G. J. Hughes, K. H. Winterhalter, and K. J. Wilson, *FEBS Lett.* **108,** 81 (1979).
[136] K. J. Wilson, A. Honegger, R. P. Stoetzel, and G. J. Hughes, *Biochem. J.* **199,** 31 (1981).
[137] K. J. Wilson, A. Honegger, and G. J. Hughes, *Biochem. J.* **199,** 43 (1981).
[138] J. E. Shively, H. Pande, P.-M. Yuan, and D. Hawke, in: M. Elzinga (ed.): *Methods in Protein Sequence Analysis,* p. 447. Humana Press Clifton, New Jersey 1982.
[139] M. Rubinstein, *Anal. Biochem.* **98,** 1 (1979).
[140] M. Rubinstein, S. Chen-Kiang, S. Stein, and S. Udenfriend, *Anal. Biochem.* **95,** 117 (1979).
[141] R. E. Majors, *J. Chromatogr. Sci.* **18,** 488 (1980).
[142] M. van der Rest, H. P. J. Bennett, S. Solomon, and F. H. Glorieux, *Biochem. J.* **191,** 253 (1980).
[143] K. J. Wilson, E. van Wieringen, S. Klauser, M. W. Berchtold, and G. J. Hughes, *J. Chromatogr.* **237,** 407 (1982).
[144] C. A. Bishop, L. J. Meyer, D. R. Harding, W. S. Hancock, and M. T. W. Hearn, *J. Liqu. Chromatogr.* **4,** 661 (1981).
[145] M. T. W. Hearn, B. Grego, and C. A. Bishop, *J. Liqu. Chromatogr.* **4,** 1725 (1981).
[146] W. A. Bradley, A. M. Gotto, and J. T. Sparrow, in: M. Elzinga (ed.): *Methods in Protein Sequence Analysis,* p. 479. Humana Press Clifton, New Jersey 1982.
[147] D. B. Wetlaufer, *Adv. Protein Chem.* **17,** 320 (1962).
[148] H. Mabuchi, and H. Nakahashi, *J. Chromatogr.* **213,** 275 (1981).
[149] M. Rubinstein, S. Stein, L. D. Gerber, and S. Udenfriend, *Proc. Natl. Acad. Sci. USA* **74,** 3052 (1977).
[150] H. Nakamura, C. L. Zimmerman, and J. J. Pisano, *Anal. Biochem.* **93,** 423 (1979).
[151] K. A. Gruber, S. Stein, L. Brink, A. Radhakrishnan, and S. Udenfriend, *Proc. Natl. Acad. Sci. USA* **73,** 1314 (1976).
[152] A. N. Radhakrishnan, S. Stein, A. Licht, K. A. Gruber, and S. Udenfriend, *J. Chromatogr.* **132,** 552 (1977).
[153] T. P. Bohan, and J. L. Meek, *Neurochem. Res.* **3,** 367 (1978).
[154] T. Isobe, T. Takayasu, N. Takai, and T. Okuyama, *Anal. Biochem.* **122,** 417 (1982).
[155] H. Nika, and T. Hultin, *Anal. Biochem.* **98,** 178 (1979).
[156] M. van der Rest, W. G. Cole, and F. H. Glorieux, *Biochem. J.* **161,** 527 (1977).
[157] W. Voelter, H. Bauer, S. Fuchs, and E. Pietrzik, *J. Chromatogr.* **153,** 433 (1978).
[158] T. Isobe, N. Ishioka, and T. Okuyama, *Biochem. Biophys. Res. Comm.* **102,** 279 (1981).
[159] N. Takahashi, T. Isobe, H. Kasai, K. Seta, and T. Okuyama, *Anal. Biochem.* **115,** 181 (1981).
[160] M. Dizdaroglu, and M. G. Simic, *J. Chromatogr.* **195,** 119 (1980).
[161] B. Larsen, V. Viswanatha, S. Y. Chang, and V. J. Hruby, *J. Chromatogr. Sci.* **16,** 207 (1978).
[162] E. Lundanes, and T. Greibrokk, *J. Chromatogr.* **149,** 241 (1978).
[163] B. Larsen, B. L. Fox, M. F. Burke and V. J. Hruby, *Int. J. Pept. Prot. Res.* **13,** 12 (1979).

[164] C. Hunter, K. Sugden, and J. G. Lloyd-Jones, *J. Liqu. Chromatogr.* **3**, 1335 (1980).

[165] J.-Y. Chang, *Biochem. J.* **199**, 537 (1981).

[166] J.-Y. Chang, R. Knecht, R. Ball, S. S. Alkan, and D. G. Braun, *Eur. J. Biochem.* **127**, 625 (1982).

[167] T. J. Yu, H. Schwartz, R. W. Giese, B. L. Karger, and P. Vouros, *J. Chromatogr.* **218**, 519 (1981).

[168] W. S. Hancock, C. A. Bishop, R. L. Prestidge, D. R. K. Harding, and M. T. W. Hearn, *J. Chromatogr.* **153**, 391 (1978).

[169] F. Widmer, K. Breddam, and J. T. Johansen, *Carlsberg Res. Comm.* **45**, 453 (1980).

[170] V. V. Ulyashin, V. I. Deigin, V. T. Ivanov, and Yu. A. Ovchinnikov, *J. Chromatogr.* **215**, 263 (1981).

[171] N. Ling, R. Burgus, and R. Guillemin, *Proc. Natl. Acad. Sci. USA,* **73**, 3942 (1976).

[172] J. J. Hansen, T. Greibrokk, B. L. Currie, K. N. Johansson, and K. Folkers, *J. Chromatogr.* **135**, 155 (1977).

[173] R. W. Frei, L. Michel, and W. Santi, *J. Chromatogr.* **126**, 665 (1976).

[174] W. S. Hancock, C. A. Bishop, and M. T. W. Hearn, *FEBS Lett.* **72**, 139 (1976).

[175] K. Krummen, and R. W. Frei, *J. Chromatogr.* **132**, 429 (1977).

[176] H. P. J. Bennett, A. M. Hudson, C. McMartin, and G. E. Purdon, *Biochem. J.* **168**, 9 (1977).

[177] W. Mönch, and W. Dehnen, *J. Chromatogr.* **140**, 260 (1977).

[178] W. S. Hancock, C. A. Bishop, L. J. Meyer, D. R. K. Harding, and M. T. W. Hearn, *J. Chromatogr.* **161**, 291 (1978).

[179] S. Gentleman, L. I. Lowney, B. M. Cox, and A. Goldstein, *J. Chromatogr.* **153**, 274 (1978).

[180] R. Burgus, and J. Rivier, in: A. Loffet (ed.): *Peptides 1976,* p. 85. Univ. Brüssel, Belgium 1976.

[181] H. P. J. Bennett, A. M. Hudson, L. Kelly, C. McMartin, and G. E. Purdon, *Biochem. J.* **175**, 1139 (1978).

[182] C. Gianoulakis, N. G. Seidah, R. Routhier, and M. Chrétien, *J. Biol. Chem.* **254**, 11903 (1979).

[183] N. W. Pedigo, N. C. Ling, T. D. Reisine, and H. I. Yamamura, *Life Sci.* **24**, 1645 (1979).

[184] M. T. W. Hearn, B. Grego, and W. S. Hancock, *J. Chromatogr.* **185**, 429 (1979).

[185] J. Spiess, J. E. Rivier, J. A. Rodkey, C. D. Bennett, and W. Vale, *Proc. Natl. Acad. Sci. USA* **76**, 2974 (1979).

[186] J. Meienhofer, T. F. Gabriel, J. Michalewsky, and C. H. Li, in: J. Z. Siemion, and G. Kupryszewski (eds.): *Peptides 1978,* p. 243. Wroslaw University Press, Poland 1978.

[187] R. A. Martinelli, and H. A. Scheraga, *Anal. Biochem.* **96**, 246 (1979).

[188] G. E. Gerber, R. J. Anderegg, W. C. Herlihy, C. P. Gray, K. Biemann, and H. G. Khorana, *Proc. Natl. Acad. Sci. USA* **76**, 227 (1979).

[189] S. Terabe, R. Konaka, and K. Inouye, *J. Chromatogr.* **172**, 163 (1979).

[190] M. E. F. Biemond, W. A. Sipman, and J. Olivié, *J. Liqu. Chromatogr.* **2**, 1407 (1979).

[191] T. A. Stoming, F. A. Garver, M. A. Gangarosa, J. M. Harrison, and T. H. J. Huisman, *Anal. Biochem.* **96**, 113 (1979).

[192] S. Kimura, R. V. Lewis, L. D. Gerber, L. Brink, M. Rubinstein, S. Stein, and S. Udenfriend, *Proc. Natl. Acad. Sci. USA* **76**, 1756 (1979).

[193] I. M. Chaiken, and C. J. Hough, *Anal. Biochem.* **107**, 11 (1980).

[194] M. Abrahamsson, and K. Gröningsson, *J. Liqu. Chromatogr.* **3**, 495 (1980).

[195] N. Larivière, N. G. Seidah, G. de Serres, J. Rochemont, and M. Chrétien, *FEBS Lett.* **122**, 279 (1980).

[196] L. Pradayrol, H. Jörnvall, V. Mutt, and A. Ribet, *FEBS Lett.* **109**, 55 (1980).

[197] T. D. Schlabach, J. A. Fulton, P. B. Mockridge, and E. C. Toren, *Clin. Chem.* **26**, 707 (1980).

[198] R. Maurer, *J. Biochem. Biophys. Meth.* **2**, 183 (1980).

[199] N. G. Seidah, M. Dennis, P. Corvol, J. Rochemont, and M. Chrétien, *Anal. Biochem.* **109**, 185 (1980).

[200] M. Lebl, *Coll. Czechoslov. Chem. Comm.* **45**, 2927 (1980).

[201] K. Breddam, F. Widmer, and J. T. Johansen, *Carlsberg Res. Comm.* **45**, 237 (1980).

[202] B. Sharp, A. E. Pekary, N. V. Meyer, and J. M. Hershman, *Biochem. Biophys. Res. Comm.* **95**, 618 (1980).

[203] K. Krummen, *J. Liqu. Chromatogr.* **3**, 1243 (1980).

[204] J. F. M. Kinkel, G. Heuver, and J. C. Kraak, *Chromatographia* **13**, 145 (1980).

[205] G. Lindeberg, *J. Chromatogr.* **193**, 427 (1980).

[206] D. Pearson, J. E. Shively, B. R. Clark, I. I. Geschwind, M. Barkley, R. S. Nishioka, and H. A. Bern, *Proc. Natl. Acad. Sci. USA* **77**, 5021 (1980).

[207] Y. Takagaki, G. E. Gerber, K. Nihei, and H. G. Khorana, *J. Biol. Chem.* **255**, 1536 (1980).

[208] S. Benjannet, N. G. Seidah, R. Routhier, and M. Chrétien, *Nature* **285**, 415 (1980).

[209] B. Grego, and M. T. W. Hearn, *Proc. Univ. Otago Med. Sch.* **58**, 41 (1980).

[210] K. J. Wilson, *Chimia* **34**, 469 (1980).

[211] J. Verhoef, J. G. Loeber, J. P. H. Burbach, W. H. Gispen, A. Witter, and D. de Wied, *Life Sci.* **26**, 851 (1980).

[212] P. Böhlen, F. Castillo, N. Ling, and R. Guillemin, *Int. J. Pept. Prot. Res.* **16**, 306 (1980).

[213] M. T. W. Hearn, *J. Liqu. Chromatogr.* **3**, 1255 (1980).

[214] R. W. Swann, and C. H. Li, *Proc. Natl. Acad. Sci. USA* **77**, 230 (1980).

[215] M. Knight, Y. Ito, and T. N. Chase, *J. Chromatogr.* **212**, 356 (1981).

[216] D. M. Desiderio, S. Yamada, F. S. Tanzer, J. Horton, and J. Trimble, *J. Chromatogr.* **217**, 437 (1981).

[217] L. Gozzini, and P. C. Montecucchi, *J. Chromatogr.* **216**, 355 (1981).

[218] W. S. Hancock, J. D. Capra, W. A. Bradley, and J. T. Sparrow, *J. Chromatogr.* **206**, 59 (1981).

[219] E. Spindel, D. Pettibone, L. Fisher, J. Fernstrom, and R. Wurtman, *J. Chromatogr.* **222**, 381 (1981).

[220] N. G. Seidah, S. Benjannet, and M. Chrétien, *Biochem. Biophys. Res. Comm.* **100**, 901 (1981).

[221] K. J. Wilson, and G. J. Hughes, *Chimia* **35**, 327 (1981).

[222] C. Olieman, E. Sedlick, and D. Voskamp, *J. Chromatogr.* **207**, 421 (1981).

[223] W. O. Richter, P. Weisweiler, and P. Schwandt, *J. Clin. Chem. Clin. Biochem.* **19**, 812 (1981).

[224] J. C. Crawhall, and B. Posner, *J. Clin. Chem. Clin. Biochem.* **19**, 641 (1981).

[225] L. Haeffner-Gormley, N. H. Poludniak, and D. B. Wetlaufer, *J. Chromatogr.* **214**, 185 (1981).

[226] J. P. Sellers, and H. G. Clark, *Thromb. Res.* **23**, 91 (1981).

[227] D. D. Gay, and R. A. Lahti, *Int. J. Pept. Protein Res.* **18**, 107 (1981).

[228] D. E. Mais, P. D. Lahr, and T. R. Bosin, *J. Chromatogr.* **225**, 27 (1981).

[229] M. C. Kemp, W. L. Hollaway, R. L. Prestidge, J. C. Bennett, and R. W. Compans, *J. Liqu. Chromatogr.* **4**, 587 (1981).

[230] B. Oray, M. Jahani, and R. W. Gracy, *Anal. Biochem.* **125**, 131 (1982).

[231] H. Mabuchi, and H. Nakahashi, *J. Chromatogr.* **228**, 292 (1982).

[232] B. Fransson, U. Ragnarsson, and Ö. Zetterqvist, *Anal. Biochem.* **126**, 174 (1982).

[233] H.-J. Schneider, U. Illig, E. Müller, B. Linzen, F. Lottspeich, and A. Henschen, *Hoppe-Seyler's Z. Physiol. Chem.* **363**, 487 (1982).

[234] C. M. Riley, L. A. Sternson, and A. J. Repta, *Anal. Biochem.* **124**, 167 (1982).

[235] P. Angwin, and J. D. Barchas, *J. Chromatogr.* **231**, 173 (1982).

[236] P. O'Farell, *J. Biol. Chem.* **250**, 4007 (1975).

[237] M. Lebl, *J. Chromatogr.* **242**, 342 (1982).

[238] K. Tatemoto, M. Carlquist, and V. Mutt, *Nature* **296**, 659 (1982).

[239] W. Mönch, and W. Dehnen, *J. Chromatogr.* **147**, 415 (1978).

[240] L. F. Congote, H. P. J. Bennett, and S. Solomon, *Biochem. Biophys. Res. Comm.* **89**, 851 (1979).

[241] W. C. Mahoney, and M. A. Hermodson, *I. Biol. Chem.* **255**, 11199 (1980).

[242] L. Henderson, R. Sowder, and S. Oroszlan, in: M. Elzinga (ed.): *Methods in Protein Sequence Analysis,* p. 409. Humana Press Clifton, New Jersey 1982.

[243] L. E. Henderson, R. Sowder, and S. Oroszlan, in: Liu, Schechter, Heinrikson, and Condliffe (eds.): *Chemical Synthesis and Sequencing of Peptides and Proteins,* p. 251, Elsevier, North Holland 1981.

[244] M. van der Rest, and P. Fietzek, *Eur. J. Biochem.* **125**, 491 (1982).

[245] J. D. Pearson, N. T. Lin, and F. E. Regnier, *Anal. Biochem.* **124**, 217 (1982).

[246] M. Kehl, F. Lottspeich, and A. Henschen, *Hoppe-Seyler's Z. Physiol. Chem.* **363**, 1501 (1982).

[247] R. V. Lewis, A. Fallon, S. Stein, K. D. Gibson, and S. Udenfriend, *Anal. Biochem.* **104**, 153 (1980).

[248] G. Vanecek, and F. E. Regnier, *Anal. Biochem.* **121**, 156 (1982).

[249] J. D. Pearson, W. C. Mahoney, M. A. Hermodson, and F. E. Regnier, *J. Chromatogr.* **207**, 325 (1981).

[250] K. Titani, T. Sasagawa, K. Resing, and K. A. Walsh, *Anal. Biochem.* **123**, 408 (1982).

[251] H.-J. Friesen, S. Stein, M. Evinger, P. C. Familletti, J. Moschera, J. Meienhofer, J. Shively, and S. Pestka, *Arch. Biochem. Biophys.* **206**, 432 (1981).

[252] B. N. Jones, R. V. Lewis, S. Pääbo, K. Kojima, S. Kimura, and S. Stein, *J. Liqu. Chromatogr.* **3**, 1373 (1980).

[253] M. Green, and K. H. Brackmann, *Anal. Biochem.* **124**, 209 (1982).

[254] A. Fallon, R. V. Lewis, and K. D. Gibson, *Anal. Biochem.* **110**, 318 (1981).
[255] C. B. Klee, M. D. Oldewurtel, J. F. Williams, and J. W. Lee, *Biochem. Int.* **2**, 485 (1981).
[256] P. Schwandt, W. O. Richter, and P. Weisweiler, *J. Chromatogr.* **225**, 185 (1981).
[257] R. A. Barford, B. J. Sliwinski, A. C. Breyer, and H. L. Rothbart, *J. Chromatogr.* **235**, 281 (1982).
[258] P. Schwandt, W. O. Richter, and E. Reuschel-Janetschek, *J. Neurochem.* **39**, 357 (1982).
[259] K. Shimizu, J. B. Wilson, and T. H. J. Huisman, *Hemoglobin* **4**, 487 (1980).
[260] K. J. Wilson, M. W. Berchtold, P. Zumstein, S. Klauser, and G. J. Hughes, in: M. Elzinga (ed.): *Methods in Protein Sequence Analysis*, p. 401. Humana Press Clifton, New Jersey 1982.
[261] U. Certa, and G. von Ehrenstein, *Anal. Biochem.* **118**, 147 (1981).
[262] M. Rubinstein, S. Rubinstein, P. C. Familletti, R. S. Miller, A. A. Waldman, and S. Pestka, *Proc. Natl. Acad. Sci. USA* **76**, 640 (1979).
[263] H. G. Barth, *Anal. Biochem.* **124**, 191 (1982).
[264] D. J. McKean, and M. Bell, in: M. Elzinga (ed.): *Methods in Protein Sequence Analysis*, p. 417. Humana Press Clifton, New Jersey 1982.
[265] M. P. Strickler, M. J. Gemski, and B. P. Doctor, *J. Liqu. Chromatogr.* **4**, 1765 (1981).
[266] F. E. Regnier, and K. M. Gooding, *Anal. Biochem.* **103**, 1 (1980).
[267] F. E. Regnier, *Anal. Biochem.* **126**, 1 (1982).
[268] D. N. Vacik, and E. C. Toren, *J. Chromatogr.* **228**, 1 (1982).
[269] O. Mikes, P. Strop, J. Zbrozek, and J. Coupek, *J. Chromatogr.* **119**, 339 (1976).
[270] S. H. Chang, R. Noel, and F. E. Regnier, *Anal. Chem.* **48**, 1839 (1976).
[271] S. H. Chang, K. M. Gooding, and F. E. Regnier, *J. Chromatogr.* **125**, 103 (1976).
[272] P. J. Kudirka, R. R. Schroeder, T. E. Hewitt, and E. C. Toren, *Clin. Chem.* **22**, 471 (1976).
[273] T. D. Schlabach, A. J. Alpert, and F. E. Regnier, *Clin. Chem.* **24**, 1351 (1978).
[274] W. D. Bostick, M. S. Denton, and S. R. Dinsmore, *Clin. Chem.* **26**, 712 (1980).
[275] K. M. Gooding, K.-C. Lu, and F. E. Regnier, *J. Chromatogr.* **164**, 506 (1979).
[276] S. M. Hanash, and D. N. Shapiro, *Hemoglobin* **5**, 165 (1981).
[277] D. L. Gooding, C. Chatfield, and B. Coffin, *Am. Lab.* August 1980, 48.
[278] G. Vanecek, and F. E. Regnier, *Anal. Biochem.* **109**, 345 (1980).
[279] G. S. Ott, and V. G. Shore, *J. Chromatogr.* **231**, 1 (1982).
[280] T. D. Schlabach, and S. R. Abbott, *Clin. Chem.* **26**, 1504 (1980).
[281] C. A. Frolik, L. L. Dart, and M. B. Sporn, *Anal. Biochem.* **125**, 203 (1982).
[282] Sj. van der Wal, and J. F. K. Huber, *Anal. Biochem.* **105**, 219 (1980).
[283] O. Mikes, *Int. J. Pept. Prot. Res.* **14**, 393 (1979).
[284] O. Mikes, P. Strop, J. Zbrozek, and J. Coupek, *J. Chromatogr.* **119**, 339 (1976).
[285] O. Mikes, P. Strop, and J. Sedlackovà, *J. Chromatogr.* **148**, 237 (1978).
[286] R. A. Cole, J. S. Soeldner, P. J. Dunn, and H. F. Bunn, *Metabolism* **27**, 289 (1978).
[287] T. D. Schlabach, J. A. Fulton, P. B. Mockridge, and E. C. Toren, *Clin. Chem.* **25**, 1600 (1979).
[288] T. D. Schlabach, J. A. Fulton, P. B. Mockridge, and E. C. Toren, *Anal. Chem.* **52**, 729 (1980).
[289] M. S. Denton, W. D. Bostick, S. R. Dinsmore, and J. E. Mrochek, *Clin. Chem.* **24**, 1408 (1978).
[290] T. D. Schlabach, S. H. Chang, K. M. Gooding, and F. E. Regnier, *J. Chromatogr.* **134**, 91 (1977).
[291] W. D. Bostick, S. R. Dinsmore, J. E. Mrochek, and T. P. Waalkes, *Clin. Chem.* **24**, 1305 (1978).
[292] F. H. Bissett, *J. Chromatogr.* **178**, 515 (1979).
[293] K.-C. Lu, K. M. Gooding, and F. E. Regnier, *Clin. Chem.* **25**, 1608 (1979).
[294] A. N. Kotake, and Y. Funae, *Proc. Natl. Acad. Sci. USA* **77**, 6473 (1980).
[295] C. A. Gruber, and M. D. Koets, *Clin. Chem.* **25**, 1970 (1979).
[296] E. C. Abraham, N. D. Cope, N. N. Braziel, and T. H. J. Huisman, *Biochem. Biophys. Acta* **577**, 159 (1979).
[297] A. N. Radhakrishnan, S. Skin, A. Licht, K. A. Gruber, and S. Udenfried, *J. Chromatogr.* **132**, 552 (1977).
[298] F. B. Rudolph, and S. W. Clark, *Anal. Biochem.* **127**, 193 (1982).
[299] L. Gozzini, and P. C. Montecucchi, in: F. Lottspeich, A. Henschen, and K. P. Hupe (eds.): *High Performance Liquid Chromatography in Protein and Peptide Chemistry*, p. 349. Walter de Gruyter, Berlin-New York 1981.
[300] V. Brantl, in: F. Lottspeich, A. Henschen, and K. P. Hupe (eds.): *High Performance Liquid Chromatography in Protein and Peptide Chemistry*, p. 365. Walter de Gruyter, Berlin-New York 1981.

[301] H. Engelhardt, G. Ahr, and M. T. W. Hearn, *J. Liqu. Chromatogr.* **4**, 1361 (1981).

[302] K. Fukano, K. Komiya, H. Sasaki, and T. Hashimoto, *J. Chromatogr.* **166**, 47 (1978).

[303] Y. Kato, K. Komiya, Y. Sawada, H. Sasaki, and T. Hashimoto, *J. Chromatogr.* **190**, 305 (1980).

[304] T. Someno, K. Katoh, K. Niijima, and H. Miyazaki, *J. Chromatogr.* **188**, 185 (1980).

[305] H. von Bahr-Lindström, M. Carlquist, V. Mutt, and H. Jörnvall, in: M. Elzinga (ed.): *Methods in Protein Sequence Analysis*, p. 455. Humana Press Clifton, New Jersey 1982.

[306] R. Somack, V. S. McKay, and J. W. Giles, *J. Am. Chem. Soc.* **16**, 285 (1980).

[307] G. P. Dimenna, and H. J. Segall, *J. Liqu. Chromatogr.* **4**, 639 (1981).

[308] D. H. Calam, and J. Davidson, *J. Chromatogr.* **218**, 581 (1981).

[309] T. Tomono, S. Yoshida, and E. Tokunaga, *J. Polymer Sci.* **17**, 335 (1979).

[310] A. P. Toste, *J. Chromatogr.* **197**, 207 (1980).

[311] K. T. Suzuki, T. Motomura, Y. Tsuchiya, and M. Yamamura, *Anal. Biochem.* **107**, 75 (1980).

[312] E. Keshavarz, and S. Nakai, *Biochim. Biophys. Acta* **576**, 269 (1977).

[313] S. Rokushika, T. Ohkawa, and H. Hatano, *J. Chromatogr.* **176**, 456 (1979).

[314] Y. Kato, K. Komiya, H. Sasaki, and T. Hashimoto, *J. Chromatogr.* **190**, 297 (1980).

[315] C. T. Wehr, and S. R. Abbott, *J. Chromatogr.* **185**, 453 (1979).

[316] M. E. Himmel, and P. G. Squire, *J. Pept. Prot. Res.* **17**, 365 (1981).

[317] D. Ratge, and H. Wisser, *J. Chromatogr.* **230**, 47 (1982).

[318] M. Okazaki, N. Hagiwara, and I. Hara, *J. Biochem.* **92**, 517 (1982).

[319] D. L. Busbee, D. M. Payne, D. W. Jasheway, S. Carlisle, and A. G. Lacko, *Clin. Chem.* **27**, 2052 (1981).

[320] R. A. Jenik, and J. W. Porter, *Anal. Biochem.* **111**, 184 (1981).

[321] N. Ui, *Anal. Biochem.* **97**, 65 (1979).

[322] Y. Kato, K. Komiya, H. Sasaki, and T. Hashimoto, *J. Chromatogr.* **193**, 458 (1980).

[323] N. Ui, *J. Chromatogr.* **215**, 289 (1981).

[324] T. Osumi, T. Hashimoto, and N. Ui, *J. Biochem.* **87**, 1735 (1980).

[325] M. Kehl, and A. Henschen, in: F. Lottspeich, A. Henschen, and K. P. Hupe (eds.): *High Performance Liquid Chromatography in Protein and Peptide Chemistry*, p. 339. Walter de Gruyter, Berlin-New York 1981.

[326] H. Ponstingl, E. Krauhs, M. Little, T. Kempf, R. Hofer-Warbinek, and W. Ade, in: F. Lottspeich, A. Henschen, and K. P. Hupe (eds.): *High Performance Liquid Chromatography in Protein and Peptide Chemistry*, p. 325. Walter de Gruyter, Berlin-New York 1981.

[327] T. Imamura, K. Konishi, and M. Yokoyama, *J. Biochem.* **86**, 639 (1979).

[328] Y. Kato, K. Komiya, H. Sasaki, and T. Hashimoto, *J. Chromatogr.* **193**, 29 (1980).

[329] T. Takagi, *J. Chromatogr.* **219**, 123 (1981).

[330] T. Konishi, *Methods Enzymol.* **88**, 202 (1982).

[331] T. Konishi, and M. Sasaki, *Chem. Pharm. Bull.* **30**, 4208 (1982).

[332] T. Takagi, K. Takeda, and T. Okuno, *J. Chromatogr.* **208**, 201 (1981).

[333] J. Bergmeyer, J. Straub, and D. Oesterhelt, in: F. Lottspeich, A. Henschen, and K. P. Hupe (eds.): *High Performance Liquid Chromatography in Protein and Peptide Chemistry*, p. 315. Walter de Gruyter, Berlin-New York 1981.

[334] H. D. Lemke, and D. Oesterhelt, in: F. Lottspeich, A. Henschen, and K. P. Hupe (eds.): *High Performance Liquid Chromatography in Protein and Peptide Chemistry*, p. 307. Walter de Gruyter, Berlin-New York 1981.

[335] Y. Shioya, H. Yoshida, and T. Nakajima, in: H. Yonehara (ed.): *Peptide Chemistry*, p. 127. Protein Research Foundation, Osaka 1980.

[336] K. Kojima, T. Manabe, T. Okuyama, T. Tomono, T. Suzuki, and E. Tokunaga, *J. Chromatogr.* **239**, 565. (1982).

[337] C. H. Williams jr., L. D. Arscott, R. P. Swonsorr, V. Massey, R. H. Schirmer, G. E. Schulz, and R. Untucht-Grau, in: F. Lottspeich, A. Henschen and K. P. Hupe (eds.): *High Performance Liquid Chromatography in Protein and Peptide Chemistry*, p. 293. Walter de Gruyter, Berlin-New York 1981.

[338] Y. Kato, K. Komiya, H. Sasaki, and T. Hashimoto, J. HRC & CC. **3**, 145 (1980).

[339] T. Someno, K. Katoh, K. Niijima, and H. Miyazaki, *J. Chromatogr.* **253**, 81 (1982).

[340] A. Feste, and J. C. Gan, *J. Chromatogr.* **248**, 417 (1982).

[341] K. Stüber, and K. Bayreuther, in: F. Lottspeich, A. Henschen, and K. P. Hupe (eds.): *High

Performance Liquid Chromatography in Protein and Peptide Chemistry, p. 205. Walter de Gruyter, Berlin-New York 1981.

[342] K. T. Suzuki, *Anal Biochem.* **102**, 31 (1980).

[343] G. J. Hughes, K. H. Winterhalter, and K. J. Wilson, in: F. Lottspeich, A. Henschen, and K. P. Hupe (eds.): *High Performance Liquid Chromatography in Protein and Peptide Chemistry*, p. 175. Walter de Gruyter, Berlin-New York 1981.

[344] T. Flatmark, and M. Grønberg, *Biochem. Biophys. Res. Comm.* **99**, 292 (1981).

[345] H. von Bahr-Lindström, U. Moberg, J. Sjödahl, and H. Jörnvall, *Biosci. Rep.* **2**, 803 (1982).

[346] T. Hashimoto, H. Sasaki, M. Aiura, and Y. Kato, *J. Chromatogr.* **160**, 301 (1978).

[347] Y. Kato, K. Komiya, H. Sasaki, and T. Hashimoto, *J. Chromatogr.* **193**, 311 (1980).

[348] I. Hara, K. Shiraishi, and M. Okazaki, *J. Chromatogr.* **239**, 549 (1982).

[349] M. Okazaki, Y. Ohno, and I. Hara, *J. Chromatogr.* **221**, 257 (1980).

[350] Y. Ohno, M. Okazaki, and I. Hara, *J. Biochem.* **89**, 1675 (1981).

[351] J. Germershausen, and J. D. Karkas, *Biochem. Biophys. Res. Comm.* **99**, 1020 (1981)

[352] K. Rittinghaus, and K.-H. Franzen, *Fresenius Z. Anal. Chem.* **301**, 144 (1980).

[353] F. Hefti, *Anal. Biochem.* **121**, 378 (1982).

[354] N. C. Robinson, and L. Talbert, *Biochem. Biophys. Res. Comm.* **95**, 90 (1980).

[355] J. M. Dayer, M. L. Stephenson, E. Schmidt, W. Karge, and S. M. Krane, *FEBS Lett.* **124**, 253 (1981).

[356] K. A. Gruber, J. M. Whitaker, and M. Morris, *Anal. Biochem.* **97**, 176 (1979).

[357] K. Rittinghaus, and K.-H. Franzen, in: F. Lottspeich, A. Henschen, and K. P. Hupe (eds.): *High Performance Liquid Chromatography in Protein and Peptide Chemistry*, p. 83. Walter de Gruyter, Berlin-New York 1981.

[358] P. Roumeliotis, K. K. Unger, J. Kinkel, G. Brunner, R. Wieser, and G. Tschank, in: F. Lottspeich, A. Henschen, and K. P. Hupe (eds.): *High Performance Liquid Chromatography in Protein and Peptide Chemistry*, p. 71. Walter de Gruyter, Berlin-New York 1981.

[359] W. Kopaciewicz, and F. E. Regnier, *Anal. Biochem.* **126**, 8 (1982).

[360] W. Schwarz, H. Tiedemann, and H. Tiedemann, *Molec. Biol. Rep.* **8**, 7 (1981).

[361] B. Sebille, N. Thuaud, and J.-P. Tillement, *J. Chromatogr.* **167**, 159 (1978).

[362] P. Roumeliotis, and K. K. Unger, *J. Chromatogr.* **185**, 445 (1979).

[363] D. E. Schmidt, R. W. Giese, D. Conron, and B. L. Karger, *Anal. Chem.* **52**, 177 (1980).

[364] S. Ohlson, L. Hansson, P. O. Larsson, and K. Mosbach, *FEBS Lett.* **93**, 5 (1978).

[365] J. R. Sportsman, and G. S. Wilson, *Anal. Chem.* **52**, 2013 (1980).

[366] H. Löbermann, F. Lottspeich, W. Bode and R. Huber, *Hoppe-Seyler's Z. Physiol. Chem.* **363**, 1377 (1982).

[367] S. Kano, K. Matsumoto, H. Nakamura, and T. Hashimoto, *J. Clin. Chem. Clin. Biochem.* **19**, 723 (1981).

[368] M. J. Bertolini, *Vox Sang.* **43**, 87 (1982).

[369] S. Weiner, *J. Chromatogr.* **245**, 148 (1982).

[370] R. van der Zee, and G. W. Welling, *J. Chromatogr.* **244**, 134 (1982).

[371] M. Gazdag, and G. Szepesi, *J. Chromatogr.* **218**, 603 (1981).

[372] B. D. Catherwood, and L. J. Deftos, *Calcif. Tissue Int.* **31**, 86 (1980).

[373] S. A. Borman, *Anal. Chem.* **54**, 21 A (1982).

[374] L. F. Congote, *Blood* **57**, 353 (1981).

[375] C. L. Hinman, H. C. Rauch, and R. F. Pfeifer, *Life Sci.* **30**, 989 (1982).

[376] E. C. Nice, M. Capp, and M. J. O'Hara, *J. Chromatogr.* **185**, 413 (1979).

[377] P. Schwandt, and W. O. Richter, *Biochim. Biophys. Acta* **626**, 376 (1980).

[378] W. S. Hancock, C. A. Bishop, P. L. Prestidge, D. R. K. Harding, and M. T. W. Hearn, *Science* **200**, 1168 (1978).

[379] P. E. Petrides, R. T. Jones, and P. Böhlen, *Anal. Biochem.* **105**, 383 (1980).

[380] S. Terabe, H. Nishi, and T. Ando, *J. Chromatogr.* **212**, 295 (1981).

[381] K. Seta, M. Washitake, T. Anmo, N. Takai, and T. Okuyama, *J. Liqu. Chromatogr.* **4**, 129 (1981).

[382] W. Richter, and P. Schwandt, *J. Neurochem.* **36**, 1279 (1981).

[383] R. A. Glasel, *J. Chromatogr.* **145**, 469 (1978).

[384] J. B. Shelton, J. R. Shelton, and W. A. Schroeder, *J. Liqu. Chromatogr.* **4**, 1381 (1981).

[385] D. R. Burger, A. A. Vandenbark, W. Dunnick, W. Kraybill, G. D. Daves, and R. M. Vetto, *J. Immunol.* **122**, 1091 (1979).

[386] M. Kimura, and Y. Itokawa, *J. Chromatogr.* **211**, 290 (1981).
[387] L. Menard, M. E. Dempsey, L. A. Blankstein, H. Aleyassine, M. Wacks, and J. S. Soeldner, *Clin. Chem.* **26**, 1598 (1980).
[388] E. J. Hayes, R. E. Gleason, J. S. Soeldner, M. Wacks, and L. Blankstein, *Clin. Chem.* **27**, 476 (1981).
[389] C. Persiani, P. Cukor, and K. French, *J. Chromatogr. Sci.* **14**, 417 (1976).
[390] H. D. Crone, and R. M. Dawson, *J. Chromatogr.* **129**, 91 (1976).
[391] R. J. Blagrove, and M. J. Frenkel, *J. Chromatogr.* **132**, 399 (1977).
[392] I. Hara, M. Okazaki, and Y. Ohno, *J. Biochem.* **87**, 1863 (1980).
[393] H. Murofushi, *J. Biochem.* **87**, 979 (1980).
[394] T. Takagi, *J. Biochem.* **89**, 363 (1981).
[395] E. Nishida, T. Kuwaki, S. Maekawa, and H. Sakai, *J. Biochem.* **89**, 1655 (1981).
[396] A. I. Smith, and J. R. McDermott, *Regulatory Peptides* **4**, 6 (1982).
[397] M. Rubinstein, W. P. Levy, J. A. Moschera, C.-Y. Lai, R. D. Hershberg, R. T. Bartlett, and S. Pestka, *Arch. Biochem. Biophys.* **210**, 307 (1981).
[398] J. Rivier, C. Rivier, J. Spiess, and W. Vale, *Anal. Biochem.* **127**, 258 (1982).
[399] J. Verhoef, E. E. Codd, J. P. H. Burbach, and A. Witter, *J. Chromatogr.* **233**, 317 (1982).
[400] Y. Kato, K. Nakamura, and T. Hashimoto, *J. Chromatogr.* **253**, 219 (1982).
[401] J. Heukeshoven, and R. Dernick, *J. Chromatogr.* **252**, 241 (1982).
[402] H. Aoshima, *Anal. Biochem.* **95**, 371 (1979).
[403] Y. Kato, K. Nakamura, and T. Hashimoto, *J. Chromatogr.* **245**, 193 (1982).
[404] E. Pfannkoch, K. C. Lu, F. E. Regnier, and H. Barth, *J. Chromatogr. Sci.* **18**, 430 (1980).
[405] N. Kaneda, M. Sato, and K. Yagi, *Anal. Biochem.* **127**, 49 (1982).
[406] Dj. Josić, W. Reutter, and I. Molnar, in: I. Molnar (ed.): *Practical Aspects of Modern HPLC*, p. 109. Walter de Gruyter, Berlin-New York 1982.
[407] W. Schwarz, J. Born, H. Tiedemann, and I. Molnar, in: I. Molnär (ed.): *Practical Aspects of Modern HPLC*, p. 123. Walter de Gruyter, Berlin-New York 1982.
[408] M. Kehl, F. Lottspeich, and A. Henschen, in: I. Molnar (ed.): *Practical Aspects of Modern HPLC*, p. 137. Walter de Gruyter, Berlin-New York 1982.
[409] M. Ritschmann, L. Kuehn, B. Dahlmann, and H. Reinauer, *Anal. Biochem.* **124**, 134 (1982).
[410] S. Hara, A. Ohsawa, and A. Dobashi, *J. Liqu. Chromatogr.* **4**, 409 (1981).
[411] K. Buchholz, A. Borchert, and S. V. Kasche, in: I. Molnar (ed.): *Practical Aspects of Modern HPLC*, p. 187. Walter de Gruyter, Berlin-New York 1982.
[412] M. Griffin, J. Wilson, and L. Lorand, *Anal. Biochem.* **124**, 406 (1982).
[413] W. C. Mahoney, *Biochim. Biophys. Acta* **704**, 284 (1982).
[414] D. P. Kosow, S. Morris, C. L. Orthner, and M.-J. Rhee, *Anal. Biochem.* **126**, 425 (1982).
[415] Y. Kato, K. Komiya, and T. Hishimoto, *J. Chromatogr.* **246**, 13 (1982).
[416] R. V. Lewis, and D. DeWald, *J. Liqu. Chromatogr.* **5**, 1367 (1982).
[417] J. A. Fulton, T. D. Schlabach, J. E. Kerl, and E. C. Toren, *J. Chromatogr.* **175**, 283 (1979).
[418] A. J. Alpert, and F. E. Regnier, *J. Chromatogr.* **185**, 375 (1979).

5 Peptide Hormones

by *Wolfgang Voelter*

5 Peptide Hormones

5.1 Introduction

High Performance Liquid Chromatography provides the peptide hormone chemist with an efficient tool for rapid separation, purification and structural analysis for his field of research.

5.2 Separation Principles

5.2.1 Reversed-Phase High Performance Liquid Chromatography

Reversed-Phase High Performance Liquid Chromatography (RP-HPLC) especially attracts the peptide hormone researchers. This is because the columns available provide remarkable efficiency and excellent selectivity; they are pressure-stable; re-equilibration is rapidly achieved; bleeding seldom occurs; and the column material is resistant to organic solvents and mild acids. Reversed-phase material, suitable for the separation of peptide hormones is available from many commercial sources e. g.: Biorad ODS (specially suitable for the separation of hydrophilic peptides); μBondapak alkylphenyl; μBondapak C_{18}; μBondapak cyanopropyl (specially suitable for hydrophobic peptides); C_{18} Corasil; C_{18}-LP-1; Hypersil ODS; LiChrosorb C_2; LiChrosorb diol; LiChrosorb RP-8; LiChrosorb RP-18 (suitable for the separation of hydrophilic peptides); Nucleosil C_8; Nucleosil C_{18}; Nucleosil 5CN (suitable for the separation of hydrophobic peptides); Partisil ODS-1 (suitable for hydrophobic peptides); Partisil ODS-2 (suitable for hydrophilic peptides); Partisal 10-(Valine-Alanine-Proline); Partisil 10-(Valine-Phenylalanine-Valine); Phenyl-Sil-X-1; Poragel PN; Poragel PS; Silica CT-(Valine-Alanine-Serine); Silica-Diamine; Spherisorb ODS; and Zorbax C-8 or Zorbax ODS (suitable for hydrophilic peptides).

For the separations of peptides or peptide hormones by RP-HPLC, aqueous solutions of e. g. H_3PO_4 [1], phosphate buffers [2,3], triethylammonium phosphate [4,5], $HClO_4$ [6], HCl [7], CH_3COOH [7], CF_3COOH [8], NH_4OAc [9 to 11] or NH_4HCO_3 [12] are usually mixed with an organic water-soluble solvent for mobile phases. Suitable organic solvents, with increasing eluotropic power are: methanol; acetic acid; ethanol; acetonitrile; 2-propanol; dimethylformamide; acetone; n-propanol or dioxan. Usually, a 10% increase in organic solvent concentration decreases the capacity factor k by a factor of 2 to 3 [13]. According to O'Hare and Nice [14], the retention order for small peptides and peptide hormones can be correlated with the sum of hydrophobicity values (based on octanol/water partition coefficients) for most hydrophobic residues of peptides. As there is often a discrepancy between predicted and experimental values, Meek derived retention coefficients for amino acids, peptides and peptide hormones directly from HPLC data [15]. The retention coefficients of amino acid residues were calculated on the basis of retention times of 25 peptides or peptide hormones separated on an

ODS column (Bio-Rad) at room temperature with linear gradients from 0.1 mol/L $NaClO_4$ of pH 7.4 and 2.1 at 0 min to 60% acetonitrile/0.1 mol/L $NaClO_4$ at 80 min (Table 5-1).

Table 5-1. Retention Times (min) of 25 Peptides and Peptide Hormones Separated by HPLC. Chromatographic Conditions: Column: Bio-Rad ODS; linear gradient elution: initial eluent 0.1 mol/L $NaClO_4$/0% acetonitrile (pH 7.4 resp. 2.1) and final eluent 0.1 mol/L $NaClO_4$/60% acetonitrile (at 80 min, 0.75%/min); room temperature. For separations at pH 7.4, the starting buffer contained 5 mmol/L phosphate buffer; for those at pH 2.1, 0.1% phosphoric acid [15].

| Compound | Retention Time (min) | |
	pH 7.4	pH 2.1
1. Triglycine	2.0	3.0
2. Pentaalanine	4.6	8.1
3. Divaline	6.9	14.5
4. Dimethionine	10.5	21.0
5. Thyrotropin-releasing hormone	11.5	11.2
6. Tuftsin	11.7	12.0
7. Trityrosine	19.5	29.7
8. (Met)-Enkephalin	27.5	38.0
9. Trileucine	28.0	36.8
10. (Leu)Enkephalin	29.3	42.0
11. Ditryptophan	31.6	44.3
12. Angiotensin II	32.2	47.5
13. α-Endorphin	32.3	47.7
14. Caerulein	34.2	42.2
15. Oxytocin	36.4	37.9
16. Gastrin-(12-15)	36.5	42.4
17. Neurotensin	39.0	48.0
18. Physalaemin	41.0	43.0
19. Triphenylalanine	41.6	49.5
20. Luteinising hormone – releasing hormone	42.8	49.5
21. α-Melanotropin	46.2	46.2
22. Bradykinin	48.0	45.0
23. Eledoisin	53.0	44.0
24. Glucagon	53.6	60.0
25. Somatostatin	57.5	55.0

On the basis of the data in Table 5-1, the retention coefficients for the amino acid residues were calculated by a computer program which changes the retention coefficients for all amino acids sequentially, up to the best correlation between actual and predicted retention times (Table 5-2).

By summing the retention coefficients, listed in Table 5-2, and by adding t_0 (2 min), retention times were calculated for a series of peptides and peptide hormones and compared with experimental values. As is seen from Table 5-3, predicted and experimentally determined retention times are reasonably close.

Table 5-2. Calculated Retention Coefficients of Amino Acid Residues. (N) Number of peptides (Table 5-1) used for the calculation. The retention times of the peptides were determined under conditions given for Table 5-1 [15].

Amino Acid (N)	Retention Coefficients	
	pH 7.4	pH 2.1
Tryptophan (7)	14.9	18.1
Phenylalanine (13)	13.2	13.9
Isoleucine (4)	13.9	11.8
Leucine (9)	8.8	10.0
Tyrosine (11)	6.1	8.2
Methionine (9)	4.8	7.1
Valine (5)	2.7	3.3
Proline (10)	6.1	8.0
Threonine (5)	2.7	1.5
Arginine (7)	0.8	− 4.5
Alanine (4)	0.5	− 0.1
Glycine (13)	0.0	− 0.5
Histidine (5)	− 3.5	0.8
Cystine (2)	− 6.8	− 2.2
Lysine (8)	0.1	− 3.2
Serine (6)	1.2	− 3.7
Asparagine (5)	0.8	− 1.6
Glutamine (4)	− 4.8	− 2.5
Aspartic acid (5)	− 8.2	− 2.8
Glutamic acid (3)	−16.9	− 7.5
Amino (19)	2.4	− 0.4
-COOH (17)	− 3.0	6.9
-Amide (8)	7.8	5.0
Pyroglutamyl- (5)	− 1.1	− 2.8
Acetyl- (1)	5.6	3.9
Tyrosine sulfate (1)	10.9	6.5

Table 5-3. Comparison of Predicted and Experimentally Determined Retention Times. Predicted retention times are calculated by summing retention coefficients, listed in Table 5-2 for each peptide and adding 2 min (t_o) [15].

Compound	Retention Time (min)	
	Predicted	Experimentally determined [14]
(Met)-Enkephalin	18.4	19.0
(Leu)Enkephalin	20.9	22.0
ACTH-(5-10)	11.9	17.0
ACTH-(34-39)	27.0	31.0
ACTH-(4-10)	12.4	20.5
ACTH-(4-11)	33.1	30.0
Angiotensin II	27.4	23.0

Table 5.3. (Continued).

Compound	Retention Time (min)	
	Predicted	Experimentally determined [14]
Substance P-(4-11)	33.1	30.0
Oxytocin	27.4	23.0
(Arg)Vasopressin	9.0	14.0
(Lys)Vasopressin	10.2	13.0
(Arg)Vasotocin	7.2	12.0
Substance P	33.3	29.0
α-MSH	27.3	26.0
Neurotensin	28.9	24.5
Somatostatin	25.5	32.0
Bombesin	22.6	26.0
Gastrin-1	26.8	28.5
ACTH-(18-39)	20.2	30.5
ACTH-(1-24)	34.9	21.5
Melittin	61.3	46.0
Glucagon	39.7	36.0
β-Endorphin	41.5	34.0

5.2.2 Ion-Exchange Chromatography

Amino acids, small peptides and peptide hormones (below 30 residues) are well separated on high-efficiency ion-exchange column material in which the ionic functional group is bonded to a polystyrene-divinylbenzene resin. The applicability of silica-based ion-exchange columns is limited because of the chemical instability of the packing material [16]. Stronger binding forces of larger peptides to the polystyrene-divinylbenzene resin make it difficult to purify longer peptide chains by this technique [17]. Since the development of the two-column system by Spackman et al [18], many improvements were made in the field of amino acid and peptide separation, by single-column analysis, the use of stable resins of small particle size and new derivatization reactions for the detection of amino acids and peptides.

A modified, commercially available, high-performance liquid chromatograph, equipped with an automatic gradient-generating system, permits the detection of amino acids, peptides and peptide hormones in the picomole range if fluorescamine is used as a detection reagent and if separation is performed on ion-exchange resins of small particle size (5 to 8 μm) [19].

Figure 5-1 shows a functional diagram of an automatic HPLC amino acid analyzer using fluorescamine as a detection reagent. Two citrate buffers (pH 2.6 and 6.3, 0.2 and 1.2 mol/L in Na^+) are used for gradient elution. The column effluent is mixed with borate buffer to adjust the pH to 9, the optimum pH-value for maximum fluorescence [19].

Figure 5-1. Functional diagram of an automatic HPLC amino acid, peptide and peptide hormone analyzer using fluorescamine as detection reagent [19].

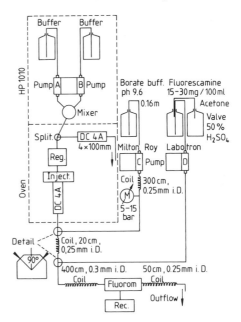

o-Phthalaldehyde forms in the presence of 2-mercaptoethanol fluorescent derivatives with the primary amino group of amino acids, peptides and peptide hormones. However, only a tenfold increase in the concentration of 2-mercaptoethanol, originally suggested by Roth [20, 21], enlarges the detection sensitivity for o-phthalaldehyde products of amino acids and peptides [22]. Compared to fluorescamine, o-phthaldehyde has two advantages: the reagent is five to ten times more sensitive than fluorescamine; and it is also soluble in aqueous solutions [22 to 24].

5.2.3 Ion-Pair High Performance Liquid Chromatography

For the technique which applies "pairing ions" [25 to 28] for the separation of ionic compounds such as amino acids, peptides and peptide hormones with reversed-phase chromatography, different expressions are in use:

- Detergent-based cation-exchange [29];
- ion-pair chromatography [30, 31];
- soap chromatography [27];
- solvent-generated ion-exchange chromatography [32];
- solvophobic-ion chromatography [33];
- surfactant chromatography [34].

Different retention theories, including solvophobic [25, 35, 36] and ion-exchange mechanisms [33, 37, 38] are discussed. However, the dynamic equilibrium is most probably affected by electrostatic, eluophilic, eluophobic, adsorbophilic and adsorbophobic forces.

Alkylsulfonates or dodecyl-ammonium phosphate [39, 40], added in concentrations of 0.05 to 5 mmol/L to the mobile phase, are common surface active ions for the performance of ion-pair chromatography [41 to 43]. According to Horváth et al. [36], there is the following relationship between the capacity factor k for polar molecules and the concentration of the pairing ion:

$$k = (k_0 + \beta (X) \cdot (1 + k_2 (X))^{-1} \cdot (1 + k_3 (X)^{-1} \quad (1)$$

where k_0 is capacity factor in the absence of the counter-ion X and β, k_2 and k_3 are equilibrium association constant terms.

If RP-HPLC of peptide hormones yields tailing, poor recovery or bad resolution, ion-pair liquid chromatography is an attractive alternative, as was demonstrated recently for thyrotropin-releasing hormone, substance P, arginine-vasopressin and the encephalins [44].

5.3 HPLC Separations of Peptide Hormones

5.3.1 Hypothalamic Hormones

The hypothalamus is a center of neurosecretion in our body. Oxytocin and vasopressin are produced in the regions of the *nucleus supraopticus* and *nucleus paraventricularis* and the biosynthesis of the hypothalamic neurosecretory regulating hormones takes place in the region of the *eminentia mediana* [45].

A survey of the names (with abbreviations), structures and regulatory effects of the hypothalamus-releasing hormones are given in Table 5-4. Table 5-5 lists the names, including their abbreviations, structures and regulatory effects, of the hypothalamus-inhibiting hormones.

Table 5-4. Names (with Abbreviations), Structures and Regulatory Effects of Hypothalamus-Releasing Hormones [46, 47].

Names	Iupac terminology	Structure (suggested)	Regulatory effect
Corticitropin-releasing hormone (CRH)	Corticoliberin	Ac-Ser-Tyr-Cys-Phe-His-(Asn, Gln)-Cys-(Pro, Val)-Lys-Gly-NH$_2$	ACTH*) production
Follicle-stimulating hormone-releasing hormone (FSH-RH)	Folliberin	Pyr-His-Trp-Ser-Tyr-Gly-Leu-Arg-Pro-Gly-NH$_2$	FSH*) production
Luteinizing hormone-releasing hormone (LH-RH)	Luliberin	Pyr-His-Trp-Ser-Tyr-Gly-Leu-Arg-Pro-Gly-NH$_2$	LH*) production
Melanocyte-stimulating hormone-releasing hormone (MRH)	Melanoliberin	Cys-Tyr-Ile-Gln-Asn	MSH*) production
Prolactin-releasing hormone (PRH)	Prolactoliberin		PRL*) production
Thyrotropin-releasing hormone (TRH)	Thyreoliberin	Pyr-His-Pro-NH$_2$	TSH*) production

Table 5-4. (Continued).

Names	Iupac terminology	Structure (suggested)	Regulatory effect
Growth hormone-releasing hormone (GRH)	Somatoliberin	H-Tyr-Ala-Asp-Ala-Ile-Phe-Thr-Asn-Ser-Tyr-Arg-Lys-Val-Leu-Gly-Gln-Leu-Ser-Ala-Arg-Lys-Leu-Leu-Gln-Asp-Ile-Met-Ser-Arg-Gln-Gln-Gly-Glu-Ser-Asn-Gln-Glu-Arg-Gly-Ala-Arg-Ala-Arg-Leu-NH$_2$	GH*) production

*) For abbreviations see Table 5-5.

Table 5-5. Names (with Abbreviations), Structures and Regulatory Effects of Hypothalamus-Inhibiting Hormones [46, 47].

Names	Iupac terminology	Structure (suggested)	Regulatory effect
Melanocyte-stimulating hormone release-inhibiting hormone (MRIH)	Melanostatin	Pro-Leu-Gly-NH$_2$ Pro-His-Phe-Arg-Gly-NH$_2$ Cys-Tyr-Ile-Gln-Asn-Cys-OH	Suppression of MSH*) release
Prolactin release-inhibiting hormone (PIH)	Prolactostatin		Supression of PRL*) release
Growth hormone release-inhibiting hormone (GIH)	Somatostatin	Ala-Gly-Cys-Lys-Asn-Phe-Phe-Trp- Lys-Thr-Phe-Thr-Ser-Cys-OH	Supression of GH*) release

*) Abbreviations used in Tables 5-4 and 5-5: ACTH Adrenocorticotropic hormone; FSH Follicle-stimulating hormone; GH Growth hormone (somatotropin); LH Luteinizing hormone; MSH Melanocyte-stimulating hormone; PRL Prolactin; TSH Thyrotropin (Thyroid-stimulating hormone).

From Tables 5-4 and 5-5, it is obvious that the hypothalamus is a source of unknown peptide hormones [46, 47] which have not yet been isolated, in pure form, by conventional methods. With the availability of conventional chromatographic techniques, and without the help of HPLC, about 300000 ovine hypothalami had to be collected for the isolation of 1 mg of almost pure thyreolibrin (TRH) (Table 5-6) which was needed for its structure elucidation [46].

The combination of gel filtration and RP-HPLC allows the isolation of pure peptides from several hundred hypothalamic fragments much more conveniently than the methods used 10 years ago [48]. A similar separation method was applied recently for the isolation of the growth hormone-releasing hormone from human pancreatic tumors [49]. The tumor tissue was extracted with 0.3 mol/L HCL, filtered on a Sephadex G-75 column and further processed by two subsequent HPLC separations on reversed-phase columns (Ultrasphere C$_{18}$, 5 μm, 25 × 0.4 cm last column) [49].

Several detailed studies are already available on HPLC of hypothalamic hormones [50 to 63] and the data for the conditions of separation are collected in Table 5-7.

By a combination of gel filtration on Sephadex G-25, counter current distribution, chromatography on CM-cellulose, partition and SE-Sephadex chromatography and RP-HPLC (µBondapak C_{18}, water, acetonitrile, propan-2-ol) the group of Schally [57] isolated ten peptides (Arg-Phe, Phe-Tyr, Val-Trp, Tyr-Phe, Lys-Phe-Tyr, Gly-Lys-Val-Asn, Phe-Glu-His-Glu, Val-Val-Tyr-Pro-Trp-Thr-Gln-Arg-Phe, Leu-Val-Val-Tyr-Pro-Trp-Thr-Gln-Arg-Phe, Phe-Leu-Gly-Phe-Pro-Thr-Thr-Lys-Thr-Tyr-Phe-Pro-His-Phe-Asn-Leu) some of which showed some biological activity.

Table 5-6. The Scheme of Purification of Ovine TRH used by Burgus et al. [46] without the Aid of HPLC.

No.	Stage	Number of hypo-thalamic fragments	Weight	TRF Units/mg
1	Lyophilized sheep hypothalami	294 000	25 kg	
2	Alcohol-chloroform extract	294 000	294 g	1
3	Ultrafiltration 'UM-3'	294 000	71 g	3
4 and 5	Double gel filtration (Sephadex G-25, 0.5 mol/L acetic acid)	286 000	16 g	16
6 and 7	Double partition chromatography, 0.01 % acetic acid-n-butanol-pyridine (11 : 5 : 3)	280 000	246 mg	800
8 and 9	Double adsorption chromatography, Norit/H_2O-ethanol-phenol	275 000	4.2 mg	30 500
10	Partition chromatography, n-butanol-acetic acid-H_2O (4 : 1 : 5), (upper phase)	273 000	2.0 mg	58 500
11	Repeat 10	270 000	1.0 mg	57 000

Table 5-7. Experimental Conditions for HPLC Separations of Hypothalamic Hormones resp. Hypothalamic Hormone Derivatives (Structures see Tables 5-4 and 5-5).

Hormone (resp. Derivative)	Stationary Phase	Eluent	Column (mm)	Detection (nm)	k-Value	Reference
Thyreoliberin	μBondapak C_{18} (10 μm)	Acetonitrile/0.01 mol/L NH_4OAc (pH 4), 0.5:99.5 (3 mL/min)	4 × 300	UV (210)	–	[50]
Thyreoliberin	Fatty Acid Analysis, analytic column, Waters (10 μm)	0.1% Acetic acid/methanol, 2:3 (1.5 mL/min)	3.9 × 300	UV (215)	–	[52]
Thyreoliberin	μBondapak C_{18} (10 μm)	A: Triethylamine-phosphoric acid (pH 3.2), B: triethyl-amine-phosphoric acid (pH 3.2)/acetonitrile, 40:60, gradient from 2% to 70% B in 78 min (1.5 mL/min)	4 × 300	UV (210)	1.18 $(t_A = t_r - t_0)$	[55]
Thyreoliberin	μBondapak C_{18} (10 μm)	A: 0.1% Phosphoric acid, B: 70% acetonitrile in A, linear gradient from 5 – 70% B (20 min) (1 mL/min)	3.9 × 300	UV (206)	–	[61]
Thyreoliberin	μBondapak C_{18} (10 μm)	Acetonitrile/1-hexanesul-fonic acid/0.02 mol/L acetic acid, 2.75:0.1:97.15 (2 mL/min)	3.9 × 300	UV (210)	–	[62]
Thyreoliberin	μBondapak C_{18} (10 μm)	Acetonitrile/1-heptanesul-fonic acid/0.02 mol/L acetic acid, 6.5:0.1:93.4 (2 mL/min)	3.9 × 300	UV (210)	–	[62]

Table 5-7. (Continued).

Hormone (resp. Derivative)	Stationary Phase	Eluent	Column (mm)	Detection (nm)	k-Value	Reference
Thyreoliberin	μBondapak C_{18} (10 μm)	Acetonitrile/1-pentane-sulfonic acid/0.02 mol/L acetic acid, 2:0.1:97.9 (2 mL/min)	3.9 × 300	UV (210)	—	[62]
Pyr-His-Pro-OH	μBondapak C_{18} (10 μm)	Acetonitrile/1-hexanesulfonic acid/0.02 mol/L acetic acid, 2.75:0.1:97.15 (2 mL/min)	3.9 × 300	UV (210)	—	[62]
Pyr-His-Pro-OH	μBondapak C_{18} (10 μm)	Acetonitrile/1-heptane-sulfonic acid/0.02 mol/L acetic acid, 6.5:0.1:93.4 (2 mL/min)	3.9 × 300	UV (210)	—	[62]
Pyr-His-Pro-OH	μBondapak C_{18} (10 μm)	Acetonitrile/1-pentanesulfonic acid/0.02 mol/L acetic acid, 2:0.1:97.9 (2 mL/min)	3.9 × 300	UV (210)	—	[62]
Pyr-His-Pro-Gly-NH_2	μBondapak C_{18} (10 μm)	Acetonitrile-1-hexanesulfonic acid/0.02 mol/L acetic acid, 2.75:0.1:97.15 (2 mL/min)	3.9 × 300	UV (210)	—	[62]
Pyr-His-Pro-Gly-NH_2	μBondapak C_{18} (10 μm)	Acetonitrile/1-heptanesulfonic acid/0.02 mol/L acetic acid, 6.5:0.1:93.4 (2 mL/min)	3.9 × 300	UV (210)	—	[62]
Pyr-His-Pro-Gly-NH_2	μBondapak C_{18} (10 μm)	Acetonitrile/1-pentanesulfonic acid/0.02 mol/L acetic acid, 2:0.1:97.9 (2 mL/min)	3.9 × 300	UV (210)	—	[62]

Compound	Packing	Mobile phase	Column	Detection	Retention	Ref.
Pyr-3-methyl-His-Pro-NH$_2$	μBondapak C$_{18}$ (10 μm)	Acetonitrile/1-hexanesulfonic acid/0.02 mol/L acetic acid, 2.75:0.1:97.15 (2 mL/min)	3.9 × 300	UV (210)	—	[62]
Pyr-3-methyl-His-Pro-NH$_2$	μBondapak C$_{18}$ (10 μm)	Acetonitrile/1-heptanesulfonic acid/0.02 mol/L acetic acid, 6.5:0.1:93.4 (2 mL/min)	3.9 × 300	UV (210)	—	[62]
Pyr-3-methyl-His-Pro-NH$_2$	μBondapak C$_{18}$ (10 μm)	Acetonitrile/1-pentanesulfonic acid/0.02 mol/L acetic acid, 2:0.1:97.9 (2 mL/min)	3.9 × 300	UV (210)	—	[62]
L-Pyr-L-His-L-3,3-dimethylprolinamide	Spherisorb-CN (5 μm)	Acetonitrile/0.01 mmol/L copper-(II) acetate, 30:70 (0.5 mL/min)	4.6 × 250	UV (210)	—	[58]
L-Pyr-D-His-L-3,3-dimethylprolinamide	Spherisorb-CN (5 μm)	Acetonitrile/0.01 mmol/L copper-(II) acetate, 30:70 (0.5 mL/min)	4.6 × 250	UV (210)	—	[58]
L-Pyr-L-His-D-3,3-dimethylprolinamide	Spherisorb-CN (5 μm)	Acetonitrile/0.01 mmol/L copper-(II) acetate, 30:70 (0.5 mL/min)	4.6 × 250	UV (210)	—	[58]
D-Pyr-L-His-L-3,3-dimethylprolinamide	Spherisorb-CN (5 μm)	Acetonitrile/0.01 mmol/L copper-(II) acetate, 30:70 (0.5 mL/min)	4.6 × 250	UV (210)	—	[58]
(D-His^2)-Thyreoliberin	μBondapak C$_{18}$ (10 μm)	Acetonitrile/0.01 mol/L NH$_4$OAc(pH 4), 0.5:99.5 (3 mL/min)	4 × 300	UV (210)	—	[50]
Luliberin	μBondapak C$_{18}$ (10 μm)	Ethanol/0.01 mol/L NH$_4$OAc (pH 4.0), 22:78 (1.5 mL/min)	4 × 300	UV (210)	11.8 min (ret. time)	[50]

Table 5-7. (Continued).

Hormone (resp. Derivative)	Stationary Phase	Eluent	Column (mm)	Detection (nm)	k-Value	Reference
Luliberin	μBondapak C$_{18}$ (10 μm)	Acetonitrile/0.01 mol/L NH$_4$OAc(pH 4.0), 22:78 (2 mL/min)	4 × 300	UV (210)	6.2 min (ret. time)	[50]
Luliberin	μBondapak C$_{18}$ (10 μm)	Acetonitrile/0.01 mol/L NH$_4$OAc(pH 4.0), 17:83 (2.5 mL/min)	4 × 600	UV (210)	–	[50]
Luliberin	Phenyl-Corasil	Acetonitrile/water, 1:4 (1.0 mL/min)	3 ftx 1/8 in.	UV (254, 220)	>20	[51]
Luliberin	Phenyl-Corasil	Acetonitrile/water 2:3 (1.0 mL/min)	3 ftx 1/8 in.	UV (254, 220)	>20	[51]
Luliberin	Phenyl-Corasil	Acetonitrile/water 7:3 (1.0 mL/min)	3 ftx 1/8 in.	UV (254, 220)	>20	[51]
Luliberin	Poragel PN (37 to 75 μm)	Acetonitrile/water 2:3 (1.0 mL/min)	3 ftx 1/8 in.	UV (254, 220)	≈10	[51]
Luliberin	Poragel PN (37 to 75 μm)	Acetonitrile/water 7:3 (1.0 mL/min)	3 ftx 1/8 in.	UV (254, 220)	>10	[51]
Luliberin	Poragel PS (37 to 75 μm)	Water (1.0 mL/min)	3 ftx 1/8 in.	UV (254, 220)	>20	[51]
Luliberin	Poragel PS (37 to 75 μm)	Acetonitrile/water, 2:3 (1.0 mL/min)	3 ftx 1/8 in.	UV (254, 220)	0.2	[51]
Luliberin	Poragel PS (37 to 75 μm)	Acetonitrile/water 7:3 (1.0 mL/min)	3 ftx 1/8 in.	UV (254, 220)	2.1	[51]

Compound	Column	Mobile phase	Column dimensions	Detection	Retention	Ref.
Luliberin	Fatty Acid Analysis, analytic column, Waters (10 μm)	8% Acetic acid/methanol, 2:3 (1.5 mL/min)	3.9 × 300	UV (254)	—	[52]
Luliberin	Fatty Acid Analysis, analytic column, Waters (10 μm)	8% Acetic acid/methanol, 1:1 (1.5 mL/min)	3.9 × 300	UV (254)	—	[52]
Luliberin	Fatty Acid Analysis, analytic column, Waters (10 μm)	8% Acetic acid/methanol 3:2 (1.5 mL/min)	3.9 × 300	UV (254)	—	[52]
Luliberin	TSK-GEL 2000 SW (10 μm)	0.05 mol/L Sodium phosphate (pH 7.2)/SDS, 99.7:0.3 (0.3 mL/min)	7.5 × 600	UV (210, 280)	14.9 (elution volume)	[59]
Luliberin	μBondapak C_{18} (10 μm)	A: 0.1% Phosphoric acid, B: 70% acetonitrile in A, linear gradient from 5 to 70% B (20 min) (1 mL/min)	3.9 × 300	UV (206)	—	[61]
(L-Ala⁶)-Luliberin	μBondapak C_{18} (10 μm)	Acetonitrile/0.01 mol/L NH_4OAc (pH 4.0), 22:78 (2 mL/min)	4 × 300	UV (210)	7.7 min (ret. time)	[50]
(L-Ala⁶)-Luliberin	μBondapak C_{18} (10 μm)	Ethanol/0.01 mol/L NH_4OAc (pH 4.0), 22:78 (4 mL/min)	4 × 300	UV (210)	6.5 min (ret. time)	[50]
(D-Ala⁶)-Luliberin	μBondapak C_{18} (10 μm)	Ethanol/0.01 mol/L NH_4OAc (pH 4.0), 22:78 (4 mL/min)	4 × 300	UV (210)	5.9 min (ret. time)	[50]
(D-Tyr⁶)-Luliberin	μBondapak C_{18} (10 μm)	Acetonitrile/0.01 mol/L NH_4OAc (pH 4.0), 22:78 (2 mL/min)	4 × 300	UV (210)	13.0 min (ret. time)	[50]

Table 5-7. (Continued).

Hormone (resp. Derivative)	Stationary Phase	Eluent	Column (mm)	Detection (nm)	k-Value	Reference
(D-His^2)-Luliberin	μBondapak C$_{18}$ (10 μm)	Acetonitrile/0.01 mol/L NH$_4$OAc (pH 4.0), 17:83 (2.5 mL/min)	4 × 600	UV (210)	–	[50]
(D-Lys^6)-Luliberin	μBondapak C$_{18}$ (10 μm)	Acetonitrile/0.01 mol/L NH$_4$OAc (pH 4.0), 22:78 (2 mL/min)	4 × 300	UV (210)	3.5 min (ret. time)	[50]
(Sar^{10})-Luliberin	μBondapak C$_{18}$ (10 μm)	Ethanol/0.01 mol/L NH$_4$OAc (pH 4.0) 22:78 (1.5 mL/min)	4 × 300	UV (210)	13.0 min (ret. time)	[50]
Des-Gly^6-Luliberin	μBondapak C$_{18}$ (10 μm)	Ethanol/0.01 mol/L NH$_4$OAc (pH 4.0), 22:78 (1.5 mL/min)	4 × 300	UV (210)	12.7 min (ret. time)	[50]
Des-Ser^4-Luliberin	μBondapak C$_{18}$ (10 μm)	Ethanol/0.01 mol/L NH$_4$OAc (pH 4.0), 22:78 (1.5 mL/min)	4 × 300	UV (210)	12.5 min (ret. time)	[50]
Melanostatin, dansyl derivative	μBondapak C$_{18}$ (10 μm)	Acetonitrile/0.01 mol/L sodium sulfate (pH 7), 45:55 (3 mL/min)	300 × 3.9	UV (254), fluorescence (360/487)	24	[54]
Melanostatin, dansyl derivative	μBondapak phenyl (10 μm)	Acetonitrile/0.01 mol/L sodium sulfate (pH 7), 45:55 (3 mL/min)	300 × 3.9	UV (254), fluorescence (360/487)	3.2	[54]
Melanostatin, dansyl derivative	μBondapak C$_{18}$ (10 μm)	Acetonitrile/0.01 mol/L sodium sulfate (pH 7), 40:60 (3 mL/min)	300 × 3.9	UV (254), fluorescence (360/487)	>30	[54]

Substance	Column	Mobile phase	Dimensions	Detection		Ref.
Melanostatin, dansyl derivative	μBondapak C$_{18}$ (10 μm)	Acetonitrile/0.01 mol/L sodium sulfate (pH 7), 43.5:56.5 (3 mL/min)	300 × 3.9	UV (254), fluorescence (360/487)	5.0	[54]
Melanostatin, dansyl derivative	μBondapak C$_{18}$ (10 μm)	Acetonitrile/0.01 mol/L sodium sulfate (pH 7), 43.5:56.5 (3 mL/min)	300 × 3.9	UV (254), fluorescence (360/487)	5.3	[54]
Melanostatin, dansyl derivative	μBondapak C$_{18}$ (10 μm)	Acetonitrile/0.01 mol/L sodium sulfate (pH 7), 41.5:58.5 (3 mL/min)	300 × 3.9	UV (254), fluorescence (360/487)	7.0	[54]
Melanostatin, dansyl derivative	μBondapak C$_{18}$ (10 μm)	Acetonitrile/0.01 mol/L sodium sulfate (pH 7), 41.5:58.5 (3 mL/min)	300 × 3.9	UV (254), fluorescence (360/487)	8.0	[54]
Melanostatin, dansyl derivative	μBondapak C$_{18}$ (10 μm)	Acetonitrile/0.01 mol/L sodium sulfate (pH 7), 50:50 (3 mL/min)	300 × 3.9	UV (254), fluorescence (360/487)	4.5	[54]
Melanostatin, dansyl derivative	μBondapak phenyl (10 μm)	Acetonitrile/0.01 mol/L sodium sulfate (pH 7), 50:50 (3 mL/min)	300 × 3.9	UV (254), fluorescence (360/487)	3.2	[54]
Melanostatin, dansyl derivative	μBondapak C$_{18}$ (10 μm)	Acetonitrile/0.01 mol/L sodium sulfate (pH 7), 20:80 (3 mL/min)	300 × 3.9	UV (254), fluorescence (360/487)	>30	[54]
Melanostatin, dansyl derivative	μBondapak C$_{18}$ (10 μm)	Acetonitrile/0.01 mol/L sodium sulfate (pH 7), 80:20 (3 mL/min)	300 × 3.9	UV (254), fluorescence (360/487)	0.4	[54]
Melanostatin, dansyl derivative	μBondapak phenyl (10 μm)	Methanol/0.01 mol/L sodium sulfate (pH 7), 50:50 (3 mL/min)	300 × 3.9	UV (254), fluorescence (360/487)	>30	[54]
Melanostatin, dansyl derivative	μBondapak C$_{18}$ (10 μm)	Isopropanol/1% acetic acid, 5:95 (3 mL/min)	300 × 3.9	UV (254), fluorescence (360/487)	0.6	[54]

Table 5-7. (Continued).

Hormone (resp. Derivative)	Stationary Phase	Eluent	Column (mm)	Detection (nm)	k-Value	Reference
Melanostatin, dansyl derivative	Radical Pak C$_{18}$ (10 μm)	Acetonitrile/0.01 mol/L sodium sulfate (pH 7) 45:55 (3 mL/min)	200 × 8	Fluorescence (350/470)	–	[63]
Melanostatin, ethansyl derivative	μBondapak C$_{18}$ (10 μm)	Acetonitrile/0.01 mol/L sodium sulfate (pH 7), 45:55 (3 mL/min)	300 × 3.9	UV (254), fluorescence (360/487)	>30	[54]
Melanostatin, ethansyl derivative	μBondapak phenyl (10 μm)	Acetonitrile/0.01 mol/L sodium sulfate (pH 7), 45:55 (3 mL/min)	300 × 3.9	UV (254), fluorescence (360/487)	7.6	[54]
Melanostatin, ethansyl derivative	μBondapak C$_{18}$ (10 μm)	Acetonitrile/0.01 mol/L sodium sulfate (pH 7), 40:60 (3 mL/min)	300 × 3.9	UV (254), fluorescence (360/487)	21	[54]
Melanostatin, ethansyl derivative	μBondapak C$_{18}$ (10 μm)	Acetonitrile/0.01 mol/L sodium sulfate (pH 7), 43.5:56.5 (3 mL/min)	300 × 3.9	UV (254), fluorescence (360/487)	12	[54]
Melanostatin, ethansyl derivative	μBondapak phenyl (10 μm)	Acetonitrile/0.01 mol/L sodium sulfate (pH 7), 43.5:56.5 (3 mL/min)	300 × 3.9	UV (254), fluorescence (360/487)	11	[54]
Melanostatin, ethansyl derivative	μBondapak C$_{18}$ (10 μm)	Acetonitrile/0.01 mol/L sodium sulfate (pH 7), 41.5:58.5 (3 mL/min)	300 × 3.9	UV (254), fluorescence (360/487)	16	[54]
Melanostatin, ethansyl derivative	μBondapak phenyl (10 μm)	Acetonitrile/0.01 mol/L sodium sulfate (pH 7), 41.5:58.5 (3 mL/min)	300 × 3.9	UV (254), fluorescence (360/487)	13	[54]
Melanostatin, ethansyl derivative	μBondapak C$_{18}$ (10 μm)	Acetonitrile/0.01 mol/L sodium sulfate (pH 7), 50:50 (3 mL/min)	300 × 3.9	UV (254), fluorescence (360/487)	6.6	[54]

Melanostatin, ethansyl derivative	μBondapak phenyl (10 μm)	Acetonitrile/0.01 mol/L sodium sulfate (pH 7), 50:50 3 mL/min	300 × 3.9	UV (254), fluorescence (360/487)	6.8	[54]
Melanostatin, ethansyl derivative	μBondapak phenyl (10 μm)	Methanol/sodium sulfate (pH 7), 50:50 (3 mL/min)	300 × 3.9	UV (254), fluorescence (360/487)	>30	[54]
Melanostatin, propansyl derivative	μBondapak C$_{18}$ (10 μm)	Acetonitrile/0.01 mol/L sodium sulfate (pH 7), 45:55 (3 mL/min)	300 × 3.9	UV (254), fluorescence (360/487)	>30	[54]
Melanostatin, propansyl derivative	μBondapak phenyl (10 μm)	Acetonitrile/0.01 mol/L sodium sulfate (pH 7), 45:55 (3 mL/min)	300 × 3.9	UV (254), fluorescence (360/487)	>30	[54]
Melanostatin, propansyl derivative	μBondapak C$_{18}$ (10 μm)	Acetonitrile/0.01 mol/L sodium sulfate (pH 7), 40:60 (3 mL/min)	300 × 3.9	UV (254), fluorescence (360/487)	>30	[54]
Melanostatin, propansyl derivative	μBondapak C$_{18}$ (10 μm)	Acetonitrile/0.01 mol/L sodium sulfate (pH 7), 43.5:56.5 (3 mL/min)	300 × 3.9	UV (254), fluorescence (360/487)	>30	[54]
Melanostatin, propansyl derivative	μBondapak phenyl (10 μm)	Acetonitrile/0.01 mol/L sodium sulfate (pH 7), 43.5:56.5 (3 mL/min)	300 × 3.9	UV (254), fluorescence (360/487)	>30	[54]
Melanostatin, propansyl derivative	μBondapak C$_{18}$ (10 μm)	Acetonitrile/0.01 mol/L sodium sulfate (pH 7), 41.5:58.5 (3 mL/min)	300 ×3.9	UV (254), fluorescence (360/487)	>30	[54]
Melanostatin, propansyl derivative	μBondapak phenyl (10 μm)	Acetonitrile/0.01 mol/L sodium sulfate (pH 7), 41.5:58.5 (3 mL/min)	300 × 3.9	UV (254), fluorescence (360/487)	>30	[54]
Melanostatin, propansyl derivative	μBondapak C$_{18}$ (10 μm)	Acetonitrile/0.01 mol/L sodium sulfate (pH 7), 50:50 (3 mL/min)	300 × 3.9	UV (254), fluorescence (360/487)	14	[54]

Table 5-7. (Continued).

Hormone (resp. Derivative)	Stationary Phase	Eluent	Column (mm)	Detection (nm)	k-Value	Reference
Melanostatin, propansyl derivative	μBondapak phenyl (10 μm)	Acetonitrile/0.01 mol/L sodium sulfate (pH 7), 50:50 (3 mL/min)	300 × 3.9	UV (254), fluorescence (360/487)	7.8	[54]
Melanostatin, propansyl derivative	μBondapak phenyl (10 μm)	Methanol/0.01 mol/L sodium sulfate (pH 7), 50:50 (3 mL/min)	300 × 3.9	UV (254), fluorescence (360/487)	>30	[54]
Melanostatin, butansyl derivative	μBondapak C$_{18}$ (10 μm)	Acetonitrile/0.01 mol/L sodium sulfate (pH 7), 45:55 (3 mL/min)	300 × 3.9	UV (254), fluorescence (360/487)	>30	[54]
Melanostatin, butansyl derivative	μBondapak phenyl (10 μm)	Acetonitrile/0.01 mol/L sodium sulfate (pH 7), 45:55 (3 mL/min)	300 × 3.9	UV (254), fluorescence (360/487)	>30	[54]
Melanostatin, butansyl derivative	μBondapak C$_{18}$ (10 μm)	Acetonitrile/0.01 mol/L sodium sulfate (pH 7), 40:60 (3 mL/min)	300 × 3.9	UV (254), fluorescence (360/487)	>30	[54]
Melanostatin, butansyl derivative	μBondapak C$_{18}$ (10 μm)	Acetonitrile/0.01 mol/L sodium sulfate (pH 7), 43.5:56.5 (3 mL/min)	300 × 3.9	UV (254), fluorescence (360/487)	>30	[54]
Melanostatin, butansyl derivative	μBondapak phenyl (10 μm)	Acetonitrile/0.01 mol/L sodium sulfate (pH 7), 43.5:56.5 (3 mL/min)	300 × 3.9	UV (254), fluorescence (360/487)	>30	[54]
Melanostatin, butansyl derivative	μBondapak C$_{18}$ (10 μm)	Acetonitrile/0.01 mol/L sodium sulfate (pH 7), 41.5:58.5 (3 mL/min)	300 × 3.9	UV (254), fluorescence (360/487)	>30	[54]
Melanostatin, butansyl derivative	μBondapak phenyl (10 μm)	Acetonitrile/0.01 mol/L sodium sulfate (pH 7), 41.5:58.5 (3 mL/min)	300 × 3.9	UV (254), fluorescence (360/487)	>30	[54]

Compound	Column	Mobile phase	Dimensions	Detection		Ref.
Melanostatin, butansyl derivative	μBondapak C$_{18}$ (10 μm)	Acetonitrile/0.01 mol/L sodium sulfate (pH 7), 50:50 (3 mL/min)	300 × 3.9	UV (254), fluorescence (360/487)	29	[54]
Melanostatin, butansyl derivative	μBondapak phenyl (10 μm)	Acetonitrile/0.01 mol/L sodium sulfate (pH 7), 50:50 (3 mL/min)	300 × 3.9	UV (254), fluorescence (360/487)	12	[54]
Melanostatin, butansyl derivative	μBondapak phenyl (10 μm)	Methanol 0.01 mol/L sodium sulfate (pH 7), 50:50 (3 mL/min)	300 × 3.9	UV (254), fluorescence (360/487)	30	[54]
Melanostatin, monoisopropansyl derivative	μBondapak C$_{18}$ (10 μm)	Acetonitrile/0.01 mol/L sodium sulfate (pH 7), 45:55 (3 mL/min)	300 × 3.9	UV (254), fluorescence (360/487)	6.2	[54]
Melanostatin, monoisopropansyl derivative	μBondapak phenyl (10 μm)	Acetonitrile/0.01 mol/L sodium sulfate (pH 7), 45:55 (3 mL/min)	300 × 3.9	UV (254), fluorescence (360/487)	3.2	[54]
Melanostatin, monoisopropansyl derivative	μBondapak C$_{18}$ (10 μm)	Acetonitrile/0.01 mol/L sodium sulfate (pH 7), 40:60 (3 mL/min)	300 × 3.9	UV (254), fluorescence (360/487)	11	[54]
Melanostatin, monoisopropansyl derivative	μBondapak C$_{18}$ (10 μm)	Acetonitrile/0.01 mol/L sodium sulfate (pH 7), 43.5:56.5 (3 mL/min)	300 × 3.9	UV (254), fluorescence (360/487)	7.0	[54]
Melanostatin, monoisopropansyl derivative	μBondapak phenyl (10 μm)	Acetonitrile/0.01 mol/L sodium sulfate (pH 7), 43.5:56.5 (3 mL/min)	300 × 3.9	UV (254), fluorescence (360/487)	5.3	[54]
Melanostatin, monoisopropansyl derivative	μBondapak C$_{18}$ (10 μm)	Acetonitrile/0.01 mol/L sodium sulfate (pH 7), 41.5:58.5 (3 mL/min)	300 × 3.9	UV (254), fluorescence (360/487)	8.2	[54]
Melanostatin, monoisopropansyl derivative	μBondapak phenyl (10 μm)	Acetonitrile/0.01 mol/L sodium sulfate (pH 7), 41.5:58.5 (3 mL/min)	300 × 3.9	UV (254), fluorescence (360/487)	8.0	[54]

Table 5-7. (Continued).

Hormone (resp. Derivative)	Stationary Phase	Eluent	Column (mm)	Detection (nm)	k-Value	Reference
Melanostatin, monoisopropansyl derivative	µBondapak C_{18} (10 µm)	Acetonitrile/0.01 mol/L sodium sulfate (pH 7), 50:50 (3 mL/min)	300 × 3.9	UV (254), fluorescence (360/487)	4.0	[54]
Melanostatin, monoisopropansyl derivative	µBondapak phenyl (10 µm)	Acetonitrile/0.01 mol/L sodium sulfate (pH 7), 50:50 (3 mL/min)	300 × 3.9	UV (254), fluorescence (360/487)	3.2	[54]
Melanostatin, monoisopropansyl derivative	µBondapak phenyl (10 µm)	Methanol/0.01 mol/L sodium sulfate (pH 7), 50:50 (3 mL/min)	300 × 3.9	UV (254), fluorescence (360/487)	>30	[54]
L-Pro-N-methyl-D-Leu-Gly-NH₂ (pareptide)	Radial Pak C_{18} (10 µm)	Acetonitrile/0.01 mol/L sodium sulfate (pH 7), 45:55 (3 mL/min)	200 × 8	Fluorescene (350/470)	–	[63]
Somatostatin	µBondapak C_{18} (10 µm)	Ethanol/0.01 mol/L NH₄OAc (pH 4.0), 35:65 (1.5 mL/min)	4 × 300	UV (210)	12.5 min (ret. time)	[50]
Somatostatin	Fatty Acid Analysis, analytic column, Waters (10 µm)	8% Acetic acid/methanol 1:1 (1.5 mL/min)	3.9 × 300	UV (254)	–	[52]
Somatostatin	µBondapak C_{18} (10 µm)	Acetonitrile/0.01 mol/L ammonium acetate (pH 4.0), 32.5/67.5 (1.4 mL/min)	–	UV (210)	–	[53]
Somatostatin	µBondapak C_{18}	A: Triethylamine-phosphoric acid (pH 3.2), B: triethyl-amine-phosphoric acid (pH 3.2) (pH 3.2)/acetoni-	4 × 300	UV (210)	51.72 $(t_r - t_o)$	[55[

...trile, 40:60, gradient from 2% to 70% B in 78 min (1.5 mL/min)

Compound	Packing	Mobile phase	Column	Detection	Result	Ref.
Somatostatin	TSK-GEL 2000 SW (10 µm)	0.05 mol/L Sodium phosphate (pH 7.2)/ SDS, 99.7:0.3 (0.3 mL/min)	7.5 × 600	UV (210, 280)	15.4 (elution volume)	[59]
Somatostatin	µBondapak C$_{18}$ (10 µm)	A: 0.1% Phosphoric acid, B: 70% acetonitrile in A, linear gradient from 5 – 70% B (20 min), (1 mL/min)	3.9 × 300	UV (206)	–	[61]
(Asp^5)-Somatostatin	µBondapak C$_{18}$ (10 µm)	Ethanol/0.01 mol/L NH$_4$OAc (pH 4.0), 35:65 (1.5 mL/min)	4 × 300	UV (210)	24.2 min (ret. time)	[50]
(D-Cys^{14})-Somatostatin	µBondapak C$_{18}$ (10 µm)	Ethanol/0.01 mol/L NH$_4$OAc (pH 4.0), 35:65 (1.5 mL/min)	4 × 300	UV (210)	15.1 min (ret. time)	[50]
(D-Phe^{11})-Somatostatin	µBondapak C$_{18}$ (10 µm)	Ethanol/0.01 mol/L NH$_4$OAc (pH 4.0), 35:65 (1.5 mL/min)	4 × 300	UV (210)	12.7 min (ret. time)	[50]
(D-Ser^{13})-Somatostatin	µBondapak C$_{18}$ (10 µm)	Ethanol/0.01 mol/L NH$_4$OAc (pH 4.0), 35:65 (1.5 mL/min)	4 × 300	UV (210)	15.2 min (ret. time)	[50]
(D-Thr^{12})-Somatostatin	µBondapak C$_{18}$ (10 µm)	Ethanol/0.01 mol/L NH$_4$OAc (pH 4.0), 35:65 (1.5 mL/min)	4 × 300	UV (210)	15.6 min (ret. time)	[50]
(D-Phe^6)-Somatostatin	µBondapak C$_{18}$ (10 µm)	Ethanol/0.01 mol/L NH$_4$OAc (pH 4.0), 35:65 (1.5 mL/min)	4 × 300	UV (210)	19.4 min (ret. time)	[50]

5.3.1.1 Thyroliberin (TRH)

For the smallest peptide hormone TRH, RP-HPLC is the most efficient analytical separation technique we know of [15, 50, 52, 55, 56, 58, 60 to 62, 64 to 66]. This is demonstrated by the fact that even 0.7% of the (D-His^2) isomer of thyreoliberin can be determined in the presence of TRH (Figure 5-2) [50].

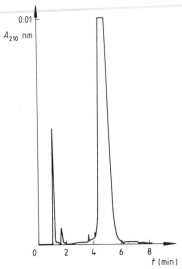

Figure 5-2. Chromatogram of the separation of (D-His^2)-TRH and TRH by HPLC. Column: μBondapak C$_{18}$, 300 × 4 mm i. d., eluent: 0.5% CH$_3$CN/0.01 mol/L NH$_4$OAc (pH4); flow-rate: 3 mL/min; detection: 210 nm; quantity: 50 μg TRH + 0.36 μg (0.7%) (D-His^2)-TRH (similar to reference [50]).

Though TRH lacks a well-absorbing chromophore, detection at 215 nm is sufficient to follow the degradation in aqueous solution (Figure 5-3) [52].

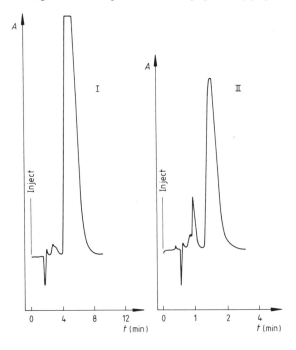

Figure 5-3. Chromatograms of aqueous TRH solutions, (I) freshly prepared and (II) stored (27 days, 4 °C). Column: Fatty Acid Analysis (10 μm), 300 × 3.9 mm i. d.; eluent: 60% methanol in 0.1% acetic acid; flow-rate: 1.5 mL/min; detection: 215 nm (similar to reference [52]).

An even better resolution is achieved if a ligand-exchange technique, based upon complexation with Cu^{2+}, is applied, as is demonstrated for the separation of four isomers of the TRH derivative pyroglutamyl-histidyl-3,3-dimethylprolinamide (Figures 5-4 and 5-5) [58].

Figure 5-4. Structure of pyroglutamyl-histidyl-3,3-dimethylprolinamide.

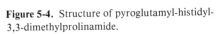

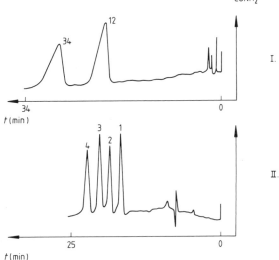

Figure 5-5. Chromatogram of L-pyroglutamyl-L-histidyl-L-3,3-dimethylprolinamide and its isomers. Column: Spherisorb-CN (5 μm), 250 × 4.6 mm i.d.; detection: UV absorption at 210 nm; peaks: 1 L-L-D, 2 L-D-L, 3 L-L-L, 4 D-L-L isomer. I: Eluent: acetonitrile/0.01 mmol/L sodium acetate (30:70); flow-rate: 2 mL/min; II: Eluent: acetonitrile/0.01 mmol/L copper-(II) acetate (30:70); flow-rate: 0.5 mL/min (similar to reference [58].

In principle, all analytical HPLC separations are transferable to preparative [67] or semipreparative [68] scale. A comparison of selected parameters between an analytical and a preparative HPLC column is given in Table 5-8.

Table 5-8. Comparison Between Analytical and Preparative HPLC Column Parameters.

	Analytical column	Preparative column
Column length (cm)	20 to 25	~ 50
Column diameter (internal) (mm)	3.5 to 4.5	8 to 20
Packing weight (g)	2 to 3	20 to 150
Flow-rate (mL/min)	1 to 2	5 to 20

A schematic diagram of an HPLC system applied for the preparative separation of synthetic TRH and its analogues using strongly acidic ion-exchange resins and volatile elution media is shown in Figure 5-6 [69]. Pyridine acetic acid buffers (1.5 mL/min) are pumped on a Biotronic glass-jacketed high-performance glass column (550 × 9 mm), filled with DC-1A cation-exchange resin.

A small amount (5%) of the effluent is used for hydrolysis with 5 mol/L NaOH solution in a 20 m × 0.7 mm PTFE reaction coil at 100 °C and detection with ninhydrin reagent. 95% of the

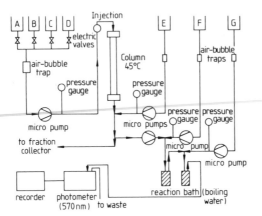

Figure 5-6. Schematic diagram of a peptide analyzer, equipped with an ion-exchange column. A, B, C, D: buffer reservoirs; E: water reservoir; F: 5 mol/L NaOH reservoir; G: ninhydrin reagent-acetic acid reservoir [69].

effluent is brought to the fraction collector. The HPLC system was succesfully applied for the purification of synthetic analogues of the thyrotropin-releasing hormone from multicomponent mixtures. The chromatogram in Figure 5-7 demonstrates the large number of compounds that are formed when Glu^2-tripeptides are reacted with boiling trifluoroacetic acid (TFA). It was not surprising that Boc-Phe-Glu(OBzl)-Pro-NH$_2$ with boiling TFA yields a reaction mixture from

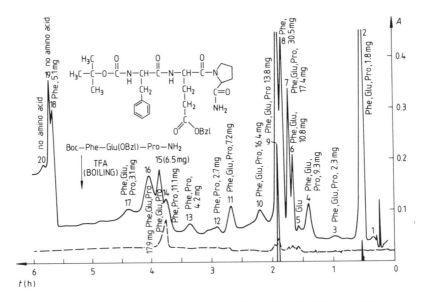

Figure 5-7. Chromatogram of a reaction mixture of Boc-Phe-Glu (OBzl)-Pro-NH$_2$ treated with boiling TFA for 2.5 h. Column: DC-1 A (Durrum, Palo Alto, Calif., USA), cation-exchange resin, 18 ± 3 µm, 550 × 9 mm i. d.; eluent: (see text and legend to Figure 5-6) pyridine/acetic acid buffer, A: 0.2 mol/L pyridine, pH 3.4 (60 min), B: 0.5 mol/L pyridine, pH 4.25 (120 min), C: 1.0 mol/L pyridine, pH 5.0 (120 min), D: 4.0 mol/L pyridine, pH 5.6 (180 min); temperature: 45 °C; pressure: 80 to 95 bar; flow-rate: 1.5 mL/min; ratio of effluent splitting: 1 : 22 = 4.4% loss of sample for detection; solid line: detection after partial hydrolysis, amount injected: 166 mg, separated collected material: 155 mg; broken line: detection without partial hydrolysis, amount injected, 109 mg [69].

which not a single purified product could be gained by crystallization. The peptide analyzer allows separation and purification of 20 different products which are pure enough for further structure elucidation work.

In Figure 5-8, preparative chromatograms of TRH and (D-His^2)-TRH are compared with each other. The chromatogram of (D-His^2)-TRH shows that the TRH sample is contaminated with about 8% of the natural hormone. According to several reports in the literature [46], (D-His^2)-TRH should have considerable biological activity. However, the chromatographically pure (D-His^2)-TRH is completely inactive which demonstrates that the preparative peptide analyzer (Figure 5-6) is also suitable for separation of peptide diastereomers on a preparative scale [69].

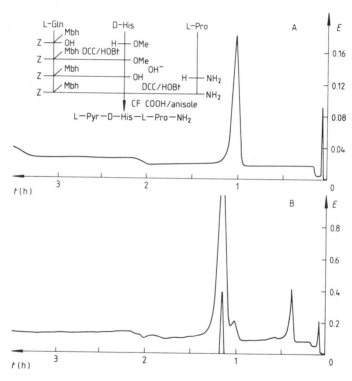

Figure 5-8. Preparative chromatograms of TRH and D-His^2-TRH. Column: DC-1 A (Durrum, Palo Alto, Calif., USA), cation-exchange resin, 18 ± 3 μm, 550 × 9 mm i. d.; eluent: (see text and legend for Figure 5-6). A, 0.1 mol/L pyridine acetate, pH 3.2 (15 min), B, 0.2 mol/L pyridine acetate, pH 3.5 (45 min), C, 0.3 mol/L pyridine acetate, pH 4.0 (60 min.), D, 0.6 mol/L pyridine acetate, pH 4.2 (60 min), E, 1.0 mol/L pyridine acetate, ph 4.6 (80 min); temperature: 43 °C; pressure: 70 to 90 bar; flow-rate: 1.5 mL/min; detection with ninhydrin (570 nm) after partial hydrolysis (5% with 5 mol/L NaOH); quantities: A: 8.7 mg, B: 250 mg [69].

5.3.1.2 Luliberin

As with TRH, numerous studies about HPLC separations on luliberin appeared recently in the
literature [4, 15, 50 to 52, 56, 59 to 61, 64, 66, 70, 71]. Because the luliberin molecule has two
aromatic side chains, detection at 245 nm is possible and allows quantitative determination of
nanomolar amounts [52]. The HPLC method is sensitive enough to demonstrate that most
commercially available peptides, and also luliberin, lack purity. Even small amounts of
impurities can be determined by HPLC as is demonstrated by the separation of 0.5 µg luliberin
from 94 µg (D-His^2)-luliberin (Figure 5-9) [50].

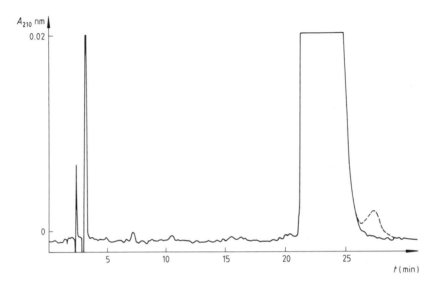

Figure 5-9. Chromatogram of the separation of (D-His^2)-luliberin and luliberin by HPLC. Column:
µBondapak C$_{18}$ (10 µm), 600 × 4 mm i. d.; eluent: 17% acetonitrile/0.01 mol/L ammonium acetate
(pH 4); flow-rate; 2.5 mL/min; detection: 210 nm; quantity: ————— 94 µg (D-His^2)-luliberin, ---- 94 µg
(D-His^2)-luliberin + 1 µg luliberin (similar to reference [50]).

5.3.1.3 Somatostatin

Due to its relatively small molecular weight, the tetradecapeptide somatostatin is also best suited
for purification by reversed-phase methods, as is shown by numerous reports [4, 7, 14, 15, 43,
50, 52, 53, 55, 56, 59, 60, 61, 64, 72 to 74]. The high efficiency of reversed-phase separation
becomes obvious from a HPLC chromatogram of a synthetic mixture of ten hypothalamic
peptides including somatostatin. Within 78 min these ten synthetic oligopeptides with a chain
length from 3 to 31 amino acids are separated and a sensitivity down to 5 µg is achieved (Figure 5-
10) [55].

    A combination of chromatographic separations and field desorption mass spectrometry was
developed recently which allows determination of picomole amounts of endogenous
oligopeptides like somatostatin in biologic tissue [60]. In connection with these studies a new

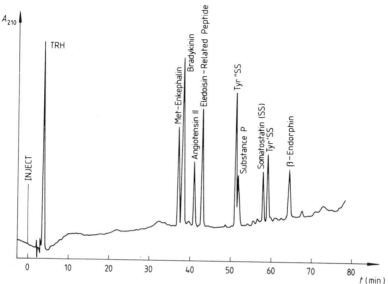

Figure 5-10. Chromatogram of a mixture of synthetic hypothalamic oligopeptides. Column: μBondapak C$_{18}$, 300 × 4 mm i. d.; eluent: linear flow program from 2 to 70% B in 78 min (A: triethylamine-phosphoric acid, pH 3.2, B: triethylamine-phosphoric acid/acetonitrile (4:6)); flow-rate: 1.5 mL/min; quantity: 2 μg/peptide; detection: 210 nm (similar to reference [55]).

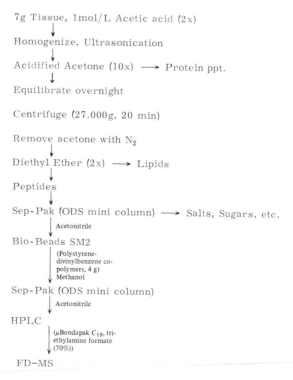

Figure 5-11. Flow chart illustrating sample preparation steps for the "picomole" procedure [60].

buffer system using dilute triethylamine − formic acid was used and somatostatin can be determined in femtomole concentrations under these conditions [60]. A flow chart illustrates this "picomole" procedure in Figure 5-11.

The method of HPLC is also more and more commonly used in the laboratories of peptide synthesis for purity control of intermediates and end products and also kinetic studies as is demonstrated in this article for a synthesis of somatostatin [75, 76]. The cystine − containing tetradecapeptide is obtained by 7 + 7 fragment condensation (Figure 5-12). The N-terminal protected heptapeptide azide is coupled to the Adpoc(1-(1-adamantyl)-1-methylethoxy-carbonyl)-deprotected C-terminal heptapeptide fragment [75, 76].

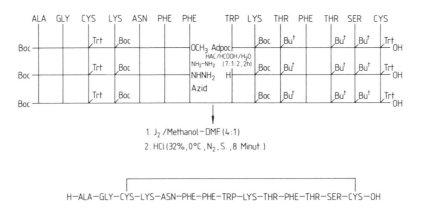

Figure 5-12. Synthesis of somatostatin by 7 + 7 fragment condensation [75, 76].

Oxidation of this protected tetradecapeptide with iodine in methanol/DMF (4:1), followed by a short treatment with hydrochloric acid (0 °C, 10 min, N_2 saturated solution), gave crude somatostatin. Purification of this product on Sephadex G-25 (eluent 2 mol/L HAc) yields 3 fractions which are examined by HPLC (Figure 5-13). The main peak of fraction II correlates with that of a reference sample. Further purification of this fraction by semipreparative HPLC yields a very pure material. The homogeneity of this final product is confirmed by HPLC (Figure 5-14), TLC in 7 different systems, electrophoresis and amino acid analysis.

This successful synthetic route to somatostatin could be achieved only by the development of a new amino protecting group, the Adpoc group, which can be cleaved under extremely mild acidolytic conditions because the reagents applied for the removal of the commonly used Boc (tert.-butyloxycarbonyl) group from Boc-Trp peptides cause alkylations in the indole part of tryptophan and yield biologically inactive peptide derivatives [68].

HPLC was the main technique working out the advantages of the Adpoc group, compared to known amino protecting groups:

● Adpoc residues can be incorporated into amino groups at high yields.
● Adpoc amino acids are crystalline compounds and stable for months at room temperature.
● Adpoc amino acids are stable in the presence of $h \cdot v$.
● Adpoc residues are cleavable under very mild conditions.
● Adpoc residues can be removed 1 000 times faster than Boc groups and permit selective cleavage.
● Adpoc residues prevent attack of the indole ring in tryptophan.

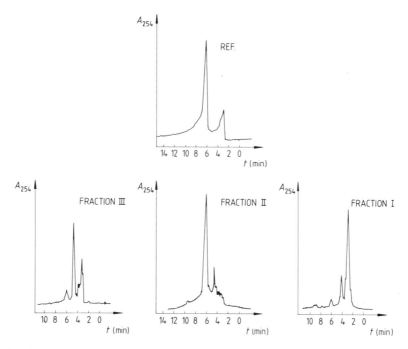

Figure 5-13. HPLC chromatograms of crude synthetic somatostatin received after purification on a Sephadex G-25 column (800 × 6 mm i. d.; solvent: 2 mol/L acetic acid). Column: RP-8 (10 µm), 250 × 4.6 mm i. d.; eluent: isopropanol/0.01 mol/L ammonium acetate (pH 4.4, 35:65); flow-rate: 1.5 mL/min; pressure: 210 bar; temperature: 25 °C; UV detection: 254 nm [75, 76].

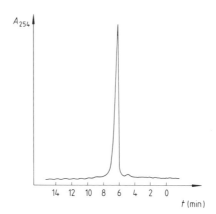

Figure 5-14. Chromatogram of pure somatostatin. Conditions see Figure 5-13 [75, 76].

Based on investigations by HPLC and mass spectrometry for the acidolytic cleavage of the Adpoc group the mechanism shown in Figure 5-15 can be assumed.

The Boc group in N^3-position of Lys has more than double the stability than in N^α-position. In the deprotection reagent, acetic acid/formic acid (83%)/water (7:1:2), it is possible to get selective cleavage of the Adpoc group in presence of N^ε-Boc groups (Figure 5-18).

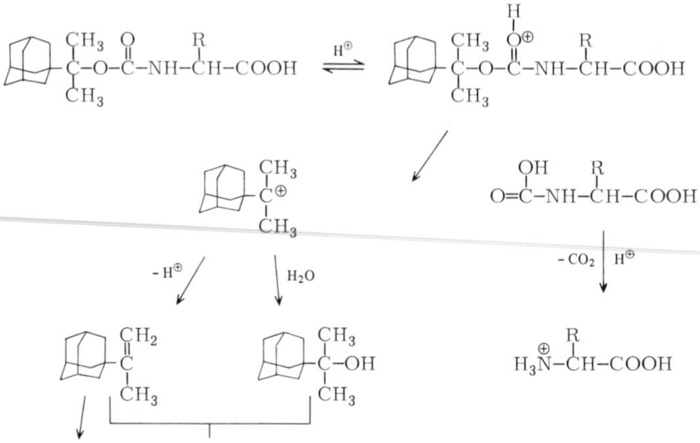

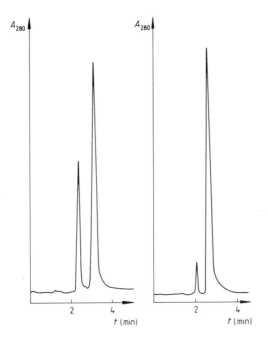

Figure 5-15. Mechanism for the acidolytic cleavage of the Adpoc group [75, 76].

Figure 5-16. HPLC chromatogram of the acidolytic cleavage of Adpoc-Trp-OH; left: 20 sec, right: 40 sec after treatment with 3% trifluoroacetic acid/methylene chloride at 25 °C; Column: RP-8 (10 µm), 250 × 4 mm i. d.; eluent: methanol (90%)/water (adjusted to pH 5.2 with sulfuric acid); flow-rate: 2.5 mL/min; pressure at column inlet: 120 atm; UV detection: 280 nm [75, 76].

In Table 5-9 data are given for the half-life times, times for a 99.9% deprotection and the velocity constants k_1' in various acidolytic solvents as determined by HPLC.

The following relations for the reaction rate constants are found for the acidolytic solvent acetic acid/formic acid (83%)/water (7:1:2):

N^α-Boc:Adpoc:Bpoc = 1:600 to 1000:1800 to 2700
N^ε-Boc:Adpoc:Bpoc = 1:1500:4900 to 6800.

Table 5-9. Rates of Deprotection of Adpoc-Trp-OH Using Various Acids (Determined by HPLC, Experimental Conditions see Figure 5-16 [75, 76]).

No	Acidolytic Solvent	Deprotection		k_1' (min^{-1})	k_{rel}' (Boc = 1)
		50% (min)	99.9% (min)		
1	3% TFA/CH$_2$Cl$_2$, 25 °C	0.18	1.78	3.87	
2	3% TFA/CH$_2$Cl$_2$, 0 °C	1.1	11.7	0.63	
3a	Acetic acid/83% (w/w) formic acid/water, 7:1:2 (v/v), 40 °C	10.8	107	$6.4 \cdot 20^{-2}$	
3b	but 25 °C	35.5	354	$1.95 \cdot 10^{-2}$	590
4	Acetic acid 80% (v/v) 40 °C	34	338	$2.00 \cdot 10^{-2}$	

For Comparison Cleavage
in Solvent 3b

Bpoc-Pro-OH, 25 °C		10.5		$6.5 \cdot 10^{-2}$	0.30
N$^\varepsilon$-Boc-Lys-OH, 25 °C		36 d		$1.3 \cdot 10^{-5}$	1470
Boc-Gly-OEt, 25 °C		14 d		$1.3 \cdot 10^{-5}$	

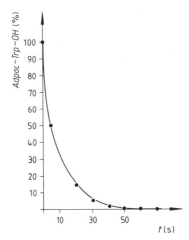

Figure 5-17. Cleavage of the Adpoc group from Adpoc-Trp-OH in the presence of 3% trifluoroacetic acid/methylene chloride at 25 °C; decrease of Adpoc-Trp-OH in (%); experimental conditions see Figure 5-16 [75, 76].

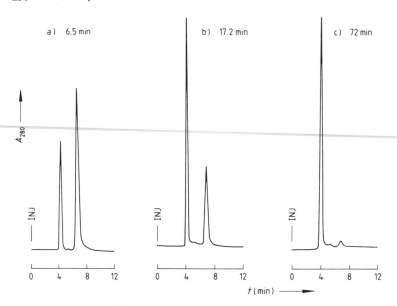

Figure 5-18. HPLC chromatogram of the cleavage of Adpoc-Trp-Lys-(Boc)-OH after treatment with acetic acid/formic acid (83%)/water (7:1:2) at 40 °C. The yield of liberated H-Trp-Lys(Boc)-OH is for a) 36.48%, b) 65.99%, c) 98.63%. No deprotection of the N^{ε}-Boc group is observed. For chromatographic conditions see Figure 5-16 [75, 76].

5.3.1.4 Melanostatin

The melanotropin-inhibiting factor (MIF, melanostatin) has gained increasing interest for the treatment of Parkinsonism [77, 78]. To measure the MIF breakdown in the body a highly efficient separation and sensitive detection method had to be developed. As the constituent amino acids of MIF lack strong absorption and the amino-terminal Pro does not react with fluorescamine or o-phthalaldehyde, fluorescent N,N-dialkylaminonaphthylenesulfonyl derivatives were chosen for MIF determination [54]. The structures of the investigated N-alkyl-aminonaphthylenesulfonyl MIF derivatives are shown in Figure 5-19.

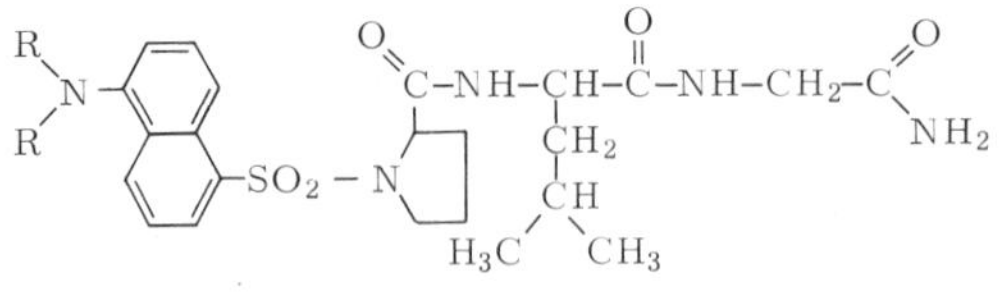

Figure 5-19. Structures of N-alkylamino-naphthylenesulfonyl derivatives of MIF; DNS: R and R': CH_3, ethansyl: R and R': $-CH_2-CH_3$, propansyl: R and R': $-Ch_2-CH_2-CH_3$, Bns: R and R': n-butyl, monoisopropansyl: R: isopropyl, R: H.

The alkylaminonaphthylenesulfonyl derivatives of MIF show strong fluorescence and allow detection at levels of 10^{-11} to 10^{-9} mol (Table 5-10) [54]. The conditions for the HPLC separations are collected in Table 5-7, Section 5.3.1.

The identical method is also suitable for the determination of pareptide (L-prolyl-N-methyl-D-leucyl-glycinamide) an analogue of MIF, which mimics the physiological function of MIF [63].

Table 5-10. Minimum Detectable Amounts of Alkylaminonaphthylenesulfonyl Derivatives of MIF $(10^{-12}$ mol) [54].

Alkylaminonaphthylenesulfonyl Derivatives of MIF	Minimum Detectable Amounts $(10^{-12}$ mol)
DNS	219
Ethansyl	1014
Propansyl	1217
Bns	3388
Monoisopropansyl	320

5.3.2 Neurohypophysial Peptide Hormones

Seven neurohypophysial peptide hormones are known to be produced in the *nucleus supraopticus* and *nucleus paraventricularis* of the hypothalamus (Table 5-11), no other group of peptide hormones has been subject to so many fundamental HPLC investigations as that of the neurohypophysial peptide hormones [2, 3, 11, 14, 15, 17, 43, 56, 59, 62, 72, 79, 80 to 86].

Table 5-11. Structures of Naturally Occurring Neurohypophysial Peptide Hormones.

Structure	Name
H-Cys-Tyr-Ile-Gln-Asn-Cys-Pro-Arg-Gly-NH$_2$ 1 2 3 4 5 6 7 8 9	Arginine vasotocin
H-Cys-Tyr-Ile-Ser-Asn-Cys-Pro-Gln-Gly-NH$_2$ 1 2 3 4 5 6 7 8 9	Glumitocin
H-Cys-Tyr-Phe-Gln-Asn-Cys-Pro-Lys-Gly-NH$_2$ 1 2 3 4 5 6 7 8 9	Lysine vasopressin
H-Cys-Tyr-Phe-Gln-Asn-Cys-Pro-Arg-Gly-NH$_2$ 1 2 3 4 5 6 7 8 9	Arginine vasopressin
H-Cys-Tyr-Ile-Gln-Asn-Cys-Pro-Ile-Gly-NH$_2$ 1 2 3 4 5 6 7 8 9	Mesotocin
H-Cys-Tyr-Ile-Ser-Asn-Cys-Pro-Ile-Gly-NH$_2$ 1 2 3 4 5 6 7 8 9	Isotocin (Ichthyotocin)
H-Cys-Tyr-Ile-Gln-Asn-Cys-Pro-Leu-Gly-NH$_2$ 1 2 3 4 5 6 7 8 9	Oxytocin

Conditions for HPLC separations and structures for hormone derivatives are seen from Table 5-12 a and b.

Table 5-12a. Experimental Conditions for HPLC Separations of Neurohypophyseal Peptide Hormones and Derivatives

Peptide	Stationary Phase	Eluent	Column (mm)	Detection (nm)	k-Value	Reference
Oxytocin	SI 60 (5 µm)	Tetrahydrofuran/0.05 mol/L acetic acid (2:1) (0.7 mL/min)	3 × 250	Fluorescence (fluorescamine)	0.4	[2]
Oxytocin	RP 8 (10 µm)	Phosphate buffer (pH 7)/ acetonitrile 4:1	3 × 250	UV (215)	3.9	[3]
Oxytocin	RP 8 (10 µm)	Phosphate buffer (pH 7)/ acetonitrile, 33:7	3 × 250	UV (215)	9.0	[3]
Oxytocin	Nucleosil C_8 (5 µm)	Phosphate buffer (pH 7)/ acetonitrile, 4:1	3 × 150	UV (215)	7.0	[3]
Oxytocin	Nucleosil C_8 (5 µm)	Phosphate buffer (pH 7)/ acetonitrile, 3:1	3 × 150	UV (215)	2.2	[3]
Oxytocin	Nucleosil C_{18} (5 µm)	Phosphate buffer (pH 7)/ acetonitrile, 4:1,	3 × 150	UV (215)	7.3	[3]
Oxytocin	ODS (Bio-Rad)	A: 5 mmol/L phosphate buffer + 0.1 mol/L $NaClO_4$ (pH 7.4), B: 0.1 mol/L $NaClO_4$/ace-tonitrile, 40:60, gradient, to B in 80 min (0.75% acetoni-trile/min)		UV (200, 220), fluorescence (fluorescamine)	36.4 (ret. time)	[15]
Oxytocin	ODS (Bio-Rad)	A: 0.1% phosphoric acid + 0.1 mol/L $NaClO_4$ (pH 2.1), B: 0.1% phosphoric acid + 0.1 mol/L $NaClO_4$/ace-tonitrile, 40:60, gradient, A to B in 80 min (0.75% ace-tonitrile/min)		UV (200, 220), fluorescence (fluorescamine)	37.9 (ret. time)	[15]

Compound	Stationary phase	Mobile phase	Dimensions	Detection	Remarks	Ref.
Oxytocin	LiChrosorb RP 8	A: 0.1% phosphoric acid + 0.1 mol/L NaClO$_4$ (pH 2.1), B: 0.1% phosphoric acid + 0.1 mol/L NaClO$_4$/acetonitrile, 40:60, gradient, A to B in 80 min (0.75% acetonitrile/min)		UV (200, 220), fluorescence (fluorescamine)	—	[15]
Oxytocin	TSK-GEL 2000 SW (10 μm)	0.005 mol/L Sodium phosphate (pH 7.2)/SDS, 99.7:0.3 (0.3 mL/min)	7.5 × 600	UV (210, 280)	15.0 mL (elution volume)	[59]
Oxytocin	μBondapak C$_{18}$ (10 μm)	Acetonitrile/0.02 mol/L acetic acid + 0.1% 1-hexane-sulfonic acid, 20:80 (2 mL/min)	3.9 × 300	UV (206)	10.1 min (elution time)	[62]
Oxytocin	RP 8 (10 μm)	Phosphate buffer (pH 7)/acetonitrile, 4:1	3 × 250	UV (210, 215, 220)	3.6 (injection of 34 μL aqueous solution)	[80]
Oxytocin	μBondapak C$_{18}$ (10 μm)	0.1 mol/L Ammonium acetate (pH 4.0)/acetonitrile, 82:18 (2.0 mL/min)	3.9 × 600	UV (254)	27 min (retention time)	[82]
Oxytocin	μBondapak C$_{18}$	0.05 mol/L Ammonium acetate (pH 4)/tetrahydrofuran, 86:14	3.9 × 300	UV	—	[85]
Oxytocin	μBondapak C$_{18}$	0.05 mol/L Ammonium acetate (pH 4)/acetonitrile, 78:22	3.9 × 300	UV	—	[85]
Oxytocin	μBondapak C$_{18}$	0.05 mol/L Ammonium acetate (pH 4)/methanol, 64:36	3.9 × 300	UV	—	[85]

Table 5-12a. (Continued).

Peptide	Stationary Phase	Eluent	Column (mm)	Detection (nm)	k-Value	Reference
Oxytocin	LiChrosorb RP-8	0.05 mol/L Ammonium acetate (pH 4)/ tetrahydrofuran, 91:9	2.1 × 250	UV	–	[85]
Oxytocin	LiChrosorb RP-8	0.05 mol/L Ammonium acetate (pH 4)/acetonitrile, 82:18	2.1 × 250	UV	–	[85]
Oxytocin	LiChrosorb RP-8	0.05 mol/L Ammonium acetate (pH 4)/methanol, 68:32	2.1 × 250	UV	–	[85]
Oxytocin	LiChrosorb RP-2	0.05 mol/L Ammonium acetate (pH 4)/ tetrahydrofuran, 88:12	2.1 × 250	UV	–	[85]
Oxytocin	LiChrosorb RP-2	0.05 mol/L Ammonium acetate (pH 4)/acetonitrile, 82:18	2.1 × 250	UV	–	[85]
Oxytocin	LiChrosorb RP-2	0.05 mol/L Ammonium acetate (pH 4)/methanol, 68:32	2.1 × 250	UV	–	[85]
Oxytocin	RP 8 (10 μm)	Phosphate buffer (pH 7)/ acetonitrile, 4:1	3 × 250	UV (210, 215, 220)	3.9 (injection of 340 μL aqueous solution)	[80]
Oxytocin	Nucleosil C$_{18}$ (10 μm)	Phosphate buffer (pH 7)/ acetonitrile, 4:1 (4.0 mL/min)	4 × 250	UV (210)	–	[80]
Oxytocin	Nucleosil C$_8$ (5 μm)	Phosphate buffer (pH 7)/ acetonitrile, 4:1 (1.8 mL/min)	4 × 150	UV (220)	–	[80]

Compound	Stationary phase	Mobile phase	Dimensions	Detection	Value	Ref.
Oxytocin	RP 8 (10 μm)	Phosphate buffer (pH 7)/acetonitrile, 4:1 (3.0 mL/min)	3 × 250	UV (215)	–	[80]
Oxytocin	Nucleosil 10 C$_{18}$	Acetonitrile (16.7%) + methanol/0.1 mol/L sodium sulfate + 0.01 mol/L phosphate buffer (pH 2.2), 4:6 (1 mL/min)	4.6 × 250	UV (215)	1.31	[86]
Oxytocin	Partisil SCX	Pyridine acetate; gradient 5 × 10^{-3} mol/L pyridine (pH 3.0) to 5 × 10^{-3} mol/L pyridine (pH 4.0), 50 min, to 5 × 10^{-1} mol/L pyridine (pH 5.0), 60 min (16 mL/h)	4.6 × 250	Fluorescamine (fluorescence)	–	[17]
Oxytocin	Si 60 (5 μm)	Tetrahydrofuran/0.05 mol/L acetic acid, 2:1 (0.7 mL/min)	3 × 250	Fluorescamine (fluorescence)	0.4	[2]
Demoxytocin	RP 8 (10 μm)	Phosphate buffer (pH 7)/acetonitrile, 4:1 (3 mL/min)	3 × 250	UV (215)	10.8	[3]
Demoxytocin	RP 8 (10 μm)	Phosphate buffer (pH 7)/acetonitrile, 33:7 (3 mL/min)	3 × 250	UV (215)	29.0	[3]
Demoxytocin	Nucleosil C$_8$ (5 μm)	Phosphate buffer (pH 7)/acetonitrile, 4:1 (2 mL/min)	3 × 150	UV (215)	17.5	[3]
Demoxytocin	Nucleosil C$_8$ (5 μm)	Phosphate buffer (pH 7)/acetonitrile, 3:1 (2 mL/min)	3 × 150	UV (215)	4.3	[3]
Demoxytocin	Nucleosil C$_{18}$ (5 μm)	Phosphate buffer (pH 7)/acetonitrile, 4:1 (2 mL/min)	3 × 150	UV (215)	21.1	[3]
Demoxytocin	RP 8 (10 μm)	Phosphate buffer (pH 7)/acetonitrile, 4:1	3 × 250	UV (210, 215, 220)	9.9 (Injection of 34 μL aqueous solution)	[80]
Demoxytocin	RP 8 (10 μm)	Phosphate buffer (pH 7)/acetonitrile, 4:1	3 × 250	UV (210, 215 220)	10.8 (Injection of 340 μL aqueous solution)	[80]

Table 5-12a. (Continued).

Peptide	Stationary Phase	Eluent	Column (mm)	Detection (nm)	k-Value	Reference
(1-Hemi-D-(α-^{2}H)-Cys)-oxytocin	μBondapak C_{18}	0.1 mol/L Ammonium acetate (pH 4.0)/acetonitrile, 82 : 18 (2.0 mL/min)	3.9 × 600	UV (254)	35 min (retention time)	[82]
(2-D-Tyr)-oxytocin	μBondapak C_{18}	0.1 mol/L Ammonium acetate (pH 4.0)/acetonitrile, 82 : 18 (2.0 mL/min)	3.9 × 600	UV (254)	38 min (retention time)	[82]
(6-Hemi-D-(α-^{2}H)-Cys)-oxytocin	μBondapak C_{18}	0.1 mol/L Ammonium acetate (pH 4.0)/acetonitrile, 82 : 18 (2.0 mL/min)	3.9 × 600	UV (254)	52 min (retention time)	[82]
(8-D-(2-^{13}C)-oxytocin	μBondapak C_{18}	0.1 mol/L Ammonium acetate (pH 4.0)/acetonitrile, 82 : 18 (2.0 mL/min)	3.9 × 600	UV (254)	43 min (retention time)	[82]
(3-L-(2-^{13}C)Leu)-oxytocin	μBondapak C_{18}	0.1 mol/L Ammonium acetate (pH 4.0)/acetonitrile, 82 : 18 (2.0 mL/min)	3.9 × 600	UV (254)	17 min (retention time)	[82]
(3-D-(2-^{13}C)Leu)-oxytocin	μBondapak C_{18}	0.1 mol/L Ammonium acetate (pH 4.0)/acetonitrile, 82 : 18 (2.0 mL/min)	3.9 × 600	UV (254)	22 min (retention time)	[82]
Arginine vasopressin	Nucleosil 10 C_{18} (10 μm)	0.05 mol/L Ammonium acetate (pH 6.5)/methanol, 61 : 39 (2 mL/min)	5 × 250	UV (220)	–	[11]
Arginine vasopressin	Partisil SCX	Pyridine acetate; gradient 5×10^{-3} mol/L pyridine (pH 3.0) to 5×10^{-2} mol/L pyridine (pH 4.0), 50 min, to 5×10^{-1} mol/L pyridine (pH 5.0), 60 min (16 mL/h)	4.6 × 250	Fluorescamine (fluorescence)	–	[17]

Compound	Stationary phase	Mobile phase	Column (mm)	Detection	Retention/elution	Ref.
Arginine vasopressin	μBondapak C$_{18}$ (10 μm)	Acetonitrile/0.02 mol/L acetic acid, + 0.1% 1-hexanesulfonic acid, 20:80 (2 mL/min)	3.9 × 300	UV (206, 210)	8.1 min (elution time)	[62]
Arginine vasopressin	μBondapak C$_{18}$	0.05 mol/L Ammonium acetate (pH 4)/ tetrahydrofuran, 86:14	3.9 × 300	UV	—	[85]
Arginine vasopressin	μBondapak C$_{18}$	0.05 mol/L Ammonium acetate (pH 4) acetonitrile, 78:22	3.9 × 300	UV	—	[85]
Arginine vasopressin	μBondapak C$_{18}$	0.05 mol/L Ammonium acetate (pH 4)/methanol, 64:36	3.9 × 300	UV	—	[85]
Arginine vasopressin	LiChrosorb RP-8	0.05 mol/L Ammonium acetate (pH 4)/ tetrahydrofuran, 91:9	2.1 × 250	UV	—	[85]
Arginine vasopressin	LiChrosorb RP-8	0.05 mol/L Ammonium acetate (pH 4)/acetonitrile, 82:18	2.1 × 250	UV	—	[85]
Arginine vasopressin	LiChrosorb RP-8	0.05 mol/1 Ammonium acetate (pH 4)/methanol, 68:32	2.1 × 250	UV	—	[85]
Arginine vasopressin	LiChrosorb RP-2	0.05 mol/L Ammonium acetate (pH 4)/ tetrahydrofuran, 88:12	2.1 × 250	UV	—	[85]
Arginine vasopressin	LiChrosorb RP-2	0.05 mol/L Ammonium acetate (pH 4)/acetonitrile, 82:18	2.1 × 250	UV	—	[85]
Arginine vasopressin	LiChrosorb RP-2	0.05 mol/L Ammonium acetate (pH 4)/methanol, 68:32	2.1 × 250	UV	—	[85]
(D-Arg^8)-vasopressin	Nucleosil 10 C$_{18}$ (10 μm)	0.05 mol/L Ammonium acetate (pH 6.5)/methanol, 61:39 (2 mL/min)	5 × 250	UV (220)	—	[11]

Table 5-12a. (Continued).

Peptide	Stationary Phase	Eluent	Column (mm)	Detection (nm)	k-Value	Reference
Lysine vasopressin	Si 60 (5 μm)	Tetrahydrofuran/0.05 mol/L acetic acid, 2:1 (0.7 mL/min)	3 × 250	Fluorescence (fluorescamine)	4.0	[2]
Lysine vasopressin	RP 8 (10 μm)	Phosphate buffer (pH 7)/acetonitrile, 4:1 (3 mL/min)	3 × 250	UV (215)	1.4	[3]
Lysine vasopressin	RP 8 (10 μm)	Phosphate buffer (pH 7)/acetonitrile, 33:7 (3 mL/min)	3 × 250	UV (215)	2.8	[3]
Lysine vasopressin	Nucleosil C_8 (5 μm)	Phosphate buffer (pH 7)/acetonitrile, 4:1 (2 mL/min)	3 × 150	UV (215)	2.7	[3]
Lysine vasopressin	Nucleosil C_8 (5 μm)	Phosphate buffer (pH 7)/acetonitrile, 3:1 (2 mL/min)	3 × 150	UV (215)	1.1	[3]
Lysine vasopressin	Nucleosil C_{18} (5 μm)	Phosphate buffer (pH 7)/acetonitrile, 4:1 (2 mL/min)	3 × 150	UV (215)	2.3	[3]
Lysine vasopressin	RP 8 (10 μm)	Phosphate buffer (pH 7)/acetonitrile, 4:1	3 × 250	UV (210, 215, 220)	1.3 (injection of 34 μL aqueous solution)	[80]
Lysine vasopressin	RP 8 (10 μm)	Phosphate buffer (pH 7)/acetonitrile, 4:1	3 × 250	UV (210, 215, 220)	1.4 (injection of 340 μL aqueous solution)	[80]
Lysine vasopressin	μBondapak C_{18}	0.05 mol/L Ammonium acetate (pH 4)/tetrahydrofuran, 86:14	3.9 × 300	UV	–	[85]
Lysine vasopressin	μBondapak C_{18}	0.05 mol/L Ammonium acetate (pH 4)/acetonitrile, 78:22	3.9 × 300	UV	–	[85]
Lysine vasopressin	μBondapak C_{18}	0.05 mol/L Ammonium acetate (pH 4)/methanol, 64:36	3.9 × 300	UV	–	[85]

Compound	Column	Mobile phase	Dimensions	Detection		Reference
Lysine vasopressin	LiChrosorb RP-8	0.05 mol/L Ammonium acetate (pH 4)/tetrahydrofuran, 91:9	2.1 × 250	UV	—	[85]
Lysine vasopressin	LiChrosorb RP-8	0.05 mol/L Ammonium acetate (pH 4)/acetonitrile, 82:18	2.1 × 250	UV	—	[85]
Lysine vasopressin	LiChrosorb RP-8	0.05 mol/L Ammonium acetate (pH 4)/methanol, 68:32	2.1 × 250	UV	—	[85]
Lysine vasopressin	LiChrosorb RP-2	0.05 mol/L Ammonium acetate (pH 4)/tetrahydrofuran, 88:12	2.1 × 250	UV	—	[85]
Lysine vasopressin	LiChrosorb RP-2	0.05 mol/L Ammonium acetate (pH 4)/Acetonitrile, 82:18	2.1 × 250	UV	—	[85]
Lysine vasopressin	LiChrosorb RP-2	0.05 mol/L Ammonium acetate (pH 4)/methanol, 68:32	2.1 × 250	UV	—	[85]
(L-Har^8)-vasopressin	Nucleosil 10 C$_{18}$ (10 µm)	0.05 mol/1 Ammonium acetate (pH 6.5)/methanol, 61:39 (2 mL/min)	5 × 250	UV (220)	—	[11]
(D-Har^8)-vasopressin	Nucleosil 10 C$_{18}$ (10 µm)	0.05 mol/L Ammonium acetate (pH 6.5)/methanol, 61:39 (2 mL/min)	5 × 250	UV (220)	—	[11]
(Mpa^1, L-Arg^8)-vasopressin	Nucleosil 10 C$_{18}$ (10 µm)	0.05 mol/L Ammonium acetate (pH 6.5)/methanol, 61:39 (2 mL/min)	5 × 250	UV (220)	—	[11]
(Mpa^1, L-Har^8)-vasopressin	Nucleosil 10 C$_{18}$ (10 µm)	0.05 mol/1 Ammonium acetate (pH 6.5)/methanol, 61:39 (2 mL/min)	5 × 250	UV (220)	—	[11]
(Mpa^1, D-Arg^8)-vasopressin	Nucleosil 10 C$_{18}$ (10 µm)	0.05 mol/L Ammonium acetate (pH 6.5)/methanol, 61:39 (2 mL/min)	5 × 250	UV (220)	—	[11]

Table 5-12a. (Continued).

Peptide	Stationary Phase	Eluent	Column (mm)	Detection (nm)	k-Value	Reference
(Mpa¹, D-Har⁸)-vasopressin	Nucleosil 10 C₁₈ (10 μm)	0.05 mol/L Ammonium acetate (pH 6.5)/methanol, 61:39 (2 mL/min)	5 × 250	UV (220)	–	[11]
Arginine vasotocin	μBondapak C₁₈ (10 μm)	Acetonitrile/0.02 mol/L acetic acid + 0.1% 1-hexanesulfonic acid, 20:80 (2 mL/min)	3.9 × 300	UV (210)	5.5 min (elution time)	[62]
Arginine vasotocin	μBondapak C₁₈	0.05 mol/L Ammonium acetate (pH 4)/tetrahydrofuran, 86:14	3.9 × 300	UV	–	[85]
Arginine vasotocin	μBondapak C₁₈	0.05 mol/L Ammonium acetate (pH 4)/acetonitrile, 78:22	3.9 × 300	UV	–	[85]
Arginine vasotocin	μBondapak C₁₈	0.05 mol/L Ammonium acetate (pH 4)/methanol, 64:36	3.9 × 300	UV	–	[85]
Arginine vasotocin	LiChrosorb Rp-8	0.05 mol/L Ammonium acetate (pH 4)/tetrahydrofuran, 91:9	2.1 × 250	UV	–	[85]
Arginine vasotocin	LiChrosorb RP-8	0.05 mol/L Ammonium acetate (pH 4)/acetonitrile, 82:18	2.1 × 250	UV	–	[85]
Arginine vasotocin	LiChrosorb RP-8	0.05 mol/L Ammonium acetate (pH 4)/methanol, 68:32	2.1 × 250	UV	–	[85]
Arginine vasotocin	LiChrosorb RP-2	0.05 mol/L Ammonium acetate (pH 4)/tetrahydrofuran, 88:12	2.1 × 250	UV	–	[85]

Compound	Column	Mobile phase	Dimensions	Detection		Ref.
Arginine vasotocin	LiChrosorb RP-2	0.05 mol/L Ammonium acetate (pH 4)/acetonitrile, 82:18	2.1 × 250	UV	—	[85]
Arginine vasotocin	LiChrosorb RP-2	0.05 mol/L Ammonium acetate (pH 4)/methanol, 68:32	2.1 × 250	UV	—	[85]
Mesotocin	µBondapak C_{18}	0.05 mol/L Ammonium acetate (pH 4)/tetrahydrofuran, 86:14	3.9 × 300	UV	—	[85]
Mesotocin	µBondapak C_{18}	0.05 mol/L Ammonium acetate (pH 4)/acetonitrile, 78:22	3.9 × 300	UV	—	[85]
Mesotocin	µBondapak C_{18}	0.05 mol/L Ammonium acetate (pH 4)/methanol, 64:36	3.9 × 300	UV	—	[85]
Mesotocin	LiChrosorb RP-8	0.05 mol/L Ammonium acetate (pH 4)/tetrahydrofuran, 91:9	2.1 × 250	UV	—	[85]
Mesotocin	LiChrosorb RP-8	0.05 mol/L Ammonium acetate (pH 4)/acetonitrile, 82:18	2.1 × 250	UV	—	[85]
Mesotocin	LiChrosorb RP-8	0.05 mol/L Ammonium acetate (pH 4)/methanol, 68:32	2.1 × 250	UV	—	[85]
Mesotocin	LiChrosorb RP-2	0.05 mol/L Ammonium acetate (pH 4)/tetrahydrofuran, 88:12	2.1 × 250	UV	—	[85]
Mesotocin	LiChrosorb RP-2	0.05 mol/L Ammonium acetate (pH 4)/acetonitrile, 82:18	2.1 × 250	UV	—	[85]
Mesotocin	LiChrosorb RP-2	0.05 mol/L Ammonium acetate (pH 4)/methanol, 68:32	2.1 × 250	UV	—	[85]

Table 5-12a. (Continued).

Peptide	Stationary Phase	Eluent	Column (mm)	Detection (nm)	k-Value	Reference
Ornipressin	Nucleosil C$_8$ (5 μm)	Phosphate buffer (pH 7) /acetonitrile, 4:1 (3 mL/min)	3 × 150	UV (210)	2.7	[3]
Ornipressin	Nucleosil C$_8$ (5 μm)	Phosphate buffer (pH 7) /acetonitrile, 3:1 (2 mL/min)	3 × 150	UV(210)	1.1	[3]
Ornipressin	Nucleosil C$_{18}$ (5 μm)	Phosphate buffer (pH 7) /acetonitrile, 4:1 (2 mL/min)	3 × 150	UV (210)	2.3	[3]
Ornipressin	RP 8 (10 μm)	Phosphate buffer (pH 7) /acetonitrile, 4:1	3 × 250	UV (210, 215, 220)	1.3 (injection of 34 μL aqueous solution)	[80]
Ornipressin	RP 8 (10 μm)	Phosphate buffer (pH 7) acetonitrile, 4:1	3 × 250	UV (210, 215, 220)	1.4 (injection of 340 μL aqueous solution)	[80]
Felypressin	RP 8 (10 μm)	Phosphate buffer (pH 7) /acetonitrile, 4:1 (3 mL/min)	3 × 250	UV (215)	5.6	[3]
Felypressin	RP 8 (10 μm)	Phosphate buffer (pH 7) /acetonitrile, 33:7 (3 mL/min)	3 × 250	UV (215)	11.7	[3]
Felypressin	Nucleosil C$_8$ (5 μm)	Phosphate buffer (pH 7) /acetonitrile, 4:1 (2 mL/min)	3 × 150	UV (210)	9.5	[3]
Felypressin	Nucleosil C$_8$ (5 μm)	Phosphate buffer (pH 7) /acetonitrile, 3:1 (2 mL/min)	3 × n 150	UV (210)	2.8	[3]

Felypressin	Nucleosil C$_{18}$ (5 μm)	Phosphate buffer (pH 7)/acetonitrile, 4:1 (2 mL/min)	3 × 150	UV (210)	10.0	[3]
Felypressin	RP 8 (10 μm)	Phosphate buffer (pH 7)/acetonitrile, 4:1	3 × 250	UV (210, 215, 220)	5.6 (injection of 340 μL aqueous solution)	[80]

Table 5-13. (Continued). (B) pH 10; mobile phase: tris (hydroxymethyl)aminomethane (buffer 0.1 mol/L, pH 10)/acetonitrile (3 : 1); column: Nucleosil C$_8$ (5 μm particle size) [3].

Sodium Chloride Concentration in the Mobile Phase (mol/L)	k		
	Ornipressin	Lysine Vasopressin	Oxytocin
0	∞	∞	2.4
0.05	2.2	2.9	2.3

Table 5-14. Detection Limits for Oxytocin and Derivatives.
Column: RP 8 (10 μm), 250 × 3 mm i. d.; eluent: phosphate buffer (pH 7)/acetonitrile (4 : 1), injection volume: 34 μL (aqueous solution); signal-to-noise ratio: 3 : 1 [80].

Substance	k (Capacity Factor)	Detection Limit (ng/injection)	Detection Wavelength (nm)
Oxytocin	3.6	30	210
		40	215
Demoxytocin	9.9	75	215
Ornipressin	1.3	30	215
Lysine vasopressin	1.3	30	215

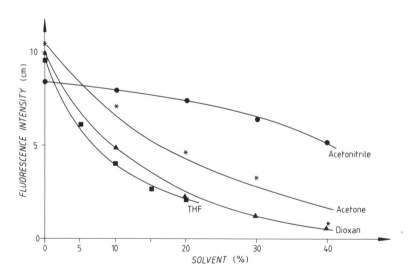

Figure 5-22. Influence of different solvents on the fluorescamine reaction of oxytocin.
Conditions at 0% 5 mL of buffer (pH 9, Titrisol, Merck) + 4 mL water + 5 μL of oxytocin (200 I. U./mL) + 1 mL of fluorescamine (30 mg/100 mL acetonitrile). Net values (blank substracted from assays (similar to reference [2]).

The primary amino groups of the neurohypophysial peptide hormones undergo a reaction with fluorescamine and form fluorescating derivatives. However, the fluorescence of the fluorescamine derivatives is strongly dependent on the type of organic solvent (Figure 5-22), the pH-value (Figure 5-23) and the concentration of fluorescamine (Figure 5-24).

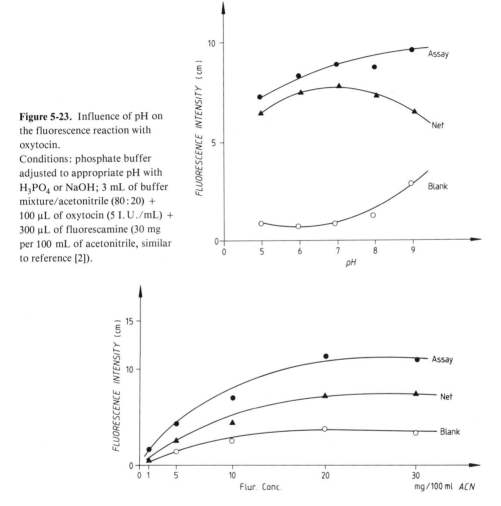

Figure 5-23. Influence of pH on the fluorescence reaction with oxytocin.
Conditions: phosphate buffer adjusted to appropriate pH with H_3PO_4 or NaOH; 3 mL of buffer mixture/acetonitrile (80:20) + 100 μL of oxytocin (5 I.U./mL) + 300 μL of fluorescamine (30 mg per 100 mL of acetonitrile, similar to reference [2]).

Figure 5-24. Influence of fluorescamine concentration on the fluorescence reaction at pH 8 (borate buffer) of oxytocin. 3 mL Borate buffer (pH 8) mixture/acetonitrile (80:20) + 100 μL oxytocin (5 I.U./mL) + 300 μL fluorescamine (30 mg per 100 mL of acetonitrile similar to reference [2]).

Based on the relationships of Figures 5-22 to 5-24 optimal conditions concerning fluorescence detection of fluorescamine derivatives of neurohypophysial peptide hormones can be selected:

a) Fluorescamine concentrations of 20 to 30 mg/mL acetonitrile give optimal fluorescence response.

b) In order to keep the organic solvent content low, the fluorescamine solution should be added at relatively low flow-rates.

c) The pH-value should be kept in the optimal range 6 to 8.

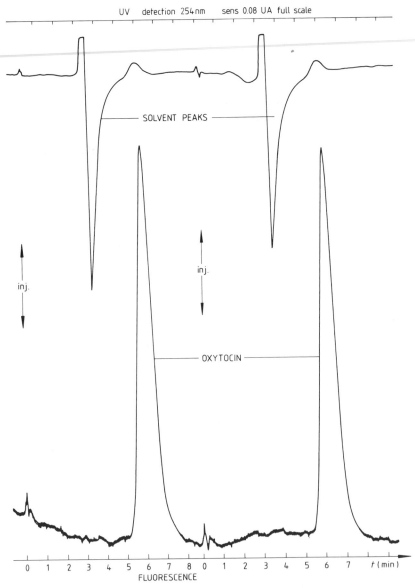

Figure 5-25. Chromatogram of oxytocin (0.88 µg per injection of 2 µL). Comparison of UV (254 nm) and fluorescence after mixing with buffer and fluorescamine. Column: Si 60 (10 µm), 250 × 3 mm i. d., eluent: tetrahydrofuran/0.05 mol/L acetic acid (2 : 1); flow-rate: 0.28 mL/min; borate buffer (pH 9), flow-rate: 0.85 mL/min; fluorescamine (30 mg per 100 mL of acetonitrile), flow-rate: 0.43 mL/min (similar to reference [2]).

Optimal mobile phase media, with regard to sepration and fluorescence signal, are buffer solutions of pH 7/acetonitrile in the proportions 80:17.5 for oxytocin and 80:15 for ornipressin and lysine vasopressin. Simultaneous detection of oxytocin by UV and fluorescence (Figure 5-25) clearly demonstrates the advantage of post-column derivatization [2].

5.3.3 Adenohypophysial Hormones

The adenohypophysis secretes several hormones of quite different structure and molecular weight: thyrotropin (TSH), adrenocoticotropin (ACTH), melanotropin (MSH), luteinizing hormone (LH, interstitial cell-stimulating hormone), follicle-stimulating hormone (FSH), prolactin (luteotropin, LTH), growth hormone (GH, somatotropin) and lipotropin(s) (LPH). Some structural characterizations for these adenohypophysial hormones are given in Table 5-15.

Table 5-15. Structural Characterization of Adenohypophysial Hormones.

Structural Characterization	Name
1 2 3 4 5 6 7 8 9 10 11 12 13 14 15 16 17 18 19 20 H-Ser-Tyr-Ser-Met-Glu-His-Phe-Arg-Trp-Gly-Lys-Pro-Val-Gly-Lys-Lys-Arg-Arg-Pro-Val- 21 22 23 24 25 26 27 28 29 30 31 32 33 34 35 36 37 38 39 Lys-Val-Tyr-Pro-Asn-Gly-Ala-Glu-Asp-Glu-Ser-Ala-Glu-Ala-Phe-Pro-Leu-Glu-Phe-OH	ACTH (human)
1 2 3 4 5 6 7 8 9 10 11 12 13 14 15 16 17 18 19 20 H-Ser-Tyr-Ser-Met-Glu-His-Phe-Arg-Trp-Gly-Lys-Pro-Val-Gly-Lys-Lys-Arg-Arg-Pro-Val- 21 22 23 24 25 26 27 28 29 30 31 32 33 34 35 36 37 38 39 Lys-Val-Tyr-Pro-Asn-Gly-Ala-Glu-Asp-Glu-Leu-Ala-Glu-Ala-Phe-Pro-Leu-Glu-Phe-OH	ACTH (porcine)
1 2 3 4 5 6 7 8 9 10 11 12 13 14 15 16 17 18 19 20 H-Ser-Tyr-Ser-Met-Glu-His-Phe-Arg-Trp-Gly-Lys-Pro-Val-Gly-Lys-Lys-Arg-Arg-Pro-Val- 21 22 23 24 25 26 27 28 29 30 31 32 33 34 35 36 37 38 39 Lys-Val-Tyr-Pro-Asn-Gly-Ala-Glu-Asp-Glu-Ser-Ala-Gln-Ala-Phe-Pro-Leu-Glu-Phe-OH	ACTH (ovine)
1 2 3 4 5 6 7 8 9 10 11 12 13 H$_3$C-CO-Ser-Tyr-Ser-Met-Glu-His-Phe-Arg-Trp-Gly-Lys-Pro-Val-NH$_2$	α-MSH
1 2 3 4 5 6 7 8 9 10 11 12 13 14 15 16 17 18 H-Asp-Ser-Gly-Pro-Tyr-Lys-Met-Glu-His-Phe-Arg-Trp-Gly-Ser-Pro-Pro-Lys-Asp-OH	β-MSH (bovine)
1 2 3 4 5 6 7 8 9 10 11 12 13 14 15 16 17 18 H-Asp-Glu-Gly-Pro-Tyr-Lys-Met-Glu-His-Phe-Arg-Trp-Gly-Ser-Pro-Pro-Lys-Asp-OH	β-MSH (porcine)
1 2 3 4 5 6 7 8 9 10 11 12 13 14 15 16 17 18 H-Ala-Glu-Lys-Lys-Asp-Glu-Gly-Pro-Tyr-Arg-Met-Glu-His-Phe-Arg-Trp-Gly-Ser-	β-MSH (human)

Table 5-15. (Continued).

Structural Characterization	Name

19 20 21 22
Pro-Pro-Lys-Asp-OH

Structural Characterization	Name
Glykoprotein (2 subunits; α: 96 amino acids; β: 120 amino acids; molecular weight (26000)	LH, ICSH (ovine, bovine)
Glycoprotein (2 subunits; molecular weight ≈ 30000)	FSH
Protein (198 amino acids, molecular weight ≈ 23000)	Prolactin (LTH, ovine)
Protein (190 amino acids, molecular weight ≈ 22000)	Growth hormone (GH, human)
Glycoprotein (2 subunits; α: 96 amino acids; β: 113 amino acids, molecular weight 28 500)	Thyrotropin (TSH, bovine)

```
  1   2   3   4   5   6   7   8   9   10  11  12  13  14  15  16  17  18
H-Glu-Leu-Ala-Gly-Ala-Pro-Pro-Glu-Pro-Ala-Arg-Asp-Pro-Glu-Ala-Pro-Ala-Glu-
 19  20  21  22  23  24  25  26  27  28  29  30  31  32  33  34  35  36  37  38
Gly-Ala-Ala-Ala-Arg-Ala-Glu-Leu-Glu-Tyr-Gly-Leu-Val-Ala-Glu-Ala-Glu-Ala-Ala-Glu-
 39  40  41  42  43  44  45  46  47  48  49  50  51  52  53  54  55  56  57  58
Lys-Lys-Asp-Glu-Gly-Pro-Tyr-Lys-Met-Glu-His-Phe-Arg-Trp-Gly-Ser-Pro-Pro-Lys-Asp-
 59  60  61  62  63  64  65  66  67  68  69  70  71  72  73  74  75  76  77  78
Lys-Arg-Tyr-Gly-Gly-Phe-Met-Thr-Ser-Glu-Lys-Ser-Glu-Thr-Pro-Leu-Val-Thr-Leu-Phe-
 79  80  81  82 83  84  85  86  87  88  89  90  91
Lys-Asn-Ala-Ile-Val-Lys-Asn-Ala-His-Lys-Lys-Gly-Gln-NH₂
```

β-Lipotropin (porcine)

```
  1   2   3   4   5   6   7   8   9   10  11  12  13  14  15  16  17  18  19
H-Glu-Leu-Ala-Gly-Ala-Pro-Pro-Glu-Pro-Ala-Arg-Asp-Pro-Glu-Ala-Pro-Ala-Glu-Gly-
 20  21  22  23  24  25  26  27  28  29  30  31  32  33  34  35  36  37  38  39
Ala-Ala-Ala-Arg-Ala-Glu-Leu-Glu-Tyr-Gly-Leu-Val-Ala-Glu-Ala-Gln-Ala-Ala-Glu-Lys-
 40  41  42  43  44  45  46  47  48  49  50  51  52  53  54  55  56  57  58
Lys-Asp-Glu-Gly-Pro-Tyr-Lys-Met-Glu-His-Phe-Arg-Trp-Gly-Ser-Pro-Pro-Lys-Asp-OH
```

γ-Lipotropin (porcine)

5.3.3.1 Corticotropin and Melanotropin

Numerous reports on the HPLC purification of corticotropins [8, 14, 15, 43, 56, 61, 70, to 72, 80, 88 to 90] and melanotropins [6, 14, 15, 43, 56, 61, 66, 71, 72, 91, 92] including theoretical considerations appeared recently in the literature. Detailed conditions for the separation of adenocorticotropic hormones and melanocyte-stimulating hormones including derivatives and fragments are given in Tables 5-16 and 5-17.

Table 5-16. Experimental Conditions for HPLC Separations of Corticotropins and Derivatives. (for Structures see Table 5-15).

Peptide	Stationary Phase	Eluent	Column (mm)	Detection (nm)	k-Value	Reference
ACTH (human)	Nucleosil 5C$_{18}$ (5 μm)	0.005 mol/L Tartrate buffer (pH 3.0) + 0.005 mol/L sodium 1-butanesulfonate + 0.05 mol/L sodium sulfate/50% acetonitrile + 50% 0.005 mol/L tartrate buffer (pH 3.0) + 0.01 mol/L sodium 1-butanesulfonate + 0.1 mol/L sodium sulfate, 2:3, (1 mL/min)	4 × 200	UV (220)	–	[70]
ACTH (human)	μBondapak C$_{18}$ (10 μm)	A: 0.08% Trifluoroacetic acid, B: acetonitrile/0.08% trifluoroacetic acid (49:51), gradient from 3.5 to 49% acetonitrile in 20 min (1 mL/min)	3.9 × 300	UV (206)	20.4 (elution time, min)	[61]
ACTH (human)	Partisil-ODS (10 μm)	A: 1% Trifluoroacetic acid, B: methanol/water/trifluoroacetic acid, 80:19:1, linear gradient from A to B (0.7 mL/min)	4 × 250	UV (280)	–	[8]
ACTH (human)	Hypersil-ODS (5 μm)	0.1 mol/L Phosphate buffer (pH 2.1)/acetonitrile, tripartite linear gradient elution (1 mL/min) to 60% acetonitrile	5 × 100	UV (225), fluorescence (275/370)	–	[88]

Table 5-16. (Continued).

Peptide	Stationary Phase	Eluent	Column (mm)	Detection (nm)	*k*-Value	Reference
ACTH (human)	Hypersil-ODS (5 μm)	Acetonitrile/0.02 mol/L phosphate buffer (pH 2.1), tripartite linear gradient, from 0% to 60% (1 mL/min) acetonitrile in 50 min	5 × 100	UV (225) fluorescence (275/370 nm)	30.5 (retention time, min)	[14]
ACTH (human)	μBondapak C$_{18}$ (10 μm)	A: 0.08% Trifluoroacetic acid, B: acetonitrile/0.08% trifluoroacetic acid (7:3), gradient from 30 to 50% B (30 min), (1 mL/min)	3.9 × 300	UV (206)	–	[61]
ACTH (porcine)	Nucleosil 5C$_{18}$ (5 μm)	0.005 mol/L Tartrate buffer (pH 3.0) + 0.005 mol/L sodium 1-butanesulfonate + 0.05 mol/L sodium sulfate/50% acetonitrile + 50% 0.005 mol/L tartrate buffer (pH 3.0) + 0.01 mol/L sodium 1-butanesulfonate + 0.1 mol/L sodium sulfate 2:3, (1 mL/min)	4 × 200	UV (220)	–	[70]
ACTH (porcine)	Hypersil-ODS (5 μm)	Acetonitrile/0.02 mol/L phosphate buffer (pH 2.1), tripartite linear gradient (1 mL/min), from 0% to 60% acetonitrile in 50 min	5 × 100	UV (225), fluorescence (275/370)	33.0 (retention time, min)	[14]
ACTH (porcine)	Hypersil-ODS (5 μm)	A: 0.2 mol/L Phosphate buffer (pH 2.1), B: acetonitrile, linear gradient	5 × 100	UV (225), fluorescence (275/370)	18.5 (retention time, min)	[14]

ACTH (porcine)	Hypersil-ODS (5 μm)	from A to B, rate change 2% acetonitrile/min	5 × 100	UV (225), fluorescence (275/370)	20.6 (retention time, min)	[14]
ACTH (porcine)	Hypersil-ODS (5 μm)	A: 0.2 mol/L Phosphate buffer (pH 2.1), B: tetrahydrofuran linear gradient from A to B, rate change 2% tetrahydrofuran/min	5 × 100	UV (225), fluorescence (275/370)	25.4 (retention time, min)	[14]
ACTH (porcine)	Hypersil-ODS (5 μm)	A: 0.2 mol/L Phosphate buffer (pH 2.1), B: dioxan, linear gradient from A to B, rate change 2% dioxan/min	5 × 100	UV (225), fluorescence (275/370)	35.4 (retention time, min)	[14]
ACTH (porcine)	Hypersil-ODS (5 μm)	A: 0.2 mol/L Phosphate buffer (pH 2.1) B: methanol, linear gradient, from A to B, rate change 2% methanol/min	5 × 100	UV (225), fluorescence (275/370)	—	[14]
ACTH (porcine)	Hypersil-ODS (5 μm)	Acetonitrile/0.1 mol/L phosphate buffer (pH 2.3), tripartite linear gradient (1 mL/min), starting with 0% acetonitrile	5 × 100	UV (225), fluorescence (275/370)	—	[14]
ACTH (porcine)	Hypersil-ODS (5 μm)	Acetonitrile/0.1 mol/L phosphate buffer (pH 6.2), tripartite linear gradient (1 mL/min), starting with 0% acetonitrile	5 × 100	UV (225), fluorescence (275/370)	—	[14]
ACTH (porcine)	Hypersil-ODS (5 μm)	Acetonitrile/0.16 mol/l hydrogen chloride + sodium chloride (pH 2.1), tripartite linear gradient (1 mL/min), starting with 0% acetonitrile	5 × 100	UV (225), fluorescence (275/370)		[14]

Table 5-16. (Continued).

Peptide	Stationary Phase	Eluent	Column (mm)	Detection (nm)	k-Value	Reference
ACTH (porcine)	Hypersil-ODS (5 µm)	Acetonitrile/0.1 mol/L phosphoric acid (pH 1.9), tripartite linear gradient (1 mL/min), starting with 0% acetonitrile	5 × 100	UV (225), fluorescence (275/370)	–	[14]
ACTH (ovine, iodinated)	µBondapak C_{18} (10 µm)	A: 0.02 mol/L Triethylamine phosphate buffer (pH 3.0), B: 0.02 mol/L triethylamine-phosphate buffer (pH 3.0)/2-propanol, 1:1, linear gradient from A to B in 75 min (1 mL/min)	–	UV (210)	–	[92]
$ACTH_{1-32}$	Nucleosil 10 C_{18}	16.7% Acetonitrile + 83.3% methanol/0.1 mol/L sodium sulfate in 0.01 mol/L phosphate buffer (pH 2.2), 35:65 (1 mL/min).	4.6 × 250	UV (215)	7.5	[86]
$ACTH_{1-32}$	Nucleosil 10 C_{18}	16.7% Isopropanol in methanol/0.1 mol/L sodium perchlorate in 0.01 mol/L phosphate buffer (pH 2.2), 35:65 (1 mL/min)	4.6 × 250	UV (215)	4.7	[86]
$ACTH_{1-28}$	Nucleosil 10 C_{18}	16.7% Acetonitrile + 83.3% methanol/0.1 mol/L sodium sulfate in 0.01 mol/L phosphate buffer (pH 2.2), 35:65 (1 mL/min)	4.6 × 250	UV (215)	10.6	[86]
$ACTH_{1-28}$	Nucleosil 10 C_{18}	16.7% Isopropanol in methanol/0.1 mol/L sodium per-	4.6 × 250	UV (215)	10.0	[86]

Compound	Stationary phase	Mobile phase	Column	Detection	Retention	Ref.
		chlorate in 0.01 mol/L phosphate buffer (pH 2.2), 35:65 (1 mL/min)				
ACTH$_{1-24}$ (pentaacetate)	μBondapak C$_{18}$ (10 μm)	Methanol/0.1% phosphoric acid 2:3	4 × 300	UV (225)	2.1 min (retention time, min)	[90]
ACTH$_{1-24}$	Nucleosil 10 C$_{18}$	16.7% Acetonitrile + 83.3% methanol/0.1 mol/L sodium sulfate in 0.01 mol/L phosphate buffer (pH 2.2), 35:65 (1 mL/min)	4.6 × 250	UV (215)	13.9	[86]
ACTH$_{1-24}$	Nucleosil 10 C$_{18}$	16.7% Isopropanol in methanol/0.1 mol/L sodium perchlorate in 0.01 mol/L phosphate buffer (pH 2.2), 35:65 (1 mL/min)	4.6 × 250	UV (215)	17.7	[86]
ACTH$_{1-24}$	Hypersil-ODS (5 μm)	0.1 mol/L Phosphate buffer (pH 2.1)/acetonitrile, 4:1 (1 mL/min)	5 × 100	UV (225) fluorescence (275/370)	–	[88]
ACTH$_{1-24}$	Hypersil-ODS (5 μm)	Acetonitrile/0.2 mol/L phosphate buffer (pH 2.1), tripartite linear gradient (1 mL/min), from 0% to 60% acetonitrile in 50 min	5 × 100	UV (225), fluorescence (275/370)	21.5 (retention time, min)	[14]
ACTH$_{1-24}$	Hypersil-ODS (5 μm)	A:0.2 mol/L Phosphate buffer (pH 2.1), B: acetonitrile, linear gradient from A to B, rate change 2% acetonitrile/min	5 × 100	UV (225) fluorescence (275/370)	13.6 (retention time, min)	[14]
ACTH$_{1-24}$	Hypersil-ODS (5 μm)	A: 0.2 mol/L Phosphate buffer (pH 2.1), B: tetrahydrofuran, linear gradient from A to B, rate change 2% acetonitrile/min	5 × 100	UV (225) fluorescence (275/370)	13.0 (retention time, min)	[14]

Table 5-16. (Continued).

Peptide	Stationary Phase	Eluent	Column (mm)	Detection (nm)	k-Value	Reference
ACTH$_{1-24}$	Hypersil-ODS (5 µm)	A:0.2 mol/L Phosphate buffer (pH 2.1), B: dioxan, linear gradient from A to B, rate change 2% dioxan/min	5 × 100	UV (225) fluorescence (275/370)	15.4 (retention time, min)	[14]
ACTH$_{1-24}$	Hypersil-ODS (5 µm)	A:0.2 mol/L Phosphate buffer (pH 2.1), B: methanol, linear gradient from A to B, rate change 2% methanol/min	5 × 100	UV (225) fluorescence (275/370)	26.0 (retention time, min)	[14]
ACTH$_{1-24}$	Hypersil-ODS (5 µm)	Acetonitrile/0.1 mol/L phosphate buffer (pH 2.3), tripartite linear gradient (1 mL/min), starting with 0% acetonitrile	5 × 100	UV (225) fluorescence (275/370)	–	[14]
ACTH$_{1-24}$	Hypersil-ODS (5 µm)	Acetonitrile/0.1 mol/L phosphate buffer (pH 6.2), tripartite linear gradient (1 mL/min), starting with 0% acetonitrile	5 × 100	UV (225) fluorescence (275/370)	–	[14]
ACTH$_{1-24}$	Hypersil-ODS (5 µm)	Acetonitrile/0.16 mol/L hydrogen chloride + sodium chloride (pH 2.1), tripartite linear gradient (1 mL/min), starting with 0% acetonitrile	5 × 100	UV (225) fluorescence (275/370)	–	[14]
ACTH$_{1-24}$	Hypersil-ODS (5 µm)	Acetonitrile/0.1 mol/L phosphoric acid (pH 1.9), tripartite linear gradient (1 mL/min), starting with 0% acetonitrile	5 × 100	UV (225) fluorescence (275/370)	–	[14]

ACTH$_{1-24}$	μBondapak C$_{18}$ (10 μm)	A: 0.08% Trifluoroacetic acid, B: acetonitrile/0.08% trifluoroacetic acid (7:3), gradient from 30 to 50% B (30 min), (1 mL/min)	3.9 × 300	UV (206)	—	[61]
ACTH$_{1-24}$	Partisil-ODS (10 μm)	A: 1% Trifluoroacetic acid, B: methanol/water/trifluoroacetic acid, 80:19:1, linear gradient from A to B (0.7 mL/min)	4 × 250	UV (280)	—	[8]
ACTH$_{1-24}$	μBondapak C$_{18}$	Acetonitrile/water/50 mol/L phosphate buffer (pH 2.5); different runs with 2% increases in acetonitrile (1 mL/min)	—	UV (254)	—	[43]
ACTH$_{1-24}$	μBondapak C$_{18}$	A: Water + 50 mmol/L sodium dihydrogen phosphate + 0.1% phosphoric acid, B: acetonitrile/water + 50 mmol/L sodium dihydrogen phosphate (1:1) + 0.1% phosphoric acid, linear gradient from A to B, (60 min), (1 mL/min)	—	UV (254)	—	[43]
ACTH$_{1-24}$ (^{3}H-labelled)	Partisil-ODS (10 μm)	A: Methanol/water/trifluoroacetic acid, 20:79:1, B: methanol/water/trifluoroacetic acid, 55:44:1, linear gradient from A to B (0.7 mL/min)	4 × 250	Radioactivity	—	[8]

Table 5-16. (Continued).

Peptide	Stationary Phase	Eluent	Column (mm)	Detection (nm)	k-Value	Reference
ACTH$_{1-24}$ sulfoxide (^{3}H-labelled)	Partisil-ODS (10 µm)	A: Methanol/water/trifluoroacetic acid, 20:79:1, B: methanol/water/trifluoroacetic acid, 55:44:1, linear gradient from A to B (0.7 mL/min)	4 × 250	Radioactivity	–	[8]
ACTH$_{1-24}$	Hypersil-ODS (5 µm)	0.1 mol/L Phosphate buffer (pH 2.1)/acetonitrile, tripartite linear gradient elution (1 mL/min) to 60% acetonitrile	5 × 100	UV (225) fluorescence (275/370)	–	[88]
ACTH$_{1-18}$	Hypersil-ODS (5 µm)	0.1 mol/L Phosphate buffer (pH 2.1)/acetonitrile, tripartite linear gradient elution (1 mL/min) to 60% acetonitrile	5 × 100	UV (225) fluorescence (275/370)	–	[88]
ACTH$_{1-18}$-NH$_2$	Nucleosil 5C$_{18}$ (5 µm)	0.005 mol/L Tartrate buffer (pH 3.0) + 0.005 mol/L sodium 1-butane sulfonate + 0.05 mol/L sodium sulfate/ 50% acetonitrile + 50% 0.005 mol/L tartrate buffer (pH 3.0) + 0.01 mol/L sodium 1-butane sulfonate + 0.1 mol/L sodium sulfate, 68:32 (1 mL/min)	4 × 200	UV (220)	–	[70]
ACTH$_{1-18}$-NH$_2$	Nucleosil 5C$_{18}$ (5 µm)	0.005 mol/L Tartrate buffer (pH 3.0) + 0.005 mol/L sodium 1-butane sulfonate +	4 × 200	UV (220)	–	[70]

		0.05 mol/L sodium sulfate/ 50% acetonitrile + 50% 0.005 mol/L tartrate buffer (pH 3.0) + 0.01 mol/L sodium 1-butane sulfonate + 0.1 mol/L sodium sulfate, 66:34 (1 mL/min)				
ACTH$_{1-18}$-NH$_2$	Nucleosil 5C$_{18}$ (5 µm)	0.005 mol/L Tartrate buffer (pH 3.0) + 0.005 mol/L sodium 1-butane sulfonate + 0.05 mol/L sodium sulfate/ 50% acetonitrile + 50% 0.005 mol/L tartrate buffer (pH 3.0) + 0.01 mol/L sodium 1-butane sulfonate + 0.1 mol/L sodium sulfate, 64:36	4 × 200	UV (220)	–	[70]
ACTH$_{1-15}$ (^{3}H-labelled)	Partisil-ODS (10 µm)	A: Methanol/water/trifluoroacetic acid, 20:79:1, B: methanol/water/trifluoroacetic acid, 55:44:1, linear gradient from A to B (0.7 mL/min)	4 × 250	Radioactivity	–	[8]
ACTH$_{1-14}$	Nucleosil 10 C$_{18}$	16.7% Acetonitrile + 83.3% methanol/0.1 mol/L sodium sulfate in 0.01 mol/L phosphate buffer (pH 2.2), 35:65 (1 mL/min)	4.6 × 250	UV (215)	10.1	[86]
ACTH$_{1-14}$	Nucleosil 10 C$_{18}$	16.7% Isopropanol in methanol/0.1 mol/L sodium perchlorate in 0.01 mol/L phosphate buffer (pH 2.2), 35:65 (1 mL/min)	4.6 × 250	UV (215)	9.1	[86]

Table 5-16. (Continued).

Peptide	Stationary Phase	Eluent	Column (mm)	Detection (nm)	k-Value	Reference
$ACTH_{1-18}$	Hypersil-ODS (5 µm)	Acetonitrile/0.2 mol/L phosphate buffer (pH 2.1), tripartite linear gradient (1 mL/min), from 0% to 60% acetonitrile in 50 min	5 × 100	UV (225) fluorescence (275/370)	18.5 (retention time, min)	[14]
$ACTH_{15-32}$	Nucleosil 10 C_{18}	16.7% Isopropanol in methanol/0.1 mol/L sodium perchlorate in 0.01 mol/L phosphate buffer (pH 2.2), 35:65 (1 mL/min)	4.6 × 250	UV (215)	0	[86]
$ACTH_{15-32}$	Nucleosil 10 C_{18}	16.7% Acetonitrile + 83.3% methanol/0.1 mol/L sodium sulfate in 0.01 mol/L phosphate buffer (pH 2.2), 35:65 (1 mL/min)	4.6 × 250	UV (215)	1.5	[86]
$ACTH_{4-10}$	Hypersil-ODS (5 µm)	0.1 mol/L Phosphate buffer (pH 2.1)/acetonitrile, tripartite linear gradient elution (1 mL/min) to 60% acetonitrile	5 × 100	UV (225) fluorescence (275/370)	–	[88]
$ACTH_{34-39}$	Hypersil-ODS (5 µm)	0.1 mol/L Phosphate buffer (pH 2.1)/acetonitrile, tripartite linear gradient elution (1 mL/min) to 60% acetonitrile	5 × 100	UV (225)	–	[88]
$ACTH_{34-39}$	Hypersil-ODS (5 µm)	Acetonitrile/phosphate buffer (pH 2.1), 6:19 (1 mL/min)	5 × 100	UV (225)	–	[88]

ACTH$_{5-10}$	Hypersil-ODS (5 µm)	Acetonitrile/0.2 mol/L phosphate buffer (pH 2.1), tripartite linear gradient (1 mL/min) from 0% to 60% acetonitrile in 50 min	5 × 100	UV (225), fluorescence (275/370)	17.0 (retention time, min)	[14]
ACTH$_{4-10}$	Hypersil-ODS (5 µm)	Acetonitrile/0.2 mol/L phosphate buffer (pH 2.1), tripartite linear gradient (1 mL/min) from 0% to 60% acetonitrile in 50 min	5 × 100	UV (225) fluorescence (275/370)	20.5 (retention time, min)	[14]
ACTH$_{18-39}$	Hypersil-ODS (5 µm)	Acetonitrile/0.2 mol/L phosphate buffer (pH 2.1), tripartite linear gradient (1 mL/min) from 0% to 60% acetonitrile in 50 min	5 × 100	UV (225) fluorescence (275/370)	30.5 (retention time, min)	[14]
ACTH$_{34-39}$	Hypersil-ODS (5 µm)	Acetonitrile/0.2 mol/L phosphate buffer (pH 2.1), tripartite linear gradient (1 mL/min), from 0% to 60% acetonitrile in 50 min	5×100	UV (225), fluorescence (275/370)	31.0 (retention time, min)	[14]
ACTH$_{11-39}$ (human)	µBondapak C$_{18}$ (10 µm)	A: 0.08% Trifluoroacetic acid, B: acetonitrile/0.08% trifluoroacetic acid (7:3), gradient from 30 to 50% B (30 min), (1 mL/min)	3.9 × 300	UV (206)	—	[61]
ACTH$_{4-10}$	Partisil-ODS (10 µm)	A: 1% Trifluoroacetic acid, B: methanol/water/trifluoroacetic acid, 80:19:1, linear gradient from A to B (0.7 mL/min)	4×250	UV (280)	—	[8]

Table 5-16. (Continued).

Peptide	Stationary Phase	Eluent	Column (mm)	Detection (nm)	k-Value	Reference
$ACTH_{17-24}$ (^{3}H-labelled)	Partisil-ODS (10 μm)	A: Methanol/water/trifluoroacetic acid, 20:79:1, B: methanol/water/trifluoroacetic acid, 55:44:1, linear gradient from A to B (0.7 mL/min)	4×250	Radioactivity	–	[8]
$ACTH_{18-24}$ (^{3}H-labelled)	Partisil-ODS (10 μm)	A: Methanol/water/trifluoroacetic acid, 20:79:1, B: methanol/water/trifluoroacetic acid, 55:44:1, linear gradient from A to B (0.7 mL/min)	4×250	Radioactivity	–	[8]
$ACTH_{9-24}$ (^{3}H-labelled)	Partisil-ODS (10 μm)	A: Methanol/water/trifluoroacetic acid, 20:79:1, B: methanol/water/trifluoroacetic acid, 55:44:1, linear gradient from A to B (0.7 mL/min)	4×250	Radioactivity	–	[8]
$ACTH_{2-20}$ (^{3}H-labelled)	Partisil-ODS (10 μm)	A: Methanol/water/trifluoroacetic acid, 20:79:1, B: methanol/water/trifluoroacetic acid, 55:44:1, linear gradient from A to B (0.7 mL/min)	4×250	Radioactivity	–	[8]
$ACTH_{3-20}$ (^{3}H-labelled)	Partisil-ODS (10 μm)	A: Methanol/water/trifluoroacetic acid, 20:79:1, B: methanol/water/trifluoroacetic acid, 55:44:1, linear gradient from A to B (0.7 mL/min)	4×250	Radioactivity	–	[8]
$ACTH_{18-39}$	Hypersil-ODS (5 μm)	0.1 mol/L Phosphate buffer (pH 2.1)/acetonitrile, tripartite linear gradient elution	5×100	UV (225) fluorescence (275/370)	–	[88]

Compound	Stationary phase	Mobile phase	Column (mm)	Detection (nm)		Ref.
(Gly^1)-$ACTH_{1-18}$-NH_2	Nucleosil $5C_{18}$- (5 μm)	(1 mL/min) to 60% acetonitrile; 0.005 mol/L Tartrate buffer (pH 3.0) + 0.005 mol/L sodium 1-butanesulfonate + 0.05 mol/L sodium sulfate/ 50% acetonitrile + 50% 0.005 mol/L tartrate buffer (pH 3.0) + 0.01 mol/L sodium 1-butanesulfonate + 0.1 mol/L sodium sulfate, 33:17 (1.0 mL/min)	4×200	UV (220)	—	[70]
(Gly^1)-$ACTH_{1-18}$-NH_2	Nucleosil $5C_{18}$ (5 μm)	0.005 mol/L Tartrate buffer (pH 3.0) + 0.005 mol/L sodium 1-butanesulfonate + 0.05 mol/L sodium sulfate/ 50% acetonitrile + 50% 0.005 mol/L tartrate buffer (pH 3.0) + 0.01 mol/L sodium 1-butanesulfonate + 0.1 mol/L sodium sulfate, 17:8 (1.0 mL/min)	4×200	UV (220)	—	[70]
(Gly^1)-$ACTH_{1-18}$-NH_2	Nucleosil $5C_{18}$ (5 μm)	0.005 mol/L Tartrate buffer (pH 3.0) + 0.005 mol/L sodium 1-butanesulfonate + 0.05 mol/L sodium sulfate/ 50% acetonitrile + 50% 0.005 mol/L tartrate buffer (pH 3.0) + 0.01 mol/L sodium 1-butanesulfonate + 0.1 mol/L sodium sulfate, 16:9 (1.0 mL/min)	4×200	UV (220)	—	[70]

Table 5-16. (Continued).

Peptide	Stationary Phase	Eluent	Column (mm)	Detection (nm)	k-Value	Reference
(Gly^1)-ACTH$_{1-18}$-NH$_2$, sulfoxide	Nucleosil 5C$_{18}$ (5 μm)	0.005 mol/L Tartrate buffer (pH 3.0) + 0.005 mol/L sodium 1-butanesulfonate + 0.05 mol/L sodium sulfate/ 50% acetonitrile + 50% 0.005 mol/L tartrate buffer (pH 3.0) + 0.01 mol/L sodium 1-butanesulfonate + 0.1 mol/L sodium sulfate, 16:9 (1.0 mL/min)	4 × 200	UV (220)	–	[70]
(β-Ala^1)-ACTH$_{1-18}$-NH$_2$	Nucleosil 5C$_{18}$ (5 μm)	0.005 mol/L Tartrate buffer (pH 3.0) + 0.005 mol/L sodium 1-butanesulfonate + 0.05 mol/L sodium sulfate/ 50% acetonitrile + 50% 0.005 mol/L tartrate buffer (pH 3.0) + 0.01 mol/L sodium 1-butanesulfonate + 0.1 mol/L sodium sulfate, 33:17 (1.0 mL/min)	4 × 200	UV (220)	–	[70]
(β-Ala^1)-ACTH$_{1-18}$-NH$_2$	Nucleosil 5C$_{18}$ (5 μm)	0.005 mol/L Tartrate buffer (pH 3.0) + 0.005 mol/L sodium 1-butanesulfonate + 0.05 mol/L sodium sulfate/ 50% acetonitrile + 50% 0.005 mol/L tartrate buffer (pH 3.0) + 0.01 mol/L sodium 1-butanesulfonate +	4 × 200	UV (220)	–	[70]

		0.1 mol/L sodium sulfate, 17:8 (1.0 mL/min)				
(Aib^1)-ACTH$_{1-18}$-NH$_2$	Nucleosil 5C$_{18}$ (5 µm)	0.005 mol/L Tartrate buffer (pH 3.0) + 0.005 mol/L sodium 1-butanesulfonate + 0.05 mol/L sodium sulfate/ 50% acetonitrile + 50% 0.005 mol/L tartrate buffer (pH 3.0) + 0.01 mol/L sodium 1-butanesulfonate + 0.1 mol/L sodium sulfate, 33:17 (1.0 mL/min)	4 × 200	UV (220)	–	[70]
(Ala^{10})-ACTH$_{1-18}$-NH$_2$	Nucleosil 5C$_{18}$ (5 µm)	0.005 mol/L Tartrate buffer (pH 3.0) + 0.005 mol/L sodium 1-butanesulfonate + 0.05 mol/L sodium sulfate/ 50% acetonitrile + 50% 0.005 mol/L tartrate buffer (pH 3.0) + 0.01 mol/L sodium 1-butanesulfonate + 0.1 mol/L sodium sulfate, 17:8 (1.0 mL/min)	4 × 200	UV (220)	–	[70]
(Ala^{10})-ACTH$_{1-18}$-NH$_2$	Nucleosil 5C$_{18}$ (5 µm)	0.005 mol/L Tartrate buffer (pH 3.0) + 0.005 mol/L sodium 1-butanesulfonate + 0.05 mol/L sodium sulfate/ 50% acetonitrile + 50% 0.005 mol/L tartrate buffer (pH 3.0) + 0.01 mol/L sodium 1-butanesulfonate + 0.1 mol/L sodium sulfate, 16:9 (1.0 mL/min)	4 × 200	UV (220)	–	[70]

Table 5-16. (Continued).

Peptide	Stationary Phase	Eluent	Column (mm)	Detection (nm)	k-Value	Reference
(D-Ala^{10})-ACTH$_{1-18}$-NH$_2$	Nucleosil 5C$_{18}$ (5 μm)	0.005 mol/L Tartrate buffer (pH 3.0) + 0.005 mol/L sodium 1-butanesulfonate + 0.05 mol/L sodium sulfate/ 50% acetonitrile + 50% 0.005 mol/L tartrate buffer (pH 3.0) + 0.01 mol/L sodium 1-butanesulfonate + 0.1 mol/L sodium sulfate, 16:9 (1.0 mL/min)	4 × 200	UV (220)	—	[70]
(Ala^{10})-ACTH$_{1-10}$-NH-NH$_2$	Nucleosil 5C$_{18}$ (5 μm)	0.005 mol/L Tartrate buffer (pH 3.0) + 0.005 mol/L sodium 1-butanesulfonate + 0.05 mol/L sodium sulfate/ 50% acetonitrile + 50% 0.005 mol/L tartrate buffer (pH 3.0) + 0.01 mol/L sodium 1-butanesulfonate + 0.1 mol/L sodium sulfate, 11:9 (1.0 mL/min)	4 × 200	UV (220)	—	[70]
(D-Ala^{10})-ACTH$_{1-10}$-NH-NH$_2$	Nucleosil 5C$_{18}$ (5 μm)	0.005 mol/L Tartrate buffer (pH 3.0) + 0.005 mol/L sodium 1-butanesulfonate + 0.05 mol/L sodium sulfate/ 50% acetonitrile + 50% 0.005 mol/L tartrate buffer (pH 3.0) + 0.01 mol/L sodium 1-butanesulfonate + 0.1 mol/L sodium sulfate, 11:9 (1.0 mL/min)	4 × 200	UV (220)	—	[70]

$(\beta\text{-Ala}^{10})\text{-ACTH}_{1-18}\text{-NH}_2$	Nucleosil 5C$_{18}$ (5 μm)	0.005 mol/L Tartrate buffer (pH 3.0) + 0.005 mol/L sodium 1-butanesulfonate + 0.05 mol/L sodium sulfate/ 50% acetonitrile + 50% 0.005 mol/L tartrate buffer (pH 3.0) + 0.01 mol/L sodium 1-butanesulfonate + 0.1 mol/L sodium sulfate, 16:9 (1.0 mL/min)	4 × 200	UV (220)	–	[70]
$(\text{Aib}^{10})\text{-ACTH}_{1-18}\text{-NH}_2$	Nucleosil 5C$_{18}$ (5 μm)	0.005 mol/L Tartrate buffer (pH 3.0) + 0.005 mol/L sodium 1-butanesulfonate + 0.05 mol/L sodium sulfate/ 50% acetonitrile + 50% 0.005 mol/L tartrate buffer (pH 3.0) + 0.01 mol/L sodium 1-butanesulfonate + 0.1 mol/L sodium sulfate, 16:9 (1.0 mL/min)	4 × 200	UV (220)	–	[70]
$(\beta\text{-Ala}^1, \text{D-Phe}^7, \text{Orn}^{15})\text{-ACTH}_{1-18}\text{-NH}_2$	Nucleosil 5C$_{18}$ (5 μm)	0.005 mol/L Tartrate buffer (pH 3.0) + 0.005 mol/L sodium 1-butanesulfonate + 0.05 mol/L sodium sulfate/ 50% acetonitrile + 50% 0.005 mol/L tartrate buffer (pH 3.0) + 0.01 mol/L sodium 1-butanesulfonate + 0.1 mol/L sodium sulfate, 16:9 (1.0 mL/min)	4 × 200	UV (220)	–	[70]
$(\text{Gly}^1, \text{Pro}^3)\text{-ACTH}_{1-18}\text{-NH}_2$	Nucleosil 5C$_{18}$ (5 μm)	0.005 mol/L Tartrate buffer (pH 3.0) + 0.005 mol/L sodium 1-butanesulfonate + 0.05 mol/L sodium sulfate/	4 × 200	UV (220)	–	[70]

Table 5-16. (Continued).

Peptide	Stationary Phase	Eluent	Column (mm)	Detection (nm)	k-Value	Reference
		50% acetonitrile + 50% 0.005 mol/L tartrate buffer (pH 3.0) + 0.01 mol/L sodium 1-butanesulfonate + 0.1 mol/L sodium sulfate, 17:8 (1.0 mL/min)				
(Lys^3, Ser^{11})-ACTH$_{1-18}$-NH$_2$	Nucleosil 5C$_{18}$ (5 μm)	0.005 mol/L Tartrate buffer (pH 3.0) + 0.005 mol/L sodium 1-butanesulfonate + 0.05 mol/L sodium sulfate/ 50% acetonitrile + 50% 0.005 mol/L tartrate buffer (pH 3.0) + 0.01 mol/L sodium 1-butanesulfonate + 0.1 mol/L sodium sulfate, 17:8 (1 mL/min)	4 × 200	UV (220)	–	[70]
(β-Ala^1, Orn^{15})-ACTH$_{1-18}$-NH$_2$	Nucleosil 5C$_{18}$ (5 μm)	0.005 mol/L Tartrate buffer (pH 3.0) + 0.005 mol/L sodium 1-butanesulfonate + 0.05 mol/L sodium sulfate/ 50% acetonitrile + 50% 0.005 mol/L tartrate buffer (pH 3.0) + 0.01 mol/L sodium 1-butanesulfonate + 0.1 mol/L sodium sulfate, 16:9 (1 mL/min)	4 × 200	UV (220)	–	[70]
(D-Ser^1, Lys^{17,18})-ACTH$_{1-18}$-NH$_2$	Partisil-ODS (10 μm)	A: 1% Trifluoroacetic acid, B: methanol/water/trifluoroacetic acid, 80:19:1, linear gradient from A to B (0.7 mL/min)	4 × 250	UV (280)	–	[8]

Table 5-17. Experimental Conditions for HPLC Separations of Melanotropins and Derivatives. (for Structures see Table 5-15).

Peptide	Stationary Phase	Eluent	Column (mm)	Detection (nm)	Retention Time (min)	Reference
α-MSH	LiChrosorb RP-8 (5 µm)	A: 0.01 mol/L Phosphate buffer (pH2.1), B: acetonitrile, from A to B, shaped gradient (2 mL/min)	4.6 × 250	UV (200)	–	[6]
α-MSH	Hypersil-ODS (5 µm)	A: 0.02 mol/L Phosphate buffer (pH 2.1), B: acetonitrile, from A to 60% B, tripartite linear gradient (1 mL/min)	5 × 100	UV (225) or fluorescence (275/370)	26.0	[14]
α-MSH	ODS (Bio-Rad)	A: 0.1 mol/L Sodium perchlorate + 5 mmol/L phosphate buffer (pH 7.4), B: 0.1 mol/L sodium perchlorate/acetonitrile, 2:3, linear gradient from A to B (0.75% acetonitrile/min)	–	UV (220) or fluorescence (fluorescemine)	46.2	[15]
α-MSH	ODS (Bio-Rad)	A: 0.1 mol/L Sodium perchlorate + 0.1% phosphoric acid, B: 0.1 mol/L sodium perchlorate + 0.1% phosphoric acid/acetonitrile (2:3), from A to B (0.75% acetonitrile/min)	–	UV (220) or fluorescence (fluorescamine)	46.2	[15]
α-MSH	µBondapak C₁₈	A:Water + 50 mmol/L sodium dihydrogen phosphate + 0.1% phosphoric acid, B:	–	UV (254)	–	[43]

Table 5-17. (Continued).

Peptide	Stationary Phase	Eluent	Column (mm)	Detection (nm)	Retention Time (min)	Reference
		acetonitrile/water + 50 mmol/L sodium dihydrogen phosphate + 0.1% phosphoric acid, 1:1, linear gradient from A to B, 60 min (1 mL/min)				
α-MSH	TSK-GEL 2000 SW (10 μm)	0.05 mol/L Sodium phosphate buffer (pH 7.2)/SDS, 99.7:0.3 (0.3 mL/min)	7.5 × 600	UV (210 or 280)	15.2 (elution volume)	[59]
α-MSH	μBondapak C$_{18}$ (10 μm)	A: 0.08% Trifluoroacetic acid, B: 49% acetonitrile in 0.08% trifluoroacetic acid, linear gradient from A to B in 20 min (1 mL/min)	3.9 × 300	UV (206)	18.9	[61]
α-MSH	Hypersil-ODS (5 μm)	A: 0.1 mol/L Phosphate buffer (pH 2.1), B: acetonitrile, tripartite gradient from A to 60% B in 50 min	5 × 100	UV (225)	–	[88]
α-MSH	μBondapak C$_{18}$	A: 0.02 mol/L Triethylamine-phosphate buffer (pH 3.0), B: 0.02 mol/L triethylamine-phosphate buffer (pH 3.0)/2-propanol, 1:1, from A to B linear gradient in 75 min (1 mL/min)	–	UV (210)	–	[92]
β-MSH$_{13-22}$	LiChrosorb RP-8 (5 μm)	A: 0.1 mol/L Phosphate buffer (pH 2.1), B: acetonitrile, from A to 100% B, shaped gradient (2 mL/min)	4.6 × 250	UV (200)	–	[6]

For reversed phase separations of weak organic acids and bases using water/methanol (acetonitrile) as mobile phases there exists the following relationship between the capacity factor k and the eluent surface tension γ (35);

$$\log k_i = C + \gamma \, \frac{N\Delta A + 4.836\,N^{1/3}(k_e - 1)\,V_m^{2/3}}{RT}$$

Where

ΔA	relative surface area of the solute molecule in contact with the stationary phase
C	is a constant,
N	Avogadro's number,
k_e	microscopic cavity factor
V_m	average molar volume of the mobile phase,
R	gas constant and
T	absolute temperature.

This linear relationship between $\log k$ and γ could be experimentally proven for $ACTH_{1-24}$ with a μBondapak C_{18} reversed phase column and acetonitrile/water or methanol/water combinations as mobile phases (Figure 5-26) [43].

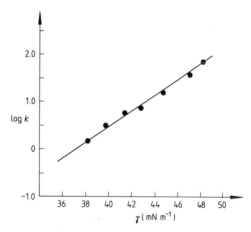

Figure 5-26. Plot of $\log k$ versus surface tension for $ACTH_{1-24}$. Chromatographic conditions: column: μBondapak C_{18}; flow-rate: 1 mL/min; mobile phase: acetonitrile/water/50 mmol/L NaH_2PO_4, with orthophosphoric acid to pH 2.5, run under isocratic conditions with 2% increases in acetonitrile content between each measurement (similar to reference [43]).

Retention times of peptides with ACTH structure are, in accordance with other polypeptides, dependent on the polarity of the organic modifier (Table 5-18).

Table 5-18. Effect of the Organic Modifier on the Retention Times of Porcine ACTH, $ACTH_{1-24}$ and α-MSH. – Chromatographic conditions: Column: Hypersil-ODS (5 μm, 100 × 5 mm i. d.); mobile phase: A: 0.2 mol/L NaH_2PO_4-H_3PO_4 (pH 2.1), B: organic solvent given below; detection: UV at 225 nm. The organic solvents are employed as the secondary solvent in a single linear gradient elution (50 min), giving a constant rate of change of 2%/min [14].

Peptide	Acetonitrile	Tetrahydrofuran	Dioxan	Methanol
$ACTH_{1-24}$	13.6	13.0	15.4	26.0
ACTH (porcine)	18.5	20.6	25.4	35.4
α-MSH	15.2	15.4	18.0	28.4

For peptides of the size of ACTH efficient separations are achieved only over a relatively small range of organic eluent concentration. At a somewhat higher percentage of organic solvent, the polypeptides are very rapidly eluted and at lower concentration of the organic modifier they are strongly bound to the reversed phase material. This effect is clearly demonstrated in Figure 5-27 for two peptides with the natural sequence of ACTH.

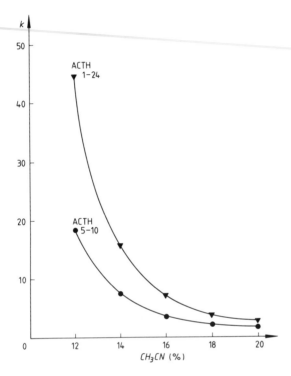

Figure 5-27. Effects of the acetonitrile concentration on the k-values of HPLC separations of $ACTH_{1-24}$ and $ACTH_{5-10}$. Chromatographic conditions: Column: Hypersil-ODS (5 µm, 100 × mm i. d.); mobile phase: 0.2 mol/L Na_2HPO_4-H_3PO_4 (pH 2.1)/acetonitrile (of different concentration as given in the figure), isocratic elution; flow-rate: 1.5 mL/min; detection: UV at 225 nm (similar to reference [14]).

As mentioned in Section 5.2.1 Meek developed a method for prediction of retention coefficients [15]. To test the applicability of this method for isocratic elution with different mobile phases, capacity factors of different ACTH derivatives were determined and compared with theoretical values. As a result a fairly good relationship between actual and predicted elution order is found (Table 5-19, Figure 5-28 [86]).

As is obvious from Table 5-15, the sequences of human ACTH and porcine ACTH differ only in position 31, the Leu residue in the porcine hormone is exhanged by a Ser residue in the human peptide. Successful separation of both hormones by RP-HPLC (Figure 5-29) makes this technique an invaluable tool in peptide research [70].

With similar conditions to those given in the legend of Figure 5-29 (content of acetonitrile in the mobile phase 18% resp. 16%) five $ACTH_{1-18}$ derivatives differing in only 1 amino acid are well separable:

(β-Ala^{10})-$ACTH_{1-18}$-NH_2, $ACTH_{1-18}$-NH_2, (L-Ala^{10})-$ACTH_{1-18}$-NH_2, (D-Ala^{10})-$ACTH_{1-18}$-NH_2 and (Aib^{10})-$ACTH_{1-18}$-NH_2 [70].

During synthesis or isolation of ACTH, the methionine residue at position 4 may be oxidized to its sulfoxide; differentiation between the oxidized and reduced form of methionine peptides is urgently required in the laboratories of peptides research. There is no better method available to

Table 5-19. Comparison of Predicted and Actual Capacity Factors of ACTH Derivatives. – Chromatographic conditions: Column: Nucleosil 10 C_{18} (250 × 4.6 mm i. d.); eluent I: acetonitrile/methanol (16.7:83.3) 0.1 mol/L sodium sulfate in 0.01 mol/L phosphate buffer (pH 2.2) 35:65; eluent II: isopropanol/methanol (16.7:83.3) 0.1 mol/L sodium perchlorate in 0.01 mol/L phosphate buffer (pH 2.2) 35:65; flow-rate: 1 mL/min; detection: UV at 215 nm. A retention time of 2.0 min is assumed for unretained compounds [86].

	No. of Residues	k Predicted pH 2.1	Actual Eluent I	Actual Eluent II
$ACTH_{15-32}$	18	2.15	1.5	0
$ACTH_{1-32}$	32	13.8	7.5	4.7
$ACTH_{1-14}$	14	20.15	10.1	9.1
$ACTH_{1-24}$	24	26.25	13.9	17.7
$ACTH_{1-28}$	28	20.8	10.6	10.0

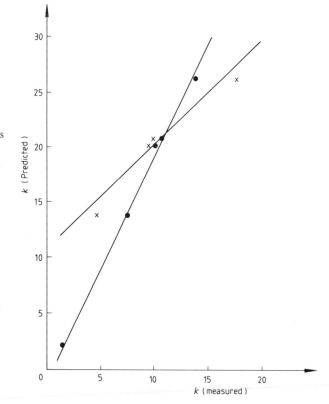

Figure 5-28. Correlation of experimentally determined versus predicted [15] k-values for ACTH derivatives ($ACTH_{15-32}$, $ACTH_{1-32}$, $ACTH_{1-14}$, $ACTH_{1-24}$ and $ACTH_{1-28}$). Experimental conditions: Column: Nucleosil 10 C_{18} (250 × 4.6 mm i. d.); flow-rate: 1 mL/min; detection UV at 215 nm; mobile phases: × – × – × acetonitrile/methanol 16.7:83.3/0.1 mol/L sodium sulfate in 0.01 mol/L phosphate buffer (pH 2.2) 35:65; •–•–• isopropanol/acetonitrile 33 3:66.7/0.1 mol/L sodium perchlorate in 0.01 mol/L phosphate buffer (pH 2.2) 4:6 (similar to reference [86]).

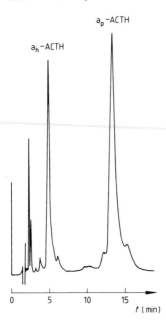

a_h-ACTH

a_p-ACTH

0   5   10   15
t (min)

Figure 5-29. HPLC separation of porcine (a_p) and human (a_h) ACTH. Column: Nucleosil $5C_{18}$ (5 μm, 200 × 4 mm i. d.); mobile phase: A: 0.005 mol/L tartrate buffer (pH 3.0) + 0.005 mol/L sodium 1-butanesulfonate + 0.05 mol/L sodium sulfate; B: acetonitrile/0.005 mol/L tartrate buffer (pH 3.0) + 0.01 mol/L sodium 1-butanesulfonate + 0.1 mol/L sodium sulfate (1 : 1), 2 : 3, (A : B); flow-rate: 1 mL/min; detection UV at 220 nm (similar to reference [70]).

fulfil this requirement than HPLC, as demonstrated in Figure 5-30 for (Gly^1)-ACTH$_{1-18}$-NH$_2$ and its sulfoxide.

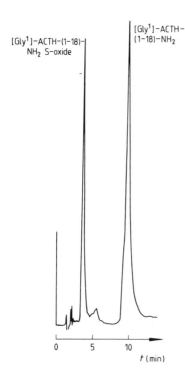

[Gly^1]-ACTH-(1-18)-NH$_2$ S-oxide

[Gly^1]-ACTH-(1-18)-NH$_2$

0   5   10
t (min)

Figure 5-30. HPLC separation of (Gly)^1-ACTH$_{1-18}$-NH$_2$ and its sulfoxide. Column: Nucleosil $5\,C_{18}$ (5 μm, 200 × 4 mm i. d.); mobile phase A: 0.005 mol/L tartrate buffer (pH 3.0) + 0.005 mol/L sodium 1-butanesulfonate + 0.05 mol/L sodium sulfate, B: acetonitrile/0.005 mol/L tartrate buffer (pH 3.0) + 0.01 mol/L sodium 1-butanesulfonate + 0.1 mol/L sodium sulfate (1 : 1), 16 : 9 (A :); flow-rate: 1 mL/min; detection: UV at 220 nm (similar to reference [70].

Similarly, the chromatogram (Figure 5-31) of a sample of α-MSH, purified by conventional methods, must convince every peptide researcher that there is no better method currently available for the control of the purity of peptides than High Performance Liquid Chromatography.

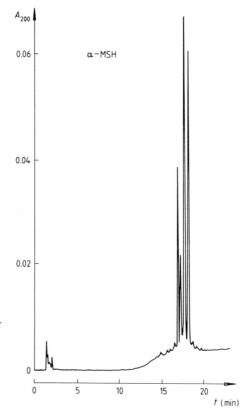

Figure 5-31. Chromatogram of α-MSH, purified by conventional methods. Column: LiChrosorb RP-8 (5 μm, 250 × 4.6 mm i. d.); mobile phase: gradient elution from 0.1 mol/L phosphate buffer (pH 2.1) with acetonitrile as the gradient former (shaped gradient from 0 to 100% acetonitrile); flow-rate: 2 mL/min; detection: UV at 200 nm (similar to reference [6].

So far the nature of the individual peaks in Figure 5-31 of the "pure" α-MSH sample have not been determined. They may be caused by different conformers, peptides of different sequence or methionine sulfoxide derivatives.

HPLC is also increasingly used to isolate natural peptides such as ACTH and its fragments from biological sources. After intravenous injection of $ACTH_{1-24}$ into rats, specifically labelled with ^{3}H in the residues 2,7 and 23, it can be shown (Figure 5-32) that within 2 min the main circulating products are the injected material and its sulfoxide. Smaller amounts of $ACTH_{17-24}$, $ACTH_{18-24}$, $ACTH_{9-24}$, $ACTH_{1-20}$, $ACTH_{2-20}$, $ACTH_{3-20}$ and $ACTH_{1-15}$ are formed by peptidases. This result is of great importance for the application of biologically active peptides in medicine [8].

A successful HPLC separation and identification by radioimmonoassay was described recently for carboxy-terminal ACTH fragments from rat pituitary pars intermedia [61]. As stationary phase a μBondapak C_{18} column (300 × 3.9 mm i. d.) was used.

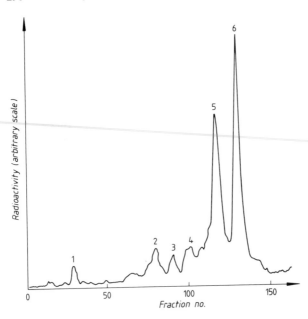

Figure 5-32. HPLC chromatogram of ^{3}H-labelled peptides extracted from plasma of ten rats after circulation 2 min after intravenous injection of ^{3}H-labelled ACTH$_{1-24}$. Plasma extracts are prepared by deproteinization with an equal volume of 30% trifluoroacetic acid and purification of the supernatant on an 0.5 mL octadecasilyl-Spherisorb (10 μm) column with 3 × 0.5 mL 1% trifluoroacetic acid and 0.5 mL methanol/water/trifluoroacetic acid (80:19:1). Conditions for the HPLC separation: Column: Partisil-ODS (10 μm, 250 × 4 mm i. d.); mobile phase: linear gradient from methanol/water/trifluoroacetic acid, 20:79:1 to methanol/water/trifluoroacetic acid, 55:44:1; flow-rate: 0.7 mL/min; detection: by radioactivity (in arbitrary scale) in 10 μL portions; 1: ACTH$_{17-24}$ and ACTH$_{18-24}$; 2: ACTH$_{9-24}$; 3: ACTH$_{1-20}$, ACTH$_{2-20}$ and ACTH$_{3-20}$; 4: ACTH$_{1-15}$; 5: ACTH$_{1-24}$, sulfoxide; 6: ACTH$_{1-24}$, (similar to reference [8].

5.3.3.2 Luteinizing Hormone (LH), Follicle-Stimulating Hormone (FSH), Prolactin, Growth Hormone (GH) and Lipotropin (LPH)

There is a relatively small number of publications about the separation of adenohypophysial hormones with protein character [14, 56, 61, 88, 93 to 95]. Structural characteristics are surveyed in Table 5-15 and experimental conditions for HPLC separations are collected in Table 5-20. In principle, two different HPLC techniques have been applied so far: Reversed phase [14, 56, 61, 88, 89, 94, 95] and gel filtration chromatography [93].

In a fundamental study, Nice et al. [94] could demonstrate that proteins can be successfully separated on stationary phases of short-chain alkylsilane-bonded silicas. Characteristics of the investigated packing material are surveyed in Table 5-21.

Retention times for different proteins on short-chain alkylsilane-bonded phase columns including prolactin (ovine and rat) and growth hormone are given in Table 5-22.

The efficient protein separation with short-chain alkylsilane-bonded silica phases is demonstrated by Figure 5-33. Though many proteins may be too hydrophobic to be successfully

Table 5-20. Experimental Conditions for HPLC Separations of Adenohypophysial Hormones with Protein Character.

Hormone (derivative)	Stationary Phase	Eluent	Column (mm)	Detection (nm)	Retention Time (min)	Reference
Luteinizing hormone	TSK G3000SW	0.1 mol/L Sodium acetate buffer (pH 7), (0.5 mL/min)	7.5 × 300	UV (216)	–	[93]
Follicle-stimulating hormone	TSK G3000SW	0.1 mol/L Sodium acetate buffer (pH 7), (0.5 mL/min)	7.5 × 300	UV (216)	–	[93]
Prolactin (rat)	LiChrosorb RP-2 (5 to 7 μm)	A: 0.155 mol/L Sodium chloride (pH 2.1, adjusted with HCl), B: acetonitrile, linear gradient from A to 75% B in 90 min (1 mL/min)	5 × 150	UV (215 or 280) or fluorescence (225/340 or 280/370)	17.3 (rel. to lysozyme = 0)	[94]
Prolactin (rat)	Ultrasphere SAC (4 to 6 μm)	A: 0.155 mol/L Sodium chloride (pH 2.1, adjusted with HCl), B: acetonitrile, linear gradient from A to 75% B in 90 min (1 mL/min)	5 × 150	UV (215 or 280) or fluorescence (225/340 or 280/370)	25.0 (rel. to lysozyme)	[94]
Prolactin (rat)	Spherisorb S5C6 (3 to 7 μm)	A: 0.155 mol/L Sodium chloride (pH 2.1, adjusted with HCl), B: acetonitrile, linear gradient from A to 75% B in 90 min (1 mL/min)	5 × 150	UV (215 or 280) or fluorescence (225/340 or 280/370)	20.0 (rel. to lysozyme)	[94]
Prolactin (rat)	Li Chrosorb RP-8 (4 to 7 μm)	A: 0.155 mol/L Sodium chloride (pH 2.1, adjusted with HCl), B: acetonitrile, linear gradient from A to 75% B in 90 min (1 mL/min)	5 × 150	UV (215 or 280) or fluorescence (225/340 or 280/370)	29.1 (rel. to lysozyme)	[94]
Prolactin (ovine)	LiChrosorb RP-2 (5 to 7 μm)	A: 0.155 mol/L Sodium chloride (pH 2.1, adjusted with HCl), B: acetonitrile, linear gradient from A to 75% B in 90 min (1 mL/min)	3 × 150	UV (215 or 280) or fluorescence (225/340 or 280/370)	13.1 (rel. to lysozyme)	[94]

Table 5-20. (Continued).

Hormone (derivative)	Stationary Phase	Eluent	Column (mm)	Detection (nm)	Retention Time (min)	Reference
Prolactin (ovine)	Ultrasphere SAC (4 to 6 μm)	A: 0.155 mol/L Sodium chloride (pH 2.1, adjusted with HCl), B: acetonitrile, linear gradient from A to 75% B in 90 min (1 mL/min)	3 × 150	UV (215 or 280) or fluorescence (225/340 or 280/370)	16.7 (rel. to lysozyme)	[94]
Prolactin (ovine)	Spherisorb S5C6 (3 to 7 μm)	A: 0.155 mol/L Sodium chloride (pH 2.1, adjusted with HCl), B: acetonitrile, linear gradient from A to 75% B in 90 min (1 mL/min)	3 × 150	UV (215 or 280) or fluorescence (225/340 or 280/370)	16.6 (rel. to lysozyme)	[94]
Prolactin (ovine)	LiChrosorb RP-8 (4 to 7 μm)	A: 0.155 mol/L Sodium chloride (pH 2.1, adjusted with HCl), B: acetonitrile, linear gradient from A to 75% B in 90 min (1 mL/min)	3 ×m 150	UV (215 or 280) or fluorescence (225/340 or 280/370)	16.6 (rel. to lysozyme)	[94]
Growth hormone (human)	TSK G2000SW	0.1 mol/L Sodium phosphate buffer (pH 7), (0.5 mL/min)	7.5 × 300	UV (210)	–	[93]
Growth hormone (human)	TSK G3000SW	0.1 mol/L Sodium phosphate buffer (pH 7), (0.5 mL/min)	7.5 × 300	UV (216)	–	[93]
Growth hormone (bovine)	LiChrosorb RP-2 (5 to 7 μm)	A: 0.155 mol/L Sodium chloride (pH 2.1, adjusted with HCl), B: acetonitrile, linear gradient from A to 75% B in 90 min (1 mL/min)	5 × 150	UV (215 or 280) or fluorescence (225/340 or 280/370)	17.3 (rel. to lysozyme = 0)	[94]
Growth hormone (bovine)	Ultrasphere SAC (4 to 6 μm)	A: 0.155 mol/L Sodium chloride (pH 2.1, adjusted with HCl), B: acetonitrile, linear gradient from A to 75% B in 90 min (1 mL/min)	5 × 150	UV (215 or 280) or fluorescence (225/340 or 280/370)	29.0 (rel. to lysozyme = 0)	[94]

Substance	Column packing	Mobile phase / conditions	Dimensions	Detection	Value	Ref.
Growth hormone (bovine)	LiChrosorb RP-8 (4 to 7 μm)	A: 0.155 mol/L Sodium chloride (pH 2.1, adjusted with HCl), B: acetonitrile, linear gradient from A to 75% B in 90 min (1 mL/min)	5 × 150	UV (215 or 280) or fluorescence (225/340 or 280/370)	39.4 (rel. to lysozyme)	[94]
β-Lipotropin (human)	Hypersil-ODS (5 μm)	A: 0.1 mol/L Phosphate buffer (pH 2.1), B: acetonitrile, gradient from A to 60% B in 50 min, tripartite linear gradient	5 × 100	UV (225) or fluorescence (275/370)	34.5	[14]
β-Lipotropin	μ-Bondapak C_{18} (10 μm)	Linear gradient from 3.5 to 49% acetonitrile containing 0.08% trifluoroacetic acid over 20 min (1 mL/min)	3.9 × 300	UV (206)	21.4	[61]
γ-Lipotropin	μ-Bondapak C_{18}	Linear gradient from 3.5 to 49% acetonitrile containing 0.08% trifluoroacetic acid over 20 min (1 mL/min)	3.9 × 300	UV (206)	19.5	[61]
β-Lipotropin 34-39 (ovine)	Hypersil-ODS (5 μm)	A: 0.1 mol/L Phosphate buffer (pH 2.1), B: acetonitrile, gradient from A to 60% B in 50 min (tripartite linear gradient in 50 min)	5 × 100	UV (225) or fluorescence (275/370)	8.5	[14]
β-Lipotropin 34-39	Hypersil-ODS (5 μm)	0.1 mol/L Phosphate buffer (pH 2.1) eluted with acetonitrile (tripartite linear gradient to 60% acetonitrile in 50 min)	5 × 100	UV (225) or fluorescence (275/370)	–	[88]
β-Lipotropin 61-65 (Met-enkephalin)	Hypersil-ODS (5 μm)	0.1 mol/L Phosphate buffer (pH 2.1) eluted with acetonitrile (tripartite linear gradient to 60% acetonitrile in 50 min)	5 × 100	UV (225) or fluorescence (275/370)	–	[88]

Table 5-20. (Continued).

Hormone (derivative)	Stationary Phase	Eluent	Column (mm)	Detection (nm)	Retention Time (min)	Reference
β-Lipotropin 61-76 (α-endorphin)	Hypersil-ODS (5 μm)	0.1 mol/L Phosphate buffer (pH 2.1) eluted with acetonitrile (tripartite linear gradient to 60% acetonitrile in 50 min)	5 × 100	UV (225) or fluorescence (275/370)	–	[88]
β-Lipotropin 61-91 (β-endorphin)	Hypersil-ODS (5 μm)	0.1 mol/L Phosphate buffer (pH 2.1) eluted with acetonitrile (tripartite linear gradient to 60% acetonitrile in 50 min)	5 × 100	UV (225) or fluorescence (275/370)	–	[88]

Table 5-21. Characteristics of Short-Chain Alkylsilane-Bonded Silica Packing Material Used for HPLC Protein Separations [94].

Packing	Carbon Chain-length	Particle Size (μm)	Pore Diameter (nm)	Pore Vol. (mL/g)	Specific Surface Area (m²/g)	Shape
LiChrosorb RP-2	1	5 to 7	–	–	500	Irregular
Ultrasphere SAC	3	4 to 6	8	0.57	180	Spherical
Spherisorb S5C6	6	3 to 7	8	0.57	200	Spherical
LiChrosorb RP-8	8	4 to 7	–	–	>250	Irregular

Table 5-22. Retention Times of Proteins Relative to Lysozyme ($= 0$) of HPLC Separations for Short Alkylsilane-Bonded Stationary Phases. Chromatographic conditions: Columns (150×5 mm i. d.); as listed in the table; mobile phase: A: 0.155 mol/L NaCl solution (pH 2.1, with hydrochloric acid), B: acetonitrile, linear gradient elution from 0 to 75% B in 90 min; flow-rate: 1 mL/min; detection: UV at 215 nm [94].

Protein	Relative Molecular Mass	LiChrosorb RP-2	Ultrasphere SAC	Spherisorb S5C6	LiChrosorb RP-8
Ribonuclease A (bovine pancreas type III A)	14 200	−10.2	−10.7	−11.3	−12.0
Epidermal growth factor (mouse)	6 000	–	−7.6	−8.0	–
Calcitonin (synthetic, human)	3 400	−4.1	−4.4	−4.1	−5.0
Cytochrome c (horse heart type III)	11 700	−2.5	−3.1	−2.3	−3.8
Parathyroid hormone (bovine)	9 500	−2.4	−2.3	−2.1	−2.6
Lysozyme (hen egg white)	14 300	0	0	0	0
Bovine serum albumin (fraction V)	68 000	3.2	3.3	5.8	7.2
Human serum albumin	66 500	3.8	3.5	–	–
α-Lactalbumin (bovine)	14 200	4.6	7.4	6.6	7.2
α-Lactalbumin (rat)	14 200	4.9	–	7.9	–
Myoglobin	17 200	7.1	9.0	9.5	8.9
α-Hemoglobin (bovine)	15 100	8.2	9.2	9.6	11.3
Carbonic anhydrase (bovine erythrocytes)	29 000	9.8	9.5	9.6	10.0
β-Lactoglobulin A (bovine milk)	18 300	10.1	10.0	–	8.8
β-Lactoglobulin B (bovine milk)	18 300	10.1	10.0	–	8.8
Elastase (porcine pankreas type III)	25 900	11.1	10.0	11.7	–
Prolactin (ovine P-S-13)	22 600	13.1	16.7	16.6	16.6
Human placental lactogen	22 100	14.3	20.2	17.6	18.5
Prolactin (rat PRL-B-2)	22 600	17.3	25.0	20.0	29.1
Growth hormone (bovine GH-B-18)	22 000	17.3	29.0	–	39.4

chromatographed under these conditions (Table 5-22, Figure 5-33), the method is certainly a valuable separation technique in combination with size-exclusion and ion-exchange chromatography.

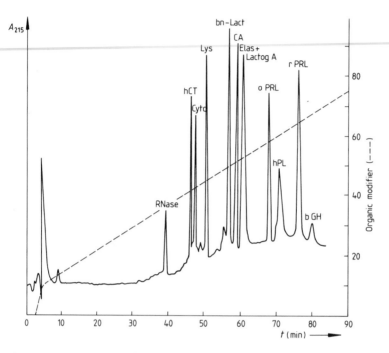

Figure 5-33. HPLC separation of 12 proteins including growth hormone and prolaction. Column: Ultrasphere SAC (4 to 6 μm); mobile phase: linear gradient of acetonitrile (dotted line) in 0.155 mol/L sodium chloride (pH 2.1); flow-rate: 1 mL/min; temperature: 45 °C; detection: UV at 215 nm; RNase: ribonuclease A (bovine pancreas type III A), hCT: calcitonin (synthetic human), Cyt c: cytochrome c (horse heart type III), Lys: lysozyme (hen egg white), b α-Lact: α-lactalbumin (bovine), CA: carbonic anhydrase (bovine erythrocytes), Elas: elastase (porcine pancreas type III), Lactog A: β-lactoglobulin A (bovine milk), o PRL: prolactin (ovine P-S-13), hPL: human placental lactogen, r PrL: prolactin (rat PRL-B-2), b GH: growth hormone (bovine GH-B-18), (similar to reference [94].

If the elution order of the proteins is compared with their net hydrophobicity (Table 5-23) then a general correlation, with some anomalies, becomes obvious. The anomalies are most probably due to conformational effects.

An attractive alternative to reversed phase chromatography on short-chain alkylsilane-bonded silica phases is high performance gel filtration chromatography, since suitable pressure-stable material is available [93, 96 to 101]. High performance gel filtration chromatography was recently successfully applied to the purification of the glycoprotein hormones follicle-stimulating hormone (FSH), luteinizing hormone (LH) and human chorionic gonadotropin (HCG) and also to the protein growth hormone [93].

Table 5-23. Correlation Between Elution Order and Hydrophobicity of Proteins in HPLC Chromatograms Using Short-Chain Alkylsilane-Bonded Silicas as Stationary Phases. Chromatographic conditions: see Figure 5-33; mole % hydrophobicity is calculated with respect to Trp, Phe, Leu, Ile, Tyr, Val and Met [94].

Protein	Relative Molecular Mass	Mole % hydrophobicity	Elution order
Ribonuclease A	13 700	21.8	1
Cytochrome c	11 700	25.0	2
Lysozyme	14 300	26.4	3
Human serum albumin	66 500	28.37	4
Bovine serum albumin	69 000	32.0	5
α-Lactalbumin (bovine)	14 200	32.5	6
Carbonic anhydrase	29 000	31.49	7
α-Haemoglobin	15 100	31.20	8
Myoglobin	17 200	31.37	8
Elastase	25 900	32.5	10
β-Lactoglobulin	18 300	34.6	10
Prolactin (ovine)	22 600	32.8	12
Human placental lactogen	22 100	33.7	13
Growth hormone (bovine)	22 000	34.0	14

5.3.4 Pancreatic Hormones

The pancreas secretes two types of hormones: the α-type of islet cells produce glucagon; and the biosynthesis of insulin takes place in the β-type of islet cells. The structures of both hormones are shown in Figure 5-33a.

The method of HPLC purification (experimental detail see Table 5-24) is elaborated in a fairly good number of communications for the insulins [7, 8, 14, 15, 43, 56, 59, 70, 71, 86, 90, 102, 104, 105] and glucagon [8, 14, 15, 50, 56, 59, 66, 90, 103, 106].

Reversed phase chromatography is one of the most useful methods for rapid investigation of the purity of insulins. The method allows detection of impurities in most commercially available samples [70]. Though human insulin differs from porcine insulin only by a single amino acid in position B 30 and the latter from bovine insulin by two amino acids all three hormones of different source can easily be separated from each other as is demonstrated by Figure 5-34.

The order of elution of the closely related insulins is explained in terms of the hydrophobicity of the amino acid residues. However, conformational effects may lead to unexpected elution order. For HPLC separation of insulins the type and concentration of the organic modifier and the salinity of the eluant have a significant influence on the mode of separation.

The separation of bovine from porcine insulin on a Nucleosil 10 C_{18} column (250 × 4.6 mm i. d.) can be achieved only if sodium sulfate (0.1 mol/L) is added to the mobile phase (methanol/acetonitrile/0.01 mol/L phosphate buffer (pH 2.2, 5 : 1 : 4) [86]. The capacity ratios for insulins increase in the order of isopropanol, tetrahydrofuran, acetonitrile, methanol for the mobile phase mixtures methanol/X (organic solvent)/0.1 mol/L sodium perchlorate (Table 5-25).

Glucagon

```
    1   2   3   4   5   6   7   8   9   10  11  12  13  14  15  16  17  18  19  20  21  22  23  24
H-His-Ser-Gln-Gly-Thr-Phe-Thr-Ser-Asp-Tyr-Ser-Lys-Tyr-Leu-Asp-Ser-Arg-Arg-Ala-Gln-Asp-Phe-Val-Gln-
   25  26  27  28  29  30
Trp-Leu-Met-Asn-Thr-OH
```

Insulin

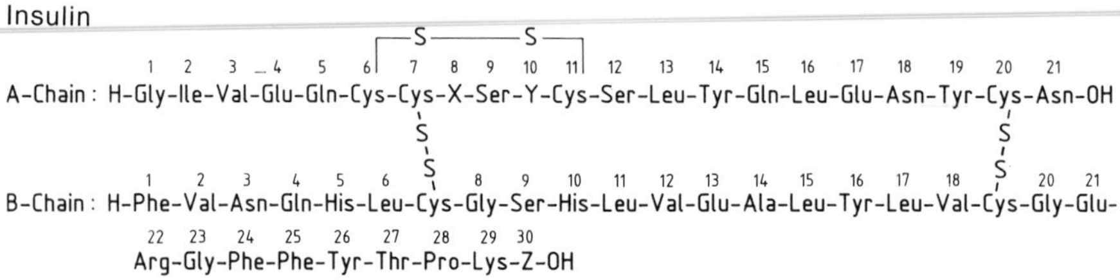

```
                                          ┌──S───────S──┐
          1   2   3  _4   5   6│  7   8   9   10  11│ 12  13  14  15  16  17  18  19  20  21
A-Chain: H-Gly-Ile-Val-Glu-Gln-Cys-Cys-X-Ser-Y-Cys-Ser-Leu-Tyr-Gln-Leu-Glu-Asn-Tyr-Cys-Asn-OH
                                          S                                           S
                                          ╎                                           ╎
          1   2   3   4   5   6   S   8   9   10  11  12  13  14  15  16  17  18  S   20  21
B-Chain: H-Phe-Val-Asn-Gln-His-Leu-Cys-Gly-Ser-His-Leu-Val-Glu-Ala-Leu-Tyr-Leu-Val-Cys-Gly-Glu-
           22  23  24  25  26  27  28  29  30
          Arg-Gly-Phe-Phe-Tyr-Thr-Pro-Lys-Z-OH
```

Insulins	A-Chain		B-Chain
	X	Y	Z
Human	Thr	Ile	Thr
Porcine	Thr	Ile	Ala
Bovine	Ala	Val	Ala

Figure 5-33a. Peptide sequences of glucagon and insulins.

Table 5-24. Experimental Conditions for HPLC Separations of Insulins and Glucagon.

Hormone (derivative)	Stationary Phase	Eluent	Column (mm)	Detection (nm)	Retention Time (min)	Reference
Insulin (porcine)	Partisil-ODS (10 μm)	A: 1% Trifluoroacetic acid, B: methanol/water/trifluoro-acetic acid, 80:19:1, linear gradient from A to B (0.7 mL/min)	4×250	UV (280)	–	[8]
Insulin (bovine)	Hypersil-ODS (5 μm)	A: 0.1 mol/L phosphate buffer (pH 2.1), B: acetonitrile, tripartite linear gradient from A to 60% B (1 to 1.5 mL/min)	5×100	UV (225) or fluorescence (275/370)	32.0	[14]
Insulin (porcine)	TSK-Gel 2000SW (10 μm)	0.05 mol/L Sodium phosphate buffer (pH 7.2)/SDS, 99.7:0.3 (0.3 mL/min)	7.5×600	UV (210 or 280)	14.6 (elution volume)	[59]
Insulin (bovine)	Nucleosil 5 C_{18} (5 μm)	A: 0.005 mol/L Tartrate buffer (pH 3.0) + 0.005 mol/L sodium 1-butanesulfonate + 0.05 mol/L sodium sulfate, B: acetonitrile (50%) + 0.005 mol/L tartrate buffer (pH 3.0) + 0.01 mol/L sodium 1-butanesulfonate + 0.1 mol/L sodium sulfate, 41.6:58.4 (1.0 mL/min)	4×200	UV (220)	–	[70]
Insulin (porcine)	Nucleosil 5 C_{18} (5 μm)	A: 0.005 mol/L Tartrate buffer (pH 3.0) + 0.005 mol/L sodium 1-butane-sulfonate + 0.05 mol/L sodium sulfate, B: acetonitrile	4×200	UV (220)	–	[70]

Table 5-24. (Continued).

Hormone (derivative)	Stationary Phase	Eluent	Column (mm)	Detection (nm)	Retention Time (min)	Reference
		(50%) + 0.005 mol/L tartrate buffer (pH 3.0) + 0.01 mol/L sodium 1-butanesulfonate + 0.1 mol/L sodium sulfate, 41.6 : 58.4 (1.0 mL/min)				
Insulin (human)	Nucleosil 5 C$_{18}$ (5 µm)	A: 0.005 mol/L Tartrate buffer (pH 3.0) + 0.005 mol/L sodium 1-butanesulfonate + 0.05 mol/L sodium sulfate, B: acetonitrile (50%) + 0.005 mol/L tartrate buffer (pH 3.0) + 0.01 mol/L sodium 1-butanesulfonate + 0.1 mol/L sodium sulfate, 41.6 : 58.4 (1.0 mL/min)	4 × 200	UV (220)	–	[70]
Insulin	µBondapak C$_{18}$ (10 µm)	Methanol/0.1% phosphoric acid, 3 : 2	4 × 300	UV (225)	6.0	[90]
Insulin (porcine)	Nucleosil 10 C$_{18}$	Methanol/acetonitrile/phosphate buffer (pH 2.2) + 0.1 mol/L sodium sulfate, 5 : 1 : 4	4.6 × 250	UV (215)	–	[86]
Insulin (bovine)	Nucleosil 10 C$_{18}$	Methanol/acetonitrile/phosphate buffer (pH 2.2), 5 : 1 : 4 (1 mL/min)	4.6 × 250	UV (215)	–	[86]
Insulin	Nucleosil 10 C$_{18}$	A: 0.05 mol/L Potassium dihydrogen phosphate/2-methoxyethanol (pH 2, adjusted	4 × 300	UV (280)	–	[102]

Compound	Packing	Mobile phase	Column (mm)	Detection		Ref.
(Thr^{B30})-insulin (bovine)	Nucleosil 5C$_{18}$ (5 μm)	with phosphoric acid), 95:5, B: isopropanol/2-methoxy-ethanol (pH 2, adjusted with phosphoric acid), 95:5, linear gradient from 90% A to 50% A	4 × 200	UV (220)	—	[70]
Glucagon	Hypersil-ODS (5 μm)	A: 0.005 mol/L tartrate buffer (pH 3.0) + 0.005 mol/L sodium 1-buta-nesulfonate + 0.05 mol/L sodium sulfate, B: acetonitrile (50%) + 0.005 mol/L tartrate buffer (pH 3.0) + 0.01 mol/L so-dium 1-butanesulfonate + 0.1 mol/L sodium sulfate, 41.6:58.4 (1.0 mL/min)	5 × 100	UV (225) or fluorescence (275/370)	36.0	[14]
Glucagon	Bio-Rad ODS (10 μm)	A:0.1 mol/L phosphate buf-fer (pH 2.1), B: acetonitrile, tripartite gradient from A to 60% B (1 to 1.5 mL/min)	—	UV (200 or 220) or fluorescence (fluorescamine)	53.6	[15]
Glucagon	Bio-Rad ODS (10 μm)	A: 0.1 mol/L Sodium per-chlorate + 5 mmol/L phos-phate buffer (pH 7.4), B: 0.1 mol/L sodium perchlora-te/60% acetonitrile, linear gradient from A to B (0.75% acetonitrile/min)	—	UV (200 or 220) or fluorescence (fluorescamine)	60.0	[15]
		A: 0.1 mol/L Sodium per-chlorate + 5 mmol/L phos-phate buffer + 0.1% phos-phoric acid (pH 2.1), B: 0.1 mol/L sodium perchlora-				

Table 5-24. (Continued).

Hormone (derivative)	Stationary Phase	Eluent	Column (mm)	Detection (nm)	Retention Time (min)	Reference
		te + 0.1% phosphoric acid/ 60% acetonitrile, linear gradient from A to B (0.75% acetonitrile/min)				
Glucagon	TSK-Gel 2000 SW (10 μm)	0.05 mol/L Sodium phosphate buffer (pH 7.2)/SDS, 99.7:0.3 (0.3 mL/min)	7.5 ×600	UV (210 or 280)	14.8 (elution volume)	[59]
Glucagon	Bondapak C$_{18}$ Corasil	Methanol/0.1% phosphoric acid, 2:3	4×300	UV (225)	4.6	[90]
Glucagon	Polygosil C$_{18}$ (10 μm)	Methanol/water/trifluoro-acetic acid, 65:35:0.1 (1.2 mL/min)	4×300	UV (205)	–	[103]

Figure 5-34. HPLC chromatogram of purified (Thr^{B30})-bovine, bovine, human and porcine insulins. Column: Nucleosil 5C$_{18}$ (5 μm, 200 × 4 mm, i. d.); mobile phase: A: 0.005 mol/L tartrate buffer (pH 3.0) + 0.005 mol/L sodium 1-butanesulfonate + 0.05 mol/L sodium sulfate, B: acetonitrile (50%)/0.005 mol/L tartrate buffer (pH 3.0) + 0.1 mol/L sodium 1-butanesulfonate + 0.1 mol/L sodium sulfate (50%), A:B = 41.6:58.4; flow-rate: 1.0 mL/min; detection: UV at 220 nm (similar to reference [70].

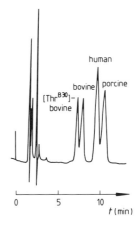

Table 5-25. Dependence of Capicity Ratios k for Bovine and Porcine Insulin on Organic Solvents. – Chromatographic conditions: Column: Nucleosil 10 C$_{18}$ (250 × 4.6 mm i. d.); mobile phase: methanol/X/0.1 mol/L sodium perchlorate (pH 2.2), 5:1:4 [86].

	Isopropanol	Tetrahydrofuran	Acetonitrile	Methanol
Bovine insulin	0.17	1.01	2.69	4.23
Porcine insulin	0.18	1.95	4.10	9.10

Prolonged use of reversed phase columns causes a decrease in their efficiency especially in the chromatography of larger sized peptides like glucagon. After silylation of the reversed phase packing material with chlorodimethyloctadecylsilane in toluene a reasonably efficient separation can be achieved again [103].

By high-performance sodium dodecyl sulfate gel chromatography on recently developed packing material (TSK-GEL 2000 SW) peptides and proteins with a molecular weight (MW) > 5000 seem to be eluted in order of their molecular size. However, smaller peptides like insulin (MW 5782) and glucagon (MW 3485) are separated according to a different mechanism [59].

5.3.5 Hormones of Different Origin

Similar HPLC techniques to those described in the previous sections were applied for neuropeptides like angiotensins [6, 15, 43, 52, 72, 90, 107], bombesin [14, 66], neurotensin [14, 15, 66], substance P [14, 43, 64, 71], for hormones like calcitonin [52, 71, 89, 108, 109], parathyroid hormone [110], secretin [111], peptides with suggested hormonal effects like sleep-inducing peptide [52], tuftsin [15, 112] or thyromimetic iodoamino acids [113 to 117].

In the sequential synthesis of secretin and analogues, RP-HPLC (LiChrosorb RP 18, 10 μm, 4 × 300 mm) proved to be an excellent method for the purification of the final desired product and all intermediate steps [111].

The potential of HPLC on alkysilane-bonded silica for separating and recovering biologically active peptides and proteins ranging up to relative molecular masses of 65 000 was tested on a Hypersil-ODS column and the fascinating results are shown in Figures 5-35 and 5-36 [14].

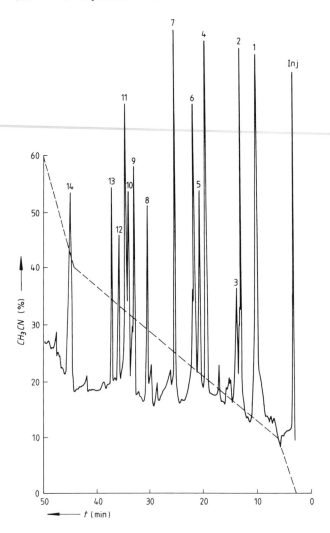

Figure 5-35. HPLC chromatogram of 13 polypeptides. Column: Hypersil-ODS (5 μm, 100 × 5 mm); mobile phase: primary solvent: 0.1 mol/L sodium dihydrogenphosphate/phosphoric acid (pH 2.1, total phosphate concentration 0.2 mol/L), secondary solvent: acetonitrile, the gradient profile is given by the dotted line; flow-rate: 1.5 mL/min; detection: UV at 225 nm; 1 to 10 μg of each polypeptide were injected in the primary solvent with 500 ng of tryptophan as an internal standard; 1 tryptophan, 2 lysine vasopressin, 3 arginine vasopressin, 4 oxytocin, 5 ACTH$_{1-24}$, 6 insulin A, 7 bombesin, 8 substance P, 9 somatostatin, 10 insulin B, 11 human calcitonin, 12 glucagon, 13 salmon calcitonin, 14 melittin (similar to reference [14]).

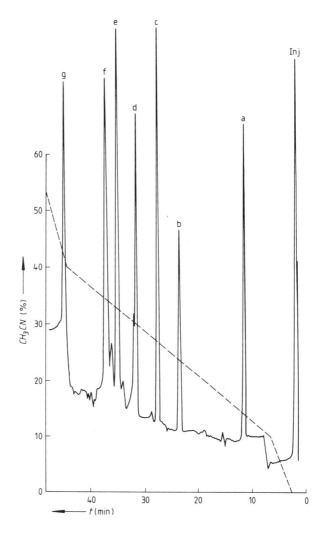

Figure 5-36. HPLC chromatogram of 6 proteins. Column: Hypersil-ODS (5 μm, 100 × 5 mm); mobile phase: primary solvent: 0.1 mol/L sodium dihydrogenphosphate/phosphoric acid (pH 2.1, total phosphate concentration 0.2 mol/L), secondary solvent: acetonitrile, the gradient profile is given by the dotted line; flow-rate: 1.5 mL/min; detection: UV at 225 nm; a tryptophan, b cobra neurotoxin 3, c ribunoclease A, d insulin, e cytochrome c, f lysozyme, g myoglobin (similar to reference [14]).

More or less efficient separation of peptides and proteins over a large range of molecular weight can be achieved by sodium dodecylsulfate gel chromatography on a recently developed TSK-GEL 2000 SW column as is clear from Table 5-26 [59].

Table 5-26. Elution volumes (V_e), k-values and Molecular Weights (MW) of Samples Chromatographed on a TSK-GEL 2000 SW Column: ($\pm$ 10, 2μm, 7.5 × 600 mm). Mobile phase: 0.05 mol/L sodium phosphate buffer (pH 7.2), containing 0.3% sodium dodecylsulfate; flow-rate: 0.3 mL/min; detection: UV at 280 nm [59].

No.	Sample	V_e mL	k	MW
1	Ferritin (V_0)	12.6	0	480 000
2	Ovalbumin	12.6	0	45 000
3	α-Chymotrypsinogen A	13.2	0.058	25 700
4	Cytochrome c	14.5	0.183	12 400
5	Aprotinin	14.5	0.183	6 520
6	Insulin (porcine)	14.6	0.192	5 782
7	Glucagon	14.8	0.211	3 485
8	Tetracosactide	14.8	0.211	2 934
9	α-Endorphin	15.9	0.317	1 746
10	Neurotensin	15.0	0.231	1 673
11	α-Melanocyte-stimulating hormone	15.2	0.250	1 665
12	Somatostatin	15.4	0.270	1 638
13	Substance P	15.1	0.240	1 348
14	Luteinizing hormone-releasing hormone	14.9	0.221	1 182
15	Bradykinin	15.2	0.250	1 060
16	Angiotensin I	15.0	0.231	1 297
17	Angiotensin II	15.8	0.308	1 046
18	Angiotensin III	15.6	0.288	931
19	Oxytocin	15.0	0.250	1 007
20	Vasopressin	15.2	0.250	1 056
21	Arg-vasotocin	15.3	0.260	1 022
22	β-Casomorphin	17.5	0.471	790
23	β-Casomorphin (1 – 5)	19.0	0.615	580
24	Thymopoietin active fragment (32 – 36)	16.8	0.404	680
25	Met-enkephalin	20.2	0.731	574
26	Leu-enkephalin	19.0	0.615	556
27	Tuftsin	16.4	0.365	501
28	Arginine	21.0	0.808	174
29	Alanine	23.0	1.000	89
30	Other amino acids	> 22.8	–	–

Up to a molecular weight of 5000, the elution order follows that of the molecular size of the samples, and therefore the elution volume can be used to estimate the molecular weights of proteins and peptides in the range of 1 000 to 45 000 [59].

5.4 References

[1] I. Molnár, and C. Horváth, in: M. Goodman, and J. Meienhofer (eds.): *Peptides,* p. 48. Halsted, New York 1977.

[2] R. W. Frei, L. Michel, and W. Santi, *J. Chromatogr.* **126**, 665 (1976).

[3] K. Krummen, and R. W. Frei, *J. Chromatogr.* **132**, 27 (1977).

[4] J. E. Rivier, *J. Liq. Chromatogr.* **1**, 343 (1978).

[5] W. Voelter, and H. Echner, unpublished results.

[6] I. Molnár and, C. Horváth, *J. Chromatogr.* **142**, 623 (1977).

[7] T. F. Gabriel, J. E. Michialewski, and J. Meienhofer, in: E. Gross, and J. Meienhofer (eds): *Peptides, Structure and Biological Function,* p. 105. Pierce Chemical Company, Rockford, Il. 1979.

[8] H. P. J. Bennet, A. M. Hudson, C. McMartin, and G. E. Purdon, *Biochem. J.* **168**, 9 (1977).

[9] T. Kronbach, and W. Voelter, unpublished results.

[10] E. Lundanes, and T. Greibrokk, *J. Chromatogr.* **149**, 241 (1978).

[11] G. Lindeberg, *J. Chromatogr.* **193**, 427 (1980).

[12] J. Schrode, and J. E. Folk, *J. Biol. Chem.* **253**, 4837 (1978).

[13] R. E. Majors, *Analusis* **10**, 549 (1974).

[14] M. J. O'Hare, and E. C. Nice, *J. Chromatogr.* **171**, 209 (1979).

[15] J. L. Meek, *Proc. Natl. Acad. Sci. USA* **77**, 1632 (1980).

[16] T. C. J. Gribnau, J. Visser, and R. J. F. Nirard: *Affinity Chromatography and Related Techniques.* Elsevier Scientific Publishing Company, Amsterdam 1982.

[17] A. N. Radhakrishnan, S. Stein, A. Licht, K. A. Gruber, and S. Udenfried, *J. Chromatogr.* **132**, 552 (1977).

[18] D. H. Spackman, W. H. Stein, and S. Moore, *Anal. Chem.* **30**, 1190 (1958).

[19] W. Voelter, and K. Zech, *J. Chromatogr.* **112**, 643 (1975).

[20] W. Voelter, *Pure Appl. Chem.* **48**, 105 (1976).

[21] M. Roth, and A. Hampai, *J. Chromatogr.* **83**, 353 (1973).

[22] J. R. Benson, and P. E. Hare, *Proc. Natl. Acad. Sci. USA* **72**, 619 (1975).

[23] E. Kraas, and W. Voelter, unpublished results.

[24] E. H. Creaser, and G. J. Hughes, *J. Chromatogr.* **144**, 69 (1977).

[25] D. P. Wittmer, N. O. Nuessle, and W. G. Haney, *Anal. Chem.* **47**, 1422 (1975).

[26] S. P. Sood, L. E. Sartori, D. P Wittmer, and W. G. Haney, *Anal. Chem.* **48**, 796 (1975).

[27] J. H. Knox, and G. R. Laird, *J. Chromatogr.* **122**, 17 (1976).

[28] J. H. Knox, and J. Jurand, *J. Chromatogr.* **125**, 89 (1976).

[29] J. C. Kraak, K. M. Jonker, and J. F. K. Huber, *J. Chromatogr.* **142**, 671 (1977).

[30] W. Voelter, K. Zech, P. Arnold, and G. Ludwig, *J. Chromatogr.* **199**, 345 (1980).

[31] B. Fransson, K.-G. Wahl, I. M. Johansson, and G. Schill, *J. Chromatogr.* **125**, 327 (1976).

[32] C. P. Terweij-Groen, S. Heemstra, and J. C. Kraak, *J. Chromatogr.* **161**, 69 (1978).

[33] N. E. Hoffmann, and J. C. Liao, *Anal. Chem.* **49**, 2231 (1977).

[34] E. Tomlinson, T. M. Jefferies, and C. M. Riley, *J. Chromatogr.* **159**, 315 (1978).

[35] C. Horváth, W. Melander, and I. Molnár, *J. Chromatogr.* **125**, 129 (1976).

[36] C. Horváth, W. Melander, I. Molnár, and P. Molnár, *Anal. Chem.* **49**, 2295 (1977).

[37] P. T. Kissinger, *Anal. Chem.* **49**, 883 (1977).

[38] J. L. M. van de Venne, J. L. H. M. Hendrikx, and R. S. Deelder, *J. Chromatogr.* **167**, 1 (1978).

[39] R. P. W. Scott, and P. Kucera, *J. Chromatogr.* **175**, 51 (1979).

[40] R. S. Deelder, H. A. J. Linssen, A. P. Konijnendijk and J. L. M. van de Venne, *J. Chromatogr.* **185**, 241 (1979).

[41] M. T. W. Hearn, B. Grego, and W. S. Hancock, *J. Chromatogr.* **185** 429 (1979).

[42] M. T. W. Hearn, and W. S. Hancock, in: J. Hawk (ed.): *Biological-Biomedical Applications of Liquid Chromatography II,* p. 243. Marcel Dekker, New York 1979.

[43] M. T. W. Hearn, and B. Grego, *J. Chromatogr.* **203**, 349 (1981).

[44] W. Voelter, H. Bauer, and T. Kronbach, unpublished results.

[45] W. Voelter, *Chem. Ztg.* **98**, 554 (1974).

[46] D. Gupta, and W. Voelter: *Hypothalamic Hormones – Structure, Synthesis and Biological Activity.* Verlag Chemie, Weinheim 1975.

[47] D. Gupta, and W. Voelter: *Hypothalamic Hormones – Chemistry, Physiology and Clinical Applications.* Verlag Chemie, Weinheim - New York 1978.

[48] S. Fuchs, and W. Voelter, unpublished results.

[49] R. Guillemin, P. Brazeau, P. Böhlen, F. Esch, N. Ling, and W. B. Wehrenberg, *Science* **218**, 585 (1982).

[50] R. Burgus, and J. Rivier, in: A. Loffet (Ed.): *Peptides,* p. 85. Editions de l'Université de Bruxelles, Bruxelles 1976.

[51] J. J. Hansen, T. Greibrokk, B. L. Currie, K. Nils-Gunnar Johansson, and K. Folkers, *J. Chromatogr.* **135**, 155 (1977).

[52] J. A. Feldman, M. L. Cohn, and D. Blair, *J. Liquid Chromatogr.* **1**, 833 (1978).

[53] E. Wünsch, in: G. Rosselin, P. Fromageot, and S. Bonfils (eds): *Hormone Receptors in Digestion and Nutrition,* p. 115. Elsevier/North-Holland Biomedical Press, Amsterdam 1979.

[54] K.-S. Hui, M. Salschutz, B. A. Davis, and A. Lajtha, *J. Chromatogr.* **192**, 341 (1980).

[55] D. M. Desiderio, J. L. Stein, M. D. Cunningham, and J. Z. Sabbatini, *J. Chromatogr.* **195**, 369 (1980).

[56] F. E. Regnier, and K. M. Gooding, *Anal. Biochem.* **103**, 1 (1980).

[57] R. C. C. Chang, W.-Y. Huang, T. W. Redding, A. Arimura, D. H. Coy, and A. V. Schally, *Biochim. Biophys. Acta* **625**, 266 (1980).

[58] K. Sugden, C. Hunter, and J. G. Lloyd-Jones, *J. Chromatogr.* **204**, 195 (1981).

[59] H. Mabuchi, and H. Nakahashi, *J. Chromatogr.* **213**, 275 (1981).

[60] D. M. Desiderio, S. Yamada, F. S. Tanzer, J. Horton, and J. Trimble, *J. Chromatogr.* **217**, 437 (1981).

[61] J. R. McDermott, A. I. Smith, J. A. Biggins, M. Chyad Al-Noaemi, and J. A. Edwardson, *J. Chromatogr.* **222**, 371 (1981).

[62] E. Spindel, D. Pettibone, L. Fisher, J. Fernstrom, and R. Wurtman, *J. Chromatogr.* **222**, 381 (1981).

[63] K.-S. Hui, M. Hui, K.-P. Cheng, and A. Lajtha, *J. Chromatogr.* **222**, 512 (1981).

[64] J. A. Feldman, and M. L. Cohn, *Chromatogr. Sci. (Biol. Biomed. Appl. Liq. Chromatogr.)* **10**, 225 (1979).

[65] E. Spindel, and R. J. Wurtman, *J. Chromatogr.* **175**, 198 (1979).

[66] J. L. Meek, in: E. Costa, and M. Trabucchi (eds): *Neural Peptides and Neuronal Communication,* p. 145. Raven Press, New York 1980.

[67] F. M. Rabel, *Int. Lab.* (1980) 91.

[68] K. Zech, W. Heinzel, W. Voelter, and K.-P. Hupe, in: F. Lottspeich, A. Henschen, and K.-P. Hupe (eds): *High Performance Liquid Chromatography in Protein and Peptide Chemistry,* p. 143. Walter de Gruyter, Berlin – New York 1981.

[69] W. Voelter, H. Bauer, S. Fuchs, and E. Pietrzik, *J. Chromatogr.* **153**, 433 (1978).

[70] S. Terabe, R. Konaka, and K. Inouye, *J. Chromatogr.* **172**, 163 (1979).

[71] H. P. J. Bennett, C. A. Browne, and S. Solomon, *J. Liq. Chromatogr.* **3**, 1353 (1980).

[72] M. T. W. Hearn, C. A. Bishop, W. S. Hancock, D. R. K.Harding, and G. D. Reynolds, *J. Liq.Chromatogr.* **2**, 1 (1979).

[73] P. D. Gesellchen, S. Tafur, and J. E. Shields, in: E. Gross, and J. Meienhofer (eds): *Peptides,* p. 117. John Wiley, New York 1979.

[74] M. Abrahamsson, and K. Groningsson, *J. Liq. Chromatogr.* **3**, 495 (1980).

[75] H. Kalbacher, and W. Voelter, in: W. Voelter, and G. Weitzel (Eds.): *Structure and Activity of Natural Peptides,* p. 383. Walter de Gruyter & Co., Berlin – New York 1981.

[76] W. Voelter, in: R. F. Beers, and E. G. Bassett (eds): *Polypeptide Hormones,* p. 135. Raven Press, New York 1980.

[77] A. J. Kastin, and A. Barbeau, *Can. Med. Assoc.* 107 (1972).

[78] F. von Gerstenbrand, H. Binder, C. Kozma, S. Pusch, and T. Reismer, *Wien. Klin. Wochenschr.* **87**, 883 (1975).

[79] K. A. Gruber, S. Stein, L. Brink, A. Radhakrishnan, and S. Udenfriend: *Proc. Natl. Acad. Sci. USA* **73**, 1314 (1976).

[80] K. Krummen, and R. W. Frei, *J. Chromatogr.* **132**, 429 (1977).

[81] D. H. Live, in: M. Goodman, and J. Meienhofer (eds): *Peptides,* p. 44. John Wiley, New York 1977.

[82] B. Larsen, V. Viswanatha, S. Y. Chang, and V. J. Hruby, *J. Chromatogr. Sci.* **16**, 207 (1978).

[83] B. Larsen, B. L. Fox, M. F. Burke, and V. J. Hruby, *Int. J. Pept. Protein Res.* **13**, 12 (1979).

[84] F. Nachtmann, *J. Chromatogr.* **176**, 391 (1979).

[85] D. D. Blevins, M. F. Burke, and V. J. Hruby, *Anal. Chem.* **52**, 420 (1980).

[86] M. Gazdag, and G. Szepesi, *J. Chromatogr.* **218**, 603 (1981).

[87] S. R. Bakalyar, R. McIlwrich, and E. Roggendorf, *J. Chromatogr.* **142**, 353 (1977).

[88] E. C. Nice, and M. J. O'Hare, *J. Chromatogr.* **162**, 401 (1979).

[89] H. P. J. Bennett, C. A. Browne, D. Goltzman, and S. Salomon, in: E. Gross, and J. Meienhofer (eds): *Peptides,* p. 121. John Wiley, New York 1979.

[90] W. S. Hancock, C. A. Bishop, R. L. Prestidge, D. R. K. Harding, and M. T. W. Hearn, *Science* **200**, 1168 (1978).

[91] T. L. O'Donohue, C. G. Charlton, C. J. Hilke, and D. M. Jacobowitz, in: E. Gross, and J. Meienhofer (eds): *Peptides,* p. 897. John Wiley, New York 1979.

[92] N. G. Seidah, M. Dennis, P. Corvol, J. Rochemont, and M. Chrétien, *Anal. Biochem.* **109**, 185 (1980).

[93] D. H. Calam, and J. Davidson, *J. Chromatogr.* **218**, 581 (1981).

[94] E. C. Nice, M. W. Capp, N. Cooke, and M. J. O'Hare, *J. Chromatogr.* **218**, 569 (1981).

[95] T. Kronbach, and W. Voelter, unpublished results.

[96] F. E. Regnier, and R. Noel, *J. Chromatogr. Sci.* **14**, 316 (1976).

[97] S. Rokushika, T. Ohkawa, and H. Hatano, *J. Chromatogr.* **176**, 456 (1979).

[98] K. A. Gruber, J. M. Whitaker, and M. Morris, *Anal. Biochem.* **97**, 176 (1979).

[99] P. Roumeliotis, and K. K. Unger, *J. Chromatogr.* **185**, 445 (1979).

[100] B. Renck, and R. Einarsson, *J. Chromatogr.* **197**, 278 (1980).

[101] Y. Kato, K. Komiya, Y. Sawada, H. Sasaki, and T. Hashimoto, *J. Chromatogr.* **190**, 305 (1980).

[102] W. Mönch, and W. Dehnen, *J. Chromatogr.* **147**, 415 (1978).

[103] C. Olieman, E. Sedlick, and D. Voskamp, *J. Chromatogr.* **207**, 421 (1981).

[104] M. T. W. Hearn, W. S. Hancock, J. G. R. Hurrell, R. J. Fleming, and B. Kemp, *J. Liq. Chromatogr.* **2**, 919 (1979).

[105] M. T. W. Hearn, and B. Grego, *J. Chromatogr.* **218**, 497 (1981).

[106] J. L. Meek, and Z. L. Rossetti, *J. Chromatogr.* **211**, 15 (1981).

[107] J. A. D. M. Tonnaer, J. Verhoef, V. M. Wiegant, and W. De Jong, *J. Chromatogr.* **183**, 303 (1980).

[108] E. C. Nice, and M. J. O'Hare, *Anal. Proc. (London)* **17**, 526 (1980).

[109] P. W. Lambert, and B. A. Roos, *J. Chromatogr.* **198**, 293 (1980).

[110] J. M. Zanelli, M. J. O'Hare, E. C. Nice, and P. H. Corran, *J. Chromatogr.* **223**, 59 (1981).

[111] J. T. M. Bakkum, H. C. Beyerman, P. Hoogerhout, C. Olieman, and D. Voskamp, *Rec. J. Royal Netherlands Chem. Soc.* **96**, 301 (1977).

[112] A. A. Amoscato, G. F. Babcock, and K. Nishioka, *J. Chromatogr.* **205**, 179 (1981).

[113] M. T. W. Hearn, W. S. Hancock, and C. A. Bishop, *J. Chromatogr.* **157**, 337 (1978).

[114] G. G. Skellern, M. Mahmoudian, and B. I. Knight, *J. Chromatogr.* **179**, 213 (1979).

[115] M. T. W. Hearn, and W. S. Hancock, *J. Chromatogr. Sci.* **18**, 288 (1980).

[116] S.-J. Su, B. Grego, and M. T. W. Hearn, *J. Liq. Chromatogr.* **4**, 1709 (1981).

[117] G. A. Brine, K. G. Boldt, M. L. Coleman, and R. S. Rapaka, *Anal. Lett.* **15**, 923 (1982).

6 Biogenic Amines

by *Karl Zech*

6 Biogenic Amines

6.1 Introduction

Cells and extracellular fluids of living organisms contain a complex mixture of compounds carrying amino groups such as peptides, amino acids and amines. Many different endogenous amines and amino acids have been identified and quantified in biological specimens during the past 25 years. Catecholamines, i. e. compounds with a 3,4-dihydroxyphenyl (pyrocatechol) ring and a side chain of either ethylamine or ethanolamine, histamine, choline, acetylcholine and indoles, gained nearly exclusive consideration. A recent trend which has developed in analytical chemistry is the study of the metabolic and functional, as well as structural, relationships of selected compounds from the same sample. For example, investigations on the metabolism of tryptophan involve analytical monitoring of tryptophan, 5-hydroxytryptophan, 5-hydroxy-tryptamine, tryptamine, N,N-dimethyltryptamine, N,N-dimethyl-5-hydroxytryptamine (bufotenin), N-acetyl-5-methoxytryptamine (melatonin), indolylacetic acid and 5-hydroxyin-dolylacetic acid as well as of conjugates of the metabolites, as shown in Figure 6-1.

Apart from aromatic amines of the pyrocatechol and indole type, particular interest has been focused during the past two decades on aliphatic polyamines, formed from the basic amino acid L-ornithine by decarboxylation. The diamine putrescine, which is the product of this reaction, is used subsequently in the biosynthesis of the polyamines spermidine and spermine. These aliphatic amines and related compounds such as diaminopropane, cadaverine and histamine, are natural metabolites occuring in nearly all living organisms [1, 2].

Up to now, little has been known about the biological function of this class of compounds. An increase in the activity of ornithine decarboxylase has been observed during growth [3], and biosynthesis of polyamines was shown to be enhanced by cancer. Much work has been done to investigate whether a correlation exists between the concentration of polyamines and the degree of tumor growth [4 to 8], and, moreover, whether this class of compounds could be used as indicators of the efficiency of cancer chemotherapy [5, 9, 10]. Although in many cases, interest may be focused preferably on a single amine, a sophisticated analytical technique will be required, as the compounds of interest usually occur at extremely low concentrations in samples containing a variety of related compounds in similar concentrations. Liquid chromatography, in combination with new detection methods, has proved to be particularly useful in the analysis of biogenic amines.

The concentration of biogenic amines in tissues and serum is usually very low. Levels below 10 nmoles per gram of wet tissue or serum concentrations of 0.1 to 0.5 µg/L are not unusual [11, 12]. Consequently, the demand for analysis of low concentrations of biogenic amines in biological fluids, discrete brain sections, and cell populations spurred the improvement of analytical methods. Enhanced specificity of the separation technique and better detectability are of equal importance. Continuing progress with analytical procedures has often led to corrections of concentration values for biogenic amines determined with less sophisticated methods, since actual levels often turned out to be much lower. β-Hydroxy-γ-aminobutyric acid [13, 14], putrescine [15, 16] and choline/acetylcholine [17] are examples where tissue concentrations had to be revised. Because of the heterogenous distribution and function of

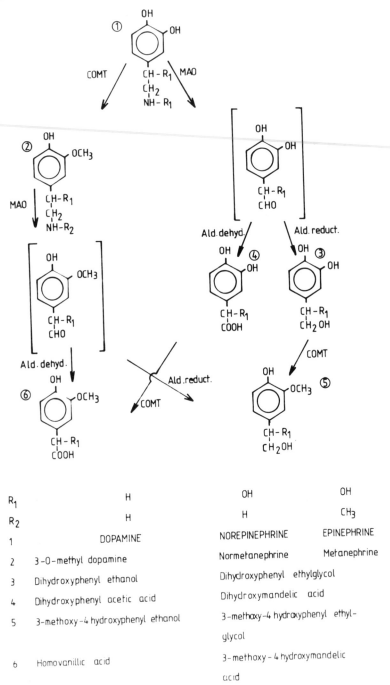

Figure 6-1. Routes of metabolism of catecholamines. The enzymes are monoamine oxidase (MAO), catechol-O-methyltransferase (COMT), aldehyde dehydrogenase (ald. dehyd.), and aldehyde reductase (ald. reduct.).

Table 6-1. Structures and Abbreviations of Catechol-, Indole- and polyamines and Related Compounds.

Compound	Structure	Abbreviation	R_1	R_2	R_3	R_4	R_5	R_6
Dopamine		3-H-Tyrm (DA)	OH	OH	H	H	H	H
Norepinephrine		NE	OH	OH	OH	H	H	H
Epinephrine		E (EPI)	OH	OH	OH	H	H	CH_3
3,4-Dihydroxyphenylalanine		DOPA	OH	OH	H	H	COOH	H
Metanephrine		MN (M)	OH	OCH_3	OH	H	H	CH_3
Normethanephrine		NM	OH	OCH_3	OH	H	H	H
Synephrine		Syn	OH	H	OH	H	H	CH_3
Norsynephrine		NSyn	OH	H	OH	H	H	H
Tyramine		Tyrm	OH	H	H	H	H	H
3-Methoxytyramine		3-M-Tyrm (3-MT)	OH	OCH_3	H	H	H	H
3,4-Dihydroxyphenyl-acetic acid		DOPAC	OH	OH	H	H	H	COOH
Homovanillic acid		HVA	OH	OCH_3	H	H	H	COOH
3,4-Dihydroxymandelic acid		DOMA	OH	OH	OH	H	H	COOH
Vanillylmandelic acid		VMA	H	OCH_3	OH	H	H	COOH
2,5-Dihydroxyphenyl-acetic acid		HGA	H	H	H	OH	OH	COOH
3-Methoxy-4-hydroxy-phenylglycol		MHPG	H	OCH_3	OH	H	H	CH_2OH
5-Hydroxytryptophan			5-HTP		OH		NH_2	COOH
Serotonin			5-HT		OH		OH	H
5-Hydroxytryptophol					OH		OH	H
5-Hydroxyindole-3-acetic acid			5-HIAA					

Table 6-1. (Continued).

Compound	Structure	Abbreviation	R_1	R_2	R_3	R_4	R_5	R_6
1,3-Diaminopropane	$H_2N\text{-}(CH_2)_3\text{-}NH_2$							
1,4-Diaminobutane (putrescine)	$H_2N\text{-}(CH_2)_4\text{-}NH_2$				PUT			
1,5-Diaminopentane (cadaverine)	$H_2N\text{-}(CH_2)_5\text{-}NH_2$				CAD			
Spermidine	$H_2N\text{-}(CH_2)_3\text{-}NH\text{-}(CH_2)_4\text{-}NH_2$				SPD			
Spermine	$H_2N\text{-}(CH_2)_3\text{-}NH\text{-}(CH_2)_4\text{-}NH\text{-}(CH_2)_3\text{-}NH_2$				SPM			

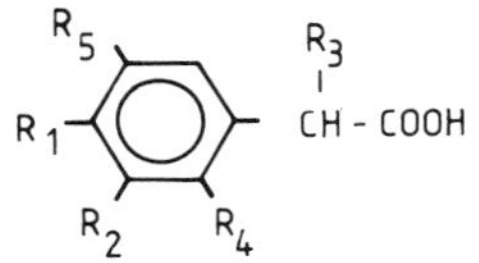

biogenic amines in the central nervous system, analytical techniques are needed which allow the analysis of selected brain sections. Apart from chromatographic procedures, therefore, techniques have been developed which are based on the specificity of enzymic reactions, often in combination with the use of radioactive substrates, as well as immunological methods [18, 19].

Thus radioenzymic methods have been developed for the determination of catecholamines [20 to 28], serotonin [29, 30], β-phenylethylamine [31, 32], histamine [33 to 35], choline, acetylcholine [36 to 41] and putrescine [16]. Radioenzymic assays were improved mainly by Da-Prada and Zürcher [83]. Determination of norepinephrine and epinephrine could be performed with a sensitivity and specificity comparable to the GC-MS technique. The procedure is based on the methylation of epinephrine and norepinephrine, catalysed by catechol-O-methyltransferase (COMT) in the presence of S-adenosylmethionine (^{3}H-methyl), leading to the products metanephrine and normetanephrine. Ion-pair extraction, followed by thin-layer chromatography separation, selective oxidation of the isolated methoxyamines and tritium counting by scintillation spectrometry allows the determination of epinephrine and norepinephrine. This procedure, which also enables the accurate determination of dopamine, was markedly improved by replacing the TLC separation step by HPLC, thus allowing some automation of the procedure [84, 85].

A breakthrough in the determination of biogenic amines was achieved in the past five years by the rapid improvement in column liquid chromatography paired with the development of new detection methods. High sensitivity and specificity, as well as flexibility in the solution of particular analytical problems, was achieved by gas chromatography with electron-capture or mass fragmentographic detection [42 to 55] as well as by HPLC involving fluorometric or electrochemical detection [56 to 75]. Electrochemical detection is used mainly for the detection of catecholamines, although it may also be used for the detection of some of the indoles.

Problems still exist with electrochemical detectors which seem to prevent the method from being used in routine analysis. For example, a great variety of detection limits were reported for dopamine, ranging from 500 pg [76], 200 pg [68], 100 pg [78], 53 pg [79], 20 pg [77] to 15 pg [80]. The further development of optical detection methods, e. g. by fluorescence [81] or chemiluminescence, [82] has certainly been stimulated because of the problems inherent in the stability of electrochemical detectors.

The simultaneous analysis of biological material of a great number of biogenic amines and their metabolites, together with related compounds, has only rarely been described in the literature. The reason for this lies in the difficulty of designing a single analytical procedure able to give the complete profile of all biogenic amines present in a single sample.

Sample work-up, separation from the surrounding matrix, and detection all give rise to problems which are very difficult to solve.

6.2   Procedures for Sample Preparation

A generally applicable procedure for sample preparation prior to analysis of biogenic amines by liquid chromatography does not exist. Moreover, catecholamines and related compounds as well as simple aliphatic diamines may be partially lost due to decomposition in alkaline media. Biogenic amines are normally assayed in discrete areas of brain, in plasma or serum, and in urine. The preparation procedure for a biological sample is equally influenced by the kind of sample matrix and the concentration of compounds to be investigated. Furthermore, free bases and the salts of many aliphatic amines and β-phenethylamines are freely soluble in water. Extraction with waterimmiscible organic solvents is usually impossible.

6.2.1 Biogenic Amines in Tissues of Biological Fluids

6.2.1.1 Aliphatic Amines and Polyamines

Homogenization of tissue with acids (0.1 to 0.4 mol/L $HClO_4$; 10% trichloroacetic acid; acetone/1 mol/L HCl (95 : 5)) may be used for work-up and extraction from tissues. As already mentioned, aliphatic amines and β-phenethylamines cannot be extracted from aqueous samples because of their high solubility in water. Concentration of larger volumes of acidic solution without losing trace amounts is difficult because of the volatility of some of the low molecular amines. Furthermore, concentration of neutralized solutions is known to cause great losses. Ion-pair extraction may present a solution to this problem [86]. Ammonium compounds, primary, secondary and tertiary amines form ion-pairs with anions. Among others [91, 92] 3,5-di-tert.-butyl-2-hydroxybenzene-sulphonate [87], tetraphenylborate [88], anthracence-2-sulphonate [89] and dimethoxyanthracene-2-sulphonate [90] form ion-pairs which may be extracted by organic solvents.

Aromatic amines and some β-phenylethylamines may, however, be extracted from alkaline solutions with organic solvents, whereas the polyamines spermidine and spermine are often extracted with n-butanol prior to chromatographic separation.

Pre-separation of biogenic amines by ion-exchange chromatography with subsequent determination of amines in the collected fractions using specific methods represents one of the more important approaches to chemical analysis. This procedure is clearly influenced by the use of ion-exchange columns in the analysis of amino acids in the more automated version [95]. The improvement of ion-exchange resins over the past twenty years has found its expression in the use of these materials for the separation and pre-separation of amines. Carboxymethyl cellulose [96] sulfonated polystyrenes and other types of cation-exchange resins (Dowex 50x8, Amberlite CG-50 or CG-100 and Bio Rex 70) have been employed [97]. The amines were eluted by salt and pH gradients, the fractions being subsequently assayed by specific methods.

6.2.1.2 Catecholamines and Other Aromatic Amines

The choice of proper sample preparation procedures for compounds of the catecholaminergic and serotoninergic system depends largely on the selectivity of the stationary phase. The procedure which is used for fluorometric assays (trihydroxyindole method) [93] is not selective enough and merely allows for determination of a group of catecholamines [94], while the same work-up might very well be used for the determination of single catecholamines if coupled with a powerful HPLC-separation system. For use in non-selective analytical procedures, modest selectivity may be achieved by an extended sample work-up procedure using selective oxidation [98]. This, however, is rather disadvantageous with powerful separation procedures. Therefore the main purpose of sample work-up for HPLC analysis of catecholamines is the separation of these compounds together with their metabolites, as a group from the surrounding matrix.

Catecholamines and metanephrines may be isolated by adsorption on a cation-exchange column in their protonated form [97]. Inclusion of a solvent extraction step offers additional selectivity, as is the case with metanephrines [97]. Separation of catecholamines from other types of biogenic amines may be accomplished by selective and reproducible adsorption on activated alumina [99 to 101]. This technique uses the reactivity of the catechole moiety which leads to adsorption on alumina due to its pyrocatechol structure. To achieve this, the eluate of the preceding ion-exchange pre-separation step is adjusted to pH 8.6 (using 0.5 mol/L tris buffer in most cases), after a small amount of acid washed alumina (typically 100 mg or less) has been added. Because of the strong retention of the resulting stable complex, the alumina may be washed in order to remove undesired compounds from the sample. The washing procedure is usually carried out with a mixture containing 100 mL double-distilled water, 100 μL of 0.1 mol/L NaHCO$_3$ and 1 mL of 0.5 mol/L tris buffer (pH 8.6). Catecholamines are eluted from alumina by addition of dilute acid (0.1 mol/L HClO$_4$ or 0.1 mol/L HCl). The alumina method, however, may result in poor recoveries if the absorbent is not properly activated.

Boric acid forms a similar complex with catecholes and this has been used for successful isolation in two methods. First is the adsorption of catechols on a boric acid gel containing dihydroxyboryl groups attached to a polymer or cellulose matrix [102 to 104]. Adsorption, complex formation, washing and elution from the column follow the same procedure as described for alumina. This method yields higher recoveries and better reproducibility than the

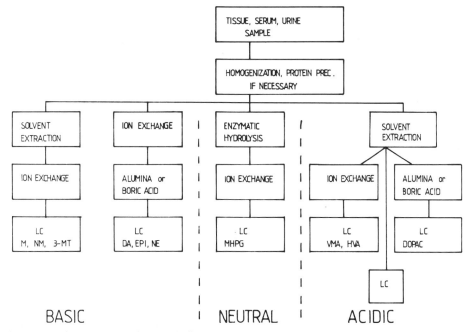

Figure 6-2. Clean up of tyrosine metabolites. Abbreviations: M metanephrine, NM normetanephrine, 3-MT 3-methoxytyramine, DA dopamine, EPI epinephrine, NE norepinephrine, MHPG 3-methoxy-4-hydroxyphenylglycol, VMA vanillylmandelic acid, HVA homovanillic acid, DOPAC 3,4-dihydroxyphenylacetic acid.

alumina method. Another approach with boric acid is to wash cation-exchange isolation volumes with boric acid for complexing and removal of catecholamines [105]. In both cases, the eluate may be injected onto the LC-column.

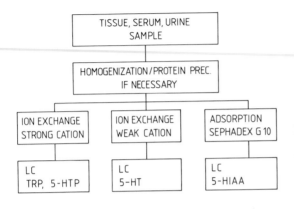

Figure 6-3. Clean up of tryptophan metabolites. Abbreviations: TRP tryptophan, 5-HTP 5-hydroxy-tryptophan, 5-HT serotonin, 5-HIAA 5-hydroxindole-3-acetic acid.

Studies of the concentration of monoamine metabolites in brain may represent a more reliable index of turnover than measurements of the concentrations of parent amines. Moreover, the metabolites have been shown to be more stable post mortem than the amines themselves [106] and are, for this reason, more suitable for measurements in brain.

As is the case with all catecholamine metabolites, extraction as a form of group isolation is generally advisable subsequent to protein precipitation and prior to LC-separation. Extraction of acidic metabolites (3,4-dihydroxyphenylacetic acid, homovanillic acid, 5-hydroxyindole-3-acetic acid) into a polar organic phase (e. g. ethyl acetate) was found to give optimal results at pH 2.0 to 4.0, whereas extraction of the neutral metabolite 3-methoxy-4-hydroxy-phenylglycol was unaffected by pH in the range 1.0 to 8.0. At pH 3.0 the following extraction efficiencies were measured [107]: (mean ± SEM) 3-methoxy-4-hydroxy-phenylglycol: 64 ± 3; 3,4-dihydroxy-phenyl-acetic acid: 86 ± 4; homovanillic acid: 98 ± 4; 5-hydroxyindole-3-acetic acid: 87 ± 3. Further separation of acidic from neutral components can often be dispensed with, and the extract can be injected directly onto the LC-system.

The catechol metabolites can be adsorbed selectively on alumina [99 to 101] or boric acid gel [102 to 104] in the same way as catecholamines. The procedure starts with protein precipitation (if necessary) followed by homogenization in acid, hydrolysis of sulfate esters, solvent extraction and, finally, adsorption onto alumina at pH 8.6. After washing the adsorbents, the molecules are eluted off the alumina by acid or an acid/methanol solution and injected onto the LC. The adsorption step contributes a great deal of selectivity; additional selectivity is achieved by electrochemical detection of the LC-column effluent.

Tryptophan metabolites (serotonin, 5-hydroxytryptophan, 5-hydroxyindole-3-acetic acid) often require a more sophisticated sample clean-up step prior to LC-analysis. A useful method is purification on small, gravity-fed, extraction columns [108]. The type of resin will be determined by the compound which has to be analyzed. Nevertheless, it is desirable to use this approach to assay several compounds concurrently. Tryptophan as well as 5-hydroxytryptophan are isolated by using a strong cation-exchange resin (e. g. DOWEX AG-50), whereas a weak cation-exchange resin (Amberlite CG-50) is employed for isolation of serotonin. 5-Hydroxyindoleacetic acid selectively adsorbs onto a gel filtration resin (Sephadex G-10). In either case, elution is followed by injection onto a liquid chromatograph. Combination of different types of resins allows the simultaneous determination of several metabolites.

6.2.1.3 Pre-Column Sample Enrichment of Serotonin and 5-Hydroxyindole-3-acetic Acid

Liquid-solid extraction columns used for the clean-up step do not fit very well the requirements of liquid chromatography. Only about 10% of the minimum volume required to elute the compounds of interest is usually injected onto the LC-column. This means a loss of about 90% of isolated compounds. On the other hand, the desire to determine serotonin and 5-hydroxyindole-3-acetic acid in localized regions of the rat brain or in punch-outs from brain slices requires a method with extremely good detector response.

Recently, a pre-column sample enrichment system for assaying serotonin or 5-hydroxyindole-acetic acid in localized areas of rat brain [109] or of serotonin in serum and plasma was described by Koch and Kissinger [110]. The whole eluate of the extraction column is transferred to a small pre-column filled with RP-18 material, thereby concentrating the compounds to be analyzed. On switching the system to the back-flush mode, the sample is transferred from the pre-column to the analytical column by the mobile phase of the analytical system. Nearly a hundred-fold enhancement of the detection limit is obtained, allowing the determination of serotonin and 5-hydroxyindole-3-acetic acid from small brain regions and punch-outs. Several publications have illustrated the advantages of this principle for various applications [111 to 113].

6.3 Column Liquid Chromatography of Biogenic Amines

6.3.1 Ion-Exchange Chromatography

6.3.1.1 Aliphatic Amines, β-Phenylethylamines, Di- and Polyamines

The use of ion-exchange separations in the analysis of biogenic amines has a long history. It started in 1958 with the development of automated devices for amino acid analysis by Spackman, Stein and Moore [95]. Many scientists [114 to 120] used columns packed with sulfonated polystyrene resins and employed pH and/or salt gradients for the successive elution of the different amines. As already known from aromatic amino acids, aromatic amines also show considerable interactions with the polymer matrix. As a consequence, the elution patterns fail to follow exactly the ion competition equilibria. The cation-exchange resins used in these experiments allowed the complete separation of a mixture of biogenic amines. The combination of ion-exchange separation with other selective separation procedures (paper chromatography, paper electrophoresis) enables the detection of aliphatic amines and phenylethylamines in the brain, urine and cerebrospinal fluid [114, 115, 121 to 125]. Further development of this technique consequently leads to the application of small ion-exchange columns as a major step in sample preparation procedures with subsequent HPLC-analysis.

The same procedure has been applied to the separation of di- and polyamines for some time. Usually, commercial amino acid analyzers must be adapted for the separation of polyamines using the reaction with ninhydrin for detection [126 to 129]. Separation is achieved similarly to amino acid analyses by application of stepwise pH- and salt gradient elution. By using fluorescamine [130, 130a] (4-phenylspiro furane-2(3H),1′-phthalan-3,3′-dione), detection limits may be lowered to the picomole range both for amino acids [131] and for amines [132 to 134]. Further advantages of fluorescamine are the fast reaction rate with amines even at room temperature (msec) and the non-fluorescence of unreacted reagent. Excessive fluorescamine is hydrolyzed to non-fluorescent products. Mixing the eluant with 0.2 mol/L sodium borate buffer (pH 9.0) brings the pH to its optimum level for the derivatization reaction, whereas the presence of boric acid prevents some catecholamines from oxidative degradation [134].

Another useful reagent besides fluorescamine is o-phthaldialdehyde [153] which, together with 2-mercaptoethanol, forms a strongly fluorescent product. The use of the most recent ion-exchange resins, combined with o-phthaldialdehyde as detection reagent, allows the routine determination of down to 3 to 6 pmol of putrescine and spermidine as well as 12 to 15 pmol of spermine.

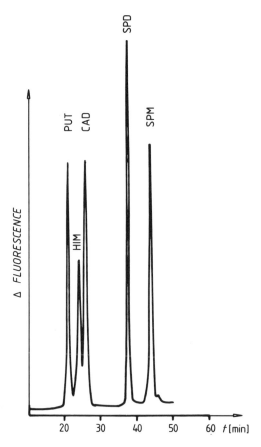

Figure 6-4. Separation of standard solution of putrescine (PUT), histamine (HIM), cadaverine (CAD), spermidine (SPD), and spermine (SPM), 1 nmol each. Chromatoraphic conditions: Column: DURRUM DC 6A (4 × 50 mm); eluent: Na-citrate 29.4 g/L, pH 5.2, step gradient with different amounts of Na/KCl additionally; flow-rate: 51 ml/h; temperature: 67 °C; detection: fluorescence at 418 nm (emission cutoff) with excitation at 355 nm; post-column reaction with o-phthaldialdehyde/mercaptoethanol.

6.3.1.2 Catechol-, Indoleamines and Their Metabolites

The development of chemically bonded, microparticulate ion-exchange packing materials on glass or silica supports played an important role in the improvement of separations. Cation-exchange chromatography has been useful for the separation of basic parent catecholamines, whereas anion-exchange columns have been very successful in assaying acidic metabolites as well as their sulfate derivatives. Although both cation- and anion-exchange columns are useful for the separation of basic amines and their acidic metabolites, respectively, the procedure is no longer optimal, if applied to mixtures containing both catecholamines and their carboxylic metabolites. Neither mode gave satisfactory separations.

Table 6-2. HPLC Ion-Exchange Separation of Norepinephrine and Epinephrine (Selected).

Column	Column Dimensions (i. d.) mm m	Mobile Phase	Flow-Rate (mL/min)	Reference
Zipax SCX	2.1 × 1.0	0.1 mol/L Na-acetate in 0.02 mol/L HCl, pH 6.3	1.0	[136]
	2.1 × 1.0	0.05 mol/L Na-acetate in 0.01 mol/L HCl	1.4	[136]
	2.1 × 1.0	0.075 mol/L NaH_2PO_4	0.5	[136]
	2.1 × 1.0	0.15 mol/L NaH_2PO_4	0.4	[136]
	2.1 × 1.0	0.05 to 0.45 mol/L NaH_2PO_4	0.4	[136]
	2.0 × 0.5	0.1 mol/L $HClO_4$	0.3	[137]
DuPont SCX	3 × 1.2	0.1 to 1 mol/L $(NH_4)_3PO_4$, pH 7.0	1.0	[138]
VYDAC cation-exchange	2 × 0.5	0.01 mol/L H_2SO_4 to 0.04 mol/L Na_2SO_4	0.4	[136]
PARTISIL-10 SCX	4.6 × 0.25	0.5 mol/L $NH_4H_2PO_4$, pH 4.36	0.76	[136]

The effect of ionic strength and pH on retention of selected catecholamines on a cation-exchange column is given in the following Table 6-3.

Table 6-3. Effect of Ionic Strength and pH on Retention Times of Catecholamines. – Chromatographic conditions: Column: 500 × 2.1 mm; resin HITACHI 3011 c; column temperature: 30 °C; flow-rate: 1.5 mL/min. (Similar to reference [137]).

Elution Buffer Concentration (mol/L)	pH	Retention Time (min) Noradrenaline	Adrenaline	Dopamine
0.2	5.1	5.6	10.0	18.5
0.1	5.1	5.6	10.2	18.6
0.05	5.1	8.0	13.4	23.4
0.2	4.4	3.9	6.4	11.5
0.075	3.65	3.2	4.8	8.4

It should be mentioned at this point that, with respect to organic separations, ion-exchange is a special type of reversed-phase chromatography involving both electrostatic and hydrophobic interactions. Moreover, among all phase systems described in the literature, the reversed-phase systems give the best selectivity and column performance. Excellent selectivity can be obtained, especially when applying ion-pair chromatography [140, 141] or dynamic cation-exchange systems [59, 142 to 150].

6.3.2 Reversed-Phase Partition Chromatography

6.3.2.1 Aliphatic Amines, β-Phenylethylamines, Di- and Polyamines

A major breakthrough in the use of liquid chromatography for the analysis of complex biological samples was intimately connected with the availabilty of chemically modified stationary phases. Maximum selectivity and column efficiency is achieved with silica supports modified with octyl- and octadecyl brushes. Application of this technique for the separation of biogenic amine was therefore desirable. Aliphatic amines, diamines and polyamines, however, created difficulties with these systems because of their pronounced polar properties and the absence of a chromophore, which makes detection very difficult.

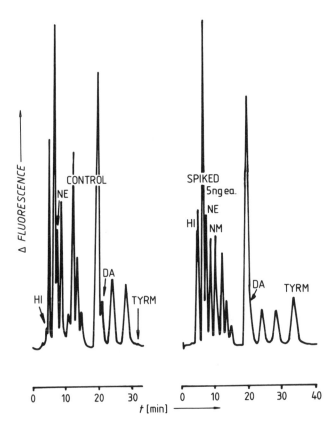

Figure 6-5. Reversed-phase HPLC separation of o-phthaldialdehyde derivatives of biogenic amines in plasma. Sample: 5 µl, equivalent to 0.05 mL plasma; column: µ Bondapak (300 × 4 mm); eluent: 0.05 mol/L NaH$_2$PO$_4$ (pH 5.10) with 480 mL of methanol per L; flow-rate: 1.5 mL/min; temperature: 35 °C (similar to reference [153]). Abbreviations: HI 5-hydroxyindole, NE norepinephrine, DA dopamine, TYRM tyramine, NM normetanephrine.

By reaction of biogenic amines with a fluorophore, a lipophilic molecule is obtained which can be detected by fluorescence measurement at very low concentrations.

Among the many alternatives offered, derivatization with dansyl chloride [151], fluorescamine [96] or o-phthaldialdehyde [153] (the latter in the presence of 2-mercaptoethanol) deserve mentioning. By application of the reversed-phase technique for analysis of fluorescent derivatives, detection of amines in the lower nanogram down to the picogram range becomes possible with a speed much greater than known from ion-exchange chromatography. This advantage, unfortunately, is partially eliminated by the need for a derivatization step.

For certain biogenic amines this technique has some limitations, as fluorescamine and o-phthaldialdehyde only react with primary amines, whereas dansyl chlorides also react with secondary amines.

6.3.2.2 Catechol-, Indoleamines and Their Metabolites

In contrast to their parent compounds, catechol- and indoleamine metabolites are acidic compounds. Cation- or anion-exchange chromatography is applicable only to the separation of basic or acidic catechol-related compounds. Reversed-phase partition mode allows for simultaneous analysis of both classes of compounds in a single chromatographic run. Hydrophobic interactions between the solute molecules and the aliphatic chain being chemically bounded to the support surface predominate in normal reversed-phase mode, whereas electrostatic and hydrophobic chromatography appears to fit best with ion-pairing (dynamic ion-exchange) models.

6.3.2.2.1 Separation System: Reversed-Phase Chromatography

Phosphoric [143], nitric, sulphuric, trichloroacetic and acetic acid buffers [148, 154] could be used as mobile phases with good efficiency to assay catechol-related compounds on non-polar stationary phase. Retention can be adjusted by varying the concentration of organic modifier (e. g. acetonitrile, methanol, propanol) and by changing the pH of the mobile phase. Increasing the pH results in shorter retention times of acidic compounds and in longer retention of the basic solutes respectively, but basic catecholamines are easily oxidized at high pH [155] and unstable columns are obtained in alkaline medium. Reduced retention with increased dissociation of the ionic functionalities shows that hydrophobic interactions predominate and electrostatic ones are negligible in reversed-phase chromatography.

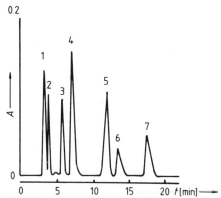

Figure 6-6. Chromatogram of 3-O-methyl metabolites of dopamine; 3-methoxy-4-hydroxy-mandelic acid (1), normetanephrine (2), metanephrine (3), 3-methoxytyramine (4), 3-methoxy-4-hydroxyphenyl-acetic acid (5), paranephrine (6), and 3-methoxy-4-hydroxyphenethanol (7).
Chromatographic conditions: Column: Partisil 1025 ODS; eluent: 50 mmol/L potassium phosphate; pH 4.6; flow-rate: 0.66 mL/min; temperature: 25 °C (similar to reference [143]).

The influence of mobile phase pH on retention of catecholamines and acidic metabolites is illustrated in Figure 6-7.

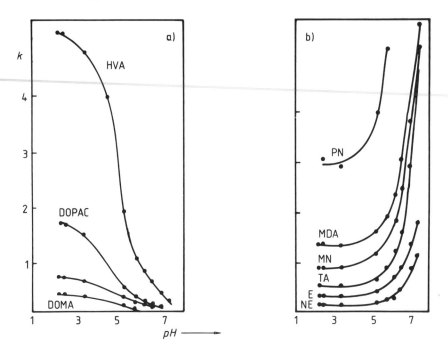

Figure 6-7. Effect of pH on the retention of acidic metabolites (a) and catecholamines (b). Column: Partisil 1025 ODS; eluent: 0.1 mol/L phosphate buffer; flow-rate: 1 mL/min; temperature: 25 °C. Symbols: Homovanillic acid (HVA); 3,4-dihydroxyphenylacetic acid (DOPAC); vanillylmandelic acid (VMA); 3,4-dihydroxymandelic acid (DOMA); paranephrine (PN); 3-O-methyl-dopamine (MDA); metanephrine (MN); tyramine (TA); epinephrine (E); norepinephrine (NE). (Similar to reference [143]).

Separation of basic compounds in reversed-phase systems becomes difficult when the selectivity of the phase systems is poor and peak tailing occurs [144, 148], probably due to the strong interaction of the highly polar groups in these compounds with non-silanized sites of the modified support. The addition of sodium salts of inorganic acids (e. g. sodium perchlorate 0.05 to 0.2 mol/L) can reduce peak tailing significantly and improve column efficiency [148]. Moreover, retention of acidic and basic compounds is affected by the addition of sodium perchlorate.

In spite of the favorable effect of sodium perchlorate and adaptation of the pH and propanol content, no complete separation of acidic metabolites and basic compounds can be achieved. Normal reversed-phase systems are mostly suitable for the separation of acidic metabolites but are less suitable for the separation of all basic compounds.

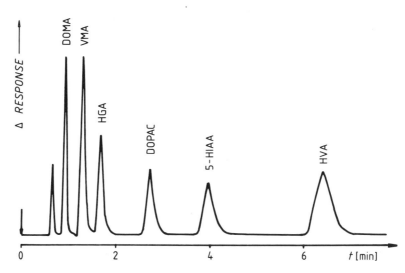

Figure 6-8. Rapid separation of a test mixture of acidic catecholamine metabolites on a reversed-phase system. Stationary phase: C_8-bonded silica; column length: 250 mm; mobile phase: 0.02 mol/L citrate (pH 2.50) + 3% (v/v) n-propanol + 0.2 mol/L $NaClO_4$; temperature: 25 °C (similar to reference [148]). Abbreviations: DOMA 3,4-dihydroxymandelic acid, VMA vanillylmandelic acid, HGA 2,5-dihydroxyphenylacetic acid, DOPAC 3,4-dihydroxyphenylacetic acid, 5-HIAA 5-hydroxyindole-3-acetic acid, HVA homovanillic acid.

6.3.2.2.2 Separation System: Dynamic Cation-Exchange (Soap Chromatography)

This technique uses reversed-phase packing material in combination with hydrophilic eluant containing an organic modifier together with a low concentration of detergent (0.1% or less). For instance, sodium 1-dodecane sulphate (SDS) as a detergent is adsorbed by the reversed-phase surface to form an anionic layer, thus exhibiting properties similar to an ion-exchanger. Other detergents in use are sodium laurylsulphate and sodium dodecylbenzenesulphonate. These dynamic cation-exchange systems using anionic surfactants were found to be suitable for the separation of amino acids [147] and basic catecholamines [58, 144]. For acidic solutes (catecholamine metabolites) physical distribution between the mobile phase and the interface is the predominant retention mechanism [155]. The improvement in retention and resolution after addition of sodium dodecylsulphate to the eluant is shown in Figure 6-9.

Speed of separation, selectivity and resolution may be readily adjusted by the sodium dodecylsulphate and counter-ion concentration, by the nature and concentration of the organic modifier or of the acid in the eluant, and by addition of salts. As these dynamic cation-exchange systems behave like conventional ion-exchange systems, the retention can be influenced in a predictable way: the greater the counter-ion (Na^+) or detergent concentration, the greater the k-value of the basic compounds. The dependence of k upon the detergent concentration in systems with an anionic detergent is qualitatively similar to those found in anion-exchange systems with cationic detergents (e. g. separation of sulphonic acids using the cationic detergent cetyltrimethylammonium bromide [157]).

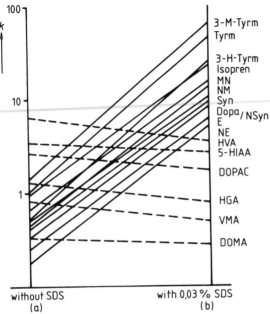

Figure 6-9. Effect of sodium dodecylsulphate (SDS) on the capacity ratio of catecholamines and related compounds. Stationary phase: C_8-bonded silica; mobile phase: (a) 0.02 mol/L citrate (pH 2.50) + 3% (v/v) n-propanol + 0.2 mol/L $NaClO_4$; temperature: 25 °C; (b) 0.02 mol/L citrate (pH 2.50) + 3% (v/v) n-propanol + 0.125 mol/L $NaClO_4$ + SDS (0.03% w/v); temperature: 25 °C (similar to reference [148]). Abbreviations: 3-M-Tyrm 3-methoxytyramine, Tyrm tyramine, 3-H-Tyrm dopamine, MN metanephrine, NM normetanephrine, Syn synephrine, DOPA 3,4-dihydroxyphenolalanine, NSyn norsynephrine, E epinephrine, NE norepinephrine, HVA homovanillic acid, 5-HIAA 5-hydroxyindole-3-acetic acid, DOPAC 3,4-dihydroxyphenylacetic acid, HGA 2,5-dihydroxyphenylacetic acid, VMA vanillylmandelic acid, DOMA 3,4-dihydroxymandelic acid.

The organic modifiers acetonitrile and methanol give the best column efficiencies [144], while, with respect to column stability, n-propanol is far superior [148].

Increasing the acid concentration reduces retention and slightly improves plate efficiency, whereas the addition of organic modifier enhances the speed of analysis but causes some loss in plate efficiency. Unfortunately, the use of acid is limited by the pH-stability of stationary phase, because acid concentrations above ca. 10^{-2} mol/L attack the solid support and therefore must be avoided in long-term runs.

By adjusting the available parameters, separation of basic catecholamines and acidic catechol related compounds can be rapidly achieved.

From Figure 6-10 it follows that catecholamines are roughly eluted in reverse order as compared to ion-pair systems or reversed-phase systems. Moreover, the addition of SDS is favourable in the case of basic solutes and less so for the resolution of acidic compounds. These metabolites may best be separated in reversed-phase systems without detergents. Therefore, a compromise had to be found: Separation of acidic compounds can be improved by decreasing the concentration of organic modifier or of SDS in the eluant, whereas decreasing the modifier concentration results in an increase in the retention of basic solutes. Decreasing the SDS concentration, however, results in a decrease in the resolution of basic compounds. The

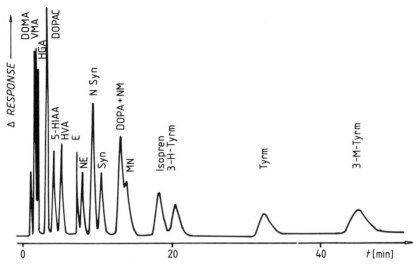

Figure 6-10. Separation of a test mixture of catecholamines and metabolites under isocratic conditions on a dynamic cation-exchange system. Stationary phase: C_8-bonded silica; mobile phase 0.02 mol/L citrate (pH 2.50) + 1% (v/v) n-propanol + 0.2 mol/L NaClO$_4$ + 0.3% (w/v) SDS; temperature: 25 °C (similar to reference [148]). Abbreviations: DOMA 3,4-dihydroxymandelic acid, VMA vanillylmandelic acid, HGA 2,5-dihydroxyphenylacetic acid, DOPAC 3,4-dihydroxyphenylacetic acid, 5-HIAA 5-hydroxyindole-3-acetic acid, HVA homovanillic acid, E epinephrine, NE norepinephrine, NSyn norsynephrine, Syn synephrine, DOPA 3,4-dihydroxyphenylalanine, NM normetanephrine, MN metanephrine, 3-H-Tyrm dopamine, Tyrm tyramine, 3-M-Tyrm 3-methoxytyramine.

compromise between modifier and SDS concentration will therefore depend on the nature of the separation problem.

An alternative for reducing SDS concentration may be loading the stationary phase with SDS and using the mobile phase without anionic detergent [148]. As already described for systems with SDS in the mobile phase, a large increase in the retention of basic compounds is observed without noticeable change in the capacity ratios of the acidic solutes. No differences in column performance were found between dynamic cation-exchange systems described, whereas the SDS-free eluant-phase systems seem to be more stable with respect to lifetime.

6.4 Detection Principles

6.4.1 Native Fluorescence Measurements

Catechols and indoles are known to exhibit native fluorescence [77, 187] or to be easily converted to trihydroxyindole derivatives by various oxidizing reagents.

The coupling of HPLC with on-line fluorimetric detection has resulted in analytical systems with maximum selectivity, whose detection limit is comparable to HPLC systems with on-line electrochemical detection.

Detection of catechols [78, 81, 189 to 193] and indoles [194 to 196] by measuring their native fluorescence was applied successfully when spectrofluorimetric HPLC detectors became commercially available. Moreover, interest in the field of fluorescence detection was renewed when problems arose with the practicability and stability of electrochemical detectors.

Fluorometric detection offers additional selectivity in the analytical system. Apart from the fact that relatively few compounds exist with inherent fluorescence, these fluorophors show different excitation and emission spectra. Catecholamines exhibit excitation maxima at 200 to 220 nm and 280 to 300 nm, with an emission maximum of 310 to 330 nm, whereas indoles typically show excitation maxima at 210 to 220 nm and 270 to 280 nm, and an emission maximum at about 360 nm. Moreover, the fluorescent derivatives of the catechols and indoles have different excitation and emission spectra, their maxima being usually shifted bathochromically. Present detection limits of about 5 to 25 pg and 100 to 500 pg for underivatized indoles and catechols demonstrate the excellent detection limit of fluorescence detection. A recent report by Yui et al. [188] describes a 1 pg detection limit for trihydroxyindole derivatives of norepinephrine and epinephrine. This may be an indication that present detection limits for certain fluorescent derivatives of indoles and catechols may be improved still further by higher absorptivities and quantum efficiencies as well as by bathochromic shifts in excitation and emission maxima of other derivatives. With excitation at 280 nm and emission at 310 to 315 nm, a strong suppression of the indole peak is obtained, whereas the intensity of catecholamine emission is little affected. Therefore, some additional selectivity could be introduced into the analysis of catecholamines in the presence of indoles [81]. Excitation at 200 nm offers better detectibility for catecholamines and serotonin, while the detection limit for other indoles is significantly lower, and no selectivity of catecholamines versus indoles is obtained.

6.4.2 Coloured and Fluorescent Derivatives

Coloured derivatives of amines have been used for the analysis of biogenic amines containing primary and secondary amino groups to a limited extent. Detection limits in the nanomole range are the main reason for this limited use. Among the possible reagents, only 2,4-dinitrofluorobenzene, the end-group reagent of Sanger [158, 159], and 2,4-dinitrobenzenesulphonic acid [160], which both lead to the same derivatives, have been used extensively. Since the development of fluorescent reagents, coloured derivatives have been gradually dismissed.

A great number of reagents have been recommended in the literature for the formation of fluorescent derivatives [176]. Sulphonyl chlorides: 5-dimethylaminonaphthalene-1-sulphonyl chloride (DNS-Cl), 5-di-n-butylaminonaphthalene-1-sulphonyl chloride [158, 159], 6-methylanilinonaphthalene-2-sulphonyl chloride [160] and 2-p-chlorosulphophenyl-3-phenylindane [161, 162]. Isothiocyanates: 4-dimethylaminonaphthalene-1-isothiocyanate [163], fluorescein isothiocyanate [164] and 9-isothiocyanatoacridine [165]. Aldehydes: o-phthaldialdehyde and pyridoxal [166, 167]. 4-Phenylspiro furan-2 (3 H),1'-phthalan-3,3'-dione (fluorescamine).

Among these reagents only DNS-Cl [168 to 172], fluorescamine [133] and o-phthaldialdehyde [173 to 175] have been used extensively for the formation of fluorescent derivatives in column liquid chromatography.

In most cases, the use of coloured or fluorescent reagents offers two possibilities [176]: either the compounds of interest in extracts or body fluids are reacted prior to the separation (precolumn derivatization); or the compound or a group of related compounds are first separated

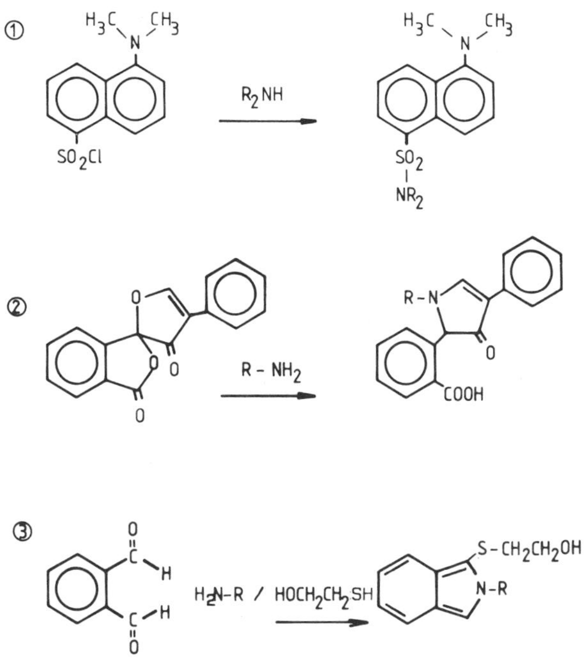

Figure 6-11. Formation of fluorescent derivatives from dansyl chloride (1), fluorescamine (2), and o-phthaldialdehyde (3).

and the derivatization reaction is performed continuously in the column eluant (post-column derivatization). The precolumn technique is preferred for DNS-Cl, whereas pre- and post-column derivatization is applied extensively with fluorescamine and o-phthaldialdehyde.

DNS-Cl reacts with primary and secondary amino groups, with phenols and imidazoles to form highly fluorescent derivatives [177 to 180]. This reagent is used in many laboratories, especially for quantification of di- and polyamines for several reasons [170, 171, 181]. These types of amines are very soluble in water and recommended only for time-consuming ion-exchange chromatography as the separation technique. Modern HPLC may be used after the introduction of a chromophore or a fluorophore for detection purposes [182] and in order to simultaneously enhance lipophilicity of the molecule. Because of their fast reaction with primary amines, fluorescamine and o-phthaldialdehyde may be used not only for pre-separation derivatization, but also for the post-column technique. As early as 1973, fluorescamine was incorporated into a system for amino acid analysis which turned out to be about 100fold more sensitive than the colorimetric reaction with ninhydrin [132]. By using pre-column derivatization, separation and quantification of amines with HPLC is superior to ion-exchange systems as regards selectivity and speed of analysis. Moreover, pre-column derivatization stabilizes the molecules and facilitates extraction. Nevertheless, the possibility of lowering HPLC detection limits to the nanogram level is the major reason for derivatization with o-phthaldialdehyde [153, 183, 184], fluorescamine [134, 185, 186] or other reagents forming fluorescent derivatives.

6.4.3 Electrochemical Detection

Since aqueous solvents were made available as eluants of modern ion-exchange or reversed-phase systems, electrochemical detectors have been used: mainly with catecholamines, but also with some indoles.

Anodic oxidation of phenols and indoles has been known for at least 50 years, yet this technique did not attract great attention because of a major problem in electrochemistry. For example, all catechols react similarly and cannot be distinguished in complex mixtures. Therefore, only by coupling electrochemical oxidation with a separation step can this technique be used successfully. Modern separation systems with ionic mobile phases containing completely dissociated ions constitute optimal solvents due to the high conductivity. An example of anodic oxidation of catechol derivatives at a graphite or glassy carbon electrode to generate the corresponding orthoquinone, two protons, and two electrons is illustrated in the following Figure 6-12.

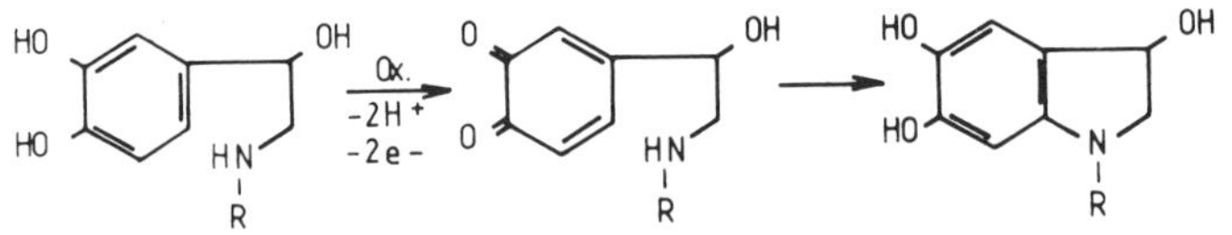

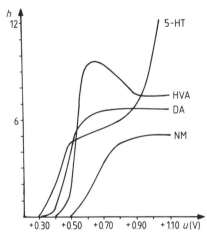

Figure 6-12. Two-electron oxidation of catecholamines followed by the pH-dependent formation of dihydroindoles.

A limiting current for dopamine is obtained at 0.60 V and for normetanephrine at 0.80 V. A current maximum at 0.60 V is obtained with homovanillic acid, while indoles follow a dual oxidation scheme. This is due to both N-oxidation and oxidation of the phenolic group of 5-hydroxy compounds [197]. 5-Hydroxytryptamine (serotonin) as a representative of this class of compounds showed a current plateau at 0.60 V and a rising current on further increasing the potential. Compounds without the phenolic group (e. g. tryptamine) give no limiting current at potentials of up to 1.10 V as illustrated in Figure 6-13. A nearly selective detection of 5-hydroxy compounds can be obtained at 0.60 V because anodic oxidation of the 5-hydroxy group started at a lower potential than the N-oxidation.

Figure 6-13. Voltammogramms of homovanillic acid (HVA), dopamine (DA), normetanephrine (NM), and serotonine (5-HT).

As is probably the case with all analytical systems sensitive enough for assaying ppb or even ppt (parts per trillion) amounts of endogenous or exogenous compounds in biological specimens, difficulties associated with reproducibility, practicability and simplicity of handling will increase with sensitivity of the analytical system. Therefore, the many reports on difficulties associated with electrochemical detection come as no surprise. In spite of careful solvent deaeration or use of an earthed Faraday cage, for example, the low stability and unidentifiable sources of noise encountered at high sensitivities have prevented its use for routine analysis.

Because electrochemistry is a surface technique, these systems are very sensitive to small changes in solvent composition. This is the reason why chromatograms with electrochemical detection give a large initial peak while in fluorescence systems there is no solvent front.

6.5 Applications

The combination of liquid chromatography with fluorimetric or amperometric detection has gained increased importance in the last few years, owing to its sensitivity and separation power which enables assays of picogram amounts of neurologically active biogenic amines and their metabolites in certain areas of the brain, blood or tissue for the first time simultaneously. Several recent applications are summarized in Table 6-4, but this selection is by no means complete.

Table 6-4. Selected Recent Neurochemical Applications of HPLC with Amperometric and Fluorimetric Detection.

Compound	Tissue or Fluid	LC-Column	Detection Method	References
5-HT	BLD	RP	EC	[110]
NE, DA,	BLD	IE	EC	[198]
DA, NE, 5-HTP, 5-HT, 5-HIAA	TH	RP	EC	[199]
DA, metabolites	incubation medium	RP	F	[192]
NE	BLD	RP	EC	[200]
NE	TH	IE	EC	[201]
NE, DA	TH	RP	EC	[202]
DOPA, DOPAC, NE, E, DA	TH	RP	EC	[79]
DA, NE, E	URN	RP	EC	[103]
NE, E	BLD	IE	F	[188]
NE, E	URN	RP	F	[191]
DA, NE	TH	IE	EC	[203]
E	TH	IE	EC	[204]
NE, E	BLD	RP	EC	[205]
NE, DA, 5-HT, Tyrm	BLD, TH, URN	RP	F	[153]
NE, DA, DOPAC	TH	RP	EC	[206]
NE, DA, 5-HT	TH	IE	EC	[207]
NE, E	BLD	IE	EC	[208]
NE, E	BLD	IE	EC	[209]
NE, E, DOPA, DA	TH	RP	EC	[59]

Table 6-4. (Continued).

Compound	Tissue or Fluid	LC-Column	Detection Method	References
DOPAC				
DOPA, metabolites	TH, BLD	RP	EC	[210]
NE, E, DA	TH	RP	EC	[211]
Diamines, polyamines	TH, BLD	IE	F	[152]
Polyamines	TH	AD	F	[171]
5-HT, 5-HIAA, 5-HTP, HVA, DOPAC	TH	RP	EC	[74]
5-HT, 5-HIAA	TH	RP	EC	[109]
VMA, E, NE, DA, metabolites	URN	RP	UV	[144]
5-HT, 5-HIAA, TRP	TH, BLD, URN	RP	EC	[108]
5-HT,	BLD	RP	EC	[110]
VMA, HVA	URN	RP	EC	[212]
DOPAC, HVA	TH	RP	EC	[69]
HVA	URN	RP	EC	[213]
5-HIAA, TRP, IAA	CSF	RP	F	[214, 215]
HVA, TYR, 5-HIAA	CSF	RP	F, EC	[216]
5-HT, 5-HIAA	TH	RP	EC	[217]
MHPG	CSF	RP	EC	[218]
MHPG, DOPAC, HVA, 5-HIAA	TH	RP	EC	[219]
E, NE, NM, DA, 5-HT	BLD	RP	F	[62]
E, NE	BLD	RP	F	[220]
5-HTP	BLD	RP	F	[215]
5-HIAA, IAA	URN	RP	F	[61]
Ne, E	BLD	IE	EC	[75]
5-HT, NE, DA	TH	RP	F	[190]
E, NE, DOPA, DA, 5-HT, TYRM, TRP	TH	RP	F	[196]

Abbreviations:

TH (tissue homogenate), BLD (blood, plasma, serum),

URN (urine);

RP (reverse-phase), IE (ion-exchange), AD (adsorption);

EC (electrochemical detection),

F (fluorimetric detection).

DA (dopamine), DOPA (3,4-dihydroxyphenylalanine), DOPAC (3,4-dihydroxyphenylacetic acid), E (epinephrine), 5-HIAA (5-hydroxyindole-3-acetic acid), 5-HT (serotonin), 5-HTP (5-hydroxytrypto-phan), HVA (homovanillic acid), IAA (indoleacetic acid), MHPG (3-methoxy-4-hydroxyphenylglycol), NE (norepinephrine), NM (normetanephrine), TRP (tryptophan), TYR (tyrosine), TYRM (tyramine), VMA (vanillylmandelic acid).

6.6 References

[1] U. Bachrach: *Function of Naturally Occuring Polyamines*. Academic Press, New York 1973.
[2] J. Jänne, H. Pösö, and A. Raina, *Biochim. Biophys. Acta.* **473**, 241 (1978).
[3] D. V. Maudsley, *Biochem. Pharmacol.* **28**, 153 (1979).

[4] H. Desser, G. W. Niebauer, and W. Gebhart, *Zbl. Vet. Med.* **A. 27**, 45 (1980).

[5] U. Bachrach, *Ital. J. Biochem.* **25**, 77 (1976).

[6] R. A. Campbell, D. R. Morris, D. Sartos, G. D. Daves, and F. Bartos: *Advances in Polyamine Research,* Vol. 2. Raven Press, New York 1978.

[7] D. H. Russell, and B. G. M. Durie: *Polyamines as Biochemical Markers of Normal and Malignant Growth.* Raven Press, New York 1978.

[8] H. Desser: *Polyamines in Biomedical Research,* J. Wiley & Sons, London 1981.

[9] D. H. Russell, C. C. Levy, S. C. Schimpff, and I. A. Hawk, *Cancer Res.* **31**, 1555 (1971).

[10] D. H. Russell, B. G. M. Durie, and S. E. Salmon, *Lancet* II, 797 (1975).

[11] M. Guggenheim: *Die biogenen Amine.* Verlag von S. Karger, Basel-New York 1951.

[12] D. F. Sharman, in: H. Blaschko and E. Muscholl: *Handbook of Experimental Pharmacology XXXIII,* p. 110, Springer Verlag, Berlin-Heidelberg-New York 1972.

[13] N. Seiler, and M. Wiechmann, *Hoppe-Seyler's Z. Physiol. Chem.* **350**, 1493 (1969).

[14] Y. Yoshino, F. V. DeFedis, and K. A. C. Elliott, *Can. J. Biochem.* **48**, 147 (1970).

[15] N. Seiler, and A. Askar, *J. Chromatogr.* **62**, 121 (1971).

[16] S. I. Harik, G. W. Pasternak, and S. H. Snyder, *Biochim. Biophys. Acta* **304**, 753 (1973).

[17] W. B. Stavinoha, S.T. Weintraub, and A. T. Modak, *J. Neurochem.* **23**, 885 (1974).

[18] M. A. Beaven, in: L. L. Iversen, S. D. Iversen, and S. H. Snyder (eds.): *Handbook of Psychopharmacology,* Vol. 1, p. 26. Plenum Press, New York-London 1975.

[19] J. M. Saavedra, *Prog. Anal. Chem.* **7**, 33 (1974).

[20] J. K. Saelens, M. S. Schoen, and G. B. Kovacsics, *Biochem. Pharmacol.* **16**, 1043 (1967).

[21] J. D. Peuler, and G. A. Johnson, *Life Sci.* **21**, 625 (1977).

[22] P. G. Passon, and J. D. Peuler, *Anal. Biochem.* **51**, 618 (1973).

[23] N. D. Vlachakis, and M. Mendlowitz, *Clin. Res.* **24**, 621 A (1976).

[24] W. J. Blaedel, and T. J. Anderson, *Anal. Chem.* **43**, 521 (1971).

[25] L. Rentzhog, *Acta Physiol. Scand. Suppl.* **377**, 1 (1972).

[26] D. P. Henry, B. J. Starman, D. G. Johnson, and R. H. Williams, *Life Sci.* **16**, 375 (1975).

[27] A. C. Cuello, R. Hiley, and L. L. Iversen, *J. Neurochem.* **21**, 1337 (1973).

[28] V. Werse, and J. Kopin, *Life Sci.* **19**, 673 (1976).

[29] F. R. Matthias, *Klin Wschr.* **50**, 243 (1972).

[30] J. M. Saavedra, M. Brownstain, and J. Axelrod, *J. Pharmacol. Exp. Ther.* **186**, 508 (1973).

[31] J. M. Saavedra and J. Axelrod, *Proc. Natl. Acad. Sci.* USA **70**, 769 (1973).

[32] J. M. Saavedra, *Anal. Biochem.* **59**, 628 (1974).

[33] S. H. Snyder, R. J. Baldessarini, and J. Axelrod, *J. Pharmacol. Exp. Ther.* **153**, 544 (1966).

[34] K. M. Taylor, and S. H. Snyder, *J. Neurochem.* **19**, 1343 (1972).

[35] Y. Kobayashi, and D. V. Maudsley, *Anal. Biochem.* **46**, 85 (1972).

[36] J. K. Saelens, M. P. Allen, and J. P. Simke, *Arch. Int. Pharmacodyn.* **186**, 279 (1970).

[37] W. D. Reid, D. R. Haubrich, and G. Krishna, *Anal. Biochem.* **42**, 390 (1971).

[38] P. A. Shea, and M. H. Aprison, *Anal. Biochem.* **56**, 165 (1973).

[39] S. Wonnacott, *Biochem. Soc. Trans.* **3**, 102 (1975).

[40] L. Waldenlind, *Biochem. Pharmacol.* **24**, 1339 (1975).

[41] R. Massarelli, T. Durkin, C. Niedergang, and P. Mandel, *Pharmacol. Res. Commun.* **8**, 407 (1976).

[42] D. B. Calne, F. Karoum, C. R. J. Ruthven, and M. Sandler, *Br. J. Pharmacol.* **37**, 57 (1969).

[43] J. C. Lhuguenot, and B. F. Maume, *J. Chromatogr. Sci.* **12**, 411 (1974).

[44] H. G. Lovelady, *Biochem. Med.* **15**, 130 (1976).

[45] M. T. Wang, K. Imai, M. Yoshioka, and Z. Taniura, *Clin. Chem. Acta.* **63**, 13 (1975).

[46] H. CH. Curtius, M. Wolfensberger, B. Steinmann, V. Redweik, and J. Siegfried, *J. Chromatogr.* **99**, 529 (1974).

[47] H. Miyezaki and Y. Hashimoto, *J. Chromatogr.* **99**, 575 (1974).

[48] M. R. Holdiness, M. T. Rosen, J. B. Justice, and D. B. Neill, *J. Chromatogr.* **198**, 329 (1980).

[49] F.-A. Wiesel, C.-G. Fri, and G. Sedvall, *J. Neurol. Transm.* **35**, 319 (1974).

[50] E. Watson, B. Travis, and S. Wilk, *Life Sci.* **15**, 2167 (1974).

[51] E. Gelpi, E. Peralta, and J. Segura, *J. Chromatogr. Sci.* **12**, 701 (1974).

[52] F. Cattabeni, S. H. Koslow, and E. Costa, *Science* **178**, 166 (1972).

[53] C.-G. Swahn, B. Sandgarde, F.-A. Wiesel, and G. Sedvall, *Psychopharmacology* **48**, 147 (1976).

[54] O. Beck, F.-A. Wiesel, and G. Sedvall, *J. Chromatogr.* **134**, 407 (1977).

[55] F. Artigas, and E. Gelpi, *Anal. Biochem.* **92**, 233 (1979).

[56] P. T. Kissinger, *Anal. Chem.* **49**, 447 A (1977).

[57] R. Keller, A. Oke, I. Mefford, and R. N. Adams, *Life Sci.* **19**, 995 (1976).

[58] R. M. Riggin, and P. T. Kissinger, *Anal. Chem.* **49**, 2109 (1977).

[59] J. Wagner, M. Palfreyman, and M. Zraika, *J. Chromatogr.* **164**, 41 (1979).

[60] J. L. Meek, and L. M. Neckers, *Brain Res.* **91**, 336 (1975).

[61] O. Beck, G. Palmskog and E. Hultman, *Clin. Chim. Acta* **79**, 149 (1977).

[62] T. P. Davis, C. W. Gehrke, C. W. Gehrke, Jr., T. D. Cunningham, K. C. Kuo, K. O. Gerhardt, H. D. Johnson, and C. H. Williams, *Clin. Chem.* **24**, 1317 (1978).

[63] J. L. Meek, *Anal. Chem.* **48**, 375 (1976).

[64] R. M. Wightman, P. M. Plotsky, E. Strope, R. Delcore, Jr., and R. N. Adams, *Brain Res.* **131**, 345 (1977).

[65] L. J. Felice and P. T. Kissinger, *Anal. Chem.* **48**, 794 (1976).

[66] L. J. Felice, C. S. Bruntlett, and P. T. Kissinger, *J. Chromatogr.* **143**, 407 (1977).

[67] S. Sasa, and C. L. Blank, *Anal. Chem.* **49**, 354 (1977).

[68] G. A. Scratchley, A. N. Masoud, S. J. Stohs and D. W. Wingard, *J. Chromatogr.* **169**, 313 (1979).

[69] F. Hefti, *Life Sci.* **25**, 775 (1979).

[70] J. J. Warsh, A. Chiu, D. D. Godse, and D. V. Coscina, *Brain Res. Bull.* **4**, 567 (1979).

[71] D. D. Koch, and P. T. Kissinger, *J. Chromatogr.* **164**, 441 (1979).

[72] J. P. Garnier, B. Bousquet, and C. Dreux, *J. Liqu. Chromatogr.* **2**, 539 (1979).

[73] I. N. Mefford, and J. D. Barchas, *J. Chromatogr.* **181**, 187 (1980).

[74] C. D. Kilts, G. R. Bresse, and R. B. Mailman, *J. Chromatogr.* **225**, 347 (1981).

[75] E. Watson, *Life Sci.* **28**, 493 (1981).

[76] G. Wenk, and R. Greenland, *J. Chromatogr.* **183**, 261 (1980).

[77] G. M. Anderson, D. K. Batter, J. G. Young, B. A. Shaywitz, and D. J. Cohen, *J. Chromatogr.* **181**, 453 (1980).

[78] J. J. Warsh, A. Chiu, P. P. Li, and D. D. Godse, *J. Chromatogr.* **183**, 483 (1980).

[79] J. Wagner, M. Palfreyman, and M. Zraika, *J. Chromatogr.* **164**, 41 (1979).

[80] S. Sasa, and C. LeRoy Blank, *Anal. Chem.* **49**, 354 (1977).

[81] H. Svendsen, and T. Greibrokk, *J. Chromatogr.* **213**, 429 (1981).

[82] S.-I. Kobayashi, J. Sekino, K. Honda, and K. Imai, *Anal. Biochem.* **112**, 99 (1981).

[83] M. Da Prada, and G. Zürcher, *Life Sci.* **19**, 1161 (1976).

[84] T. Müller, E. Hofschuster, H.-J. Kuss, and D. Welter, *J. Neurol. Transm.* **45**, 219 (1979).

[85] P. Hajdu, D. Palm, and M. Uihlein, in: *Abstracts IV European Congress of Clinical Chemistry*, Vienna 1981.

[86] G. Schill, K. O. Borg, R. Modin, and B. A. Persson, in: *Progress in Drug Metabolism*, Vol. **2**, Chap. 5. John Wiley & Sons, New York 1977.

[87] B. Ulin, K. Gustavii, and B. A. Persson, *J. Pharm. Pharmacol.* **28**, 672 (1976).

[88] F. Fonnum, *Biochem. J.* **115**, 465 (1969).

[89] D. Westerlund, *Acta Pharm. Suec.* **9**, 47 (1972).

[90] D. Westerlund, and K. O. Borg, *Anal. Chim. Acta* **67**, 89 (1973).

[91] B. A. Persson, *Acta Pharm. Suec.* **8**, 193 (1972).

[92] B. A. Persson, *Acta Pharm. Suec.* **8**, 217 (1971).

[93] N. Seiler, L. Demisch, and H. Schneider, *Angew. Chem., Int. Ed. Engl.* **10** (1), 51 (1971).

[94] H. Weil-Malherbe, and A. D. Bone *Biochem. J.* **67**, 65 (1957).

[95] D. H. Spackman, W. H. Stein, and S. Moore, *Anal. Chem.* **30**, 1190 (1958).

[96] K. Samejima, M. Kawase, S. Sakamoto, M, Okada, and Y. Endo, *Anal. Biochem.* **76**, 392 (1976).

[97] R. E. Shoup, and P. T. Kissinger, *Clin. Chem.* **23**, 1268 (1977).

[98] G. Schwedt, *Clin. Chim. Acta* **51**, 247 (1974).

[99] A. H. Anton, and D. F. Sayre, *J. Pharmacol. Exp. Ther.* **138**, 360 (1962).

[100] R. Keller, A. Oke, I. Mefford, and R. N. Adams, *Life Sci.* **17**, 995 (1976).

[101] J. F. O'Hanlon, Jr., H. C. Campuzano, and S. M. Horvath, *Anal. Biochem.* **34**, 560 (1970).

[102] S. Higa, T. Suzuki, A. Hayashi, I. Tsuge, and Y. Yamaniura, *Anal. Biochem.* **77**, 18 (1977).

[103] T. P. Moyer, N. S. Jiang, G. M. Tyce, and S. G. Sheps, *Clin. Chem.* **25**, 256 (1979).

[104] C. F. Gelijkens, and A. P. DeLeenheer, *J. Chromatogr.* **183**, 78 (1980).

[105] P. T. Kissinger, C. S. Bruntlett, and R. E. Shoup, *Life Sci.* **28**, 455 (1981).

[106] A. V. P. Mackay, C. M. Yates, A. Wright, P. Hamilton, and P. Davies, *J. Neurochem.* **30**, 841 (1978).

[107] A. J. Cross, and M. H. Joseph, *Life Sci.* **28**, 499 (1981).

[108] D. D. Koch, and P. T. Kissinger, *J. Chromatogr.* **164**, 441 (1979).

[109] D. D. Koch, and P. T. Kissinger, Life Sci. **26**, 1099 (1980).

[110] D. D. Koch, and P. T. Kissinger, *Anal. Chem.* **52**, 27 (1980).

[111] J. Lankelma, and H. Poppe, *J. Chromatogr.* **149**, 587 (1978).

[112] K. Ogan, E. Katz, and W. Slavin, *J. Chromatogr. Sci.* **16**, 517 (1978).

[113] W. Voelter, T. Kronbach, K. Zech, and R. Huber, *J. Chromatogr.* **239**, 475 (1982).

[114] T. Nakajima, F. Wolfgram, and W. G. Clark, *J. Neurochem.* **14**, 1113 (1967).

[115] S. Baba, and S. Ogiya, *Yakugaku Zasshi* **89**, 399 (1969).

[116] H. Hatano, S. Sumizu, S. Rokushika, and F. Murakami, *Anal. Biochem.* **35**, 377 (1970).

[117] R. A. Wall, *J. Chromatogr.* **60**, 195 (1971).

[118] P. Vandekerekhove, and K. Henderickx, *J. Chromatogr.* **82**, 379 (1973).

[119] C. D. Scott, *J. Chromatogr. Sci.* **11**, 379 (1973).

[120] P. Jandera, and J. Churacek, *J. Chromatogr.* **98**, 1 (1974).

[121] T. L. Perry, S. Hansen, J. G. Foulks, and G. M. Ling, *J. Neurochem.* **12**, 397 (1965).

[122] T. L. Perry, S. Hansen, and L. MacDougall, *J. Neurochem.* **14**, 775 (1967).

[123] T. L. Perry, and W. A. Schroeder, *J. Chromatogr.* **12**, 358 (1963).

[124] T. L. Perry, M. Hestrin, L. MacDougall, and S. Hansen, *Clin. Chim. Acta* **14**, 116 (1966).

[125] T.L. Perry, S. Hansen, and I. Jenkins, *J. Neurochem.* **11**, 49 (1964).

[126] L. J. Marton, D. H. Russell, and C. C. Levy, *Clin. Chem.* **19**, 923 (1973).

[127] L. J. Marton, O. Heby, C. B. Wilson and P. L. Y. Lee, *FEBS Lett.* **46**, 305 (1974).

[128] H. Adler, M. Margoshes, L. R. Snyder, and C. Spitzer, *J. Chromatogr.* **143**, 125 (1977).

[129] N. A. Dierick, I. J. Vervaeke, J. A. Decuypere, and H. K. Hendrickx, *J. Chromatogr.* **129**, 403 (1976).

[130] S. Udenfried, S. Stein, P. Böhlen, W. Dairmann, W. Leimgruber, and M. Weigele, *Science* **178**, 871 (1972).

[130a] M. Weigele, S. L. DeBernardo, J. P. Tengi, and W. Leingruber, *J. Am. Chem. Soc.* **94**, 5927 (1972).

[131] W. Voelter, and K. Zech, *J. Chromatogr.* **112**, 643 (1975).

[132] S. Stein, P. Bohlen, J. Stone, W. Dairman, and S. Udenfried, *Arch. Biochem. Biophys.* **155**, 202 (1972).

[133] S. DeBarnardo, M. Weigele, V. Toome, K. Manart, W. Leimgruber, P. Bohlen, S. Stein, and S. Udenfried, *Arch. Biochem. Biophys.* **163**, 390 (1974).

[134] K. Imai, *J. Chromatogr.* **105**, 135 (1975).

[135] L. J. Marton, and P. L. Y. Lee, *Clin. Chem.* **21**, 1721 (1975).

[136] G. Schwedt, *J. Chromatogr.* **143**, 463 (1977).

[137] R. T. Borchardt, M. F. Hegazi, and R. L. Schowen, *J. Chromatogr.* **152**, 255 (1978).

[138] K. D. McMurtrey, L. R. Meyerson, J. L. Cashaw, and V. E. Davis, *Anal. Biochem.* **72**, 566 (1976).

[139] E. Ueda, N. Yoshida, K. Nishimura, T. Joh, S. Autoku, K. Tsukada, S. Ganno, and T. Kokubu, *Clin. Chim. Acta* **80**, 447 (1977).

[140] B.-A. Persson, and B. L. Karger, *J. Chromatogr. Sci.* **12**, 521 (1974).

[141] B.-A. Persson, and P.-O. Lagerström, *J. Chromatogr.* **122**, 305 (1976).

[142] L. J. Felice, and P. T. Kissinger, *Anal. Chem.* **48**, 794 (1976).

[143] J. Molnar, and C. Horvath, *Clin. Chem.* **22**, 1497 (1976).

[144] J. H. Knox, and J. Jurand, *J. Chromatogr.* **125**, 89 (1976).

[145] R. M. Riggin, and P. T. Kissinger, *Anal. Chem.* **49**, 2109 (1977).

[146] C. Horvath, W. Melander, J. Melander, and P. Molnar, *Anal. Chem.* **49**, 2295 (1977).

[147] J. C. Kraak, K. M. Jonker, and J. F. K. Huber, *J. Chromatogr.* **142**, 671 (1977).

[148] J. P. Crombeen, J. C. Kraak, and H. Poppe, *J. Chromatogr.* **167**, 219 (1978).

[149] P. T. Kissinger, R. M. Riggin, R. L. Alcorn, and L. D. Rau, *Biochem. Med.* **13**, 299 (1975).

[150] C. D. Kilts, G. R. Breese, and R. B. Mailman, *J. Chromatogr.* **225**, 347 (1981).

[151] G. Schwedt, and H. H. Bussemas, *Z. Anal. Chem.* **283**, 23 (1977).

[152] K. Samejiama, M. Kawase, S. Sakamoto, M. Okada, and Y. Endo, *Anal. Biochem.* **76**, 392 (1976).

[153] T. P. Davis, C. W. Gehrke, C. W. Gehrke, T. D. Cunningham, K. C. Kuo, K. O. Gerhardt, H. D. Johnson, and C. M. Williams, *J. Chromatogr.* **162**, 293 (1979).

[154] P. A. Asmus, and C. R. Freed, *J. Chromatogr.* **169**, 303 (1979).
[155] G. M. J. Bijersbergen van Henegouwen, C. Kruse, and K. W. Gerritsma, *Pharm. Weekbl.* **111**, 197 (1976).
[156] C. P. Terweij-Groen, S. Heemstra, and J. C. Kraak, *J. Chromatogr.* **161**, 69 (1978).
[157] J. H. Knox, and G. R. Laird, *J. Chromatogr.* **122**, 17 (1976).
[158] N. Seiler, T. Schmidt-Glenewinkel, and H. H. Schneider, *J. Chromatogr.* **84**, 95 (1973).
[159] N. Seiler, and B. Knödgen, *J. Chromatogr.* **131**, 109 (1977).
[160] R. P. Corry, R. R. Becker, R. Rosenbluth, and T. Isenberg, *J. Am. Chem. Soc.* **90**, 1643 (1968).
[161] Ch. P. Ivanov, and Y. Vladovska-Yukhnovska, *Biochim. Biophys. Acta.* **194**, 345 (1969).
[162] I. Durko, Y. Vladovska-Yukhnovska, and C. P. Ivanov, *Clin. Chim. Acta* **49**, 407 (1973).
[163] H. Ichiwaka, T. Tanimura, T. Nakajima, and Z. Tamura, *Chem. Pharm. Bull. (Tokyo)* **18**, 1493 (1970).
[164] H. Maeda, N. Ishida, H. Kawauchi, and K. Tuzimura, *J. Biochem. (Tokyo)* **65**, 777 (1969).
[165] J. E. Sinsheimer, D. D. Hong, J. T. Stewart, M. L. Fink, and J. H. Burckhalter, *J. Pharm. Sci.* **60**, 141 (1971).
[166] N. Lustenberger, H. W. Lange, and K. Hempel, *Angew. Chem.* **84**, 255 (1972).
[167] H. W. Lange, N. Lustenberger, and K. Hempel, *Z. Anal. Chem.* **261**, 337 (1972).
[168] N. Seiler, and H. H. Schneider, *J. Chromatogr.* **59**, 367 (1971).
[169] W. Dünges, G. Naundorf, and N. Seiler, *J. Chromatogr. Sci.* **12**, 655 (1974).
[170] M. M. Abdel-Monem, and K. Ohno, *J. Chromatogr.* **107**, 416 (1975).
[171] N. E. Newton, K. Ohno, and M. M. Abdel-Monem, *J. Chromatogr.* **124**, 277 (1976).
[172] B. Kaltenegger, Thesis, University of Tübingen 1977.
[173] M. Roth, and A. Hampai, *J. Chromatogr.* **83**, 353 (1973).
[174] R. P. Maickel, and F. P. Miller, *Anal. Chem.* **38**, 13 (1966).
[175] S. S. Simons, and D. F. Johnson, *J. Am. Chem. Soc.* **98**, 7098 (1976).
[176] J. F. Lawrence, and R. W. Frei: *Chemical Derivatization in Liquid Chromatography*. Elsevier Scientific Publishing Company, Amsterdam-Oxford-New York 1976.
[177] B. S. Hartley, and V. Massey, *Biochim. Biophys. Acta.* **21**, 58 (1956).
[178] W. R. Gray, and B. S. Hartley, *Biochem. J.* **89**, 380 (1963).
[179] J. Rosmus, and Z. Deyl, *Chromatogr. Rev.* **13**, 83 (1971).
[180] N. Seiler, *Methods Biochem. Anal.* **18**, 259 (1970).
[181] H. Veening, W. W. Pitt Jr., and G. Jones Jr., *J. Chromatogr.* **90**, 129 (1974).
[182] R. W. Frei, M. Thomas and I. Frei, *J. Liqu. Chromatogr.* **1**, 443 (1978).
[183] P. M. Froehlich, and T. D. Cunnigham, *Anal, Chim. Acta* **97**, 357 (1978).
[184] L. D. Mell, A. R. Dasler, and A. B. Gustafson, *J. Liq. Chromatogr.* **1**, 261 (1978).
[185] K. Imai, M. Tsukanoto, and Z. Tamura, *J. Chromatogr.* **137**, 357 (1977).
[186] G. Schwedt, *J. Chromatogr.* **118**, 429 (1976).
[187] A. P. Graffeo, and B. L. Karger, *Clin. Chem.* **22**, 184 (1976).
[188] Y. Yui, M. Kimura, Y. Itokawa, and C. Kawai, *J. Chromatogr.* **177**, 376 (1979).
[189] O. Beck, and T. Hesselgren, *J. Chromatogr.* **181**, 100 (1980).
[190] G. P. Jackman, V. J. Carson, A. Bobik, and H. Skews, *J. Chromatogr.* **182**, 277 (1980).
[191] L. M. Nelson, and M. Carruthers, *J. Chromatogr.* **183**, 295 (1980).
[192] M. T. I. W. Schüsler-Van Hees, and G. M. J. Beijersbergen van Henegouwen, *J. Chromatogr.* **196**, 101 (1980).
[193] A. M. Krustulovic, *Adv. Chromatogr.* **17**, 279 (1979).
[194] G. M. Anderson, and W. C. Purdy, *Anal. Chem.* **51**, 283 (1979).
[195] A. M. Krustulovic, and C. Matzura, *J. Chromatogr.* **163**, 72 (1979).
[196] A. M. Krustulovic, and A. M. Powell, *J. Chromatogr.* **171**, 345 (1979).
[197] D. A. Richards, *J. Chromatogr.* **175**, 293 (1979).
[198] M. J. Cooper, R. F. O'Dea, and B. L. Mirkin, *J. Chromatogr.* **162**, 601 (1979).
[199] C. C. Loullis, D. L. Felten, and P. A. Shea, *Pharmacol. Biochem. Behavior* **11**, 89 (1979).
[200] G. C. Davis, P. T. Kissinger, and R. E. Shoup, *Anal. Chem.* **53**, 156 (1981).
[201] A. Oke, R. Keller, I. Mefford, and R. N. Adams, *Science* **200**, 1411 (1978).
[202] L. J. Felice, J. D. Felice, and P. T. Kissinger, *J. Neurochem.* **31**, 1461 (1978).
[203] C. L. Blank, S. Sasa, R. Isernhagen, L. R. Meyerson, D. Wassil, P. Wong, A. T. Modak, and W. B. Stavinoha, *J. Neurochem.* **33**, 213 (1979).

[204] K. H. Milby, I. N. Mefford, R. W. Keller, and R. N. Adams, *Brain Res.* **169**, 398 (1979).
[205] D. S. Goldstein, G. Feuerstein, J. L. Izzo, Jr., I. J. Kopin, and H. R. Keiser, *Life Sci.* **28**, 467 (1981).
[206] I. N. Mefford, M. Gilberg, and J. D. Barchas, *Anal. Biochem.* **104**, 469 (1980).
[207] S. Sasa, and C. L. Blank, *Anal. Chim. Acta* **104**, 29 (1979).
[208] H. Hallman, L. O. Farnebo, B. Hamberger, and G. Jonsson, *Life Sci.* **23**, 1049 (1978).
[209] P. Hjemdahl, M. Daleskog, and T. Kahan, *Life Sci.* **25**, 131 (1979).
[210] C. R. Freed, and P. A. Asmus, *J. Neurochem.* **32**, 163 (1979).
[211] T. H. Müller, and K. Unsicker, *J. Neurosci. Methods* **4**, 39 (1981).
[212] S. J. Soldin, and J. G. Hill, *Clin. Chem.* **26**, 291 (1980).
[213] J. L. Morrisey, and Z. K. Shihabi, *Clin. Chem.* **25**, 2045 (1979).
[214] G. M. Anderson, and W. C. Purdy, *Anal. Lett.* **10**, 493 (1977).
[215] G. M. Anderson, and W. C. Purdy, *Anal. Chem.* **51**, 283 (1979).
[216] G. M. Anderson, J. G. Young, and D. J. Cohen, *J. Chromatogr.* **164**, 501 (1979).
[217] W. H. Lyness, N. M. Friedle, and K. E. Moore, *Life Sci* **26**, 1109 (1980).
[218] P. J. Langlais, W. J. McEntee, and E. D. Bird, *Clin. Chem.* **26**, 786 (1980).
[219] A. J. Cross, and M. H. Joseph, *Life Sci* **28**, 499 (1981).
[220] M. T. Wang, K. Imai, M. Yoshioka, and Z. Tamura, *Clin. Chim. Acta* **63**, 13 (1975).

7 Lipids

by *Manfred Tevini* and *Dirk Steinmüller*

7 Lipids

7.1 Introduction

Lipids are a very heterogeneous class of compounds containing lipophilic chains which determine their solubility in organic solvents and their insolubility in water. They can arbitrarily be subdivided into two groups, one related to hydrocarbons and fatty acids, and another group related to terpenoids or prenols. Representatives of the first group are long-chain hydrocarbons and -alcohols, fatty acids, esters of fatty acids with different alcohols, phospholipids (mixed esters of fatty acids and phosphoric acid with glycerol or sphingosine) and glycolipids (a heterogeneous lipid class containing sugar or sugar derivatives). The second group includes long-chain terpenoids (such as carotenoids), mixed terpenoids (e. g. chlorophylls) and the long-chain polyprenols (e. g. lipophilic quinones).

Lipids are the main constituents of all plant and animal membranes. In membranes they have not only a structural role but are also involved in their function, as demonstrated in the photosynthetic membrane (thylakoids) of chloroplasts. In most membranes, lipids have a barrier function and are involved in the control of the transport of compounds through the membrane. Lipids can also be stored, either in plants or animals, and serve as an energy supply. Storage lipids in seeds or animal tissue are used for oil production and therefore serve as a food supply. Scientific and economic interest thus involve the biochemist and food technologist with lipids. New methods are being developed for separation and identification, among them high pressure (performance) liquid chromatography.

The extreme differences in the polarity of lipids make the choise of suitable stationary and mobile phases difficult. For the separation of an artificial mixture of glycerides, phospholipids, cholesterol, cerebrosides and other lipids, for example, a column of 1 m length and a gradient of three solvent mixtures with a separation time of 3 hours has been used [2]. A lipid mixture extracted from natural sources seems to be impossible to separate sufficiently into individual lipids of each class in one single run. Therefore, in most applications, separations of single lipid classes were developed. Aitzetmüller and Koch [3] separated a mixture of natural lipids containing hydrocarbons, cholesterols, wax esters, and glycerides within 30 minutes. Plant lipid extracts are now routinely separated into single components of several lipid classes such as carotenoids, chlorophylls and lipophilic quinones [4]. In most of the applications, however, a special preparation of the lipid extract prior to chromatography is necessary. Current techniques of extraction, purification, and preliminary fractionation of lipids of natural origin were recently reviewed by Zhukov and Vereshchagin [1].

The detection of lipids in most HPLC-applications is done by light absorption or by differential refraction. Most of the membrane-, storage- and surface lipids absorb in the ultraviolet wavelength band: however, the molar extinction coefficients of saturated and monoenoic lipids are low. Only highly unsaturated compounds show good absorption. Refractive index (RI) detection has the disadvantage of low sensitivity and is only practicable in the isocratic mode. The detection of lipids by flame ionization (FI) using a moving wire is sometimes described and is reviewed by Aitzetmüller [149]. In this case the lipids must have large dif-

ferences in the volatility compared to the solvent system. The combustion of separated compound excludes their further examination. The sensitivity of this detection method is similar to
RI-detection. Other detector systems, including infrared, fluorescence, radioscintillation and
electron capture, are occasionally mentioned but are mainly used for special problems [24, 131,
142, 143, 149].

According to the most common photometric detection method the authors will first describe
lipids which show reasonable absorption in the visible and near ultraviolet region up to 250 nm.
Lipids absorbing below 250 nm will follow in the second section.

Table 7-1. Chemical Structures of Some Important Lipids.

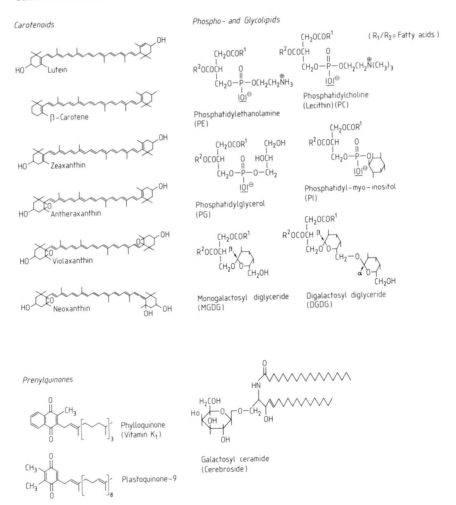

Table 7-1. (Continued).

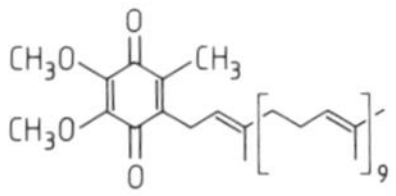

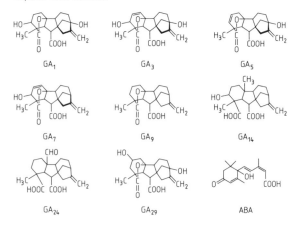

Ubiquinone – 10
(Coenzyme Q 10)

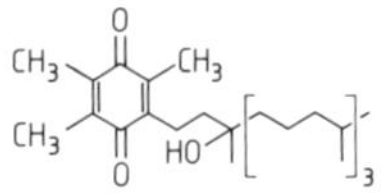

α–Tocoquinone

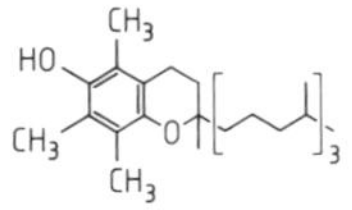

α–Tocopherol

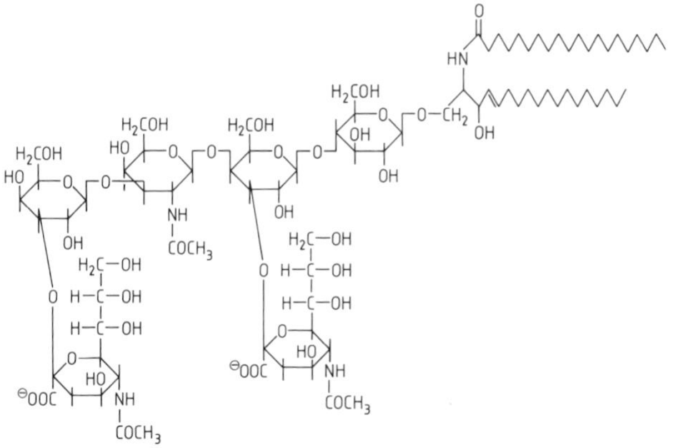

Ganglioside (GM 1)

Terpenoid Plant Hormones

GA₁

GA₃

GA₅

GA₇

GA₉

GA₁₄

GA₂₄

GA₂₉

ABA

GA : gibberellic acid derivatives

ABA : abscisic acid

7.2 Pigments and Prenyl Quinones

All lipophilic pigments having reasonable absorption in the visible waveband and also lipids absorbing in the near ultraviolet region are included in this group. All the molecules contain either a sequence of conjugated double bonds (carotenoids, vitamin A-derivatives), a chromophoric porphyrine with terpenoid alcohols in the side chain (chlorophylls), or a quinone system with open chain terpenoid alcohols, commonly referred to as prenols or prenyl compounds (plastoquinones, ubiquinones, tocopherols, vitamin K).

Pigments and prenyl quinones are important constituents of plants and animals, participating in the function and structure of cell membranes. Plant pigments are especially involved in photosynthesis, a main subject for plant physiologists. A simple method to separate these functional lipids in one chromatographic run was therefore developed in our laboratory [4]. Figure 7-1 shows an improved separation of carotenoids, chlorophylls, and relevant prenyl quinones, as well as of pheophytins (Figure 7-2), by reversed-phase chromatography (LiChrosorb 5 µm, RP-8, 25 cm column).

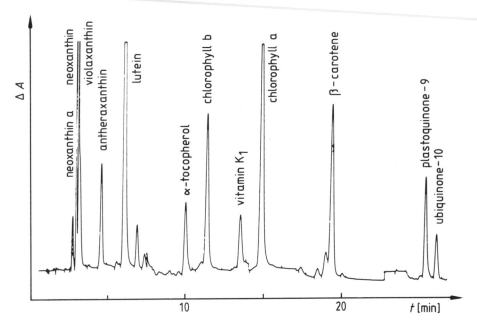

Figure 7-1. Pigment separation of green barley leaves.
Column: LiChrosorb RP-8 (5µm). Mobile phase: MeOH(B)/H_2O gradient from 85% B to 95% B within 20 min, isocratically for 1.5 min and then to 98% B within 1.5 min. Flow-rate 2.5 mL/min. Column/eluent temperature 40 °C. The variable wavelength detector was programmed to absorption maximum of each compound. From ref. [4].

The solvent system (methanol/water) gives excellent resolution when used as a gradient. For a typical separation, one can start with 85% methanol and increase methanol within 20 minutes to 95% or 98%. Plant lipids extracted in acetone or methanol can be injected without any pre-column preparation. Detection is by means of a variable wavelength detector measuring at the absorption maxima. The fixed wavelength detector (UV-detector 254 nm) can be used only for some quinones (e. g. plastoquinone) and is very insensitive for carotenoids, tocopherols and others. The high molar absorption coefficients of carotenoids ($1.5 \cdot 10^5$ cm²/mol), chlorophyll (about $8.4 \cdot 10^4$ cm²/mol), and e. g. plastoquinone (about $1.4 \cdot 10^4$ cm²/mol) allow quantification of carotenoids down to 0.7 ng, of chlorophylls to 1.7 ng (both at 430 nm). Detection of prenyl quinones is possible under the following conditions: plastoquinone (PQ-9) (oxidized form at 255 nm) 5.6 ng, Vitamin K_1 (at 265 nm) 4.2 ng and α-tocopherol (α-T) (at 290 nm) 17.5 ng. The separation of the xanthophylls lutein and zeaxanthin, however, is not possible on this column.

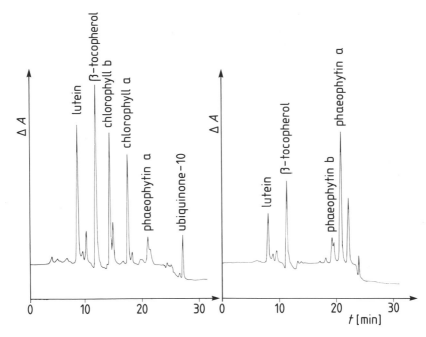

Figure 7-2. Pigment separation of commercially dried (left) and dried + boiled peas. Chromatographic conditions see Figure 7-1. Mobile phase gradient starting with 82% B (Tevini, unpublished).

The reduced form of plastoquinone PQ-H$_2$ cannot be separated from β-carotene, so that two runs are necessary for measuring the amount of β-carotene at 470 nm and of PQ-H$_2$ at 290 nm. One can also oxidize the PQ-H$_2$ by ferric chloride to PQ and measure, in a second run, the

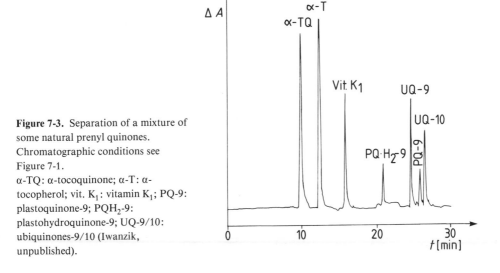

Figure 7-3. Separation of a mixture of some natural prenyl quinones. Chromatographic conditions see Figure 7-1.
α-TQ: α-tocoquinone; α-T: α-tocopherol; vit. K$_1$: vitamin K$_1$; PQ-9: plastoquinone-9; PQH$_2$-9: plastohydroquinone-9; UQ-9/10: ubiquinones-9/10 (Iwanzik, unpublished).

absorption increase of PQ at 255 nm. A separation of an artifical mixture of the following prenyl quinones α-TQ, α-T, K_1, PQ-H_2, PQ, UQ-9, UQ-10 using the same conditions as mentioned above is shown in Figure 7-3.

The separation of xanthophyll esters can also be done on RP-8 columns by increasing solvent B to 100% methanol (Figure 7-4). The retention times within one xanthophyll class depend on chain length and degree of saturation of bonded fatty acids. In yellow autumnal leaves of decidous trees the main constituents are lutein esters with a complex fatty acid composition, so that the separation of molecular species seems to be impossible under these conditions. Fatty acids do not change the molar absorption coefficient considerably so that a quantification of xanthophyll esters with different fatty acid composition is possible.

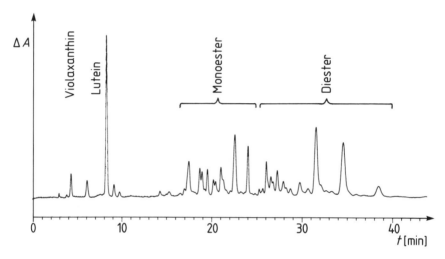

Figure 7-4. Carotenoid separation of yellow (autumn) leaves of *Aesculus hippocastanum L*. Chromatographic conditions see Figure 7-1, detection: 430 nm. Mobile phase gradient from 85% B to 100% B within 25 min. Tevini and Riedmann. (unpublished).

Similar reversed-phase or "normal-phase" columns have been used by other authors for the separation of carotenoids and chlorophylls either of higher plants or of algae [5, 6, 7, 8, 9, 10, 11]. Chlorophyllides were recently separated on RP-18 columns with methanol/water/ethyl acetate as a solvent [12]. Table 7-2 shows a summary of described separation of plant pigments.

Reversed-phase can also be used to separate different tocopherols (α-δ-tocopherols, α-δ-tocotrienols) which are present in plant oils. Fat-soluble vitamins were first separated in 1972 by Williams et al. [17]. Several other publications followed [18, 19, 20, 21]. Some authors use fluorescence emission for the detection of the tocopherols (Figure 7-5), which is somewhat more sensitive than UV-absorption [22, 23, 24]. Table 7-3 summarizes some anlytical data for tocopherols and other prenols.

Plant prenyl quinones and terpenoids have also been separated by two columns of different polarity [16, 25, 26, 27, 28].

Table 7-2. Overview of HPLC Analysis of Some Plant Pigments.

Compounds	Column	Mobile Phase	Detection (nm)	Reference
Chl a b c, ph a, l, n, v, β-c, dinoxanthins	Bondapak C-18 (37-75 μm), 61 cm, two in series	MeOH/H$_2$O Ether/MeOH (stepwise)	440	[5]
Chl a, a'b b', ph, l, n, v	Silica gel SS-05 (0.5 μm), 65 cm	i-Propanol/hexane gradient	380	[13, 14, 15]
Chl a b	Partisil PXS ODS 2	MeOH/H$_2$O 95:5	654	[6]
Chl a b, l, n, v, a, β-c	Nucleosil (5 μm)	i-Octane/EtOH 9:1	445	[7]
Chl a b, l, n, v, a, z	LiChrosorb RP-8 (5 μm)	MeOH/H$_2$O 9:1	430	[16]
Chl a a'b, ph, β-c, v, n-a, l, l-epox, n, a	SorbSil 60-D-10, C-18	EtOH/MeOH/H$_2$O (stepwise)	440	[8]
Chl a c$_1$ c$_2$, chlid a, β-c, peridinins, dinoxanthins	Partisil 10 ODS, Bondapak CN, C-18	MeOH/H$_2$O gradient	650, 440	[10]
Chl a b, ph a, b, n, n-a, l, a, β-c, xanthophyll esters, quinones	LiChrosorb RP-8 (5 μm)	MeOH/H$_2$O gradient	vw	[4, 11]
Chl a b, a, l-epox, cis/trans: n, v, l, β-c, α-c, trihydr. -α-c	LiChrosorb RP-8 (5 μm) LiChrosorb RP-18	MeOH/acetonitrile/H$_2$O 25:75 gradient	430	[9]
Chl a, chlid a, pchlid a, β-c, n, v, l, l-epox	C-18	MeOH/H$_2$O/ethylacetate gradient	436	[12]
Pheophytin esters	LiChrosorb RP-8 (5 – 10 μm), (5 – 20 μm) preparative	MeOH/H$_2$O MeOH/acetone	410, 667, 534	[147]
Bacteriochl a + b-esters	LiChrosorb RP-8 (5 – 10 μm)	MeOH/H$_2$O	vw	[148]

Abbreviations:

chl (chlorophyll), ph (pheophytin), chlid (Chlorophyllide), pchlid (protochlorophyllide), l (lutein), n (neoxanthin), n-a (neoxanthin-A), v (violaxanthin), β-c (β-carotene), α-c (α-carotene), a (antheraxanthin), z (zeaxanthin), l-epox (lutein 5,6-epoxide). vw = variable wavelength.

Remark:

The chlorophyll isomers a', b' separated by some authors were first described by Strain and Mannig (1942) and Strain (1954) and are not natural compounds of plant pigments but artificial products due to extraction procedures (Bacon and Holden, 1967).

Table 7-3. Overview of HPLC Analysis of Some Natural Prenyl quinone Derivatives. Abbreviations see Legend of Figure 7-3.

Compounds	Column	Mobile Phase	Detection (nm)	Reference
Tocopherols α, β, γ, δ Tocotrienols α, β, γ, δ	Corasil II, 2 m (37 – 50 μm)	0.5% THF in hexane	254 or 280	[18]
Tocopherols α, β, α-TQ Tocotrienols α, β, PQ-1,9, vit K$_{1,2}$, menaquinone-4, terpenoids	LiChrosorb RP-8 (5 μm) LiChrosorb SI-60 (5 μm)	4.75% H$_2$O in MeOH 1% dioxane in hexane	220, 254 265, 290	[25, 26, 27, 145]
Tocopherols α, γ	Bondapak C-18 pre-column Corasil	MeOH/H$_2$O 97:3	fluorescence 330	[22]
Tocopherols α, β, γ, δ	Spherisorb (5 μm) Partisil PXS 5 pre-column Corasil	1.4% i-Propanol in hexane	fluorescence 340	[23]
Tocopherols α, β, γ, δ, Tocotrienols α, β, γ	LiChrosorb SI-60 (5 μm)	5% Diethylether in hexane	292, fluoresc. 330	[24]
Tocopherols, UQ vit A, K	Nucleosil C-18 Partisil ODS LiChrosorb DIOL	EtOH/H$_2$O or i-Prop./hexane	UV	[28]
Vit E-quinones, tocopherol, -quinone	Bondapak C-18	100% Acetonitrile	254	[20]
Tocopherols α, β, γ, δ, vitamins D	LiChrosorb SI-60, (∅ 16 mm), prep.	0.5% i-Propanol in i-octane	296	[19]
PQ-9, PQ-H$_2$, vit K$_1$, carotenoids	Porasil Bondapak C-18 LiChrosorb SI-10	Dichlorethane/heptane 6:94 MeOH/i-prop. 3:1	254	[29]
Tocopherols α, β, α-TQ, UQ-9, 10, vit K$_1$, PQ-9, PQ-H$_2$, Chls, carotenoids	LiChrosorb RP-8 (5 μm)	MeOH/H$_2$O gradient	vw	[4]
Tocopherols α, γ, α-acetate tocoquinone, hydroxymethyl-chromanonacid	Partisil ODS (10 μm) Spherisorb ODS (5 μm) 15 cm	MeOH/H$_2$O 87:13 or gradient	285.5 275	[21]

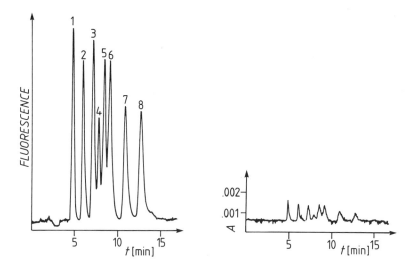

Figure 7-5. Separation of tocopherol- and tocotrienol standards.
Column: LiChrosorb SI-60 (5μm); mobile phase: 5% diethyl ether in hexane; flow-rate: 2 mL/min. Passes first through fluorescence detector (left) set at 290 nm excitation, 330 nm emission, and secondly through absorption detector (right) set at 295 nm.
1:α-tocopherol; 2: α-tocotrienol; 3: β-tocopherol; 4: antioxidant BHA; 5: γ-tocopherol; 6: β-tocotrienol; 7: γ-tocotrienol; 8: δ-tocopherol.
From ref. [24].

7.2.1 Vitamin A

Vitamin A and retinoic derivatives including retinol, retinal, retinoic acid, retinyl esters etc. can be successfully separated on reversed-phase (C-18) or "normal-phase" (silica gel, NH_2). The detection was mostly done in the UV-region between 320 nm and 365 nm [32, 33, 34, 35, 36, 37, 38, 39, 150].

7.3 Fatty acids

Gas chromatography is the most frequently used method to separate complex mixtures of fatty acid methyl esters and of unmodified fatty acids [40, 41]. Recent developments of HPLC-techniques, however, have provided many applications for fatty acid analysis (see Table 7-4 at the end of the Section). One of the major problems of using HPLC is the detection and quantification of fatty acids and related lipids. The most common detection devices are the differential refractometer detector and the ultraviolet detector. Scholfied [42, 43] studied the HPLC separation of saturated and unsaturated fatty acid methyl esters using C-18-bonded Corasil columns and the differential refractometer for detection. Acetonitrile/water mixtures eluted the unsaturated fatty acids faster than the corresponding, more saturated species and eluted the cis-isomers earlier than the corresponding trans-isomers. Plattner et al. [44] demonstrated the separation of complex mixtures of seed oils into fatty acids and triglycerides and observed a linear relationship between the carbon number and the logarithm of the retention volume.

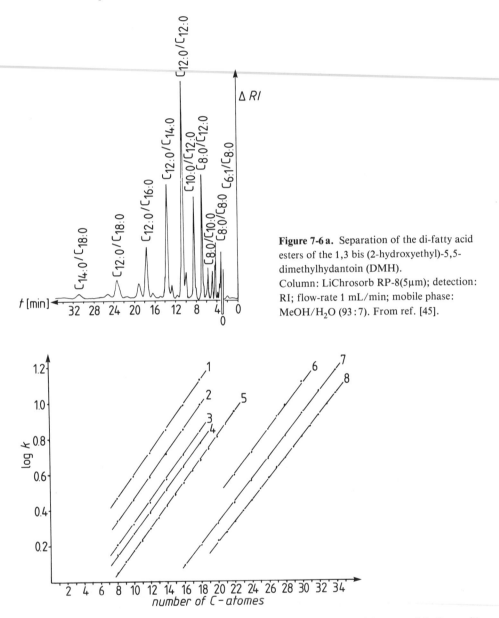

Figure 7-6 a. Separation of the di-fatty acid esters of the 1,3 bis (2-hydroxyethyl)-5,5-dimethylhydantoin (DMH). Column: LiChrosorb RP-8(5µm); detection: RI; flow-rate 1 mL/min; mobile phase: MeOH/H₂O (93:7). From ref. [45].

Figure 7-6 b. Log *k*-values as a function of the type of ester and the number of C-atoms of the fatty acid. Chromatographic conditions see Figure 7-6 a.
1 (i-octyl esters), 2 (n-hexyl esters), 3 (i-butyl esters), 4 (i-propyl esters), 5 (methyl esters), 6 (trimethylpropyl triesters), 7 (DMH-diesters), 8 (pentaerythrite tetraesters). From ref. [45].

Recently Henke and Schubert [45] separated di-fatty acid esters as DMH-esters (DMH = 1,3-bis-(2-hydroxyethyl)-5,5-dimethylhydantoin) using a reversed-phase column (RP-8) and refractometer detection (Figure 7-6a). They found a linearity between the log κ-values and the number of C-atoms of different types of esters (Figure 7-6b).

Argentation chromatography has been used for the separation of unsaturated fatty acid esters as was shown for methyl stearate, -oleate, -elaidate and some other cis- and trans-isomers [46, 47, 48]. Figure 7-7 shows a separation of cis-trans-isomers of a margarine sample on a Spherisorb S5W column impregnated with 30% $AgNO_3$.

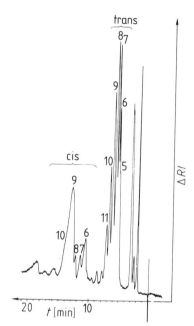

Figure 7-7. Separation of fatty acid methyl esters. Column: Spherosorb S5W, 24 cm, impregnated with 20% $AgNO_3$; detection at 205 nm; mobile phase: 1% THF in hexane; flow-rate 2.2 mL/min.
Numbers represent the position of double bond in C 18, e. g. 9 = C 18 ω 9. From ref. [48].

RI-detection is relatively insensitive to fatty acid concentrations at the ng-level [42, 43, 49, 50]. UV-detection is also not very sensitive to unmodified fatty acids apart from highly unsaturated species. Several derivatives, however, show high absorption in the UV-region. Important derivatives for UV absorption analysis are phenacyl esters, substituted phenacyl esters (bromine, chlorine, methoxy), p-nitrobenzyl esters, 2-naphthacyl esters, benzyl esters and some other derivatives for fluorescence analysis. Politzer et al. [51] converted C-16 and C-18 acids to benzyl esters and detected 1 to 2 µg as the lower limit. 2-Naphthacyl esters however reach a lower detection limit of 4 ng [52]. Several authors used the p-nitrobenzyl derivatives [53, 54]. The most commonly analyzed fatty acid derivatives are the phenacyl esters. Borch [55] separated 24 phenacyl esters of the C12 – C24 series with molar absorption coefficients up to $1.4 \cdot 10^4$ cm^2/mol (Figure 7-8). The lowest detection limit was 10 ng and the relationship of peak area to concentration of fatty acids was linear in the range of 100 ng to 100 µg. The column used was a Bondapak C-18 (90 cm), the eluant was a stepwise gradient of acetonitrile/water. N,N-diisopropylamin (catalyst) in a solution of phenacyl bromide is usually used for the derivatization process.

Another interesting method is the employment of crown ethers (e. g. 1,4,7,10,13,16-hexaoxacyclooctadecane) as catalysts and α, p-dibromoacetophenone as the acylating agent [56, 57].

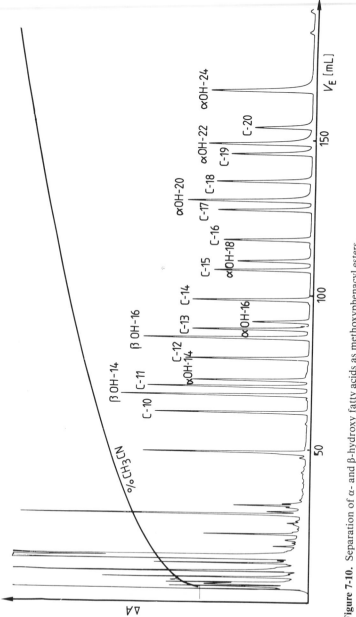

Figure 7-10. Separation of α- and β-hydroxy fatty acids as methoxyphenacyl esters.
Columns: Two µBondapak C-18 in series, 30 cm; detection at 254 nm; mobile phase: acetonitrile/H$_2$O gradient from 40 : 60 to 100% acetonitrile within 3h; flow-rate: 1 mL/min; column temperature 38 °C. From ref. [62].

Table 7-4. Overview of Fatty Acid Analysis by HPLC.

Detection	Column	Mobile Phase	Remarks	References
Phenacyl esters 254 nm	Bondapak C-18 90 cm	Acetonitrile/H_2O step program	C 12-24, 24 compounds	[55]
Phenacyl esters 254 nm	Corasil II C-9	MeOH/H_2O or heptane/chloroform	C 2-7, 12-20, 4 comp. each	[57]
FFA, RI / Methyl esters, RI	VYDAC (35-44 µm) 1 m	MeOH/H_2O	C 6-11, 20-24 / C 20:0-20:5	[49]
Methyl esters, RI, 254 nm	Corasil C-18 2 ft	Acetonitrile/H_2O MeOH/H_2O	C 12-18 doubl. bond. isomers	[42, 43]
FFA 235 nm, IR 990 cm^{-1}	Partisil (5 µm) 50 cm	0.75% EtOH in hexane	cis/trans C 18 methylhydroxy-FA	[66, 67]
FFA 215 nm, or 234 nm	TSK-gel LS 140 60 cm	Hexane/EtOH 9:1	C 18 hydroxy, hydroperoxy-FA	[68]
Methyl esters 205 nm	Spherisorb S5W + $AgNO_3$ (20%)	THF/hexane	C 18 cis/trans doubl. bond. isomers	[47, 48]
p-Chloro-bromo-nitro-phenacyl esters, 2-naphthacyl esters	Bondapak C-18 FFAP two in series	Acetonitrile or acetonitrile/H_2O gradient	C 2-24 35 compounds	[60]
Bromomethyl methoxycoumarin deriv. fluorescence	MicroPak SI-10	i-Octane:acetonitr./ methylen chloride 10:15 gradient	C 3-18 6 compounds	[69]
Methoxyphenacyl esters 254 nm or 280 nm	Bondapak C-18 FFAP two in series pre column ODS	Acetonitrile/H_2O gradient	C 8-24, 12-32 28 compounds compl. hydroxyl-FA hydrogenation unsat. FA	[59, 62, 70, 71]
Phenacyl esters 254 nm	Bondapak C-18, two in series	Acetonitrile/H_2O gradient	C 10-24 from glycerides 26 compounds	[72]
p-Bromophenacyl esters 254 nm	Spherisorb ODS	MeOH/H_2O 9:1	C 14-18 from triglyc. 7 compounds	[73]

Table 7-4. (Continued).

Detection	Column	Mobile Phase	Remarks	References
Methyl- → i-octyl esters, di-and triesters, RI	LiChrosorb RP-8 (5 μm)	MeOH/H_2O e.g. 93:7	e. g. C 8-24 C 18 isomers	[45]
Bromophenacyl esters	Porasil C-30	Acetonitr./methylchl. or acetonitr./H_2O or acetonitr./dioxane	40 compounds C 3-24, 76-82 "critical pairs"	[61]
Bromophenacyl esters	LiChrosorb RP-18 (5 μm)	Acetonitrile/H_2O ph 3.1 (H_3PO_4)	from glycerides C 9-20	[74]
p-Bromophenacyl esters	Radial Pak A C-18 (10 μm)	Acetonitrile/H_2O 87:13 or MeOH/H_2O 90:10	C 12-22 with K'-factors	[75]
FFA, RI	Bondapak FFAP	THF, Acetonitrile/H_2O	from natural fats	[76]
FFA, RI	LiChrosorb RP-8 (10 μm) Pre-Column Porasil A	THF, Acetonitrile/H_2O/ HAc	margarine samples	[146]

Abbreviations:
FFA (free fatty acids)   FA (fatty acid)
RI (refractive index detector) IR (infra red detector)
FFAP (free fatty acid phase bonded column)

HPLC [66, 67, 68]. There are many other publications concerning the separation of fatty acids, and these are summarized in Table 7-4.

7.4 Glycerides (Mono-, Di-, Triglycerides)

The glycerides can be separated into lipid classes, either unrelated to saturation and number of C-atoms, or according to the molecular species of each class. In the first case, monoglycerides (MG), diglycerides (DG) and triglycerides (TG) are separated into three different homogeneous peaks, which contain very heterogeneous mixtures of molecular species. The separation of molecular species is, as with gas chromatography, very difficult to achieve by HPLC. Most publications only describe the separation within one lipid class (mostly triglycerides) according to the number of C-atoms. Reversed- and polar-phases are used for separation of glycerides. The detection is done either by FI (moving wire) with a sensitivity of about 0.5 to 2 µg or by RI with a sensitivity of 50 µg. A total separation of each molecular species is not possible at present.

7.4.1 Glyceride Classes

The separation methods previously described deal not only with MG, DG and TG but also with several other glyceride classes. Privett et al. [77] separated lipids of soybeans into 29 compounds including TG, phospholipids and galactolipids (both mixed diglycerides), sterols, cerebrosides etc. (Fig. 7-11) using a Porasil II column, an elution program with pentane, pentane/diethyl ether, chloroform/methanol/NH_4OH and a moving wire FID [2, 77].

A separation of technical lipids containing TG, 1,2-DG, 1,3-DG, and MG can be achieved within 15 min on a LiChrosorb SI-60 column [3]. The elution system CCl_4/isooctane (34:66), chloroform/dioxane/hexane (40:11:49), chloroform/methanol/di-isopropyl ether (34:36:30) also separates free fatty acids, hydrocarbons, squalene, cholesterols and cholesterol esters in addition to glycerides (Figure 7-12).

7.4.2 Molecular Species

Molecular species within one lipid class can be separated isocratically according to the number of C-atoms on a reversed-phase column combined with an RI-detector (Figure 7-13a). A linearity was found between log retention time (log RT) and number of C-atoms (Figure 7-13b) as well as a linearity between log RT and saturation at the same number of C-atoms (Figure 7-13c) [44].

Each additional double bond shortens the retention time, which then coincides with the retention time of species with fewer C-atoms. As an example, the separation of trioleate from tripalmitate is not possible. Hydroxy- or epoxygroups shorten the retention more than double bonds. Jensen [78] used an RP-18 column with the solvents acetonitrile/tetrahydrofuran/hexane (224:123.2:39.6). A linearity was found between the k-factor and the column temperature for the separation of triglycerides of vegetable oils (Figure 7-14).

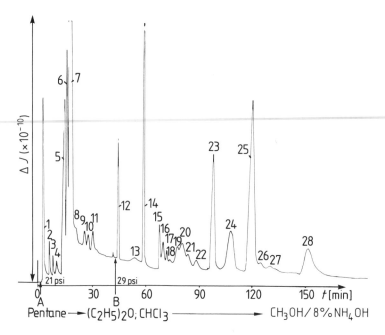

Figure 7-11. Separation of lipids of immature soybeans.

Column: Porasil II; detection: moving wire FID; mobile phase: gradient as indicated above.

1, 2, 3: (hydrocarbons, waxes, etc. and unknowns), 4, 5: (sterol esters), 6: (triglycerides), 7, 8, 9, 10, 11, 14, 18, 20, 25, 28: (unknowns), 12: (sterols), 13: (free fatty acids), 15: (esterified sterol glyc.), 19: (cerebroside), 16: (MGDG), 21: (PG), 22: (DGDG), 23: (PE), 24: (PI), 26: (PC), 27: (PA), 29: (lyso PC). From ref. [77].

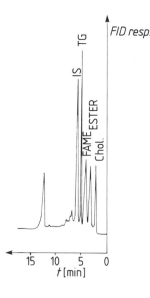

Figure 7-12. Separation of methylated lipids from human hair surface (sebum).

Column: LiChrosorb SI-60; detection: moving wire FID; mobile phase: two gradients from carbon tetrachloride/i-octane (34:66) to chloroform/dioxane/hexane (40:11:49) and to chloroform/MeOH/di-i-propyl ether (34:36:30).

Chol: (cholesterol), Ester: (wax esters + cholesterol esters), FAME: (fatty acid methyl esters), TG: (triglycerides), IS: (internal standard: monoolein diacetate). From ref. [3].

Figure 7-13 a. Separation of three common seed oil triglycerides.
Column: μBondapak C-18, 2 ft; detection: RI; mobile phase: acetonitrile/acetone (2:1); flow-rate: 1 mL/min. Numbers mean carbon numbers of the molecular species. From ref. [44].

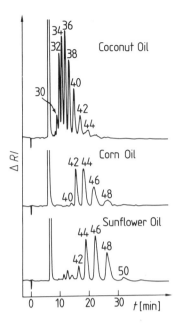

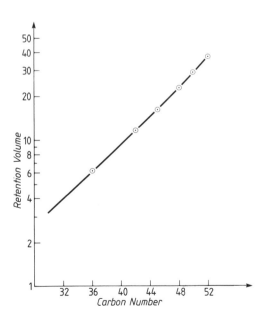

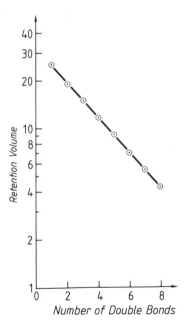

Figure 7-13 b, c. Plots of retention volume vs. carbon number (b) and vs. number of double bonds (c). Chromatographic condition as in Figure 7-13 a. From ref. [44].

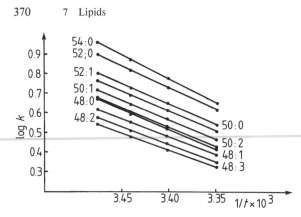

Figure 7-14. Plots of log *k*-values vs. 1/*T* (column temperature) for various triglycerides from vegetable oils.
Column: LiChrosorb RP-18 (5μm); detection: RI; mobile phase: acetonitrile/THF/hexane (224:123.5:39.6); flow-rate: 1.5 mL/min. Numbers indicate number of C-atoms e. g. 48, and the number of double bonds e. g.:3. From ref. [78].

Best separations have been found at 14.5 °C. Compton et al. [79] reported that resolution and peakshape can be improved by running a temperature program from 30° to 60 °C in the column oven. Natural mixtures of triglycerides of peanut and cotton-seed oil using an RP-18 column and a solvent mixture of acetonitrile and acetone (42:58) have been examined by Bezard and Ouedraogo [80]. Radioactive labelled ^{14}C-tri-18:1 was eluted with a 98% recovery in one chromatographic peak. However, a total separation of the mixtures, according to the number of C-atoms and degree of saturation, was not shown. The fatty acid analysis of all separated

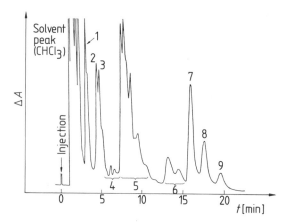

Figure 7-15. Separation of the commercial emulsifier type E 472.
Column: Partisil 5 (5μm), 15 cm; detection at 213 nm; mobile phase: hexane/i-propanol (H$_2$O 2% + HClO$_4$ 0.2%) (92:8); flow-rate: 1.5 mL/min.
1: (Acetic acid + acetylated monoglycerides),
2: (diacetyltartaric acid ester of diglycerides),
3: (acetic and diacetyltartaric acid esters of monoglycerides),
4: (monoglycerides),
5: (diacetyltartaric acid esters),
6: (acetyltartaric acid esters,
7: (tartaric acid esters),
8: (di-diacetyltartaric acid esters),
9: (acetyl + diacetyltartaric acid esters of monglycerides).
From ref. [86].

fractions by GC showed that only one fraction contained a homogeneous tri-18:2. All other fractions contained mixtures of many fatty acids.

Separations of molecular species are also possible on polar columns. This has advantages in the separation of TG having more than 54 C-atoms, as was shown for separations on a Porasil column with isooctane/ether/acetic acid (99:1:1) as the solvent system [81].

The quantification of natural mixtures of TG, DG, and MG by UV-detection is problematic. The molar absorption coefficients at 213 nm are between 63 cm²/mol and 180 cm²/mol for saturated species of C-16 or C-18-species of MG, DG and TG, separated on a LiChrosorb-Diol-column with 95% isopropanol. This is shown by Riison and Hoffmeyer [82]. Karleskind et al. developed a mixed chlorine-iodine-derivatization method to determine unsaturated species after separation at 265 nm [83]. The absorption coefficients at 265 nm were proportional to the number of double bonds.

The absorption of carbonyl groups in the infrared region at 5.75 µm has been utilized for the detection of high amounts of TG [85].

RI-detection was used for several species of tri- and divernolate (vernolic acid = cis-12,13-epoxyoleic acid) separated on a Bondapak C-18 with acetonitrile/acetone as isocratic solvent [85].

Technical emulsifiers such as acetyltartaric acid esters of MG or DG have been separated on a RP-18 column with a mixture of acetonitrile/hexane/HCl O$_4$ and measured at 213 nm (Figure 7-15) by Sudrand et al. [86]. A LiChrosorb-Diol column with a gradient elution of hexane/isopronanol has been used for emulsifiers of the polyglyceroltyp [87].

7.5 Phospholipids and Glycolipids

Phospholipids and glycolipids are mainly diglycerides which show large variations in their fatty acid chains. These lipids are of physiological importance, since they are constituents of biologically active membranes e. g. photosynthetic membranes in plants and membranes in the nervous system of man and animals (Table 7-5). The amino alcohol sphingosine can be linked to fatty acids instead of glycerol in both phospholipids and glycolipids. These sphingosines are minor constituents of plants but major components in animals. Phospholipids possessing a vinyl ether linkage instead of the ester bond are called plasmalogens and are abundant in nerve tissues. The proper analysis of all these compounds is necessary for an accurate measurement of physiological alterations in the lipid composition of the cell caused by environmental changes or diseases. Therefore the analysis by HPLC of membrane lipids, especially of phospholipids, has recently become of interest in biology, agriculture and medicine.

Quantitative analysis of phospholipids and glycolipids by HPLC was recently reviewed by McCluer and Jungalwala [88].

Table 7-5. Polar Lipid Contents of Some Plant and Animal Tissue[a].

	MGDG	DGDG	SL	PC	PG	PE	PI	PS	PA	DPG	PEPL	SP
Impatiens balsamina												
– green leaves	373.0	210.0	23.7	41.1	19.4	30.5	7.1	0.4	–	1.3	n. d.	–
– stems	50.0	32.5	2.5	5.3	2.4	9.7	3.7	1.8	–	0.3	–	–
– roots	20.6	38.6	5.2	16.2	3.1	26.3	3.0	2.9	–	–	–	–
– red floral leaves	19.3	18.5	9.6	25.0	4.7	19.8	0.5	1.7	–	–	–	–
– rat brain[b]	–	–	–	15.1	–	7.4	1.4	4.7	1.0	0.6	15.8	3.7

[a] Abbreviations see Table 7-1.
[b] μM/gfw (ref. [144])

7.5.1 Phospholipids

Phospholipids can be separated either as derivatives or as unmodified lipids. The detection and quantification of lipids as diphenylcarbonyl- or nitrobenzoate derivatives can easily be done in the UV-region near 260 nm. However the derivatization method is not suitable for all phospholipids and needs a time-consuming pre-column preparation, which is not necessary for the detection of unmodified lipids in the shortwave region of UV at 205 nm. Unsaturated lipids have high absorption, while saturated lipids show a low absorption at this wavelength. The individual phospholipid peaks, however, usually contain a mixture of several molecular species of the same phospholipid carrying both unsaturated and saturated fatty acids. In this respect, the quantification of unmodified lipids is difficult. In addition the complete separation of molecular species is possible with some artificial lipid mixtures but seems to be impossible with complex natural lipid mixtures.

7.5.1.1 Phospholipid Derivatization

Phospholipids containing primary amino groups such as phosphatidyl ethanolamine (PE), phosphatidyl serine (PS), their lyso-compounds (LPE, LPS) or the related plasmalogens can be derivatized by 4-biphenyl carbonylchloride [89]. The biphenyl carbonyllipids have absorption maxima at 268 nm and absorption coefficients near $2.3 \cdot 10^4$ cm^2/mol. The lowest detection limit is 0.3 to 0.4 ng with a linearity between 10 pmol/L and 20 nmol/L. The lipid derivatives have been separated on a MicroPak SI-10 with the solvent mixture dichlormethane/methanol/ NH_4OH (92:8:1 or 80:15:3).

The second derivatization method (by converting mono- and diacylglycerols to their p-nitrobenzoates) is very time-consuming but applicable for all phospholipids. Phospholipase C (commercially available) has been used for enzymatic conversion to 1,2 diglycerides [90]. The benzoate lipids, and even some of the molecular species, have been separated on a RP-18 column by eluting the lipids with a mixture of isopropanol and acetonitrile (35:65 v/v) and have been detected at 254 nm down to 1 nmol/L (≈ 0.6 µg). Figure 7-16 shows the separation of 1,2-di-laureate, -myristate, -palmitate, -stearate and some other mixed species.

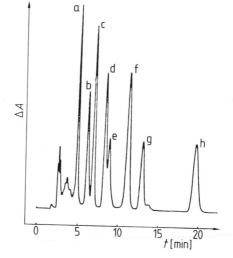

Figure 7-16. Separation of diglyceride p-nitro-benzoates.
Column: Brownlee RP-8 (10µm); detection at 254 nm; mobile phase: i-propanol/acetonitrile (35:64); flow-rate: 1 mL/min.
a: (1,2 di-12:0), b: (1,2 di-16:1(9)), c: (1,2 di-14:0), d: (1,3 di-18:1(11)), e: (1,2 di-18:1(11)), f: (1,2 di-16:0), g: (1-18:0-2-18:1), h: (1,2 di-18:0).
From ref. [90].

A very sensitive method for the determination of lipids by labelling with ^{32}P has been successfully used for minor phospholipid components of blood and yeast cells by Blom et al. [91]. The incubated lipids are injected into a LiChrosorb SI-60 column, eluted by a gradient of different solvent mixtures (chloroform, propanol, acetic acid and water) and detected by a bench-top liquid scintillation counter (Figure 7-17).

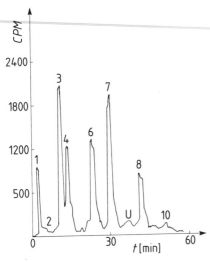

Figure 7-17. Separation of a total phospholipid extract of ^{32}P-labelled yeast cells.
Column: LiChrosorb SI-60 (10μm); detection: Scintillation counter; mobile phase: gradient of chloroform/propanol/acetic acid/H_2O (50:55:2.5:5, 50:55:2.5:8.75, and 50:55:5:10); flow-rate: 0.6 mL/min.
1: (PA), 2: (DPG), 3: (PE), 4: (PG), 6: (PS), 7: (PI), 8: (PC), 10: (DPI), U: unidentified.
From ref. [91].

A solvent system consisting of propanol/toluene/acetic acid/H_2O and propanol/ethyl acetate/benzene/H_2O ensures good separation of PG, PE, PI, PS, PC, lyso-PC, and sphingomyeline [151]. The detection was achieved by ^{32}P-labeled lipids with a radioactive flow detector in combination with a conventional liquid scintillation counter. Both detector systems show good conformity.

7.5.1.2 Unmodified Phospholipids

For the detection of unmodified lipids most investigators utilize the absorption in the shortwave UV-region between 203 nm and 213 nm. Since many solvents have strong absorption at this region, mixtures of acetonitrile/methanol/water or hexane/isopropanol/water have primarily been used. The separation of phosphatidyl cholines (PC) and sphingomyeline was already achieved on a MicroPak SI-10 column several years ago by Jungalwala et al. [92]. The absorption coefficients at 203 nm are between 200 cm^2/mol for the saturated PC-18:0 and $3.46 \cdot 10^4$ cm^2/mol for the highly unsaturated PC-20:4. Recently Chen and Kou [93] separated nearly all major phospholipids including PI, PS, PE, PC and sphingomyeline also using acetonitrile and methanol as solvents, but substituting 85% phosphoric acid (130:5:1.5) for water, which increases selectivity (Figure 7-18).

Unfortunately phosphoric acid destroys the plasmalogens and prevents a possible post-column determination of phosphate. Geurts van Kessel and Hax [94, 95] extended phospholipid separations to PA, PC, PE, PI, PS, LPC, LPE, sphingomyeline and cholesterol by using a LiChrosorb SI-60 column and gradient elution with a mixture of hexane/isopropanol/water (6:8:1.4 → 6:8:0.75), detecting the lipids at 206 nm. At this wavelength the absorption

Figure 7-18. Separation of phospholipid standards.
Column: MicroPak SI-10 (10μm); detection at 203 nm; mobile phase: acetonitrile/MeOH/H$_3$PO$_4$ (85%) (130:5:1.5); flow-rate: 1 mL/min.
PMME: (phosphatidyl monomethyl ethanolamine),
PDME: (phosphatidyl diymethyl ethanolamine),
SPH: (sphingomyeline).
From ref. [93].

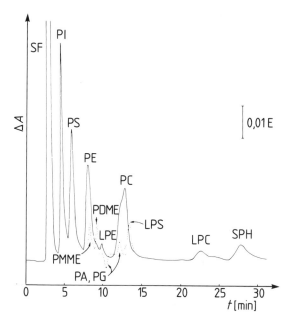

coefficients are between 600 cm^2/mol for the PC-16:0 and 1100 cm^2/mol for the PC-18:1. It should be noted, that dioxane and tetrahydrofuran are unsuitable because of peroxide production. PG, PA, PS, PC and triglycerides had been quantitatively determined by using a moving wire-FID after the separation of the lipids on a Bondapak-NH$_2$-column. Linearity between the detector signal and the concentration was achieved in the range of 50 to 250 μg. The NH$_2$-column (Ultrasil-NH$_2$) is also suitable for the separation of several phospholipids, cholesterol, cerebrosides and some molecular species of these compounds as shown by Hanson et al. [96]. A multistep gradient with mixtures of hexane/isopropanol (5.5:8) and hexane/isopropanol/methanol/water (5.5:8:1:1.5) can be used for this purpose. Wheat phospholipids have been separated by a similar solvent system consisting of hexane and iso-propanol (6:8 v/v) with a linear increase of water from 0.5 to 1.5% [97]. After elution of the lipids from the column (Porasil) the phosphate content was determined according to Bartlett [98] or Fiske-Subbarow [99]. The detector signal at 206 nm can be calibrated by this procedure, however, a constant fatty acid composition of the detected peak must be assumed [100]. Briand et al. [101] made a quantitative comparison of calibrated phospholipids separated by HPLC and TLC and showed good agreement within the linear part of the calibration curve between 2.5 and 20 μg. Furthermore it was recommended that a 3 cm SI-60 column be used prior to the LiChrosorb Diol column for a better resolution of PC and sphingomyeline (Figure 7-19).

In general, better selectivity can be achieved by properly balancing the solvent mixture, especially by addition of acids or other ionic modifiers to the solvent systems [79, 102]. Optimized chromatograms of natural phospholipid extracts of rat brain and rat liver are shown in Figure 7-20.

The analysis of molecular species of all phospholipids in one chromatographical run seems to be impossible. The separation of molecular species of different phospholipids of egg yolk was attempted using 8 columns (Biosil HA, 1 m each) in a row by Fager et al. [103]. Nevertheless, the separation into single species was not complete. On the other hand, the separation of synthetic

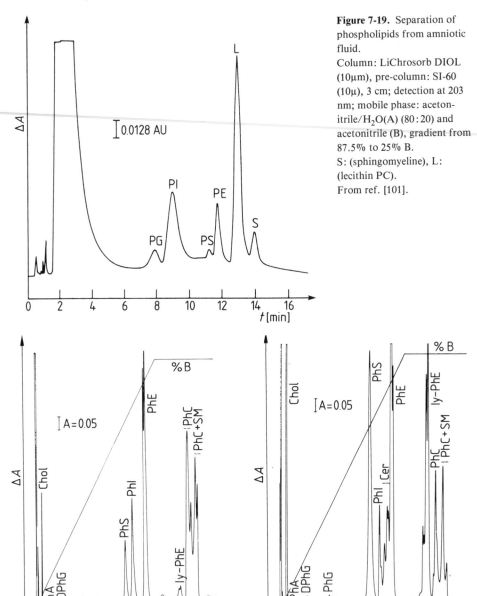

Figure 7-19. Separation of phospholipids from amniotic fluid.
Column: LiChrosorb DIOL (10μm), pre-column: SI-60 (10μ), 3 cm; detection at 203 nm; mobile phase: acetonitrile/H$_2$O(A) (80:20) and acetonitrile (B), gradient from 87.5% to 25% B.
S: (sphingomyeline), L: (lecithin PC).
From ref. [101].

Figure 7-20. Separation of a lipid extract from rat liver (left) and rat brain (right).
Column: MicroPak SI-5, pre-column: VYDAC, 4 cm; detection at 205 nm; mobile phase: hexane/ i-propanol/H$_2$O/H$_2$SO$_4$ (A) (97:3:0:0.02) and (B) (75:24:0.9:0) gradient to 100% B; flow-rate 1.5 mL/min.
Chol: (cholesterol), ph-: (phosphatidyl-), cer: (cerebrosides), SM: (sphingomyeline).
From ref. [102].

species of phosphatidyl choline can be achieved by using two columns, as was shown for Bondapak C-18 and a FA-column (Fatty Acid-column, Waters Ass.) and an isocratic solvent system containing methanol, water and chloroform [104]. The retention time followed the order of "effective carbon number", which was defined by the authors as the number of acyl-C-atoms minus the number of double bonds. A separation of natural egg yolk lecithine species is shown in Figure 7-21.

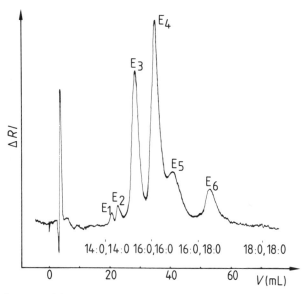

Figure 7-21. Separation of prepurified commercial egg lecithin molecular species.
Column: μBondapak C-18; detection: RI; mobile phase: MeOH/H_2O/chloroform (100:10:1).
E_1 + E_2: oxidation products with the effective carbon number of about 29.
E_3: 1-16:0-2-18:2
E_4: 1-16:0-2-18:1
E_5: 1-18:0-2-18:2
E_6: 1-18:0-2-18:1.
From ref. [104].

For good detection by RI the amounts of the lipid species should be higher than 500 nmol/L. UV-detection (203 nm) of PC-species was described by Smith and Jungalwala [105]. They used a reversed-phase Nucleosil-5-C-18 column and methanol/phosphate buffer pH 7.4 (9.5:0.5) as a solvent. The fatty acid analysis of the collected peaks showed a linearity between log RT and number of C-atoms. They also determined the HCN (hydrophobic carbon number) which is the number of C-atoms and double bonds in relation to the localization in the chromatogram. So PC-di-18:1 has a different HCN-value (and a different retention time) to PC-18:0/18:2. The separation of molecular species from several natural phospholipids has been described by Patton et al. [106] (Figure 7-22). The single phospholipids had been separated first on a LiChrosorb Si-100 column and then again in a second run on an Ultrashere-ODS-column which separated according to the molecular species. 28 peaks were detected, of which 22 represented single molecular species, whereas 6 peaks were eluted as a mixture of two molecular species, e. g. C-18:2/18:3 and C-14:0/20:4.

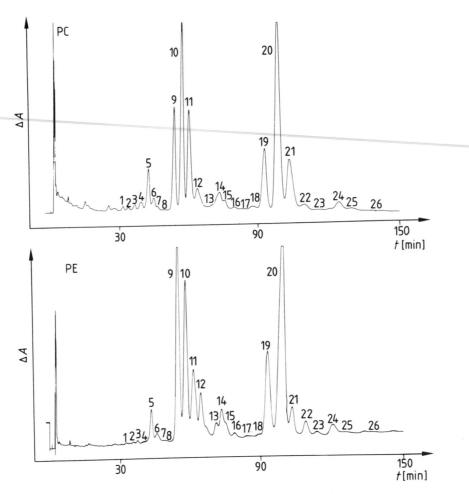

Figure 7-22. Separation of the molecular species of rat liver PC and PE.
Column: Ultrasphere ODS; detection at 205 nm; mobile phase: 20 mmol/L choline chloride in
MeOH/H₂O/acetonitrile (90.5:7:2.5); flow-rate: 2.0 mL/min.
1: (14:0/22:6), 2: (18:2/18:3 + 14:0/20:4), 3: (16:1/18:2), 4: (18:2/22:6 + 15:0/22:6),
5: (16:0/20:5 + 18:2/20:4), 6: (18:2/18:2), 7: (16:0/16:1), 8: (16:1/18:1), 9: (16:0/22:6),
10: (16:0/20:4), 11: (16:0/18:2), 12: (18:1/18:2), 13: (16:0/22:5n-3), 14: (16:0/22:5n-6 +
18:0/20:5), 15: (16:0/20:3n-6), 16: (17:0/18:2 + 16:0/20:3n-9), 17: (16:0/18:1), 18: (18:1/18:1),
19: (18:0/22:6), 20: (18:0/20:4), 21: (18:0/18:2), 22: (18:0/17:1 + 17:0/18:1), 23: (18:0/22:5n-3),
24: (18:0/22:5n-6), 25: (18:0/20:3n-6), 26: (18:0/18:1), 27: (20:0/22:6), 28: (20:0/20:4).
From ref. [106].

Silver nitrate impregnated columns, which are now commercially available, might open a new
field for the complete separation of molecular species. Smith et al. [107] described the separation
of sphingomyeline and cerebroside using reversed-phase and argentation columns (see Figure
7-24, Section 7.5.2.1.2).

7.5.2 Glycolipids

Glycolipids will be divided into two classes: those based on sphingosine and those based on glycerol. Glycolipids contain fatty acids and sugar moieties. The lipopolysaccharides of bacteria are different from glycolipids because they are water-soluble and therefore do not fulfil the definition of lipids. Several phospholipids such as glucosaminyl phosphatidyl glycerol, also contain sugar but have not yet been separated by HPLC. The sphingosine derived glycolipids can be subdivided into ceramides and gangliosides (definition below), which are widespread among animal tissues. Ceramides have also been found in higher plants but seem to be rare in micro-organisms. Glycolipids based on glycerol are major constituents of plants and micro-organisms, although small amounts have been found in animal tissue. The analysis and quantification of the glycolipids will cause the same problems as already described for phospholipids. Therefore glycolipids have mostly been separated and detected as benzoyl derivatives which show reasonable absorption at 230 nm.

7.5.2.1 Ceramides and Gangliosides

Different authors often used their own nomenclature for these compounds, which can be very confusing. For classification the following comments should help the reader:

N-acyl-sphingosine is called ceramide and is the framework for the glycosyl ceramides, which might contain one or more different sugar residues. The galactosyl ceramide (Cer-gal) was originally called cerebroside. The old trivial name for the diglycosyl ceramides (Cer-glc-gal, Cer-gal-gal) is cytoside. The tetraglycosyl ceramide (Cer-glc-gal-gal-N-actyl galactosamine) was called globoside. In HPLC literature many authors devide ceramides according to whether the fatty acids are carrying hydroxy groups (HFA-Cer) or not (NFA-Cer).

The gangliosides contain one or more molecules of sialic acid linked to one or more of the ceramide sugar residues. Sialic acid is chemically known as N-acetyl neuraminic acid (NANA). The most common nomenclature used in HPLC analysis is that of Svennerholm, which is given for several gangliosides in the legend of Figure 7-25 (Section 7.5.2.1.2).

7.5.2.1.1 Derivatization and Quantitative Determination

Several glycolipid derivatization methods have been examined by McCluer and Evans [108, 109] and as a standard procedure the conversion of the dried lipids with benzoyl chloride (10% in pyridine) at 60 °C was recommended. The incubation time for quantitative conversion is 30 min for NFA-Cer and only 15 min for HFA-Cer. Benzoyl chloride concentrations below 10% result in a lower yield. The derivatives can be extracted with hexane and should be washed several times with methanol (95%). It should be mentioned that during this procedure O-acylation occurs in addition to N-amide-acylation. The conversion with benzoic anhydride results only in O-acylation, but requires an incubation time of 16 h at 110 °C. Side reactions of the cerebrosides might occur at this temperature; for a mixture of glycosyl cerebrosides an incubation temperature 37 °C at 16 h with benzoyl chloride as the acylation reagent is recommended [110]. The benzoylated lipids can be detected by absorption measurements at 230 nm and quantitatively calibrated by using benzoylated Cer-glc or Cer-lac-standards. The number of benzoyl groups for Cer-glc should be 6, for Cer-lac 9 and for Cer-gal-lac 12 at complete conversion. The molar absorption coefficients have been estimated for all other glycosyl ceramides under the assumption that the absorption increases additively with the possible number of benzoyl groups and that O-benzoyl- and N-benzoyl groups have the same coefficients. The recovery after derivatization and HPLC separation is approximately between 77% to 90% using ^{14}C-labelled ceramides. The lowest detection limit is 70 pmol/L. Suzuki et al. [111] separated 6 glycosyl ceramides as O-acetyl-N-p-nitrobenzoyl derivatives with a recovery of 75% (Figure 7-23). The amounts of glycosyl ceramides of human erythrocytes differ considerably when different derivatization methods are compared, so that an improvement of the current methods is highly desirable.

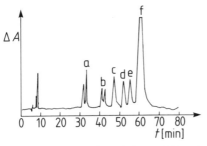

Figure 7-23. Separation of O-acetyl-N-p-nitrobenzoyl glycolipid derivatives. Column: Zorbax SIL; detection at 254 nm; flow-rate: 0.5 mL/min; mobile phase: i-propanol (1%) in hexane/dichlorethane (2:1) for 5 min then gradient from 1% to 5% i-propanol.
a: (Glucosyl ceramide),   b: (lactosyl ceramide),
c: (Lactotriaosyl ceramide),   d: (globotriaosyl ceramide),
e: (neolactotetraosyl ceramide), f: (globotetraosyl ceramide).
From ref. [111].

7.5.2.1.2 Separation Conditions

HFA-Cer can be separated from NFA-Cer on a Zipax-column (50 cm) using 7% ethyl acetate in hexane as the solvent and a further separation of NFA-Cer-glc and NFA-Cer-gal can be achieved by using a MikroPak-NH$_2$-10 column with 1.2% propanol in cyclobutane as solvents [109]. When dioxane is used instead of ethyl acetate the absorption of the compounds can be measured at 230 nm, which is 14 times more sensitive than at 280 nm. Since gradient elution causes a sharp ascent of the baseline, it is recommended by Jungalwala et al. that a reference cell with the same gradient should be provided [112]. Their system allows the separation and detection of single lipid classes without precleaning at a lowest detectable amount of 10 pmol/L. A better method was described for the analysis of Cer-glc, Cer-lac, tri- and tetraglycosyl-Cer (globosides), and N-acetyl-sphingosine [113]. They used a Zipax column and a linear gradient of 1% to 20% dioxane in hexane and determined 2 pmol/L Cer-glc as well as 20 pmol/L of tetragloboside. Nitrobenzoyl derivatives can be separated on a Sorbax SIL by a gradient of 1% to 5% isopropanol in hexane/dichlorethane (2:1) and detected at 254 nm [111].

A combination of argentation and reversed-phase columns is useful for the separation of molecular species [107]. The saturated and monoenoic NFA-Cer can be separated on a Chrompak silver column with a mixture of hexane and isopropanol (9:1) first and then be separated into molecular species on a Nukleosil C-18 column with pure methanol as the solvent (Figure 7-24). Unmodified HFA-Cer have also been separated by this method and detected at 203 nm.

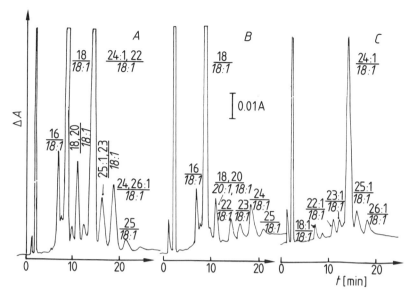

Figure 7-24. Separation of 3-O-benzoylated NFA-ceramides from beef brain. The NFA-cer were first separated into two main peaks by argentation chromatography on a Chrompak silver column, hexane/i-propanol (9:1), flow-rate 0.5 mL/min (not shown). Further separation of the molecular species was done by reversed-phase HPLC. Column: Nucleosil-5 C-18; detection at 230 nm; flow-rate: 2 mL/min; mobile phase: MeOH.

A: Total NFA-ceramides,

B: NFA-ceramides collected from the silver column (peak 1) (saturated/monounsaturated fatty acid species),

C: NFA-ceramides collected from the silver column (peak 2) (di-monounsaturated fatty acid species). From ref. [107].

A moving wire FID is useful for the detection of unmodified glycosyl ceramides and gangliosides (GM3, GM2, GM1, GD1a, GD1b etc.) after separation of the lipids on a Si-60 column as shown by Tjaden et al. [114]. The optimal solvent system for glycosyl ceramides was chloroform/methanol and for gangliosides chloroform/methanol/aqueous hydrochloric acid (Figure 7-25). Interfering phospholipids can be removed by hydrolysis with NaOH, which does not destroy the glycosphingosines.

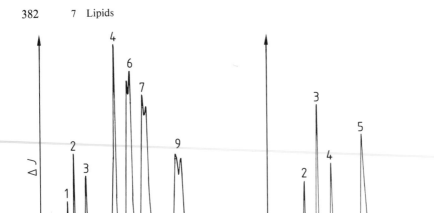

Fig. 7-25. Separation of ganglioside- (left) and neutral glycosphingolipid standards from bovine brain. Column: LiChrosorb SI-60 (9 μ); detection: moving-wire FID; mobile phase: Chloroform/MeOH/aq. HCl 0.01 mol/L (60:35:4).
Left: 1, 5, 8: unknown. 2: GM3 (cer-glc-gal-sialo), 3: GM2 (cer-glc-galsialo-galNAc), 4: GM1 (cer-glc-galsialo-galNAc-gal), 6: GD1a (cer-glc-galsialo-galNAc-galsialo), 7: GD1b (cer-glc-gal-disialo-galHAc-gal), 9: GT1 (cer-glc-gal-disialo-galNAc-galsialo).
Right: 1: unknown. 2: GL1a (cer-glc), 3: GL2a (cer-lac), 4: GL3 (cer-di-gal-glc), 5: GL4 (cer-glc-gal-galNAc-galN).
From ref. [114].

7.5.2.2 Glycosyl Glycerides

Among the glycosyl glycerides the galactosyl diglycerides are the main constituents of chloroplast membranes of higher plants and algae. Additionally a sulphoquinovosyl diglyceride (plant sulfolipid) is found in all photosynthetic plants, whereas mannosyl diglycerides are abundant in bacteria. Nevertheless little analytical work has been done on HPLC for these lipids. The galactolipids have been separated, together with other lipids (see Section 7.4.1 and Figure 7-11) on a Porasil II column [77] or on a Spherisorb ODS column [115] using either a moving wire FID or RI-detector. In our laboratory we separate the galactolipids directly from plant lipid extracts on LiChrosorb RP-8 columns (25 cm) with a solvent mixture of methanol and water (9:1) and detect them in parallel by RI- and UV-absorption. Figure 7-26 shows a chromatogram of a plant lipid extract with RI-detection of the galactolipids and parallel detection of the pigments at 430 nm monitored with a second recorder. Because of the high content of dienoic and trienoic fatty acids (linoleic and linolenic acid) a detection at 208 nm is also possible.

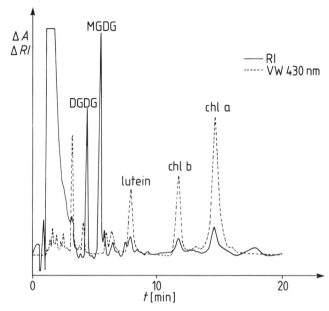

Figure 7-26. Separation of a lipid extract from green corn leaves.
Column: LiChrosorb RP-8 (5 μm); parallel detection with RI and absorption at 430 nm; mobile phase:
MeOH/H₂O (9:1); flow-rate: 2 mL/min; column temperature: 40 °C. From Iwanzik 1980, unpublished.

Carotenoids and chlorophylls do not interfere, as shown for green and chlorophyll-free tissue by Riedmann and Tevini [11]. In the presence of high amounts of pigments the RI-detector is recommended because the pigments show very low refraction. The RI-detection of galactolipids however, is four times less sensitive than the UV-detection at 208 nm. Linearity of the UV-detector signal was determined between 0.2 μg and 200 μg. Higher sensitivity can be achieved at 206 nm with acetonitrile instead of methanol as organic solvent. Quantitative comparisons of TLC and HPLC separated lipids result in good conformity. Figure 7-27 shows a comparison of chromatograms of plant lipids separated on a RP-2 (5 cm × 4.6 mm i. d., 5 μm) detected at 430 nm, 224 nm and 204 nm.

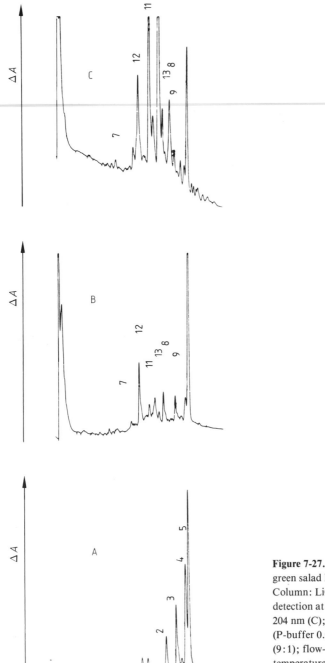

Figure 7-27. Separation of a lipid extract of green salad leaves.
Column: LiChrosorb RP-2 (5 µm), 5 cm; detection at 430 nm (A), 224 nm (B), and 204 nm (C); mobile phase: acetonitrile/H$_2$O (P-buffer 0.01 mol/L adjusted to pH 7.7) (9:1); flow-rate: 2.0 mL/min; column temperature: 40 °C.
2,3: (carotenoids), 4,5: (chlorophylls), 7: (PI + PG), 8: (PE), 9: (PC-di-18:0), 11: (MGDG), 12, 13: (DGDG). From ref. [11].

7.6 Hydrocarbons, Alcohols, Wax Esters, Terpenoid Derivatives

Hydrocarbons, alcohols and wax esters have often been combined under the general topic of waxes. These substances generally occur at the cuticles of plants and animals. Together with other mechanisms, lipids are responsible for water conservation of the organism. Waxes also act as protective barriers against the environemnt. The composition of waxes is very different and apparently related to the function of the surface. The proportion of hydrocarbons in insect waxes may be about 50% and in mammalian waxes usually less than 1%. Natural oils and gases also contain high amounts of hydrocarbons, which are technically fractionated to olefins, paraffins and many other compounds. Nevertheless, the analysis of these compounds by HPLC is not common and gas chromatographic methods are primarily used.

Under this topic we will also describe HPLC-separations of some phytohormones synthesized via the terpenoid pathway as well as of some essential oils.

7.6.1 Hydrocarbons and Lipophilic Alcohols

The fractionation of hydrocarbons, aldehydes, ketones and triterpenes for further gas chromatographic analysis can be achieved on a 1.4 m silica gel column with hexane/ethyl acetate as solvent [116]. As already described in section 7.4 hydrocarbons can be separated from glycerides on a SI-60 column [3]. The same column was used for the separation of technical olefins which were eluted by isooctane and detected by RI [117, 118, 119]. For complex mixtures of polycyclic aromatic hydrocarbons reversed-phases are commonly in use. Sorbax ODS and LiChrosorb PR-18 are suitable for these compounds [120] as well as VYDAC 201 TP [121]. As eluents, acetonitrile/water mixtures give the best resolutions. The retention times increase with increasing ratio of chain length and width of the molecules. In addition to RI-, UV- and fluorescence-detection are possible [122]. Long chain fatty alcohols with chain length from C49 to C58 have been separated as dinitrobenzoyl esters [123]. Prefractionating into saturated and unsaturated alcohols was achieved by argentation TLC. For further analysis a 10 cm RadialPak C-18 column was used to separate the saturated species whereas the unsaturated alcohols were resolved on a 30 cm MicroPak MCH C-18 column with p-dioxane/acetonitrile (3:2, resp. 3:13) as eluants.

7.6.2 Wax Esters, Essential Oils, Terpenoid Plant Hormones

Wax esters are esters of long chain (10 to 30 carbon atoms) alcohols with long chain fatty acids. They cover mainly the outer surface of organisms. Surface lipids have been extensively studied and reviewed by Kolattukudy [124, 125]. However, very little information is available about the analysis of these compounds by HPLC. The reason for this might be that these complex substances are very difficult to identify, since in most cases no standards are available. Indentification is usually only possible by physical methods such as mass spectroscopy.

Wax esters of jojoba oil have been separated according to the chain length on two BondaPak C-18 columns (30 cm each), which were combined in tandem. Five fractions, eluted by acetonitrile/water (2:1) mixtures and detected by RI (Figure 7-28), have been identified chemically as esters of fatty acids and alcohols with a chain length between 36 and 46 C-atoms [126]. The same column was used for the separation of some essential oils [127]. Over 20 substances have been eluted with methanol : water (2 : 1) and detected spectrophotometrically at 254 nm but most of them could not be identified.

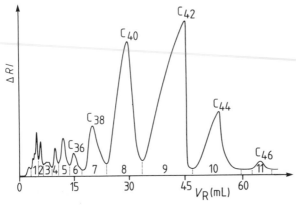

Figure 7-28. Separation of *Apache Jojoba* oil.
Column: Bondapak C-18, two 12 inch. in tandem; mobile phase: acetonitrile/acetone (2 : 1); detection: RI. From ref. [126].

Mono-, sesqui-, diterpenes and sesquiterpenoid lactones can be separated in one chromatographic run on reversed-phase (RP-8, RP-18) with a gradient of acetonitrile/water (50% → 100%) within 60 minutes (Figure 7-29) [128, 129]. The different absorption of several terpenoids can be utilized to detect them at variable wavelength between 200 nm and 254 nm. The detection limit was measured at 5 µg and linearity up to 20 µg.

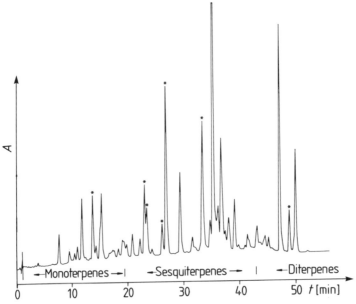

Figure 7-29. Separation of the pentane eluted fraction of the essential oils of *Cistus ladanifer*.
Column: LiChrosorb RP-18 (5 µm); detection at 220 nm. Asterisked peaks also can be detected at 240 nm.
Mobile phase: acetonitrile/H$_2$O (1 : 1) gradient to 100% acetonitrile within 45 min.
Most peaks were identified by the authors. From ref. [128].

Farnesol isomers can be separated on a Porasil column (30 cm) with a solvent mixture of trimethyl pentane and ethylether (90 : 10) or enriched on PAK 500-silica cartridges [130].

The separation and quantification of natural waxes into hydrocarbons, wax esters, fatty acid methyl esters, glycerides (mono-, di-, tri-), aldehydes, and ketones was recently described by Atkin et al. [131]. Two Spherisorb SSW columns (20 cm, 5 µ) were connected and the substances eluted with several mixtures of hexane, tetrahydrofuran, isopropanol, and acetonitrile. The hydrocarbons eluted first (isocratic, hexane) were detected by RI. All other compounds were detected by infrared adsorption of the carbonyl group at 5.75 µm, since the absorption of the hydroxy group at 3.3 µm is not very sensitive. The conversion of fatty acids to fatty methyl esters is recommended. 1.2 µg is close to the detection limit for tripalmitate.

Two plant growth regulators − abscisic acid (ABA) and gibberellic acid (GA) − belong to the general classification of terpenoids showing absorption in the UV-region. GA is one compound of a heterogeneous group of more than fifty gibberellins bearing different substitutes at the gibban skeleton. Because of their central role during plant growth and development these and other phytohormones have had considerable attention. The quantity of these compounds and all other phytohormones, however, is rather small in plant tissues e. g. about 10 000 barley coleoptiles contain 1 µg gibberellic acid. Therefore pre-column enrichment and purification is usually necessary. Reversed-phase columns are also used for purification as well as for separation of phytohormones [132 to 139, 152]. ABA can be detected at 254 nm or 280 nm, whereas GA absorption is in the 200 to 208 nm region. Gibberellins, separated on "normal-phase" columns can be detected at 256 nm after their derivatization to the p-nitrobenzoyl esters [140, 141]. [3]H- or [14]C- labelled gibberellins were monitored with an on-stream radioactive scintillation counter [142, 143]. Figure 7-30 shows chromatograms of ABA, phaseic acid and indolyl acetic acid directly separated from Sorghum leaf extracts and further purified on normal-phase columns. The detection limits are less than 1 µg and the recovery about 75%.

Modern methods for plant hormone analysis including HPLC, were recently reviewed [153].

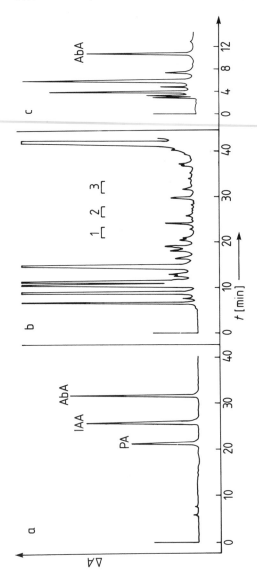

Figure 7-30. Separation of a plant hormone mixture (a) comparing to an extract from *Sorghum* leaves (b). Column: Ultrasphere ODS, 25 cm; mobile phase: gradient from (60:40:0.5) water/MeOH/HAc to (30:70:0.5); flow-rate: 1.6 mL/min; detection: UV 254 nm.

PA: phaseic acid, IAA: indolyl acetic acid, ABA: abscisic acid. The fractions 1 to 3 were collected corresponding to each hormone and further analyzed as shown in (c) for ABA:

Column: Ultrasphere SI; mobile phase: chloroform/acetonitrile/HAc (94:5:1); flow-rate: 1 mL/min. From ref. [152].

7.7 References

[1] Zhukov A. V., and Vereshchagin A. G., *Adv. Lipid Res.* **18**, 247 – 282 (1981).
[2] Stolyhwo A., and Privett O. S., *J. Chromatogr. Sci.* **11**, 20 – 25 (1973).
[3] Aitzetmüller K., and Koch J., *J. Chromatogr.* **145**, 195 – 202 (1978).
[4] Tevini M., Iwanzik W., and Thoma U., *Planta* **153**, 388 – 394 (1981).
[5] Eskins K., Scholfield C. R., and Dutton H. J., *J. Chromatogr.* **135**, 217 – 220 (1977).
[6] Shoaf W. T., *J. Chromatogr.* **152**, 247 – 249 (1978).
[7] Stransky H., *Z. Naturforsch.* **33 c**, 836 – 840 (1978).
[8] Braumann T., and Grimme L. H., *J. Chromatogr.* **170**, 264 – 268 (1979).
[9] Braumann T., and Grimme L. H., *Biochem. Biophys. Acta* **637**, 8 – 17 (1981).
[10] Davies D., and Holdsworth E. S., *J. Liqu. Chromatogr.* **3(1)**, 123 – 132 (1980).
[11] Riedmann M., and Tevini M., *Hewlett Packard Application Note* **232/13** (1980).
[12] Eskins K., and Harris L., *Photochem. Photobiol.* **33**, 131 – 133 (1981).
[13] Iriyama K., Yoshiura M., and Shiraki M., *J. Chromatogr.* **154**, 302 – 305 (1978).
[14] Yoshiura M, Iriyama K., and Shiraki M., *Chem. Lett.* **6**, 281 – 282 (1978).
[15] Iriyama K., and Shiraki M., *J. Liq. Chromatogr.* **2(2)**, 255 – 276 (1979).
[16] Prenzel U., and Lichtenthaler H. K., in: Liljenberg C., and Appelqvist L.-A. (eds.): *Advances in the Biochemistry and Physiology of Plant Lipids.* Elsevier Biomedical Press 1979.
[17] Williams R. C., Schmidt J. A., and Henry R. A., *J. Chromatogr. Sci.* **10**, 494 (1972).
[18] Cavins J. F., and Inglett G. E., *Am. Ass. Cereal Chem.* **51**, 605 – 609 (1974).
[19] Tiebach, R. K. D., and Schramm M., *Chromatographia* **13(7)**, 403 – 407 (1980).
[20] Rao G. H. R., Krick T. P., and White J. G., *J. Chromatogr.* **196**, 506 – 511 (1980).
[21] Howell S. K., and Wang Y.-W., *J. Chromatogr.* **227**, 174 – 180 (1982).
[22] McMurry C. H., and Blanchflower W. J., *J. Chromatogr.* **178**, 525 – 531 (1979).
[23] Tangney C.C., Driskell J. A., and McNair H. M., *J. Chromatogr.* **172**, 513 – 515 (1979).
[24] Thompson J. N., and Hatina G., *J. Liq. Chromatogr.* **2(3)**, 327 – 344 (1979).
[25] Lichtenthaler H. K., and Prenzel U., *J. Chromatogr.* **135**, 493 – 498 (1977).
[26] Lichtenthaler H. K., and Prenzel U., *ISF/AOCS World Congress New York 1980.*
[27] Abe K., Hiroshima O., Ikenoya S., Ohmae M., and Kawabe K., *ISF/AOCS World Congress NY 1980.*
[28] Lominski A., and Rienits K. G., *Phytochemistry* **20(5)**, 993 – 996 (1981).
[29] Strain H. H., and Mannig W. M., *J. Biol. Chem.* **146**, 275 (1942).
[30] Strain H. H., *J. Agr. Food Chem.* **2**, 1222 – 1225 (1954).
[31] Bacon M. F., and Holden M., *Phytochemistry* **6**, 193 – 210 (1967).
[32] Puglisi C. V., and de Silva J. A. F., *J. Chromatogr,* **120**, 457 – 464 (1976).
[33] Puglisi C. V., and de Silca J. A. F., *J. Chromatogr.* **152**, 421 – 430 (1978).
[34] Paanakker J. E., and Groenendijk G. W. T., *J. Chromatogr.* **168**, 125 – 132 (1979).
[35] Besner J.-G., Leclaire R., and Band P. R., *J. Chromatogr.* **183**, 346 – 351 (1980).
[36] Frolik C.-A., Tavela T. E., Peck G. L., and Sporn M. B., *Anal. Biochem.* **86**, 743 – 750 (1978).
[37] Palmskog G., *J. Chromatogr.* **221**, 345 – 351 (1980).
[38] Wang C.-C., Campbell S., Furner R. L., and Hill D. L., *Drug Metab. Dispers.* **8**, 8 (1980).
[39] Vane F. M., Stoltenberg J. K., and Buggé J. L., *J. Chromatogr.* **227**, 471 – 484 (1982).
[40] Kuksis A., in: Kuksis A. (ed.): *Handbook of Lipid Research,* Vol. **1**, pp. 1-122. Plenum press New York 1978.
[41] Lie Ken Jie M., in: Giddings J. C., Gushka E., Keller R. A., and Cazes J. (eds.): *Advances in Chromatography,* Vol. **18**, pp. 1 – 57. Marcel Dekker New York 1979.
[42] Scholfield C. R., *Anal. Chem.* **47(8)**, 1417 – 1420 (1975 a).
[43] Scholfield C. R., *Lipids* ●, 36 – 37 (1975 b).
[44] Plattner R. D., Wade K., and Kleiman R., *J. Am. Oil Chem. Soc.* **54**, 511 – 515 (1977).
[45] Henke H., and Schubert J. C., *J. High Resol. Chrom. & Chromat. Com.* **3**, 69 – 78 (1980).
[46] Miles F., and Schuring V., Gil-Av E., *J. Chromatogr.* 83, 91 (1973).
[47] Battaglia R., *Mitt. Geb. Lebensmittelunters. Hyg.* **68**, 28 (1977).
[48] Battaglia R., and Fröhlich D., *Chromatographia* **13(7)**, 428 – 431 (1980).
[49] Pei P. T.-S., Henly R. S., and Ramachandran S., *Lipids* **10(3)**, 152 – 156 (1975).

[50] Warthen J. D., Jr., *J. Am. Oil Chem. Soc.* **52**, 151 (1975).

[51] Politzer I. R., Griffin G. W., Dowty B. J., and Leseter J. L., *Anal. Lett.* **6**, 539 (1973).

[52] Cooper M. J., and Anders M. W., *Anal. Chem.* **46**, 1849 (1974).

[53] Knapp D. R., and Krüger S., *Anal. Lett.* **8**, 603 (1975).

[54] *Regis Lab. Notes,* **16**, (1974).

[55] Borch R. F., *Anal. Chem.* **47(14)**, 2437 – 2439 (1975).

[56] Durst H. D., *Tetrahedron Lett.* **2421** (1974).

[57] Durst H. D., Milano M., Kikta E. J., Jr. Connelly S. A., and Grushka E., *Anal. Chem.* **47(11)**, 1797 – 1801 (1975).

[58] Pei P. T.-S., Kossa W. C., Ramachandran S., and Henly R. S., *Lipids* **11**, 814 (1976).

[59] Miller R. A., Bussell N. E., and Ricketts C., *J. Liq. Chromatogr.* **1**(3), 291 – 304 (1978).

[60] Jordi H. C., *J. Liq. Chromatogr.* **1**(2), 215.230 (1978).

[61] Takayama K., Jordi H. C., and Benson F., *J. Liq. Chromatogr.* **3**(1), 61 – 69 (1980).

[62] Bussell N. E., and Miller R. A., *J. Liq. Chromatogr.* **2**(5), 697 – 718 (1979).

[63] Smith W. L., and Lands W. E. M., *J. Biol. Chem.* **247**, 1038 – 1047 (1972).

[64] Galliard T., and Chan H. W. S., in: Stumpf P. K. (ed.): *Biochemistry of Plants,* Vol. **4**, pp. 132 – 162. Academic Press New York 1980.

[65] Galliard T., in: Galliard T., and Mercer E. J. (eds.): *Recent Advances in Chemistry and Biochemistry of Plant Lipids-Proceedings of the Phytochemical Society No.* **12**, pp. 319 – 358. Academic Press New York 1975.

[66] Chan H. W. S., Prescott F. A. A., and Swoboda P. A. T., *J. Am. Oil Chem. Soc.* **53**, 572 – 576 (1976).

[67] Chan H. W. S., and Levett G., *Lipids* **12**(10), 837 – 840 (1977).

[68] Aoshima H., *Anal. Biochem.* **87**, 49 – 55 (1978).

[69] Zelenski S. G., and Huber J. W., *Chromatographia* **11**(11), 645 – 646 (1978).

[70] Bussell N. E., Gross A., and Miller R. A., *J. Liq. Chromatogr.* **2**(9), 1337 – 1365 (1979).

[71] Mell L. D., Joseph S. W., and Bussell N. E., *J. Liq. Chromatogr.* **2**(3), 407 – 416 (1979).

[72] Hullett D. A., and Eisenreich S. J., *Anal. Chem.* **51**(12), 1953 – 1960 (1979).

[73] Tweeten T. N., and Wetzel D. L., *Cereal Chem.* **56**(5), 398 – 402 (1979).

[74] Passi S., Rothschild-Boros M. C., Fasella P., Nazzaro-Porro M., and Whithouse D., *J. Lipid Res.* **22**, 778 – 784 (1981).

[75] Roggero J. P., and Coen S. V., *J. Liq. Chromatogr.* **4**(10), 1817 – 1829 (1981).

[76] King J. W., Adams E. C., and Bidlingmeyer B. A., *J. Liq. Chromatogr.* **5**(2), 275 – 304 (1982).

[77] Privett O. S., Dougherty K. A., Erdahl W. L., and Stolyhwo A., *J. Am. Oil Chem. Soc.* **50**, 516 (1973).

[78] Jensen G. W., *J. Chromatogr.* **204**, 407 – 411 (1981).

[79] Compton B. J., and Purdy W. C., *J. Liq. Chromatogr.* **3**(8), 1183 – 1194 (1980).

[80] Bezard J. A., and Ouedraogo M. A., *J. Chromatogr.* **196**, 279 – 293 (1980).

[81] Plattner R. D., and Payne-Wahl K., *Lipids* **14**(2), 152 – 153 (1979).

[82] Riison T., and Hoffmeyer L., *J. Am. Oil Chem. Soc.* **55**, 649 – 652 (1978).

[83] Karleskind A., Valmalle G., Midler O., and Blanc M., *Analusis* **5**(2), 79 – 84 (1977).

[84] Parris N. A., *J. Chromatogr.* **149**, 615 – 624 (1978).

[85] Plattner R. D., Wade K., and Kleiman R., *J. Am. Oil Chem. Soc.* **55**, 381 – 382 (1977).

[86] Sudrand G., Coustard J. M., Retho C., Hagemann R., Gaudin D., and Virelizier H., *J. Chromatogr.* **204**, 397 – 406 (1981).

[87] Garti N., and Aserin A., *J. Liq. Chromatogr.* **4**(7), 1173 – 1194 (1981).

[88] McCluer R. H., and Jungalwala F. B., in: Hawk G. L. (ed.): *Biological/Biomedical Applications of Liquid Chromatography,* pp. 7 – 30. Marcel Dekker New York 1979.

[89] Jungalwala F. B., Turel R. J., Evans J. E., and McCluer R. H., *Biochem. J.* **145**, 517 – 526 (1975).

[90] Batley M., Packer N. H., and Redmond J. W., *J. Chromatogr.* **198**, 520 – 525 (1980).

[91] Blom C. P., Deirekauf F. A., and Riemersma J. C., *J. Chromatogr.* **171**, 331 – 338 (1979).

[92] Jungalwala F. B., Evans J. E., and McCluer R. H., *Biochem. J.* **155**, 55 – 60 (1976).

[93] Chen S. S. H., and Kou A. E., *J. Chromatogr.* **227**, 25 – 31 (1982).

[94] Geurts van Kessel W. S. M., Hax W. M. A., Demel R. A., and De Gier J., *Biochem. Biophys. Acta* **486**, 524 – 530 (1977).

[95] Hax W. M. A., and Geurts van Kessel W. S. M., *J. Chromatogr.* **142**, 735 – 741 (1977).

[96] Hanson V. L., Park J. Y., Osborn T. W., and Kiral R. M., *J. Chromatogr.* **205**, 393 – 400 (1981).
[97] Ashworth E. N., John J. B. S., Christiansen M. N., and Patterson G. W., *J. Agric Food Chem.* 879 – 881 (1981).
[98] Bartlett G. R., *J. Biol. Chem.* **234**, 466 (1959).
[99] Fiske C. H., and Subbarow Y., *J. Biol. Chem.* **66**, 375 (1925).
[100] Gross R. W., and Sobel B. E., *J. Chromatogr.* **197**, 79 – 85 (1980).
[101] Briand R. L., Harold S., and Blass K. G., *J. Chromatogr.* **223**, 277 – 284 (1981).
[102] Yandrasitz J. R., Berry G., and Segal S., *J. Chromatogr.* **225**, 319 – 328 (1981).
[103] Fager R. S., Shapiro S., and Litman B. J., *J. Lipid Res.* **18**, 704 – 709 (1977).
[104] Porter N. A., Wolf R. A., and Nixon J. R., *Lipids* **14**(1), 20 – 24 (1978).
[105] Smith M., and Jungalwala F. B., *J. Lipid Res.* **22**, 697 – 704 (1981).
[106] Patton G. M., Fasulo J. M., and Robins S. J., *J. Lipid Res.* **23**, 190 – 196 (1982).
[107] Smith M., Monchamp P., and Jungalwala F. B., *J. Lipid Res.* **22**, 714 – 719 (1981).
[108] McCluer R. H., and Evans J. E., *J. Lipid Res.* **14**, 611 – 617 (1973).
[109] McCluer R. H., and Evans J. E., *J. Lipid Res.* **17**, 412 – 418 (1976).
[110] Ullman M. D., and McCluer R. H., *J. Lipid Res.* **18**, 371 – 378 (1977).
[111] Suzuki A., Kundu S. K., and Marcus D. M., *J. Lipid Res.* **21**, 473 – 477 (1980).
[112] Jungalwala F. B., Hayes L., and McCluer R. H., *J. Lipid Res.* **18**, 285 – 292 (1977).
[113] Ullman M. D., and McCluer R. H., *J. Lipid Res.* **19**, 910 – 913 (1978).
[114] Tjaden U. R., Krol J. H., van Hoeven R. P., Oomen-Menlemans E. P. M., and Emmelot P., *J. Chromatogr.* **136**, 233 – 243 (1977).
[115] Chung O. K., Tweeten T. N., and Wetzel D. L., *ISF/AOCS World Congress New York 1980*.
[116] Anderson L. A., Doggett N. S., and Ross M. S. F., *J. Lipid Chromatogr.* **2**(3), 455 – 461 (1979).
[117] Suatoni J. C., and Swab R. E., *J. Chromatogr. Sci.* **13**, 361 – 366 (1975).
[118] Suatoni J. C., and Swab R. E., *J. Chromatogr. Sci.* **14**, 535 – 537 (1976).
[119] Suatoni J. C., and Swab R. E., *J. Chromatogr. Sci.* **18**, 375 – 377 (1980).
[120] Katz E., and Ogan K., *Chromatogr. Newslett.* **8**, 20 – 22 (1980).
[121] Wiese S. A., Bonnett W. J., Guenther F. R., and May W. E., *J. Chromatogr. Sci.* **19**, 457 – 465 (1981).
[122] Nielson T., *J. Chromatogr.* **170**, 147 – 156 (1979).
[123] Quereshi N., Takayama K., and Schnoes H. K., *J. Lipid Chromatogr.* **4**(7), 1207 – 1218 (1981).
[124] Kolattukudy P. E., in: Tevini M., and Lichtenthaler H. K. (eds.): *Lipids and Lipid Polymers in Higher Plants*, pp. 272 – 292. Springer Berlin-New York 1977.
[125] Kolattukudy P. E., in: Stumpf P. K., and Conn E. E. (eds.): *The Biochemistry of Plants*, Vol. **4** pp. 571 – 645, Academic Press New York 1980.
[126] Spencer G. F., Plattner R. D., and Miwa T., *J. Am Oil Chem. Soc.* **54**, 187 – 189 (1977).
[127] Komae H., and Hayashi N., *J. Chromatogr.* **114**, 258 – 260 (1975).
[128] Strack D., Proksch P., and Gülz P.-G., *Z. Naturforsch.* **35c**, 675 – 681 (1980a).
[129] Strack D., Proksch P., and Gülz P.-G., *Z. Naturforsch.* **35c**, 915 – 918 (1980b).
[130] Warthen J. D., Jr., *J. Lip. Chromatogr.* **3**(2), 279 – 286 (1980).
[131] Atkin D. S. J., Hamilton R. J., Mitchell S. F., and Sewell P. A., *Chromatographia* **15**(2), 97 – 100 (1982).
[132] Dühring H., and Bachmann O., *Physiol. Plant.* **34**, 201 – 203 (1975).
[133] Sweetser P. B., and Vatvars A., *Anal. Biochem.* **71**, 68 – 78 (1976).
[134] Ciha A. J., Brenner M. L., and Brun W. A., *Plant Physiol.* **59**, 821 – 826 (1977).
[135] Arteca R. N., Poovaiak B. W., and Smith O. E., *Plant Physiol.* **65**, 1216 – 1219 (1980).
[136] Durley R. C., Kannangara T., and Simpson G. M., *J. Chromatogr.* **236**, 181 – 188 (1982).
[137] Norman S. M., Maier V. P., and Echols L. C., *J. Liquid Chromatogr.* **5**(1), 81 – 91 (1982).
[138] Yamaguchi I., Yokoto T., Yoshida S., and Takahashi N., *Phytochemistry* **18**, 1699 – 1702 (1979).
[139] Jones M. G., Metzger J. D., and Zeevaart J. A. D., *Plant physiol.* **65**, 218 – 221 (1980).
[140] Heftmann E., Saunders G. A., and Haddon W. F., *J. Chromatogr.* **156**, 71 – 77 (1978).
[141] Reeve D. R., Crozier A., in: Hillman J. R. (ed.): *Isolation of Plant Growth Substances*, pp. 41 – 77. Cambridge University Press 1978.
[142] Reeve D. R., Yokota T., Nash L. J., and Crozier A., *J. Exp. Bot.* **27**, 1243 – 1258 (1976).
[143] Reeve D. R., and Crozier A., *J. Chromatogr.* **137**, 271 (1977).
[144] Ansell G. B., in: *Form and Function of Phospholipids, B. B. A. Library*, Vol. **3**, p. 377 – 422. Elsevier 1973.

[145] Prenzel U., and Lichtenthaler H. K., *J. Chromatogr.* **242**, 9 – 19 (1982).

[146] Bailie A. G., Terry D. W., O'Brien R. K., Beebe J. M., Stuart J. D., McCosh-Lilie E. J., and Hill D. W., *J. Chromatogr. Sci.* **20**, 466 – 470 (1982).

[147] Schoch S., *Z. Naturforsch.* **33c**, 712 – 714 (1978).

[148] Steiner R., Wieschhoff H., and Scheer H., *J. Chromatogr.* **242**, 127 – 134 (1982).

[149] Aitzetmüller K., *J. Chromatogr.* **113**, 231 – 266 (1975).

[150] Stancher B., and Zonta F., *J. Chromatogr.* **238**, 217 – 225 (1982).

[151] Alam J., Smith J. B., Silver M. J., and Ahern D., *J. Chromatogr.* **234**, 218 – 221 (1982).

[152] Durley R. C., Kannangara T., and Simpson G. M., *J. Chromatogr.* **236**, 181 – 188 (1982).

[153] Horgan R., in: Reinhold L., Harborn J. B., and Swain T. (eds.) *Progress in Phytochemistry*, Vol. 7, pp. 137 – 170. Pergamon Press London 1981.

8 Carbohydrates

by *Hermann Bauer* and *Wolfgang Voelter*

8 Carbohydrates

8.1 Introduction

The enormous number of stereo isomers of carbohydrates (e. g. 32 isomers of none-side-branched neutral hexoses of identical molecular weight) and the molecular accumulation of hydroxyl groups makes it extraordinarily difficult to find efficient methods for their separation.

Different analytical and preparative techniques for the separation and identification of carbohydrates were developed in the past. First, paper chromatography [1] was used, which was followed by thin-layer chromatography [2], liquid-solid [3,4], liquid-liquid column chromatography [5-7], ion-exchange chromatography of boric acid esters [8-11] and gas chromatography of volatile derivatives [12, 13].

8.2 General Techniques

8.2.1 Liquid-Solid Chromatography

In several cases, good separations under low pressure conditions are described using charcoal as the stationary phase [14]; at present, however, no suitable material for HPLC separations of carbohydrates is commercially available.

Silica gel cannot be used very successfully for the separation of free sugars because the adsorbtive forces between the silanol and the hydroxyl groups of the carboxydrates are too high [15]. Furthermore, the solubility in non-aqueous solvents is restricted. Silica gel, however, is an excellent stationary phase if less polar derivatives have to be separated. So it might be advantageous to convert sugars into less polar derivatives, e. g. to corresponding peracetates, for separation.

The behaviour of alumina does not differ very much from that of silica gel but it is less inert to carbohydrates and chemical reactions occur more frequently [16].

8.2.2 Liquid-Liquid Chromatography (LLC)

Celluloses, which were successfully applied to low pressure LLC of carbohydrates, were replaced by ion-exchange resins with different counter-ions [6, 17, 18]. Polystyrene divinyl benzene as a matrix proved to be a pressure-stable stationary phase. The relative amount of water in the stationary phase is greater than in the mobile phase if aqueous-organic solvents are used, e. g. ethanol water. Therefore, polar molecules like carbohydrates are retarded by such resins.

Both, cation- and anion-exchange resins are successfully used for carbohydrate separation [19, 20]. In the literature, however, more papers are published about strong acidic polystyrene-divinyl-benzene sulfonic acid resins as they have been more easily commercially available in small and uniform particle sizes. This material is commonly used in amino acid analyzers. Besides calcium-, barium-, lithium-, sodium- and potassium-ions, organic bases, as methyl-, dimethyl- and trimethyl-ammonium-ions, are used as cationic counter-ions.

Sulfate and chloride are preferred for anionic counter-ions. In general, the k-value depends on the structure, the number of free hydroxyl groups and the stereochemistry of the carbohydrate molecule. The k-values increase with the number of hydroxyl groups per molecule, and furthermore depend on the column temperature. Operation temperatures of $80\,°C$ and more have been used successfully to shorten the time of analysis and also to improve the column efficiency [19]. Interactions between the different counter-ions and the solutes, as well as sieve effects of the resin matrix, may also influence the separation [19].

For fast liquid-liquid chromatographic separations, pressure-stable stationary phases, based on silica gel, are usually used. Unmodified silica gel, which is coated *in situ* with a film of water or with polyfunctional amines [15, 21] can be used successfully as the stationary phase. The eluants have to be chosen carefully because only a very small concentration of water can be used and sugars are nearly insoluble in most organic solvents. Furthermore, unmodified silica gel may interact with carbohydrates and cause loss in reproducibility of the separation.

Chemically-bonded stationary phases with amino or other polar groups (e. g. diol groups), can be used successfully [22, 23] without the disadvantages discussed above. Suitable eluants are, e. g. acetonitrile ($< 70\%$) water or ethanol ($< 70\%$) water mixtures. Recently, stationary phases were described which allow application of concentrations of only about 40% of organic solvent [24].

8.2.3 Ion-Exchange Chromatography

Neutral sugars show extremely small acidity. Their ability to form enediolates should not be used as a basis for ion-exchange chromatography as the resulting isomerisation products may lead to undesired chromatograms.

Acidic or basic sugar derivatives can be separated successfully on ion-exchange resins [25, 26, 27]. The order of elution depends on the pK-values of the solutes, the molality of the counter-ion, the pH of the eluant and the temperature. Furthermore, additional contributions from liquid-liquid- and gel chromatography have to be taken into account.

The most efficient method for the separation of complex mixtures of carbohydrates is ion-exchange chromatography on strong, basic, ion-exchange resins in the borate form, using borate buffers as the eluant. This method was introduced by Khym and Zill [8] and thereafter improved by several authors [9, 11, 28 to 30].

Carbohydrates form anionic complexes with boric acid [31] as all compounds bearing neighbouring hydroxyl groups with a dihedral angle of not more than $60\,°$. The stability of these complexes and thus their acidity depends on the stereochemistry of the hydroxyl groups (cis, trans/equatorial, axial) of the diol residue [10]. Isocratic as well as gradient elution, with buffers of 0.05 to 1.0 mol/L in boric acid and pH-values of 7 to 10, are successfully used [9, 28 to 30].

8.3 Detection

Free carbohydrates bear no groups detectable with commercially available high sensitivity detectors for HPLC. For example, UV-detection can be used successfully only at wavelengths below 200 nm as hydroxyl groups do not absorb at higher wavelengths.

In general, the eluted carbohydrates can be detected either by their physical properties or by pre- or post-column reactions which convert the sugars into derivatives of high detection sensitivity. Whereas, with the first principle of detection, the fractions are eluted as pure components, the second type of determination cannot be used, at least in most cases, for preparative purposes, because the separated compounds are used for derivatization. However, splitting of the eluate, fractionation of one part and post-column derivatization of the second one can be advantageous.

8.3.1 Detection via Physical Properties

Optical rotation of carbohydrates can be used for detection only if relatively large amounts of optically active sample is available, as the method suffers from low detection sensitivity [32]. The chromatograms are difficult to interpret if overlapping peaks of different signs occur. The detection by ultraviolet absorption can be used for free sugars and polyols only below 200 nm, with low sensitivity. However, sugar acids as well as acylated derivatives can be detected by absorption of the carboxyl resp. carbonyl group (200 to 220 nm). Benzyl or trityl ether, aromatic ester or aromatic aglycon derivatives can be detected with ease and good sensitivity if the appropiate wavelength is applied.

Although refractometers are widely used as detectors for carbohydrates, this bulk detector sometimes is too unselective and often not sensitive enough.

Carbohydrates and derivatives with free anomeric hydroxyl groups can be detected with high selectivity and sensitivity with the aid of electrochemical detectors.

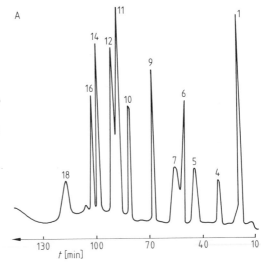

Figure 8-1. Separations of a standard mixture with different post-column derivatization methods. Column: 6 × 180 mm; stationary phase: strong basic ion-exchange resin, 11 ± 1 µm, borate form; eluent: borate buffers, 0.2 to 1.4 mol/L in borate, pH 8.6 to 9.5, flow-rate: 0.6 mL/min; column temperature: 40 to 67 °C; amount injected; 10 nmol per component (A + B) and 50 nmol per component (C). Post-column reaction:
A: Copper bicinchoninate: 0.1% sodium bicinchoninate, 0.05% copper sulfate × 5 H_2O, 0.25% aspartic acid in 1 mol/L sodium carbonate solution; flow-rate: 0.45 mL/min; reaction coil: PTFE 0.3 × 3000 mm, 100 °C; detection: absorption at 570 nm.

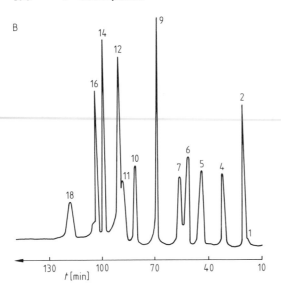

B: Orcinol-sulfuric-acid: 0.1% orcinol in concentrated sulfuric acid; flow-rate: 0.65 mL/min; reaction coil: PTFE (0.5 × 2500 mm), 100 °C; detection: absorption at 420 nm.

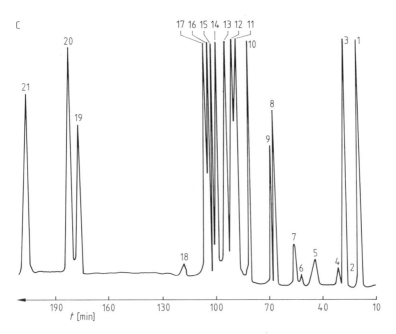

C: Periodate-acetylactone: reagent I: 0.1% sodium periodate in 0.5 mol/L ammonium acetate/acetic acid buffer, pH 3.8; flow-rate:0.3 ml/min; reaction coil: PTFE (0.3 × 1000 mm), 100 °C; reagent II: 0.75% sodium arsenite/1% acetylacetone in 0.5 mol/L sodium acetate/acetic acid buffer pH 4.0; flow-rate: 0.3 ml/min; reaction coil: PTFE (0.3 × 1500 mm), 100 °C; detection: absorption at 420 nm.
1 2-Deoxyribose, 2 sucrose, 3 glycerol, 4 cellobiose, 5 maltose, 6 rhamnose, 7 lactose, 8 meso-erythritol, 9 ribose, 10 mannose, 11 fructose, 12 arabinose, 13 sobitol, 14 xylose, 15 arabitol, 16 glucose, 17 mannitol, 18 melibiose, 19 glucuronic acid, 20 gluconic acid, 21 galacturonic acid.

8.3.2 Post-Column Reactions

Three principal different types of post column reactions with different selectivities are applied for the detection of carbohydrates and their derivatives. The methods are based on the reducing properties of free sugars, the potential formation of furfurals under acid conditions and the oxidative glycol bond cleavage.

In Figure 8-1, the different selectivities of an oxidizing (Cu-bicinchoninate reagent), an acid-destructive (orcinol-sulfuric acid reagent) and a glycol bond cleaving reagent (periodate-acetylactone reagent) are compared with each other.

In Table 8-1 the selectivities of different reagents are listed.

Table 8-1. Selectivity of Some Post-Column Reaction Reagents for Carbohydrates.

Compound/ class of compound	Cu-Bicin-choninate	Tetrazolium sulfonic acid	Orcinol/ sulfuric acid	Periodic-reagent	Note
Formalaldehyde	−	−	+	+	According to definition no sugars
Glycolaldehyde	+	+	+	+	
Aldoses	+	+	+	+	
Ketoses	+	+	+	+	
Polyols	−	−	−	+	
Aldonic acids	−	−	−	+	
Uronic acids	+	+	+	(+)	
Saccharic acids	−	−	−	(+)	
Saccharinic acids	−	−	−	+	
Amino sugars	+	+	(−)	(+)	
Sugar phosphates	(+)	(+)	+	(+)	
Deoxy sugars	+	+	(+)	(+)	
Reducing oligo-saccharides	+	+	+	(+)	
Non-reducing oligosaccharides	−	−	+	(+)	
Polysaccharides	−	−	+	(+)	
Glycosides	−	−	+	(+)	

Carbohydrates and derivatives with free anomeric hydroxyl groups reduce copper(II) ions in basic media to copper(I) which reacts with sodium bicinchoninate (4,4'-2,2'-bicarboxybiquinoline) to a violet coloured [33] complex or they can reduce [19] a tetrazolium sulfonic acid [10] to formazans of intense colour. The detection limit is in the range of less than 10^{-9} mol.

Figure 8-2 shows the flow scheme of the copper-bicinchoninate post-column reaction detector based on the copper-bicinchoninate reaction.

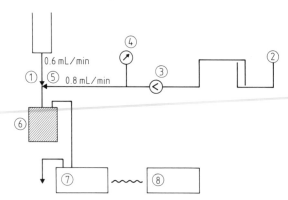

Figure 8-2. Flow scheme of the copper bicinchoninate post-column reaction detector. 1. Effluent from separation column, 2. reagent (0.05% sodium bicinchoninate, 0.025% copper (II) sulfate, 0.10% aspartic acid in 1.2 mol/L aqueous potassium carbonate), 3. minipump, 4. pressure gauge, 5. mixing T, 6. reaction coil: PTFE (0.3 × 3000 mm), 100 to 130°C, 7. photometer (570/420 nm), 8. recorder.

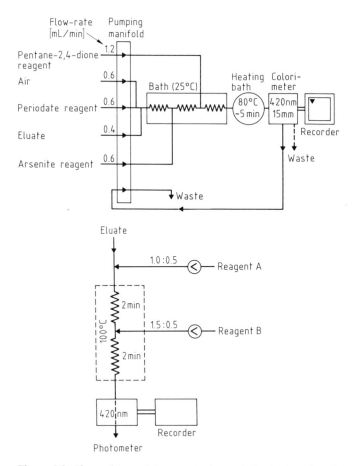

Figure 8-3. Flow scheme of two post-column derivatization detection systems for the periodate-acetylacetone reaction.
3 a. Multi-reagent system according to Samuelson [6];
3 b. Simplified system [10].

Under strongly acidic conditions, carbohydrates form furfurals and smaller degraded units. This behaviour is the basis of several analytical techniques for detection and determination of carbohydrates. The formed products react with several aromatic phenols and amines to mostly not yet exactly defined dyes. For post-column reactions, the anthrone-sulfuric acid [34] and the orcinol-sulfuric acid reagent proved to be most suitable. The flow scheme of such reactors is similar to that of the bicinchoninate detection system. As reagents 0.1% anthrone or orcinol, dissolved in concentrated sulfuric acid, should be used [10]. Selectivities for these reagent are collected in Table 8-1 (see also Figures 8-1).

1,2-Diols undergo an oxidative carbon-carbon bond cleavage with periodic acid. Terminal 1,2-diols form formaldehyde and other oxidation products. The formaldehyde reacts with acetylacetone, in the presence of ammonia, to a yellow dye. Unfortunately, an excess of periodic acid and the formed iodic acid decompose the dye by oxidation. A complicated multi-reagent post-column reactor was designed (Figure 8-3 a) [18]. The combination of different steps allows the use of only two reagents for post-column reaction detection (Figure 8-3 b) [10]. The column effluent is mixed with a solution of 0.25% sodium periodate and 1.5% ammonium acetate in a 0.8 mol/L sodium acetate buffer of pH 3.2. After reaction of 2.5 to 3 min in a coil of 0.3 mm inner diameter at 100 °C, the second reagent, 0.75% sodium arsenite and 2% acetylacetone in 0.5 mol/L sodium acetate buffer of pH 4.5, is added. A reaction time of 1.5 to 2.0 min in a further coil of 0.3 mm inner diameter at 100 °C is sufficient for the development of the dye, which is detected at 420 nm by a filter photometer. The sensitivity is somewhat below that of the above mentioned reagents.

8.4 Monodeoxy- and Oligosaccharides

Carbohydrates with a free anomeric hydroxyl group mutarotate in solution to form an equilibrium of their α- and β-anomers of the furanose- and pyranose forms. This equilibrium is disturbed by the chromatographic process, thus causing additional contributions to band broadening. These contributions can be considerable, especially if a relatively low temperature is applied.

Free carbohydrates may be separated by adsorption, partition, ion-exchange and gel permeation chromatography. Adsorption chromatography has lost its former importance, whereas the other three methods have been improved and represent today the most important techniques in carbohydrate analysis.

8.4.1 Liquid-Liquid Chromatography on Iion-Exchange Resins

This method was introduced by Samuelson et al. [6, 17, 18]. Anion-exchange resins, in the sulfate and chloride form, and cation-exchange resins, in the alkali, calcium and barium form, are in use, based on polystyrene divinyl benzene copolymers. Aqueous ethanol ($\approx 90\%$) is applied as the eluent and the eluted carbohydrates are detected with the orcinol-sulfuric acid method.

Fast separation at elevated temperatures was achieved on a Technicon type S (20 μm) resin in the sulfatic form, using 89% aqueous ethanol as an eluent [19]. Eight sugars could be separated by this means within 3 hours. The detection was carried out with the tetrazolium blue reagent.

The selectivity of this method depends on the alcohol concentration of the eluent and the counter-ion, as well as on the cros linkage of the resin. Alkali, alkaline earth metal and some transition metal ions form complexes with polyhydroxyl compounds and also with potential enediolates. For example, it is extremely difficult to separate allose, altrose and mannose on basic resins in the sulfate form, whereas on acid resins in the lithium form, excellent separations are achieved.

This matrix can also be used successfully for separation of oligosaccharides. In some cases, however, the k-values do not increase with the order of number of residues if the ethanol concentration is varied.

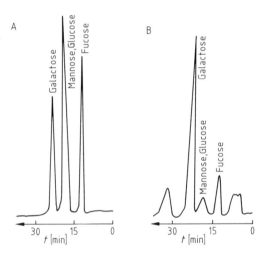

Figure 8-4. Separation of a standard mixture (A) and a hydrolysate of a glycoprotein (B) of gastrointenstinal mucosa. Column: 4 × 3000 nm; stationary phase: strong acid ion-exchange resin, DC-4A, Durrum, Palo Alto, USA., 8 ± 1 μm; Li-form; column temperature 65 °C; eluent: 89% ethanol; flow-rate: 0.3 mL/min; detection: bicinchoninate; post-column derivatization method.

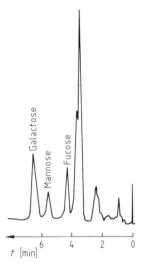

Figure 8-5. Separation of a hydrolysate of a glycoprotein of gastrointestinal mucosa (same sample as in Figure 4 b). Column: 4 × 200 mm; stationary phase: Nucleosil 5 SA (5 μm); flow-rate: 0.8 mL/min; eluent: acetonitrile/water (88 : 12); detection: UV at 195 nm.

In contrast to the chromatography on ion-exchange resins in the borate form, it is relatively easy to separate the common neutral sugars mannose, galactose and fucose expexted in glycoproteins. The time for an analysis is only about 10 to 20 minutes (Figure 8-4).

Unfortunately, it is difficult to separate glucose from mannose. Glucose is found as an impurity in almost every isolated glycoprotein.

Replacing the polystyrene divinylbenzene matrix by silica, at least in the case of strongly acidic ion-exchange material in the lithium form, gives excellent results [23] as demonstrated by Figure 8-5.

8.4.2 Liquid-Liquid Chromatography on Silica Gel with *in situ* Coated or Bonded Polar Layers

The separation of mono- and oligosaccharides on normal silica gel is not recommended. Even small amounts of water in e. g. acetonitrile/water eluents may be sufficient to elute all sugars quickly and, usually, with tailing.

Addition of polyamines to the eluent has been reported by several authors [15, 21]. After *in situ* impregnation of the silica gel, a strong polar stationary phase of slightly basic character is formed. Silanol groups are more acidic hydroxyl groups than those of carbohydrates.

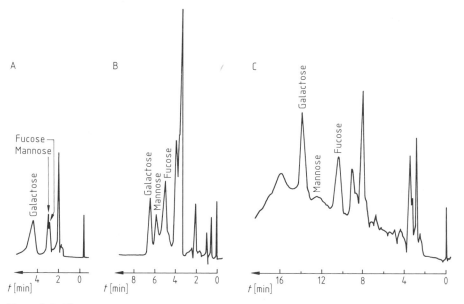

Figure 8-6. Chromatograms obtained from a hydrolysate of a glycoprotein of gastrointestinal mucosa. Column: 4 × 250 mm; flow-rate: 0.8 mL/min; detection; UV at 215 nm.

A: Stationary phase: silica gel (Merck Si 60, 5 μm); eluent: acetonitrile/water (91%);

B: Stationary phase: same as A; eluent: 0.5% piperazine in acetonitrile/water (88%);

C: Stationary phase: amino phase (Merck Lichrosorb-Amin 5 μm), eluent: acetonitrile/water (88%).

Stronger bonds with the polyamines therefore occur. The resulting modified surface of the stationary phase behaves more or less like a bonded amino phase to the eluent, however, a small amount of polyamine has to be added to maintain the conditions of the stationary phase. The influence of polyamine (piperazine) on the separation of some monosaccharides is demonstrated in Figure 8-6. The elution profile of the same mixture on a bonded amino phase is included. All three chromatograms were obtained from a hydrolysate of a glycoprotein of gastrointestinal mucosa (as in Figure 8-4).

New, chemically-bonded amino phases were recently described which allow the application of solvents containing about 40% of water [24].

According to the sequence of elution the separation should be mainly liquid-liquid partition chromatography.

In special series of carbohydrates, e. g. aldoses and ketoses, a systematic increase of the k-values with the number of hydroxyl groups per molecule occurs. First deoxysugars are eluted, followed by ketoses, aldoses and finally polyols. Differentiation within a series, e. g. hexoses, seems to be more difficult.

For the separation of oligosaccharides, chemically modified silica gel and bonded amino phases prove to be suitable (Figure 8-7). The elution sequence is the reverse of that of gel permeation chromatography [35].

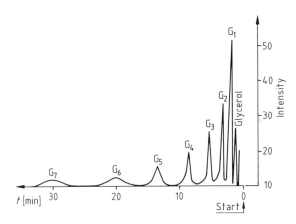

Figure 8-7. Separation of maltooligosaccharides of corn sirup. Column: 4 × 250 mm; stationary phase: μ Bondapak carbohydrate; detection: UV at 195 nm; mobile phase: acetonitrile/water (89:11).

8.4.3 Liquid-Liquid Chromatography on Non-Polar Stationary Phases, Reversed-Phase Chromatography

As carbohydrates show more or less strong polar character, they have to be transformed into suitable non-polar derivatives if reversed-phase liquid chromatography on non-polar stationary phases as ODS is applied. Peracylation with aromatic residues proved to be most convenient [36]. The necessary pre-column derivatization is easy to carry out and yields, in most cases, complete reaction. The aromatic residues show excellent interaction with non-polar stationary phases and result in a fast and highly sensitive separation of oligosaccharides.

8.4.4 Ion-Exchange Chromatography on Resins in the Borate Form

The separation of carbohydrates as borate complexes is influenced strongly by the configuration and the conformation of the suger moiety. The retention ratio depends on the number and type of hydroxyl groups, the dihedral angle of the glycol groups, the pH-value and the temperature.

Anomeric hydroxyl groups show stronger affinity to the borate ion than alcoholic hydroxyls. Furthermore, the stability of the complexes, and thus the capacity factor, depends on the anomeric distribution of the pyranose and furanose forms. Neighbouring hydroxyl groups in equatorial-equatorial position are more stable than those in equatorial-axial position. Complexation with 1,3-diols may also occur; for example, the separations of galactose and fucose (6-deoxy-galactose) show pH-dependency. 0.01 to 1.0 mol/L borate buffers of pH 5 to 10 are applied as eluants for carbohydrate mixtures.

The separations are carried out at elevated temperatures. Unfortunately, several sugars may be degraded under such conditions if relatively high temperatures are applied. Some authors use borate buffers in the presence of diols (which show low affinity to the borate ion at moderate pH-values) to minimize any alkaline rearrangement of the saccharides [37]. However, below 40 °C no considerable degradation is observed if moderate pH-values are applied. With the use of a temperature gradient excellent separation can be achieved, as Figure 8-8 demonstrates [20].

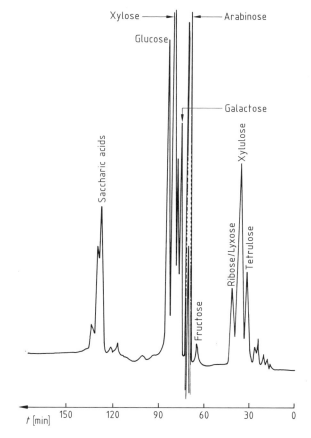

Figure 8-8. Separation of a complex mixture of carbohydrates received from the formose reaction. Column: 6 × 180 mm; stationary phase: strong basic ion-exchange resin; DA-X-8-11, 11 μm, Durrum, Palo Alto, USA; eluent: borate buffers 0.2 to 1.4 mol/L in borate, pH 8.6 to 9.5; flow-rate: 0.6 mL/min; column temperature; 38 to 67 °C; detection: periodate-acetylacetone post-column derivatization, UV at 420 nm.

A chromatogram obtained with isocratic elution from a hydrolysate of a glycoprotein of gastrointestinal mucosa is shown in Figure 8-9 (same sample as in Figures 8-4 and 8-6).

A combined system for the separation of neutral sugars, amino sugars and amino acids is discussed below (see Section 8.5).

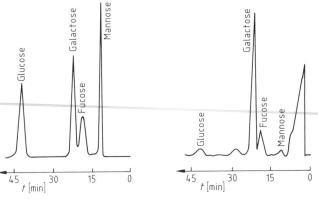

Figure 8-9. Separation of a hydrolysate of a glycoprotein of gastrointestinal mucosa. Eluent: borate buffer, 0.4 mol/L in borate, pH 9.3; column temperature: 56 °C; further conditions: see legend to Figure 8-8.

The application of the borate method to clinical problems allowed, for example, investigation of the occurrence of ganglioside sugars in the cerebrospinal fluid influenced by brain diseases [38]. For this purpose a fast and efficient separation technique is required, as a large number of samples has to be analyzed. Due to the highly specific orcinol-sulfuric acid post-column reaction, only proteins of molecular weight $>10^3$ had to be removed from the samples by ultramembrane filtration.

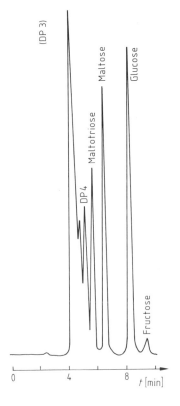

Figure 8-10. Separation of corn sirup oligosaccharides. Column: 6.5 × 300 mm, Interaction JC 6020 carbohydrate column; eluent: water; column temperature: 90 °C; flow-rate: 0.5 mL/min; detection: R.I.

8.4.5 Gel Permeation Chromatography (GPC)

This method is especially suitable for the separation of carbohydrate mixtures of different molecular weights. Unfortunately only a few suitable stationary phases are available, so this method is still the domain of low pressure chromatography on polyacrylamide gels, sepharoses etc. In Figure 8-10 the separation of a series of maltoses on a polystyrene matrix is shown.

8.5 Amino Sugars

Free amino sugars should be separated applying ion-exchange chromatography. For elution from acid resins, in some cases diluted acids but preferably acidic buffers, are in use [39]. Standard amino acid analyzers with post-column ninhydrin reaction are often used succesfully for this purpose. However, in the presence of amino acids the molarity and the pH of the elution buffers has to be modified to elute the amino sugars after phenylalanine but before the basic amino acids. This is very easily done, as demonstrated in Figure 8-11.

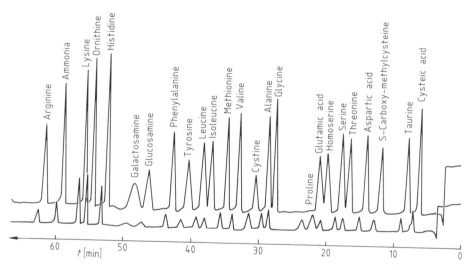

Figure 8-11. Separation of amino sugars in presence of amino acids. Column: 3.2 × 200 mm; stationary phase: strong acid ion-exchange resin BTC 2710/7 μm (Biotronik, Frankfurt, FRG); flow-rate: 0.4 mL/min; eluent: sodium citrate: 0.1 mol/L to 1.0 mol/L, pH 3.4 to 4.6; temperature gradient: 46 to 68 °C; sample: 5 nmol/component.

A simultaneous determination of amino sugars, amino acids and neutral sugars was also described [27]. Using a small pre-column containing a protonated acid ion-exchange resin and automatic column switching, submicrogram amounts of glycoprotein can be analyzed without an additional internal standard (Figure 8-12).

Preparative separations can be carried out with volatile eluents like pyridine-acetic acid buffers to facilitate the work-up of the fractions.

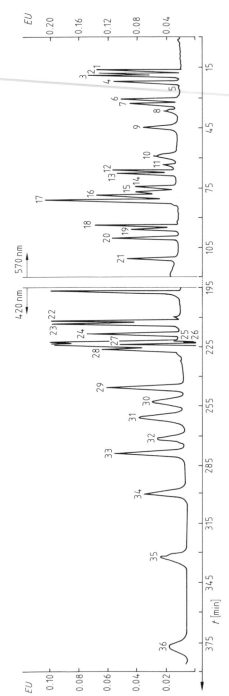

Figure 8-12. Chromatogram of a mixture of amino acids, amino sugars and neutral sugars. Pre-separation column: 5 × 4 mm, DC-8-9-resin; amino acid and amino sugar column: 250 × 4 mm, DC-8-9-resin; neutral sugar column: 160 × 4 mm, DA-X-8-8 resin; flow-rate: 0.24 mL/min; pressure: 80 to 110 bar; recorder range: 0 to 0.2 A (ninhydrin, 570 nm) or 0 to 01 A (orcinol-sulfuric acid, 420 nm); peaks: 1 aspartic acid, 2 threonine, 3 serine, 4 glutamic acid, 5 proline, 6 glycine, 7 alanine, 8 cystine, 9 valine, 10 methionine, 11 unknown, 12 isoleucine, 13 leucine, 14 tyrosine, 15 phenylalanine, 16 galactosamine, 17 glucosamine, 18 lysine, 19 ammonia, 20 histidine, 21 arginine, 22 sucrose, 23 trehalose, 24 cellobiose, 25 maltose, 26 rhamnose, 27 lactose, 28 ribose, 29 mannose, 30 fructose, 31 arabinose, 32 galactose, 33 xylose, 34 glucose, 35 gentiobiose, 36 melibiose, 37 fucose. Each peak represents 2.05 nmol per amino acid and 4.40 nmol per amino sugar and neutral sugar [27].

Separation of amino sugars can also be achieved via their derivatives. The chromatographic behaviour of the derivatives depends on the nature and the number of the substituents. If the amino group is blocked, as in various naturally occurring N-acetylated amino sugars, the basic character is lost and ion-exchange chromatography has to be replaced by other techniques. Such derivatives behave more or less like neutral sugars and consequently separation techniques used for this class of compounds should be applied.

8.6 Alditols

Because of the accumulation of hydroxyl groups in the molecule, the separation conditions for alditols do not differ much from those of neutral sugars. Liquid-liquid and ion-exchange chromatography represent the most important techniques in this field. The borate method shows more selectivity. The order of elution strongly obeys the rule of Boeseken [31]: Cis-diols undergo stronger complexation than trans-diols. The influence of terminal diol groups is lower. Thus the elution order of pentitols is xylitol, arabinitol = lyxitol and ribitol.

Figure 8-13 shows a chromatogram obtained by isocratic elution on a basic ion-exchange resin of 8 μm particle size in the borate form. Detection was carried out with the periodate reagent.

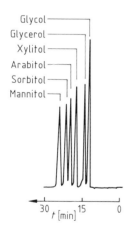

Figure 8-13. Chromatogram of some polyols. Column: 6 × 250 mm; stationary phase: basic ion-exchange resin, Durrum DA-X 8-11; 11 μm; eluent: borate buffer, 0.8 mol/L in borate, pH 9.4; detection: periodateacetylacetone, post-column derivatization.

8.7 Sugar Acids

The most efficient method for preparative isolation and for analysis of aldonic, uronic, saccharic saccharinic acids and other acid sugar derivatives is doubtless anion-exchange chromatography. The application of eluents containing boric acid results in some cases, in additional selectivity.

8.7.1 Uronic Acids

Most of the chromatographic methods, described for the isolation of uronic acids, are based on low pressure liquid chromatography. E. g. the separation of galacturonic and glucuronic acid on Dowex 1 with 0.15 mol/L acetic acid as eluent has been described [40].

The application of a low particle size resin resulted in a separation of more than 10 components [41]. The elution with potassium borate buffers of pH 8 to 10 and 0.6 to 1.0 mol/L in boric acid on 8% cross-linked spherical polystyrene divenylbenzene resins of particle size 8 μm showed more selectivity and the uronic acids could be eluted after elution of neutral sugars [42].

8.7.2 Aldonic, Saccharic and Saccharinic Acids

The most efficient separations of this class of compounds are carried out on strongly basic ion-exchange resins in the borate form [20]. The presence of borate allows, in most cases, separation of acids of the same pk, according to their ability to form boric acid complexes. In a mixture resulting from the formose reaction [43], several aldonic and saccharinic acids could be separated and detected as well as neutral sugars and polyols (see Figure 8-8). The order of elution follows besides the pK-value again the rules of Boeseken.

The separation of ascorbic acid, neutral sugars, uronic acids and isoascorbic acids was also successfully carried out on an ion-exchange resin column [44, 45].

8.8 Sugar Phosphates

For this class of acidic sugar derivatives, ion-exchange chromatography is the most important method for the analysis and the isolation from natural sources. However, the stability of these compounds, especially under acidic or basic conditions, is not very high. Apart from this property, sugar phosphates behave chromatographically similarly to other sugar acids. Consequently, in most cases, similar elution conditions (see Section 8.7) are used.

8.9 Glycosides, Esters, Ethers and Acetals

The chromatographic behaviour of glycosides with simple aglycones is similar to that of free monosaccharides and polyols. For partition chromatography, polar stationary phases based on silica or polystyrene divinyl benzene are suitable (see Sections 8.4.1 and 8.4.2). However, ion-exchange chromatography on resins in the borate form shows significant difference compared to free sugars and polyols. Loss of the reactive anomeric hydroxyl group results in less strong boric acid complexes and thus in smaller k-values [10]. Bulky and unpolar aglycones can influence the dominant chromatographic properties. Reversed-phase or even gel permeation chromatography can thus be used. Ethers, acetals and esters of carbohydrates lose the characteristic behaviour of free sugars according to the number and type of the residues. Most of the partially or completely derivatized carbohydrates show more or less unpolar properties. Therefore, acetylated, benzoylated, benzylated, methylated isopropylidene or benzylidene derivatives should be separated via liquid-solid chromatography e. g. on silica gel or, most preferentially, via reversed-phase chromatography.

8.10 Polysaccharides

No general method can be recommended for the chromatographic isolation, purification and analytical characterization of polysaccharides. Neutral polysaccharides can be separated by gel permeation. In several cases more selectivity can be achieved via their borate esters on ion-exchange resins. Differentiation in a series of homologeous saccharides, however, is more difficult. Unfortunately, only a few suitable pressure-stable column packing materials for this purpose are currently available commercially. Most of the chromatographic separations in this field are still performed by low pressure liquid chromatography. For the separation of some acidic or basic polysaccharides, ion-exchange resins can be used for the stationary phase with good success.

The exclusion range of pressure-stable resins is relatively low (10^3 to 10^5 relative molecular mass). Therefore this method is restricted if large molecular weight saccharides have to be separated.

8.11 References

[1] F. Cramer, *Angew. Chem.* **62**, 73 (1950).
[2] E. Stahl, and U. Kaltenbach, *J. Chromatogr.* **5**, 351 (1961).
[3] R. L. Whistler, and D. F. Durso, *J. Am. Chem. Soc* **72**, 677 (1950).
[4] H. W. McNeely, W. W. Binley, and M. L. Wolfrom, *J. Am. Chem. Soc.* **67**, 527 (1945).
[5] L. Hough, J. K. N. Jones, and W. A. Wadman, *J. Chem. Soc.* (1949), 2511.
[6] B. Arwidi, and O. Samuelson, *Svensk. Kem. Tidskr.* **722**, 84 (1965).
[7] S. Roseman, R. H. Abeles, and A. Dorman, *Arch. Biochem. Biophys.* **36**, 232 (1952).
[8] J. Y. Khym, and L. P. Zill, *J. Am. Chem. Soc.* **74**, 2090 (1952).
[9] R. B. Kesler, *Anal. Chem.* **39**, 1416 (1967).
[10] H. Bauer, Thesis, Tübingen University, 1975.
[11] H. Bauer, and W. Voelter, *Chromatographia* **9**, 433 (1976).
[12] C. C. Sweeley, R. Bentley, M. Makita, and W. W. Wells, *J. Am. Chem. Soc.* **85**, 2497 (1963).
[13] W. A. König, H. Bauer, W. Voelter, and E. Bayer, *Chem. Ber.* **106**, 1905 (1973).
[14] S. A. Baker, J. J. Bourne, and O. Theander, *J. Chem. Soc.* 4276 (1955).
[15] M. Boumahraz, V. Ya. Davydov, and A. V. Kiselev, *Chromatographia* **15**, 751 (1982).
[16] K. S. Ennor, J. Honeyman, C. J. B. Shaw, and T. C. Stening, *J. Chem. Soc.* 2921 (1958).
[17] J. Havlicek, G. Petersson, and O. Samuelson, *Acta Chem. Scand.* **26**, 2205 (1972).
[18] H. Matsui, E. Päärt, and O. Samuelson, *Chem. Scr.* **1**, 45 (1971).
[19] K. Mopper, and E. T. Degens, *Anal. Biochem.* **45**, 147 (1972).
[20] A. R. Hernanto, Thesis, Tübingen University, 1983.

[21] K. Aitzetmüller, *Chromatographia* **13**, 432 (1980).

[22] M. T. Yang, L. P. Milligan, and G. W. Mathison, *J. Chromatogr.* **209**, 316 (1981).

[23] H. Bauer, A. Shalaby, and W. Voelter, in press.

[24] P. Orth, and H. Engelhardt, *Chromatographia* **15**, 9 (1982).

[25] E. Martinsson, and O. Samuelson, *Chromatographia* **3**, 405 (1970).

[26] A. Hjerpe, C. A. Antonopoulos, B. Classon, and B. Engfeldt, *J. Chromatogr.* **202**, 453 (1980).

[27] M. M. Tikhomirov, A. Ya. Khorlin, W. Voelter, and Hermann Bauer, *J. Chromatogr.* **167**, 197 (1978).

[28] R. B. Kesler, Anal. Chem. **39**, 1416 (1967).

[29] W. Voelter, and H. Bauer, *Chem. Exp. Didakt.* **1**, 203 (1975).

[30] W. Voelter, and H. Bauer, *J. Chromatogr.* **126**, 693 (1976).

[31] J. Boeseken, *Rec. Trav. Chem.* **61**, 82 (1942).

[32] J. C. Kuo, and E. S. Yeung, *J. Chromatogr.* **223**, 321 (1981).

[33] K. Mopper, and E. M. Gindler, *Anal. Biochem.* **56**, 440 (1973).

[34] E. E. Moose, *Anal. Chem.* **19**, 1012 (1947).

[35] K. Kainuma, T. Nakakuki, and T. Ogawa, *J. Chromatogr.* **212**, 126 (1981).

[36] P. F. Daniel, I. T. Lott, and R. H. McCluer, in: G. L. Hawk (ed.): *Biological/Biomedical Applications of Liquid Chromatography* **III**, p. 363. Marcel Dekker, Inc. New York, 1981.

[37] E. F. Walborg, D. B. Ray, and L. E. Öhrberg, *Anal. Biochem.* **29**, 433 (1969).

[38] R. Seuffer, W. Voelter, and H. Bauer, *J. Clin. Chem. Clin. Biochem.* **15**, 663 (1977).

[39] K. Brendel, N. O. Roszel, R. W. Wheat, and E. A. Davidson, *Anal. Biochem.* **18**, 147 (1967).

[40] J. X. Khym, and D. G. Doherty, *J. Am. Chem. Soc.* **74**, 3199 (1952).

[41] B. Carlsson, and O. Samuelson, *Anal. Chim. Acta* **49**, 247 (1970).

[42] H. Bauer, unpublished results.

[43] A. R. Hernanto, W. Voelter, and H. Bauer, in: *Proceedings XIth Intenational Carbohydrate Symposium, Vancouver, Canada, 1982.*

[44] J. Geigert, D. S. Hirano, and S. L. Neidleman, *J. Chromatogr.* **206**, 396 (1981).

[45] M. H. Bui-Nguyên, *J. Chromatogr.* **196**, 163 (1980).

9 Nucleobases, Nucleosides, Nucleotides

by *Herbert Schott*

9 Nucleobases, Nucleosides, Nucleotides

9.0 Abbreviations

Thy	thymine	IMP	inosine 5'-monophosphate
Ade	adenine	AMP	adenosine 5'-monophosphate
Gua	guanine	TMP	thymidine 5'-monophosphate
Cyt	cytosine	UMP	uridine 5'-monophosphate
Ura	uracil	CMP	cytidine 5'-monophosphate
Thd	ribosylthymine	GMP	guanosine 5'-monophosphate
dGuo	deoxyguanosine	XMP	xanthosine 5'-monophosphate
dAdo	deoxyadenosine	dAMP	deoxyadenosine 5'-monophosphate
G	guanosine	dTMP	deoxythymidine 5'-monophosphate
C	cytidine	ADP	adenosine 5'-diphosphate
T	thymidine	ATP	adenosine 5'-triphosphate
A	adenosine	GTP	guanosine 5'-triphosphate

9.1 Introduction

Numerous problems in nucleic acid research, e. g. in analysis, isolation and synthesis of nucleic acids and their building blocks, have recently been approached with HPLC, often with satisfactory results. Naturally, questions dealing with nucleobases, nucleosides, and mononucleotides can be clarified more easily than problems involving oligonucleotides, polynucleotides, and nucleic acids. Nevertheless, substantial achievements have been made in the latter area, as will be shown in the present paper.

Nucleic acids are known to be the carriers of genetic information. They are subdivided in deoxyribonucleic acid (DNA) and ribonucleic acid (RNA). DNA, like RNA, is a long, unbranched macromolecule consisting of nucleotides joined by 3'-5' phosphodiester bonds (see Figure 9-1). The backbone of DNA consists of deoxyriboses linked by phosphodiester bridges. The variable part of DNA is its sequence of bases. DNA contains four kinds of general bases. The two purines are adenine (Ade) and guanine (Gua). The two pyrimidines are thymine (Thy) and cytosine (Cyt). The covalent structure of RNA differs from that of DNA in two ways. The sugar unit in RNA is ribose rather than deoxyribose. The other difference is that one of the four major bases in RNA is uracil (Ura) instead of thymine. RNA also contains numerous modified bases. RNA molecules are single-stranded, except in some viruses.

The monomeric units of the nucleic acids are thus the mononucleotides, which consist of one of the possible nucleobases and the respective sugar residue (ribose or deoxyribose). Nucleic acid fragments (Figure 9-1) with up to ca. 10 monomeric units are referred to as oligonucleotides, longer fragments as polynucleotides. In the present review, examples of HPLC applications with nucleic acid building blocks will initially be presented. Subsequently, problems of oligonucleotide and polynucleotide separation will be discussed. Finally, the recent application of HPLC to oligonucleotide synthesis, which has resulted in substantial simplification of the complicated synthesis method, will be reported.

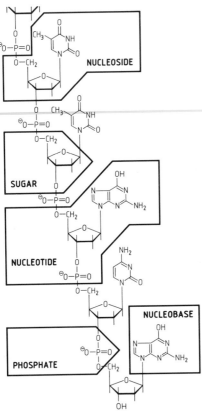

Figure 9-1. Scheme of a single stranded DNA-fragment.

9.2 Separation Processes of Nucleobases, Nucleosides and Mononucleotides

HPLC procedures have been developed for analysis of nucleobases, nucleosides and mononucleotides [1, 2]. In most cases, a cation-exchanger resin is employed for the separation of bases or nucleosides, and an anion-exchanger is used for nucleotides.

9.2.1 Ion-Exchangers

The application of ion-exchangers in HPLC has been investigated thoroughly [3]. Optimal conditions for the separation of nucleobases using cation-exchangers have been reported [4]. Bases are also resolved on Aminex A-7 with 1 mol/L phosphate at pH 2.75 and 50 °C. The optimal conditions for the same analysis on Aminex A-28 are elution with 0.4 mol/L phosphate-borate, pH 8.25, at 45 °C. The dependence of the charge of various analogues of the nucleic acid bases on the pH of the solution has been tabulated. The retention behavior of nucleobases (purine and pyrimidine bases) and their nucleosides, in systems consisting of water/ethanol mixtures with added electrolytes as mobile phase and Aminex A-28 as stationary phase, has been systematically investigated [5]. The effect of pH, type and concentration of the counter-ion, ethanol content of the mobile phase, and temperature on the retention and column efficiency has been determined. The results show that all these parameters have a significant effect and have to be optimized in order to separate nucleobases and nucleosides using isocratic elution. The separation of fourteen compounds has been achieved in ca. 30 min (Figure 9-2).

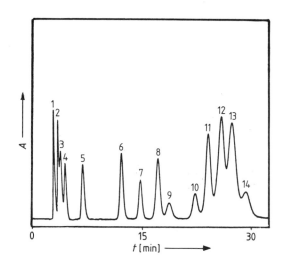

Figure 9-2. Separation of a mixture of nucleobases and nucleosides on an Aminex A-28 column (250 × 3 mm i. d.) [5]; mobile phase: 5 mmol/L citrate + 50 mmol/L phosphate buffer (pH 9.25) + 55% ethanol; elution temperature: 70 °C; detection: 260 nm. Peak identification: 1 5-methylcytosine, 2 cytosine, 3 adenosine, 4 cytidine, 5 thymidine, 6 thymine, 7 uracil, 8 uridine, 9 adenine, 10 guanine, 11 hypoxanthine, 12 xanthine and guanosine, 13 inosine, 14 xanthosine.

   The ability of the phase system is demonstrated by analysis of a calf thymus DNA hydrolyzate.
   A large variety of nucleic acid constituents have been separated with HPLC on a silica-based weak anion-exchange column [6]. This technique has permitted some relatively difficult separations, such as separation of 2'-, 3'- and 5'-AMP, or of a mixture of ribo- and deoxyribonucleosides and nucleotides. A number of other separations are demonstrated by isocratic or gradient elution, e. g. separation of a mixture of nucleoside mono-, di-, and triphosphates; of a mixture of nucleosides and bases; and of a mixture of nucleotide oligomers. These chromatographic separations were accomplished using relatively simple experimental procedures at ambient temperatures and involved relatively short analysis times. In most cases, excellent separations were obtained by adjustment of buffer concentration and pH, or by addition of an organic modifier. In some cases, gradient elution was required to achieve optimum resolution.
   A method has been reported for rapid purification of radioactive labelled deoxyribonucleoside triphosphates from their spontaneously emerging hydrolysis products of deoxyribonucleoside diphosphate, deoxyribonucleoside monophosphate, and deoxyribonucleoside [7]. The separations are finished within 3 min or less and are carried out on a 0.1 × 5 cm column filled with LiChrosorb-NH_2, using isocratic elution with 0.025 mol/L potassium phosphate, pH 6.8 at room temperature and a flow-rate of 30 mL/h.

9.2.2 Reversed-Phase

It is desirable to separate nucleic acid constituents using a simple chromatographic system with a single column and a single solvent. Seven of the naturally occuring nucleosides and their bases have been analyzed using the reversed-phase partition mode of HPLC. With microparticle chemically bonded packings, nucleosides and their bases can be determined quantitatively within 30 min in the presence of nucleotides; sensitivity, accuracy, and reproducibility are high. Peaks in chromatograms of cell extracts were identified by absorbance ratios and enzymatic peak shift methods. Applications of this technique to biochemical studies have been reported [8].

Four components of three sets of DNA constituents; bases, nucleosides and mononucleotides, were sufficiently resolved under one set of chromatographic conditions using Zorbax ODS column and 0.4 mol/L $NH_4H_2PO_4$ (pH 3.5) as solvent (Figure 9-3) [9].

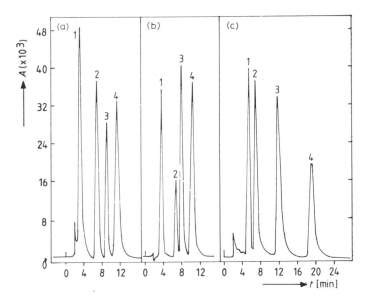

Figure 9-3. Separation of a mixture of (a) nucleobases, (b) deoxyribonucleoside 5'-monophosphates, and (c) 2'-deoxyribonucleosides, on a Zorbax ODS column (250 × 2.1 mm i. d.) [9]; mobile phase: 400 mmol/L ammonium phosphate (pH 3.5); elution temperature: 40 °C; detection: 260 nm. Peak identification: (a), 1 cytosine, 2 guanine, 3 thymine, 4 adenine; (b) 1 deoxycytidine 5'-monophosphate, 2 deoxythymidine 5'-monophosphate, 3 deoxyguanosine 5'-monophosphate, 4 deoxyadenosine 5'-monophosphate; (c) 1 deoxycytidine, 2 deoxyguanosine, 3 deoxyadenosine, 4 deoxythymidine.

The base composition of 1 μg of DNA has been analyzed using this method. The reported results revealed that the separation of dGuo from dTMP and dAdo from dAMP were not satisfactory. Improved resolution would be expected from a system utilizing a longer column or gradient elution. The chromatographic behavior of Ade, dAdo and dAMP was somewhat different from that of the others. The retention times of these three compounds were increased substantially as the pH of the solvent increased. dAMP was found to have a somewhat shorter retention time than the other two fragments. Only the retention of Ade and dAdo was reduced with increasing ammonium phosphate concentration, the retention of dAMP and other compounds being either unaffected or slightly increased. The elution profiles of bases traced by radioactivity indicated that small amounts of Gua, Thy and Ade were retarded near the position of Cyt and that Ade eluted with tailing. These would be reasons for the lower recoveries of these compounds. Moreover, it cannot be excluded that this method could result in a slightly higher content of Cyt in DNA than the other methods.

A procedure for the selective determination of adenosine in the presence of other nucleic acid components has been reported [10]. Reversed-phase microparticle columns and an isocratic elution mode of dilute potassium dihydrophosphate and anhydrous methanol were used. The analysis is specific for adenosine and is achieved in <10 min. An example of the use of this analysis in a biochemical study has been reported.

A fast, quantitative procedure for determining the percentage of guanine (G) plus cytosine (C) in DNA preparations after acid hydrolysis in 88% formic acid has been described [11]. As little as 10 µg of DNA is amenable to this analysis. Although thymine is sometimes poorly resolved from impurities at the solvent front, the percentage of G + C was found to be accurately determined using adenine (A) simply from the ratio of concentrations from C/(A + C) or (G + C)/(2 A + G + C). The HPLC method gave values for the percentage of G + C in close agreement with thermal melting point and buoyant density values determined for the DNA of 10 bacterial species and 2 fungi.

A rapid and complete separation of the four Thy < > Thy dimers on a conventional octadecyl reversed-phase column and on the new radial-PAK A cartridge with the Waters radial compression separation system (RC 55) has been reported [12]. Separations of the optically active stereoisomers as well as the meso pairs of cyclobutadithymidine (thymidine dimers, Thd < > Thd) by reversed-phase HPLC have also been described. Cyclobutadipyrimidines represent the major class of DNA lesions induced by the action of far and near ultraviolet light on biological systems.

An HPLC method was developed for the monitoring of hydrolytic decomposition of 5-iodo-2'deoxyuridine in aqueous solution and for the stability assay of this compound [13]. The separation of 5-iodo-2'-deoxyuridine and its decomposition products was performed on a µ Bondapak C_{18} column using a mixture of water and methanol as the eluant. On the basis of the experimental data, the kinetic order and the rate constants of both consecutive reactions were determined.

The groups UMP, CMP, AMP, and GMP; and AMP, ADP and ATP have been separated by HPLC isocratically on a reversed-phase column in the presence of tetra-n-butylammonium ion [14]. The 12 nucleoside phosphates and cyclic AMP could not be separated isocratically but could be separated by gradient elution with increasing ionic strength and methanol concentration. Uracil, cytosine, adenine and guanine were separated in the presence of 10-camphorsulfonate ions. The ribonucleosides of these bases also were separated in the presence of the latter ion.

The introduction of quaternary ammonium alkylates as ion pair-forming counter-ions has enabled the rapid separation of polar water-soluble compounds on reversed-phases [15, 16]. Compared to ion exchange, paired-ion chromatography on reversed-phases requires less sophisticated chromatographic equipment. Moreover, regeneration of the column is no longer required and the time of analysis is thereby considerably reduced. The isocratic separation of 6 naturally occuring 5'-ribonucleoside monophosphates by reversed-phase HPLC was achieved using solvents containing tetramethylammonium, tetraethylammonium, or tetrabutylammonium ions (Figure 9-4). Their effectiveness in resolving the nucleoside monophosphates increases with increasing alkyl chain length (butyl > ethyl > methyl). In an acidic aqueous solvent containing methanol, these ion-pair reagents effect discrete separations of all the nucleoside monophosphates. The described systems also provide for virtually quantitative recovery of the separated nucleotides and utilize phosphate-free solvents consisting of volatile components easily removed by evaporation [17].

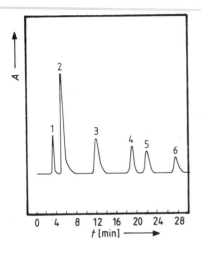

Figure 9-4. Separation of a mixture of ribonucleoside 5'-monophosphates on an Ultrasphere ODS column (250 x 4.6 mm i. d.) [17]; mobile phase: 2.5 mmol/L tetrabutylammonium hydroxide + 12% methanol, adjusted to pH 2.5 with formic acid; elution temperature: room temperature; detection: 254 nm. Peak identification: 1 cytidine 5'-monophosphate, 2 adenosine 5'-monophosphate, 3 guanosine 5'-monophosphate, 4 uridine 5'-monophosphate, 5 inosine 5'-monophosphate, 6 xanthosine 5'-monophosphate.

The common adenine nucleotides (adenosine mono-, di-, triphosphate) have been separated by paired-ion chromatography from their sulphated derivatives (adenosine 5'-sulphatophosphate, adenosine 3'-phosphate 5'-sulphatophosphate) [18]. With tetrabutylammonium hydroxide as the ion pair-forming reagent, nicotinamide adenine dinucleotide phosphate, flavin-adenine dinucleotide and adenosine 3', 5'-bisphosphate were also separated from these nucleotides by rapid isocratic elution. The method is highly reliable, as shown by the capacity factors, and its compatibility with the requirements of a continuous-flow radio detection for ^{35}S-labelled nucleotides is demonstrated. It has been applied to an investigation of the kinetics of an adenosine 3'-phosphate 5'-sulphatophosphate sulphotransferase reaction involved in higher plant assimilative sulphate reduction.

9.2.3 Affinity Chromatography

The separation of bases and nucleosides employing a column packed with porous thymine-coupled spherical resins of diameter 12 to 15 μm has been described [19]. The resins were synthesized by suspension polymerization of glycidyl methacrylate and ethylene glycol dimethacrylate in the presence of diluent. Chromatographic measurements were carried out at 25 °C on an HPLC chromatograph using distilled water as solvent. The retention volumes of bases and nucleosides revealed that adenine and adenosine were retained most strongly and that guanine and guanosine were more retarded than 3 pyrimidine bases or 3 nucleosides of pyrimidine bases. Moreover, the retention volumes of the 3 pyrimidine bases or 3 nucleosides of pyrimidine bases were conveniently different, and 5 nucleic acid bases or 5 nucleosides could be separated in a short time. From the results of measurements performed on the same column with 0.1 mol/L sodium chloride and 1 mol/L urea solutions as solvents and on a column packed with non-thymine-bound resins, it was evident that the retardation of nucleic acid bases and nucleosides in the column packed with resins containing thymine was due mainly to interactions between thymine and the bases.

The use of boronic acid-substituted polymers for the separation of diol-containing molecules such as nucleosides, nucleotides, catecholamines, carbohydrates and transfer RNA has been well documented. The vicinal diols of these substances are able to form reversibly cyclic boronate esters with the boronate anion at high pH. The formation of these complexes is dependent on pH, ionic strength, temperature and − in the case of nucleic acid components − on the structure of the base. 3-aminobenzene boronic acid was bound covalently to small, 10 μm, solid beads of polychlorotrifluoroethylene [20] or porous silica particles [21] and used in HPLC for the separation of mixtures of nucleosides, nucleotides or carbohydrates (Figure 9-5).

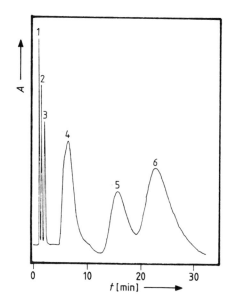

Figure 9-5. Separation of a mixture of ribo- and deoxyribonucleosides on a boronic acid silica column (100 x 5 mm i. d.) [21]. Mobile phase: 100 mmol/L sodium phosphate (pH 7.5); elution temperature: room temperature; detection: 260 nm. Peak identification: 1 thymidine and deoxycytidine, 2 deoxyguanosine, 3 deoxyadenosine, 4 cytosine and uridine, 5 guanosine, 6 adenosine.

The direct analysis of plasma nucleosides has been especially difficult because of the extremely low, variable, endogenous levels in the normal human population, and the tendency for the compound of interest to be obscured by other components found in plasma. It has been found that boronic acid-substituted polymers, e. g. "Affi-gel" (Bio-Rad, Labs., Richmond, Calif. USA [22] and "Boronic Acid Gel" (Aldrich, Milwaukee, Wisconsin USA) [23] can be used for the prefractionation and concentration of plasma nucleosides prior to injection in HPLC, thus greatly increasing sensitivity as well as selectivity. The normal human plasma levels of at least two nucleosides, inosine and adenosine, were reliably measured in all subjects examined using this type of boronate affinity gel. The identity and absolute quantitative value of these two compounds has been verified by the enzymatic peak-shift method.

9.2.4 Metal-Solute Complexes

The potential of metal-ion bonded phases in HPLC has been recently demonstrated [24, 25]. A new bonded phase, containing a $Co(en)_3^{3+}$ moiety, was prepared in order to study the chromatographic behavior of solutes capable of forming outersphere complexes with cobalt compounds [26]. The test solutes were nucleotides and nucleosides. It was found that solute-stationary phase interactions could be quite strong, resulting in long retention times. This was particularly so with triphosphate nucleotide. To overcome this difficulty Mg(II) was added to the mobile phase. Under these conditions selectivity, efficiency and analysis times were greatly improved. The behavior of the $Co(en)_3^{3+}$ phase was compared to that of a C_{18} column and a diamine system. The importance of adding Mg(II) to the mobile phase is demonstrated on all systems.

9.3 Analysis of Nucleic Acid Constituents in Biological Samples

The analysis of nucleic acid constituents in biological samples has been carried out using different HPLC procedures including ion-exchange and reversed-phase. Most of these techniques were developed for the separation of bases and nucleosides [27, 28] or nucleotides [20

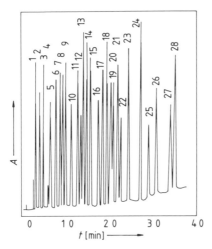

Figure 9-6. Separation of 0.1 to 0.5 nmol of nucleobases, nucleosides, nucleotides, aromatic amino acids and metabolites [32]. Column: reversed-phase (C_{18}) on 10 µm totally porous silica support. Injection volume: 40 µL of a solution $1 \cdot 10^{-5}$ mol/L in each standard. Eluents: low-strength, 0.02 mol/L KH_2PO_4, pH 5.6; high strength, 60% methanol. Gradient: slope 0.69 %/min (0 – 60% methanol in 87 min), linear. Temperature, ambient; flow-rate 1.5 mL/min; detection 254 nm. Peak identification: 1 cytosine, 2 orotidine, 3 uracil, 4 L-tyrosine, 5 cytidine, 6 hypoxanthine, 7 uridine, 8 5-aminoimidazolcarboxamide riboside, 9 7-methylinosine, 10 7-methylxanthosine, 11 7-methylguanosine, 12 beta-nicotinamide adenine dinucleotide, 13 inosine, 14 guanosine, 15 2'-deoxyinosine, 16 2'-deoxythymidine, 17 1-methylinosine, 18 N_1-methylguanosine, 19 N_2-methylguanosine, 20 kynurenic acid, 21 adenosine, 22 theobromine, 23 N_2N_2-dimethylguanosine, 24 theophylline, 25 dyphylline, 26 6-methyladenosine, 27 indole-3-propionic acid, 28 caffeine.

to 31] alone by removing interfering components prior to analysis. In characterization of the different DNA or RNA types, the analysis of nucleobases and their nucleosides in DNA and RNA hydrolyzates is of great importance. Alterations in the purine and pyrimidine metabolic pathways caused by genetic diseases such as the Lesch-Nyhan syndrome, or adenosine deaminase or nucleoside phosphorylase deficiencies, can sometimes be recognized from quantitative analysis of the nucleobases and nucleosides in cell extracts. Moreover, the measurement and metabolism of purine and pyrimidine analogues, used as therapeutic agents in the treatment of cancer, provides valuable informations. Alterations of the serum nucleoside and base profiles in patients with neoplastic diseases have been of particular interest, as concentrations of several modified nucleosides and bases have been found to be elevated in the urine of patients suffering from various types of malignancies.

9.3.1 Nucleosides and Mononucleotides alone

A comprehensive investigation has been conducted on the HPLC separation of nucleosides, their bases and other low-molecular-weight UV-absorbing compounds that can be found in serum. A buffer/methanol gradient was used in conjunction with chemically bonded, microparticulate columns to separate many of the biologically important compounds under study in minimal time with maximal resolution (Figure 9-6).

Retention data (see Table 9-1), absorbance rations (280/254 nm) and fluorescence responses are reported for 86 nucleosides, bases, nucleotides and other UV-absorbing compounds commonly encountered in biological studies [32].

Table 9-1. Observed Retention Times of Nucleobases, Nucleotides and Metabolites [32]. – Chromatographic conditions: Column: reversed-phase (C_{18}) on 10 μm totally porous silica support. Injection volume: 40 μL of a solution $1 \cdot 10^{-5}$ mol/L in each standard. Eluents: low-strength, 0.02 mol/L KH_2PO_4, pH 5.6; high-strength, 60% methanol. Gradient: slope 0.69%/min (0 to 60% methanol in 87 min), linear. Temperature: ambient; flow-rate: 1.5 mL/min.

Compound	Observed Retention Time (min)	Compound	Observed Retention Time (min)
Cytosine	2.28	Cytidine	5.85
Uridine diphosphoglucose	2.35	Riboflavin	6.84
Uridine monophosphate	2.54	Hypoxanthine	7.31
Orotidine	3.25	1-Methylcytidine	7.25
Nicotinamide mononucleotide	3.41	Guanine	7.56
Uric Acid	4.31	Uridine	8.27
Uracil	4.13	Xanthine	8.53
Pseudouridine	4.31	5-Aminoimidazolocarboxamide riboside	8.77
4-Amino-5-imidazolocarboxamide	4.31		
5-Fluorouracil	4.36	Thymidine monophosphate	8.89
Guanosine monophosphate	4.52	Nicotinamide adenine dinucleotide phosphate	8.91
Xanthosine monophosphate	4.75		
Adenosine monophosphate	5.04	Thymine	9.30
1-Methyladenine	5.77	7-Methylinosine	9.46

Table 9-1. (Continued.)

Compound	Observed Retention Time (min)	Compound	Observed Retention Time (min)
Adenosine monophosphate	9.53	2'-Deoxyguanosine	16.86
Flavin adenine dinucleotide	9.98	2'-Deoxythymidine	17.29
Alpha-nicotinamide adenine	10.15	1-Methylinosine	18.22
dinucleotide		6-Methylpurine	18.98
Adenosine 5'-diphosphoribose	10.26	2-Methyladenine	19.13
Allopurinol	10.52	N^1-Methylguanosine	19.22
7-Methylxanthosine	10.69	Indole-3-lactic acid	19.28
3',5'-Cyclic cytidine monophosphate	10.76	Purine riboside	19.69
5-Methylcytidine	10.79	Tubercydin	19.73
Purine	11.20	7-Methyladenine	19.92
Anthranilic Acid	11.23	N^2-Methylguanosine	20.23
7-Methylguanosine	11.82	Kynurenic acid	20.80
Pyrimidine	11.92	Adenosine	21.77
Xanthosine	12.40	Indole-3-acetic acid	21.99
Nicotinamide	12.55	5-Methylpyrimidine	23.23
3',5'-Cyclic uridine monophosphate	12.86	3',5'-Cyclic adenosine	23.47
Beta-nicotinamide adenine	13.00	monophosphate	
dinucleotide		2'-Deoxyadenosine	23.55
Inosine	13.52	N^2,N^2-Dimethylguanosine	24.42
Adenine	13.54	6-Methyladenine	24.90
Guanosine	14.40	Theophylline	27.20
7-Methylguanine	14.65	Flavin mononucleotide	27.58
3',5'-Cyclic guanosine	15.12	Dyphylline	29.11
monophosphate		6-Methyladenosine	30.86
N^2-Methylguanine	15.22	Indole-3-acetamide	31.41
2'-Deoxyinosine	15.29	Indole-3-propionic acid	34.66
3',5'-Cyclic inosine monophosphate	15.92	Caffeine	35.08
Hippuric acid	15.98	3-Indole-anthranilic acid	41.11

Nucleotide profiles of the acid-soluble extracts of normal and abnormal platelets have been determined [33]. Standard curves obtained for each of three major nucleotides were linear throughout the range studied and the recovery of standards added to the platelet homogenates was efficient and reproducible. The values obtained by HPLC agreed closely with the published data using other methods. Platelets of patients with storage-pool deficiency have been analyzed with this method and the findings are in agreement with the observations of other workers. The technique is simple and reproducible with a high degree of accuracy, and has great potential for studies on nucleotide metabolism of blood platelets.

A methodology for the determination of the intracellular levels of free deoxyribonucleotides has been reported [34]. The analysis of free deoxyribonucleotides was carried out on a Lichrosorb-NH_2 column with a single buffer of potassium phosphate. The elution order of nucleotides was CMP, AMP, UMP, IMP, GMP, and XMP. This procedure, employing HPLC for the detection of deoxyribonucleotides in the epidermis, makes it possible to elucidate the biological characteristics and significance of DNA metabolism in normal epidermis, as well as changes which occur in pathological conditions.

Separation and quantitation of purine and pyrimidine nucleotides has been described using HPLC on a pellicular anion-exchange resin [35]. The method has been applied to extracts of cultered human lymphoid cell lines. Analyses can be carried out on 1 to 2×10^6 cells in 150 min. The soluble intracellular nucleotides appeared to increase rapidly in amount after subculture, but this was probably related more to increase in cell size than to increasing intracellular concentrations of nucleotides. No differences were found in soluble purine nucleotide levels between normal cells and cells deficient in hypoxanthine-guanine phosphoribosyltransferase. However, the enzyme-deficient cells had higher concentrations of soluble pyrimidine nucleotides, an unexpected finding. Growth of normal cells was inhibited by 5×10^{-5} or 10^{-4} mol/L guanine or guanosine. This was associated with a marked expansion of the GTP pool accompanied by marked decrease of the adenine and pyrimidine nucleotides.

A method for determining tissue pools of uridine deoxyuridine; cytidine; deoxycytidine; and thymidine mono-, di-, and triphosphates has been presented [36]. The method utilizes anion-exchange and, after conversion of nucleotides to nucleosides by acid phosphatase, HPLC on a preparative column with UV detection at 254 and 280 nm. The yield of this procedure is $80 \pm 2\%$ with a detection limit of 100 pmol nucleotide per sample. A detectability of 10 pmol can be achieved for each compound by rechromatographing appropriate nucleoside fractions on an analytical column. The recovery, including this step, is $66 \pm 7\%$. The assay is reproducible and highly selective, with a lower sensitivity limit of approximately 0.1 μmol/L using 150 to 250 mg (wet weight) tissue samples. Nucleotide pools have been determined in Balb/c mouse liver and in mouse lymphoma (S-49) cell culture, the latter with and without addition of 5-fluorouracil to the medium.

An assay for the fourteen major cellular purine ribonucleotides and 2'-deoxyribonucleotides has been presented [37]. Following an initial separation by anion-exchange HPLC, the nucleotides are hydrolyzed to their respective nucleosides by alkaline phosphatase and quantified by reversed-phase HPLC and UV-absorbance detection. The assay is reproducible, specific and has a detection limit of 10 pmol per sample. The recovery of nucleosides derived from nucleotides is 85%. Purine nucleotide pool sizes have been measured in cultured mouse T lymphoma (S-49) cells before and after treatment with 2.0 μmol/L mycophenolic acid, an inhibitor of the enzyme IMP dehydrogenase, for 3 h. Control nucleotide levels obtained by this method are consistent with those reported for S-49 cells using other methods, and the observed decrease in guanine nucleotides and increase in IMP after treatment with mycophenolic acid agree with previous reports.

9.3.2 Bases, Nucleosides and Mononucleotides Simultaneously

Pyrimidine and purine mononucleotide metabolism consists of a complex network of biochemical pathways essential to the function and reproduction of cells. Perturbation of this tightly controlled substrate pattern by genetic alterations or antimetabolite treatment leads to changes in cell function and, potentially, to cell toxicity by largely unknown mechanisms. It is clearly desirable to measure changes throughout the mononucleotide metabolism network in order to investigate the mechanisms leading to cell damage. Thus, simultaneous measurement of all of the purine and pyrimidine metabolites in cells from affected individuals may provide very important informations. Simultaneous analysis of bases, nucleosides, and nucleotides has been very difficult to achieve [38]. However, the HPLC system [39] reported to have accomplished the separation and quantitation of all of the purine bases, ribonucleosides, and ribonucleotides in a single analysis has provided very useful information for metabolic studies [40]. The capabilities of this system have been extended [41]. Separation of purine and pyrimidine bases, ribonucleosides, and ribonucleotides in a single analysis using an anion-exchange (Animex A-25) resin and requiring only 160 min has been reported. The procedure is carried out on a 1.8 × 700 mm column. The column is eluted with a linear gradient of ammonium chloride (Figure 9-7).

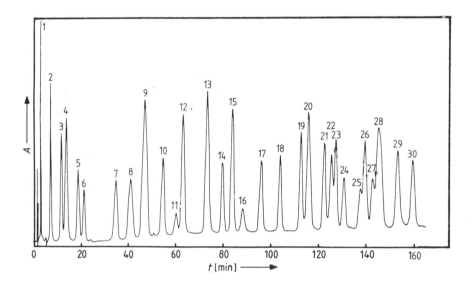

Figure 9-7. Separation of nucleobases, nucleosides and nucleotides on an Aminex A-25 column (3.2 mm o. d. x 1.8 mm i. d. x 700 mm) [41]. Mobile phase: linear gradient 70 mmol/L $Na_2B_4O_7$/45 mmol/L NH_4Cl in 2.5% ethanol (pH 9.15) − 10 mmol/L $Na_2B_4O_7$/500 mmol/L NH_4Cl (pH 8.8), with 15-min gradient; delay flow-rate, 0.5 mL/min. Elution temperature: 65 °C. Detection: 254 nm. Peak identification: 1 cytosine, 2 cytidine, 3 thymidine, 4 adenosine, 5 thymine, 6 uracil, 7 guanine, 8 adenine, 9 uridine, 10 hypoxanthine, 11 xanthine, 12 guanosine, 13 inosine, 14 cytidine 5′-monophosphate, 15 thymidine 5′-monophosphate, 16 xanthosine, 17 adenosine 5′-monophosphate, 18 uridine 5′-monophosphate, 19 cytidine 5′-diphosphate, 20 guanosine 5′-monophosphate and thymidine 5′-diphosphate, 21 inosine 5′-monophosphate, 22 adenosine 5′-diphosphate, 23 uridine 5′-diphosphate, 24 cytidine 5′-triphosphate, 25 thymidine 5′-triphosphate, 26 guanosine 5′-diphosphate, 27 uridine 5′-triphosphate, 28 adenosine 5′-triphosphate and xanthosine 5′-monophosphate, 29 guanosine 5′-triphosphate, 30 adenylosuccinate.

The potential application of this method for the quantitation of acid-soluble metabolites in fibrolasts has been described (Figure 9-8).

The advantage of the system over the many existing methods of analysis of intracellular purine and pyrimidine compounds is its capability to separate and quantitate all of the naturally existing purine and pyrimidine bases, ribonucleosides, and ribonucleotides simultaneously. This system has been applied to the study of the metabolic fate of ^{14}C-labeled purine and pyrimidine compounds. Simultaneous measurement of radioactivity in different pools provides valuable information about the functioning of metabolic pathways since the calculation of specific activities of labeled metabolites is possible. Under these elution conditions, some of the deoxy compounds are also separated from the ribose compounds.

A single-column system for the simultaneous separation of bases, nucleosides and nucleoside mono- and polyphosphates has been developed [42], in which a strong porous anion-exchange resin (Animex A-14) is used. The chromatographic run, carried out at 55 °C and at alkaline pH by using a linear gradient both of ionic strength and pH, takes 225 min. The quantitative application of the described procedure to the analysis of cell nucleotide pools has been reported.

A simultaneous analysis of ATP, ADP, AMP and other purines in human erythrocytes has been reported [43]. The method is fast and reliable for estimating adenine ribonucleotide concentration in erythrocytes and could be applied to many enzyme assays involving purine constituents.

An HPLC method [44] has been developed which is capable of detecting 1.0 to 5.0 ng of components and requires about 30 min for a complete chromatographic separation of ribo-nucleosides from deoxyribonucleosides and from bases. These separations were carried out under different pH-values and buffers, namely, phosphate buffer containing 2.5% methanol at pH 6.9 and 3.0 or 50 mmol/L sodium borate buffer, pH 9.0. These different conditions were utilized to obtain more definitive identification and quantitation of normal metabolites and their counterparts, the antimetabolites. Twenty naturally occuring components are separated from each other by an isocratic elution method, alleviating the need for a gradient elution system, which produces a drift in the baseline with increasing concentration of the eluting buffer. The drift especially occurs when the instrument is operating at maximum sensitivity, thus hindering the quantitation of the separated components. The potential application of this method to the quantitation of plasma metabolites and antimetabolites such as 1-β-D-arabino-furanosylcytosine; arabinofuranosyluracil and fluoro-pyrimidine has been described [44]. This method can be utilized for plasma analysis directly without concentration and reconstitution, thus speeding the analysis and eliminating losses and possible breakdown of components during concentration. The presence of endogenous contaminating components does not affect the separation, identification, and quantitation of metabolites found in plasma. Columns are stable and can be used for several months without any detectable changes in their quality of separation. Conditions were outlined where minimum or no interference of normal metabolites with the separation and quantitation of pyrimidine antimetabolites can be obtained.

As nucleosides and bases have been found in detectable concentrations in human serum, it was felt that serum might serve as a useful physiological fluid in which to examine the overall nucleoside and base profiles and to study alterations of these profiles during neoplastic and other disease states. As a first step in this long-range goal of studying alterations in serum nucleoside and base profiles in patients with cancer, it was necessary to determine the compounds which are found in normal serum, as well as variations in these profiles due to sex, age, diet, etc. In addition, it was necessary to study effects of sample preparation and handling on the stability of these compounds. Only after these initial studies were done could the sera of patients with various types of malignant and non-malignant diseases be studied and the sera

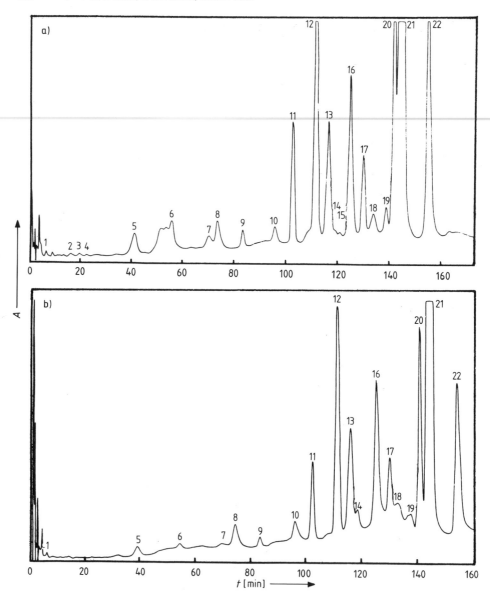

Figure 9-8. Separation of acid-soluble purine and pyrimidine metabolites in fibroblasts of normal subject (a) and of hypoxanthine phosphoribosyl transferase − deficient subject (b) on an Aminex A-25 column. Chromatographic conditions same as in Figure 9-7 [41]. Peak identification: 1 cytidine, 2 adenosine, 3 thymine, 4 uracil, 5 adenine, 6 hypoxanthine, 7 nicotinamide adenine dinucleotide, 8 inosine, 9 cytidine 5′-monophosphate, 10 adenosine 5′-monophosphate, 11 uridine 5′-monophosphate, 12 nicotinamide adenine dinucleotide phosphate, 13 uridine diphosphate galactose and cytidine 5′-diphosphate, 14 guanosine 5′-monophosphate, 15 inosine 5′-monophosphate, 16 adenosine 5′-diphosphate, 17 uridine 5′-diphosphate, 18 cytidine 5′-triphosphate, 19 guanosine 5′-diphosphate, 20 uridine 5′-triphosphate, 21 adenosine 5′-triphosphate, 22 guanosine 5′-triphosphate.

from healthy subjects be compared with those with disease states. Reversed-phase HPLC was used to investigate the profiles of low-molecular-weight, UV-absorbing compounds in human serum [45]. Identification techniques were described which allow for the identification of picomolar amounts of the nucleosides, bases and other compounds in several microliters of serum ultrafiltrate. The sera from 31 normal subjects (17 males, 14 females) showed very consistent profiles. A total of 12 compounds were identified and quantified in normal serum. The analysis of sera from over 150 patients with various types of neoplasia and other diseases showed serum profiles significantly different from normal profiles.

A rapid procedure for the isolation, separation identification and measurement of urinary pyrimidine bases and nucleosides by HPLC has been reported [46]. The initial isolation of these compounds from urine was accomplished with small, disposable ion-exchange columns. HPLC was performed on a silica gel column with a mobile phase composed of methylene chloride, methanol and 1 mol/L aqueous ammonium formiate buffer. Peaks were recorded at both 254 nm and 280 nm and the response ratio was used in conjunction with the elution volume for compound identification. The minimum detectable amount ranged from 0.2 ng for uracil to 2.2 ng for cytidine. Linearity and recovery for thymine, uracil, uridine, pseudouridine, oratic acid and orotine added to urine was demonstrated over almost a 10^3 concentration range. The potential of the application of this method to the study of inborn errors in the urea cycle is discussed.

Data on the application of a reversed-phase HPLC to the analysis of nucleosides and bases in human plasma have been presented [47]. An initial HPLC separation allowed the collection of a number of effluent fractions, each of which contained a single component of interest. The re-application of these fractions to a second HPLC separation permitted the resolution and quantification of nanogram amounts of these components. Isocratic elution with volatile buffers renders the samples amenable to a automatic sampling procedure or lyophilization.

9.3.3 Modified Constituents of DNA and RNA

The covalent binding of mutagenic and carcinogenic alkylating agents with DNA is considered a critical event in the mechanism of action of these agents. Alkylating agents can substitute at fifteen possible nucleophilic base sites, and at the phosphodiester backbone in DNA. Several studies have indicated that only certain DNA alkylation products contribute to the mutagenic or carcinogenic activity of these agents. For instance, it has been found that O^6-alkylguanines are quantitatively associated with carcinogenesis or mutagenesis, whereas the 7-alkylguanines do not appear to be involved in these processes. Much less is known about the other DNA alkylation products, especially the recently discovered O-alkylpyrimidines. This is partly due to the lack of efficient routine methods for the degradation and subsequent fractionation of alkylated DNA. Recent work with HPLC [48 – 51] showed that some of the base alkylation products and phosphotriesters could be separated and that this method could be successfully applied to the analysis of DNA hydrolysates (Figure 9-9).

Reproducible and quantitative methods of analysis for all the known methylated or ethylated products in a single DNA sample have been described [52]. The chemical and enzymatic digests

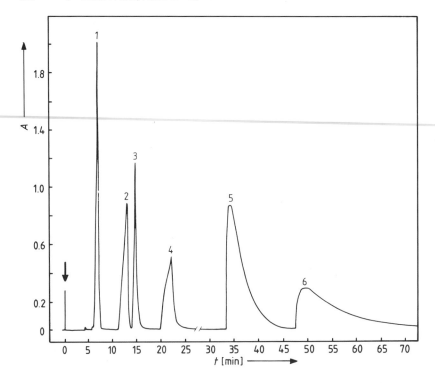

Figure 9-9. Separation of purines on a Partisil 10 SCX column (250 x 6.4 mm i. d.) [51]. Mobile phase: 30 mmol/L NH$_2$H$_4$PO$_4$ (pH 4.6). Elution temperature: 25 °C. Flow-rate: 1.2 mL/min, 925 psi for the first 27 minutes then increased (break in the tracing) to 2.1 mL/min, 1575 psi after break. Detection: 254 nm. Peak identification: 1 guanine, 2 7-methylguanine, 3 adenine, 4 O^6-methylguanine, 5 1-methyladenine, 6 3-methyladenine.

were fractionated by a combination of HPLC systems to yield quantitative estimates of the following products from methylated or ethylated DNA: 1-, 3-, and 7-alkyladenines, O^2-alkyl-cytosines, 3-, O^6-, and 7-alkylguanines and O^2-, 3-, and O^4-alkylthymines. N^6-alkyladenines, 1-alkylguanines and N^2-alkylguanines were not detected and the 3-alkylcytosines were detected but not quantified. Phosphotriesters were estimated from the amounts of recovered alkyl phosphotriesters of thymidylyl (3′– 5′) thymidine. Using these methods, it was possible to account for 98, 81, 98, and 92% of DNA bound alkyl groups obtained from DNA reacted with [^{14}C] methyl methanesulfonate, [^{3}H] ethyl methanesulfonate, N-[^{3}H]-methyl-N-nitrosourea, and N-[^{14}C] ethyl-N-nitrosourea, respectively.

Most DNA molecules contain minor amounts of bases which are methylated after DNA replication. In procaryotes and some non-vertebrate eucaryotes, 5-methylcytosine and/or N^6-methyladenine are present as minor bases. In all examined DNAs from vertebrates or higher plants, 5-methylcytosine is present as the only minor base. These minor bases may comprise less than 0.05 mol percent of the bases in some insect and bacterial DNAs or as much as 7 mol percent of the bases in higher plant DNAs.

Typically, mammalian DNA has 0.5 to 1.5 mol percent 5-methylcytosine. Several different analytical techniques, for example, reversed-phase [9] or paired ion reversed-phase HPLC [53] have been used in the determination of the major, minor or total base composition of DNAs. A method which offers good sensitivity, selectivity, precision and accuracy for the determination of all six deoxyribonucleosides without the use of harsh hydrolysis conditions, large DNA samples, difficult sample preparation procedures or *in vivo* labeling of DNA has been described [54]. This method should be a useful research tool in studies on various DNAs and DNA subfractions and should help to elucidate the functions of methylation of DNA. The DNA samples were quantitatively hydrolyzed with DNase 1, nuclease P 1, and bacterial alkaline phosphatase. The resulting deoxyribonucleosides were directly separated within 70 min by reversed-phase HPLC with detection by ultraviolet absorption at 254 nm and 280 nm. The highly sensitive and selective dual wavelength quantitation greatly enchances the precision and accuracy of the chromatographic analysis. Contamination of DNA preparations with RNA does not interfere with the DNA analysis due to the high resolution of the chromatography. The quantitation of 5-methylcytosine in 5 μg of calf thymus and salmon sperm DNA in which the 5-methylcytosine comprises only 1 to 2% of the total bases has been described.

Reversed-phase and reversed-phase ion-pair chromatographic methods have been used to determine 5-alkyluracil in the presence of purine bases (mainly adenine) in the hydrolysates of enzymatically synthesized DNA [55]. The effect of ionic strength, pH, concentration of the ion-pairing agent and methanol on the selectivity between alkyluracil and purine bases was examined in order to simplify the routine work and reduce the time neccessary for analysis. Optimal conditions were developed for the isocratic separation of the various mixtures obtained by hydrolysis of the products of enzymatic synthesis.

The chromatographic parameters affecting the reversed-phase HPLC separation of major and modified nucleosides with a Bondapak C_{18} column have been studied [56]. This investigation has resulted in the separation of eighteen nucleosides in a single analysis. The studied parameters include: mobile phase flow-rate, pH, methanol concentration, column temperature and injection volume. Each parameter was investigated individually to observe the effect on the chromatographic behavior of the nucleosides. The relationships which have been established for the elution of the nucleosides as a function of the investigated parameters can be used to predict separation. From these experiments, the chromatographic conditions for the separation of urinary nucleosides were optimized using both isocratic and step gradient conditions. The step gradient system is more suitable for determining the nucleoside compositions of tRNA hydrolysates, and permits complete separation of the major ribo- and deoxyribonucleosides. A very significant aspect of this research is the determination of the effects of various chromatographic parameters on the reversed-phase HPLC separation of the nucleosides. These findings provide great flexibility in the analysis of nucleosides in that they provide a guide for finding optimal conditions for nucleoside separations. This chromatography is of importance in the accurate determination of tRNA composition, especially for scientists investigating tRNA biosynthesis, function and sequence, also for investigations on the purity of RNA and DNA isolations, and research on DNA and its modification.

An analytical method has been presented for the quantitative determination of certain major and modified bases in unfractionated rat liver tRNA [57]. tRNA was hydrolyzed with perchloric acid and the liberated bases were separated by HPLC. Bases were selectively detected in tRNA hydrolysates at wavelengths near their UV-absorption maxima. Recovery values for individual bases generally were in the 80 to 100% range. The composition of rat liver tRNA with respect to

10 bases was determined, and the levels of these bases were in agreement with published values determined by other methods.

An analytical method that can readily be placed in operation, and which is particularly well suited to scientists investigating tRNA structure, biosynthesis, and function, and for the determination of major and modified nucleosides of tRNA has been reported [58]. The method is characterized by the following features: sensitivity at the nanogram level, high chromatographic resolution and selectivity, direct measurement of nucleosides with accuracy and precision. Analysis is nondestructive and the high capacity of this chromatographic system allows easy isolation of pure nucleosides for further characterization, rapid separation and measurement within ca. 1 h after hydrolysis to nucleosides, and quantitation without use of radiolabeled compounds, however, labeled compounds are readily isolated and measured.

A quantitative analysis of the incorporation of stable isotopes into nucleic acids for verification of the site and determination of the abundance of the label has been presented [59]. HPLC and mass spectrometry of nucleic acids and bases were used for quantitation of isotopic enrichment, with only µg amounts of available RNA. Conditions for acid hydrolysis of tRNA were optimized for quantitative yield of bases without destruction, and optimum conditions for the HPLC separation of the bases were determined. Three tRNA preparations, [^{13}C-] enriched *in vivo* by incorporation of [^{13}C$_2$-]adenine, [^{13}C$_2$]uracil and [^{13}C]methyl groups from methionine, were subjected to these procedures, followed by mass spectrometry of the bases. In natural abundance, ^{13}C is 1.08 atom%; in these tRNA preparations 27% of all adenine was labeled at position 2 with ^{13}C atoms; 43 atom% ^{13}C at position 2 of uracil and 45 atom% ^{13}C at position 2 of cytosine; and 56.9 atom% ^{13}C at the methyl of thymine, respectively. The reported techniques are important to the study of nucleic acid biosynthesis, modification and structure using nuclear magnetic resonance spectroscopy.

The naturally occuring modified nucleoside 3-[3-amino-3-carboxypropyl]-1-methylpseudouridine (am ψ) is found in eukaryotic 18 S rRNA. Am ψ was localized to sequence resolution in *D. melanogaster* 18 S rRNA. This hypermodified base causes an absolute stop in cDNA elongation. The RNA sequence bearing am ψ was determined by dideoxysequencing with reverse transcriptase, and the cDNA coding for this part of the 18 S rRNA was sequenced by the Maxam-Gilbert method. Together these 2 methods can be used to position the cDNA stop (am ψ) in the rRNA sequence. Chemical evidence for the existence of am ψ in this RNA sequence was obtained by HPLC of 18 S rRNA nucleosides from radioactive-labeled cells [60]. L 2-[^{14}C] methionine will selectively label am ψ in eukaryotic 18 S rRNA. Using HPLC, a single ^{14}C-labeled nucleotide was found in digests of 18 S rRNA. This nucleotide is in the RNA sequence bearing the cDNA stop since a restriction fragment which hybridizes to this sequence protects the modified base from RNase T 1 digestion.

9.3.4 Cytosine Arabinose and Metabolites

Information about drug levels, tissue distribution, and the persistence of drug metabolites in biological samples can be used to monitor drug effects at both the clinical and experimental level. Such information would allow drug dose adjustments to be made to accommodate inter- and intra-patient variation. 1-β-D-arabinofuranosylcytosine (Ara-C) is a pyrimidine nucleoside analog which is currently a component of several therapeutic drug combination protocols. It is metabolized to an active metabolite, Ara-C triphosphate (Ara-CTP) and to an inactive compound, 1-β-D-uracil arabinoside (Ara-U). HPLC offers a rapid method to monitor levels of Ara-C and metabolites in tissues. However, chromatographic analysis of arabinose-nucleoside analogues in biological samples is complicated by interference of naturally occuring nucleosides and nucleotides. Therefore, in the past it has been necessary to use radioactively-labeled Ara-C, chromatography, and subsequent liquid scintillation counting to separate and quantitate drug levels in biological samples. These techniques tend to be time-consuming and the expense and radioactivity of radiolabeled Ara-C limits their usefulness in obtaining pharmacokinetic information in animals and patients. Two HPLC methods have been developed [61] to separate and quantitate Ara-C and its metabolites in biological tissues. One method utilizes a quaternary ammonium anion-exchange resin (Aminex) to isocratically separate arabinose-containing analogues from all other interfering compounds. The second method utilizes a boronate-functionalized polyacrylamide resin to selectively retain cytosine, uridine and other cis-diols, while the arabinose-containing analogues are eluted. The eluted compounds are then easily quantitated on a reversed-phase C_{18} column. These methods were used to measure drug levels in mouse serum and urine and in tumor cells. Both separation methods are isocratic, thereby avoiding the drift in baseline observed with gradient elution, and can detect nanogram quantities of Ara-C and its metabolites. The anion-exchange resins (A-27 and A-29) were used to quantitate Ara-C, Ara-U and Ara-CTP levels directly from biological tissues in less than 40 min. Ara-C and Ara-U were also quantitated on a reversed-phase C_{18} column after pretreatment of samples with a boronate affinity gel. The use of the C_{18} column for drug quantitation offers the advantages of speed (Ara-C and Ara-U are eluted in approximately 20 min), less expense, greater sensitivity and is more common in clinical laboratories than the ion-exchange resin.

An HPLC method for the determination of the antineoplastic agent cytarabine and its main metabolite uracil arabinoside in human plasma and cerebrospinal fluid has been described [62]. Complete separation from endogenous constituents was achieved by isocratic reversed-phase chromatography using phosphate buffer (0.05 mol/L, pH 7.0) as the eluent. The limit of detection was 50 ng/mL. Day-to-day coefficients of variation were below 10%. The applicability of this rapid, simple and specific method for pharmacokinetic studies and monitoring of therapy was demonstrated.

9.3.5 Modified Adenine Nucleosides

A rapid, sensitive, and specific HPLC method for the estimation of 5'-methylthioadenosine in biological samples has been developed [63]. A doublestep chromatography on Dowex-50, (H^+ form) and boric acid gel was required before chromatographic separation of the sample on Partisil 10 SCX. The yield is quantitative and the procedure is simple and highly reproducible.

Identification of the naturally occuring modified adenine nucleosides (and 3'-O-methyladenosine) by HPLC which has been optimized for the separation of most nucleosides has been reported [64]. The basis for this identification is the enzyme peak shift in which the retention times of both the sample and of the N^6-deaminated product are determined, after incubation with adenosine deaminase.

9.3.6 5-Fluorouracil and 5-Fluoro-2'-deoxyuridine

The biochemical importance of 5-fluorouracil and its nucleosides and nucleotides has been reviewed [65]. Reversed-phase liquid chromatography is used for the separation of 5-fluorouracil, its deoxyribo- and ribonucleosides and nucleotides [66]. The bases and nucleosides are easily separated from their naturally occurring analogues on an octadecyl silica column eluted with $2 \cdot 10^{-2}$ mol/L KH_2PO_4 (pH 5.0) containing 5% (v/v) methanol. This system can be applied to the measurement of 5-fluoro-2'-deoxyuridine serum levels down to 0.1 µg/mL. Addition of small amounts (10^{-3} mol/L) of tetrabutylammonium phosphate to the eluant results in a large retention increase for the nucleotides, while the capacity ratios of the bases and nucleosides remain unchanged. The influence of the tetrabutylammonium phosphate and ammonium phosphate concentrations and pH of the eluant was investigated. Evidence is presented indicating that the quaternary ammonium compound is absorbed into the octadecyl silica surface; nucleotides are probably retained as adsorbed tetrabutylammonium ion-pairs.

Plasma 5-fluorouracil concentration in the micromolar and above range have been monitored using HPLC [67 to 71]. Although these assays represent a considerable improvement in terms of sensitivity and/or specificity over previously published microbiologic and gas chromatographic assays they are of limited use in pharmacokinetic studies in which 5-fluorouracil is administered by: continuous intravenous infusion, intraarterial hepatic infusion, or peritoneal dialysis. In such cases, precise drug monitoring in the 0.1 to 1.0 mol/L range is necessary.

An HPLC method which is capable of measuring 5-fluorouracil and 5-fluorodeoxyuridine at concentration of 50 nmol/L in human plasma has been presented [72]. The method employs tritium-labeled 5-fluorouracil and 5-fluorodeoxyuridine as internal standards. The fluoropyrimidines are removed from plasma by anion-exchange chromatography and are extracted into ethyl acetate. The ethyl acetate is evaporated to dryness and 5-fluorouracil and 5-fluorodeoxyuridine are chromatographed on a semipreparative µBondapak C_{18} column. The method is specific and sufficiently sensitive to measure levels of 5-fluorouracil in plasma below 1 µmol/L, such as may occur after intrahepatic or intraperitoneal drug administration.

9.4 Separation of Oligo- and Polynucleotides

9.4.1 Oligonucleotides

Trinucleoside diphosphates are valuable probes of protein biosynthesis. They have been used to decipher the genetic code, to probe the secondary structures of tRNA and of 5 S rRNA and to probe the specificity of oligonucleotide binding to the translational initiation factor IF 3. They have been synthesized enzymatically and traditionally isolated by anion-exchange chromatography. The isolation procedure usually requires an overnight elution with a salt concentration gradient followed by another day of manipulations to remove the salt. A method has been developed to simplify and shorten the amount of time required in the isolation procedure by the application of deproteinized reaction mixtures to an octadecylsilyl porous silica microsphere column, as well as elution with a gradient of increasing methanol concentration [73]. Application of this technique allows separation of all 16 nucleoside monophosphates from each other, and from trinucleoside diphosphates and synthesis byproducts.

Oligoadenylates can be analyzed according to the type of 3'terminus (A_nA, A_nA_p and $A_nA > p$, oligoadenylates that do not have phosphate at the 3'-terminus, 2' (3')-monophosphate, and a 2', 3'-cyclic phosphate, respectively) using HPLC with RPC 5 support and novel dual column technique [74]. The first column separates A_nA_p plus $A_nA > p$ from A_nA, and at the start of the second column a layer of bacterial alkaline phosphatase enzyme converts the A_nAp into A_nA. Hence, A_nA emerges separately from the original A_nA and from the $A_nA > p$. The technique can be used to analyze a 3-component mixture for a single chain length or a mixture of A_nAp and $A_nA > p$ of mixed chain lengths (n = 3 to 7). The presence of poly(U) does interfere with the analysis.

LiChrosorb RP-8, RP-18 and Diol, as well as a newly synthesized basic dimethylamino-modified silica ion-exchanger (DMA-silica), were applied to the separation of adenylic acid, cytidylic acid and uridylic acid oligoribonucleotides [75]. Using LiChrosorb RP-8 and RP-18, respectively, in aqueous buffered eluents (K_2HPO_4/H_3PO_4), the retention of oligonucleotides was increased with decreasing number of nucleotide units in the solute, i. e., with increasing hydrophobic character. The elution behavior of oligonucleotides on LiChrosorb Diol followed the same order but occurred according to a size-exclusion mechanism. The retention of oligonucleotides on DMA-silica is assumed to be based on electrostatic interactions between the charged solutes and the ionic surface sites of DMA. The relative contribution of ionic and molecular interactions to total retention of the solutes was discussed.

A rapid and highly reproducible chromatographic technique has been developed for analysis and purification of complex mixtures of oligoribonucleotides [76]. The method utilizes a column of microparticulate porous silica beads fully functionalized with octadecylsilyl groups. The column is eluted with gradients in acetonitrile/water/ammonium acetate. Most separations are completed in 5 to 15 min with usually better than 1% reproducibility of absolute retention times and about 0.1% reproducibility of relative retention times. A single column accomplishes separations of mononucleosides, mononucleotides, and larger oligomers up to at least 20-mers. The absolute detection limit is ~ 1 pmol of base, though most of the analytical separations described use ~ 1 nmol. In favourable circumstances it is possible to use the analytical columns to purify ~ 1 mg of an oligonucleotide in a single 10 to 30 min elution.

9.4.2 Sequence Isomeric Oligonucleotides

Small oligonucleotides from DNA and RNA have been separated according to their base composition by anion-exchange HPLC on Partisil-10 SAX using triethylammonium acetate buffer as the eluent [77]. Fifteen of the 16 possible deoxydinucleoside monophosphates (Figure 9-10) and all 16 dinucleoside monophosphates have been separated (Figure 9-11).

All pairs of sequence isomers were well resolved. The commercially available deoxydinucleotides were resolved into 13 fractions. A good resolution of deoxytrinucleoside diphosphates isolate from an alkaline phosphatase-Mg^{2+}-activated DNase I digest of calf thymus DNA was achieved using this technique (Figure 9-12).

A large number of sequence isomers were fully separated. The base sequence of the eluted individual constituents was determined by their hydrolysis with snake venom and spleen

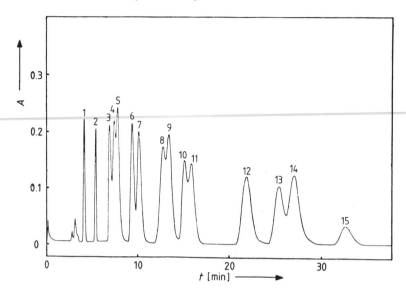

Figure 9-10. Separation of deoxyribodinucleoside monophosphates on a Partisil-10 SAX column (500 × 3 mm i.d.) [77]. Mobile phase: 10 mmol/L triethylammonium acetate (pH 3.1). Elution temperature: 60 °C. Detection: 260 nm. Peak identification: 1 (dC)$_2$, 2 d(A-C), 3 d(T − C), 4 d(C − T), 5 d(G − C), 6 d(C − G), 7 (dA)$_2$, 8 d(T − A), 9 d(A − T), 10 d(G − A), 11 d(A − G), 12 (dT)$_2$, 13 d(G − T), 14 d(T − G), 15 (dG)$_2$.

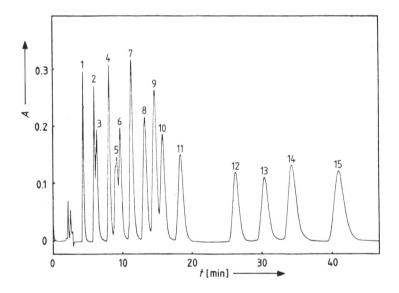

Figure 9-11. Separation of dinucleoside monophosphates. Chromatographic conditions are the same as in Figure 9-10 [77]. Peak identification: 1 (C)$_2$, 2 A − C, 3 C − A, 4 U − C, 5 C − U and (A)$_2$, 6 G − C, 7 C − G, 8 U − A, 9 A − U, 10 G − A, 11 A − G, 12 (U)$_2$, 13 G − U, 14 U − G, 15 (G)$_2$.

Figure 9-12. Separation of trinucleoside diphosphates isolated from an alkaline phosphatase-pancreatic RNase digest of yeast RNA on a Partisil-10 SAX column (500 × 3 mm i. d.) [77]. Mobile phase: linear gradient of 30 mmol/L (pH 3.1) to 400 mmol/L (pH 3.4) triethylammonium acetate; duration of gradient elution, 80 min. Elution temperature: 60 °C. Detection: 260 nm. Peak identification: 1 A−A−C, 2 G−A−C, 3 A−G−C, 4 A−A−U, 5 G−G−C, 6 G−A−U, 7 A−G−U, 8 G−G−U.

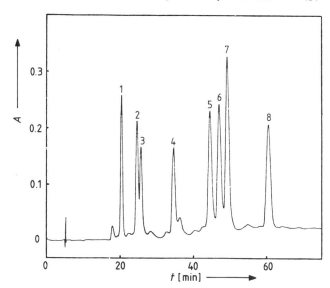

phosphodiesterase followed by HPLC analysis of the released nucleotides. The eight trinucleoside diphosphates isolated from an alkaline phosphatase pancreatic RNase digest of RNA have also been separated according to base compositions. Their sequence was determined as above. The described technique is fast and yields very good separations. Most of the sequence isomers were separated. Moreover, the eluant triethylammonium acetate can easily be removed from column effluents by freezedrying, which facilitates subsequent sequence analysis of the eluted compounds. The observed elution orders of the sequence isomers obey certain rules which are discussed in detail.

Short DNA fragments of defined sequence, the application of which is particularly widespread in gene technology, are generally only obtainable from complicated synthesis. The following alternative route has yielded 150 defined DNA fragments [78, 79]. Chemical partial hydrolysis of readily available DNA initially yields either mixtures of homologous oligonucleotides, or pyrimidine or purine oligonucleotide mixtures, in preparative amounts. Known chromatographic methods (ion-exchange, paper- and template chromatography) are combined in a separation route to fractionate the highly complex partial hydrolysates into mixtures of determinable composition [80 to 82]. Subsequent HPLC on reversed-phase yields DNA fragments of defined sequence from the preseparated mixtures [83, 84]. Generally a volatile two-component buffer: A $\triangleq$ 0.1 mol/L ammonium acetate (pH 7.5); B $\triangleq$ 60% methanol, 40% water is used for separation. When using Nucleosil 7.5 μ C_{18}, for example, one run (ca. 20 min) on an analytic HPLC column (0.46 × 11.2 cm) yields the respective DNA fragments in quantities (0.5 to 3.0 A_{260} units) which normally suffice in enzymatic synthesis of gene fragments. Identification and characterization of the desired peak products is substantially complicated by the appearance of numerous, often equivocal peaks when fractioning oligonucleotide mixtures. Homochromatography and fingerprint method, however, permit unequivocal determination of the purity and sequence of the peak products. The oligonucleotides obtainable from this method satisfy all demands currently placed on synthetic DNA fragments. This method is limited to DNA fragments of given sequence; however, this approach is much easier to perform than chemical synthesis.

9.4.3 DNA-Restriction-Fragments

HPLC (RPC-5) was used at pH 12 for preparative separation of the complementary strands of the smaller DNA fragments which are generated by the Hae III restriction endonuclease [85].

The properties of the fractionated Hae III fragments of pRZ2 DNA were studied in an effort to determine why several of the fragments bind more tightly to RPC-5 than expected on the basis of their length [86]. The purified fragments were analyzed for their nucleotide composition by direct determination of their constituent mononucleotides and by analytical CsCl and Cs_2SO_4 density gradient analysis. A-T-rich fragments elute at higher salt concentrations than fragments of equivalent size which are not A-T-rich. In addition, denaturation mapping studies by electron microscopy indicate that an A-T-rich run with an otherwise G-C-rich fragment can give rise to delayed elution. At least one other factor influences the separation of DNA restriction fragments by RPC-5 chromatography. Some of the fragments in this digest, which elute later than predicted from their size, either contain known genetic regulatory sites or bind regulatory proteins.

Uncoated Kel-F powder offers some unique features as a support for reversed-phase HPLC of oligonucleotides and DNA restriction fragments [87]. Compounds are eluted from the column by a gradient of acetonitrile (0 to 18% v/v) in 0.1 mol/L aqueous triethylammonium acetate. In contrast to RPC-5 chromatography, oligonucleotides are not eluted by aqueous salt solutions alone, and the separation of restriction fragments depends only on the chain length. The packing material is cheap, easy to pack, chemically inert, and does not bleed, so that separations are highly reproducible. The DNA loading capacity for Kel-F is presently inferior to RPC-5, but recovery of µg amounts of material is typically better than 50%.

9.4.4 RNA Fragments

The 3'-terminal fragments of *E.coli* 16S rRNA was isolated and subsequently purified by electrophoresis on 15% polyacrylamide gels containing 0.1% SDS and on a Permaphase AAX anion-exchange column, which permits fractionation in the range from mononucleotides up to polynucleotides of ~ 80 nucleotides in length [88]. Using HPLC, the RNA fragment in the low/ molecular weight range was analyzed by treatment with snake venom phosphodiesterase and separation of the digestion products on the column. The 4 common ribonucleosides-5'-phosphates were identified by their retention times, and the relative amounts corresponded well with the total base composition of the fragment. HPLC analysis of the products obtained after RNase T 1 treatment of the 49-nucleotide fragment yielded the expected set of oligonucleotides. The UV spectrum and melting curve of the purified fragment were also obtained. The rapid analysis of modified tRNA[Phe] from yeast by HPLC of oligonucleotides after RNase T 1 digestion on aminopropylsilica and assignment of fragments based on nucleoside analysis by chromatography on C_{18}-silica has been reported [89].

9.4.5 t-RNA

Solid beads of polychlorotrifluoroethylene have been coated with phenyl boronates. This material permits the separation of mammalian and bacterial aminoacyl-tRNAs from uncharged tRNAs and O-methyl nucleosides from ribose-unsubstituted nucleosides in one chromatographic step, as the substituted members of each group do not undergo boronate complex formation and are thus not as much retarded in passing through the column. Complex formation between ribofuranoses and the boronate matrix appears to be enhanced by the hydrophobic "tail" of the boronate compound, by the high ionic environment of the solvent, and by the hydrophobic nature of the inert support. This method of one-step purification of tRNAs on reversed-phase boronate columns has been tested for several tRNAs specific for amino acids of different hydrophobicity and ionic character. The results indicate that each tRNA tested can be purified with appreciable purity (70 to 95%) and high yield (80%). However, recovery of the queuine base containing aminoacyl-tRNAs is only about 6% of the applied material.

A rapid separation of tRNA isoacceptor species has been described using HPLC of tRNA samples on RPC-5 resin [90]. The technique is shown to be highly reproducible. A minimum of 8000 counts in the sample is necessary for analysis in a flow cell counting device, although less radioactive samples can be counted in a liquid scintillation counter. The technique was proposed for the analysis of changes in tRNA complements from differentiating cells or cells that have been grown under different conditions.

9.4.6 Sequence Analyses of Oligonucleotides and RNA

A simple procedure for the sequential analysis of small oligonucleotides has been reported [91]. The method is based on the simultaneous identification and quantitation of monomers released by snake venom phosphodiesterase digestion of oligonucleotides using anion-exchange chromatography on Permaphase AAX or a reversed-phase RPC-5 column [92]. In this way, the correct sequence of 5 oligomers, e. g. r(ACCUCC), r(CUGUU), r(AGGA), d(ATTACC) and d(GGAAT) was easily and unambiguously established [91].

The rapid automated sequence analysis of a synthetic deoxydecanucleotide d(TATCAAGTTG) has been described. The method is based on HPLC in combination with venom phosphodiesterase action [93].

Conditions of HPLC on columns of AS-Pellionex SAX and AL-Pellionex WAX have been investigated to attain a good separation, clearcut identification, and accurate quantification of ribonucleosides, and mono- and oligoribonucleotides produced by digestions of polyribonucleotides with several ribonucleases [94]. The RNase digests of 5S rRNA are usually resolved into about fifteen peaks. Most peaks consisted of single oligonucleotides, but several others contain two or more components. Hence, a rapid UV-scanner was connected to the HPLC apparatus to identify such coeluted materials in terms of both the times of retention on the columns and the UV-spectra. This method permitted determination of the sequences of various oligonucleotides obtained by complete and partial RNase digestions of trout liver 5S tRNA. Although this HPLC method requires a larger amount of RNA and takes more time than gel-electrophoresis methods devised for isotope-labeled RNA, it has several advantages. This method requires only about one-twentieth of the amount of time and material compared with conventional chromatographic methods, and permits the identification of modified nucleotides from their UV-spectra, which the gel-electrophoresis methods do not. It should be particularly useful in institutions where facilities for radioisotope experiments are lacking or limited.

9.5 Application in Polynucleotide Synthesis

HPLC has been developed as a rapid and efficient method for the separation of synthetic oligonucleotides which are standard intermediates in the stepwise or blockwise synthesis of polynucleotides. The methods lend themselves to separations on a preparative scale and effect a marked reduction in the time required for the synthesis of DNA or RNA fragments. The chemical synthesis of oligodeoxyribonucleotides requires the preparation of completely protected fragments followed by the liberation of the amine functions of the nucleobases, the internucleotidic phosphates and the terminal hydroxy groups of the chain. This deprotection is usually followed by purification of the oligomer obtained by HPLC. The employed support can be an ion-exchanger and/or a reversed-phase matrix (Figure 9-13, Figure 9-14, Figure 9-15). Extensive studies of the influence of the different purine and pyrimidine bases, of protecting groups, of the phosphate groups, and of the chain lengths of oligonucleotides on their retention on such columns are reported [95 to 114].

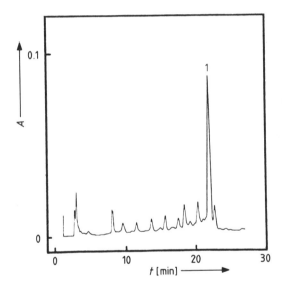

Figure 9-13. Separation of an oligodeoxyribonucleotide mixture containing the synthetic decamer d(C – C – G – A – T – A – T – C – G – G) (Peak 1) on a Partisil SAX column (250 x 4.6 mm i. d.) [116]. Mobile phase: Solvent A: 1 mmol/L KH_2PO_4 (pH 6.3) in formamide: H_2O (60:40, v/v); solvent B: 300 mmol/L KH_2PO_4 (pH 6.3) in formamide: H_2O (60:40, v/v); gradient 0 to 75% solvent B, 40 min; flow-rate 2 mL/min. Elution temperature: 45 °C. Detection: 280 nm.

Reversed-phase chromatography gives good results but this method presents certain problems when employed alone, as it is difficult to predict the elution properties of a given oligomer with respect to the other products in the mixture to be separated, and no information is afforded on the chain length of the purified oligomer. The I-125 Protein Analysis Column (Water Assoc.) a size-exclusion column has been proposed as a new support particularly adapted to separate synthetic oligonucleotides [115]. The influence of the pH and molar concentration of the mobile phase on the resolution of the column has been studied. Volatile buffers such as aqueous triethylammonium acetate yield good and rapid purifications of fully deprotected synthetic oligonucleotides.

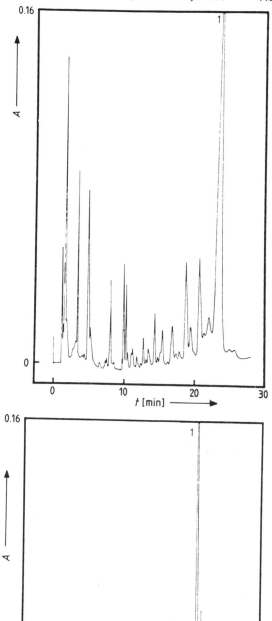

Figure 9-14. Separation of the mixture of Figure 9-13 on a Zorbax-NH$_2$ column (250 x 4.6 mm i. d.) [116]. Mobile phase: Solvent A: 10 mmol/L KH$_2$PO$_4$ (pH 4.5); solvent B: 900 mmol/L KH$_2$PO$_4$ (pH 4.5); gradient 0 to 50% solvent B, 50 min; flow-rate 2 mL/min. Elution temperature: 60 °C. Detection: 280 nm.

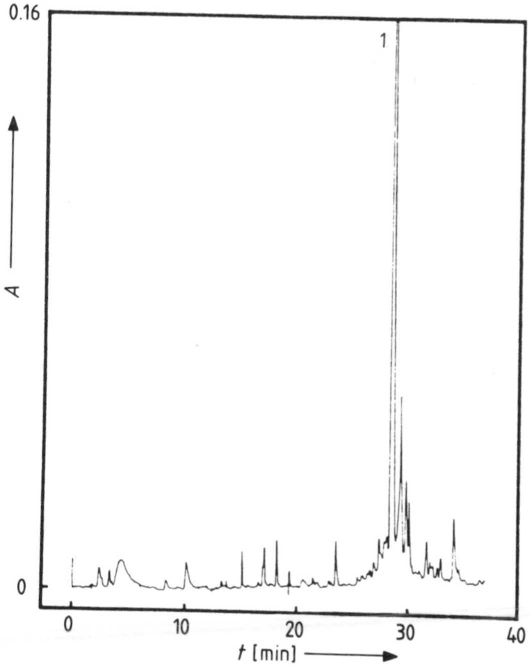

Figure 9-15. Separation of the mixture of Figure 9-13 on a Zorbax-ODS column (250 x 4.6 mm i. d.) [116]. Mobile phase: Solvent A: 10 mmol/L triethyl-ammonium acetate (pH 7.0); solvent B: 60% acetonitrile in 10 mmol/L triethylammonium acetate (pH 7.0); gradient 0 to 30% solvent B, 60 min; flow-rate 2 mL/min. Elution temperature: 45 °C. Detection: 280 nm.

9.6 References

[1]   D. R. Gere, in: J. J. Kirkland (ed.): *Modern Practice of Liquid Chromatography*, pp. 417. Wiley, New York 1971.

[2]   R. A. Holton, D. M. Spatz, E. E. van Tamelen, and W. Wierenga, *Biochem. Biophys. Res. Commun.* **58**, 605 (1974).

[3]   P. R. Brown, in: *High Pressure Liquid Chromatography*. Academic Press, New York 1973.

[4]   V. P. Demushkin, and G. Y. Plyashkevich, *Anal. Biochem.* **84**, 12 (1978).

[5]   R. Eksteen, J. C. Kraak, and P. Linssen, *J. Chromatogr.* **148**, 413 (1978).

[6]   E. H. Edelson, J. G. Lawless, C. T. Wehr, and S. R. Abbott, *J. Chromatogr.* **174**, 409 (1979).

[7]   H.-J. Breter, and R. K. Zahn, *Z. Naturforsch.* **31**c, 551 (1976).

[8]   R. A. Hartwick, and P. R. Brown, *J. Chromatogr.* **126**, 679 (1976).

[9]   A. Wakizaka, K. Kurosaka, and E. Okuhara, *J. Chromatogr.* **162**, 319 (1979).

[10] R. A. Hartwick, and P. R. Brown, *J. Chromatogr.* **143**, 383 (1977).

[11] C. Y. Ko, J. L. Johnson, L. B. Barnett, H. M. McNair, and J. R. Vercellotti, *Anal. Biochem.* **80**, 183 (1977).

[12] J. Cadet, and L. Voituriez, *J. Chromatogr.* **195**, 139 (1980).

[13] G. Szepesi, M. Gazdag, and J. Mezei, *Pharmazie* **35**, 602 (1980).

[14] N. E. Hoffman, and J. C. Liao, *Anal. Chem.* **49**, 2231 (1977).

[15] J. R. Miksic, and P. R. Brown, *J. Chromatogr.* **142**, 641 (1977).

[16] E. J. M. Pennings, and G. M. J. van Kempen, *J. Chromatogr.* **176**, 478 (1979).

[17] T. F. Walseth, G. Graff, M. G. Moos Jr., and N. D. Goldberg, *Anal. Biochem.* **107**, 240 (1980).

[18] J. D. Schwenn, and H. G. Jender, *J. Chromatogr.* **193**, 285 (1980).

[19] Y. Kato, T. Seita, T. Hashimoto, and A. Schimizu, *J. Chromatogr.* **134**, 204 (1977).

[20] R. P. Singhal, R. K. Bajaj, C. M. Buess, D. B. Smoll, and V. N. Vakharia, *Anal. Biochem.* **109**, 1 (1980).

[21] M. Glad, S. Ohlson, L. Hansson, M.-O. Mansson, and K. Mosbach, *J. Chromatogr.* **200**, 254 (1980).

[22] E. H. Pfandenhauer, and S. D. Tong, *J. Chromatogr.* **162**, 585 (1979).

[23] H. Schott, unpublished.

[24] F. K. Chow, and E. Grushka, *Anal. Chem.* **49**, 1756 (1977).

[25] F. K. Chow, and E. Grushka, *Anal. Chem.* **50**, 1346 (1978).

[26] F. K. Chow, and E. Grushka, *J. Chromatogr.* **185**, 361 (1979).

[27] C. W. Gehrke, K. C. Kuo, G. E. Davis, R. D. Suits, T. P. Waalkes, and E. Borek, *J. Chromatogr.* **150**, 455 (1978).

[28] A. M. Krstulovic, P. R. Brown, and D. M. Rosie, *Anal. Chem.* **49**, 2237 (1977).

[29] J. X. Khym, *Clin. Chem.* **21**, 1245 (1975).

[30] M. Mckeag, and P. R. Brown, *J. Chromatogr.* **152**, 253 (1978).

[31] V. Svoboda, and I. Kleinmann, *J. Chromatogr.* **176**, 65 (1979).

[32] R. A. Hartwick, P. S. Assenza, and P. R. Brown, *J. Chromatogr.* **186**, 647 (1979).

[33] G. H. R. Rao, J. G. White, A. A. Jachimowicz, and C. I. Witkop, *J. Lab. Clin. Med.* **81**, 839 (1974).

[34] R. Ogura, T. Matsuzaki, S. Kumano, A. H. Daoud, C. A. Griffin, and J. M. Knox, *Int. J. Biol. Macromol.* **2**, 58 (1980).

[35] D. P. Brenton, K. H. Astrin, M. K. Cruikshank, and J. E. Seegmiller, *Biochem. Med.* **17**, 231 (1977).

[36] J. Maybaum, F. K. Klein, and W. Sadee, *J. Chromatogr.* **138**, 149 (1980).

[37] M. B. Cohen, J. Maybaum, and W. Sadee, *J. Chromatogr.* **198**, 435 (1980).

[38] F. S. Anderson, and R. C. Murphy, *J. Chromatogr.* **121**, 251 (1976).

[39] B. Bakay, E. Nissinen, and L. Sweetman, *Anal. Biochem.* **86**, 65 (1978).

[40] B. Bakay, E. Nissinen, L. Sweetman, U. Francke, and W. L. Nyhan, *Pediat. Res.* **13**, 1365 (1979).

[41] E. Nissinen, *Anal. Biochem.* **106**, 497 (1980).

[42] A. Floridi, C. A. Palmerini, and C. Fini, *J. Chromatogr.* **138**, 203 (1977).

[43] P. D. Schweinsberg, and T. L. Loo, *J. Chromatogr.* **181**, 103 (1980).

[44] Y. M. Rustum, *Anal. Biochem.* **90**, 289 (1978).

[45] R. A. Hartwick, A. M. Krstulovic, and P. R. Brown, *J. Chromatogr.* **186**, 659 (1979).

[46] J. E. Evans, H. Tieckelmann, E. W. Naylor, and R. Guthrie, *J. Chromatogr.* **163**, 29 (1979).

[47] G. A. Taylor, P. J. Dady, and K. R. Harrap, *J. Chromatogr.* **183**, 421 (1980).

[48] D. H. Swenson, P. D. Lawley, *Biochem. J.* **171**, 575 (1978).

[49] J. V. Frei, D. H. Swenson, W. Warren, and P. D. Lawley, *Biochem. J.* **174**, 1031 (1978).

[50] H. W. Thielmann, *Cancer Lett.* **6**, 311 (1979).

[51] E. M. Faustman, and J. I. Goodman, *J. Pharm. Meth.* **4**, 305 (1980).

[52] D. T. Beranek, C. C. Weis, and D. H. Swenson, *Carcinogenis* **1**, 595 (1980).

[53] M. Ehrlich, and K. Ehrlich, *J. Chromatogr. Sci.* **17**, 531 (1979).

[54] K. C. Kuo, R. A. Mclune, and C. W. Gehrke, *Nucleic Acids Res.* **8**, 4763 (1980).

[55] A. H. Czárnyi, M. Vajda, and J. Sági, *J. Chromatogr.* **204**, 213 (1981).

[56] C. W. Gehrke, and K. V. Kuo, *J. Chromatogr.* **188**, 129 (1980).

[57] J. M. Essigmann, W. F. J. Busby, and G. N. Wogan, *Anal. Biochem.* **81**, 384 (1977).

[58] G. E. Davis, C. W. Gehrke, and K. C. Kuo, *J. Chromatogr.* **173**, 281 (1979).

[59] P. F. Agris, and J. G. Tompson, *J. Chromatogr.* **194**, 205 (1980).

[60] D. C. Youvan, and J. F. Hearst, *Nucleic Acids Res.* **9**, 1723 (1981).

[61] M. G. Pallavicini, and J. A. Mazrimas, *J. Chromatogr.* **183**, 449 (1980).

[62] H. Breithaupt, and J. Schick, *J. Chromatogr.* **225**, 99 (1981).

[63] F. D. Ragione, G. Ragosta, G. Cacciapouti, M. Porcelli, and M. Carteni-Farina, *Bull. Soc. Ital. Biol. Sper.* **56**, 2030 (1980).

[64] H. Ratech, G. J. Thorbecke, and R. Hirschhorn, *J. Chromatogr.* **183**, 499 (1980).

[65] C. Heidelberger, *Prog. Nucleic Acids Res. Mol. Biol.* **4**, 1 (1965).

[66] C. F. Gelijkens, and A. P. De Leenheer, *J. Chromatogr.* **194**, 305 (1980).

[67] W. E. MacMillan, W. H. Wolberg, and P. G. Welling, *Cancer Res.* **38**, 3479 (1978).

[68] W. D. Ensminger, A. Rosowsky, U. Raso, D. C. Levin, M. Glode, S. Come, G. Steele, and E. Frei, *Cancer Res.* **38**, 3784 (1978).

[69] D. W. Sitar, D. H. Shaw, M. P. Thirlwell, and J. R. Ruedy, *Cancer Res.* **37**, 3981 (1977).

[70] A. T. Wu, J. L. Au, and W. Sadee, *Cancer Treat. Rep.* **63**, 210 (1978).

[71] J. L. Au, A. T. Wu, M. A. Friedman, and W. Sadee, *Cancer Treat. Rep.* **63**, 343 (1979).

[72] A. R. Buckpitt, and M. R. Boyd, *Anal. Biochem.* **106**, 432 (1980).

[73] R. W. Tyson, and E. Wickstrom, *J. Chromatogr.* **192**, 485 (1980).

[74] D. A. Usher, and J. A. Rosen, *Anal. Biochem.* **92**, 276 (1979).

[75] W. Jost, K. K. Unger, R. Lipecky, and H. G. Gassen, *J. Chromatogr.* **185**, 403 (1979).

[76] G. D. McFarland, and P. N. Borer, *Nucleic Acids Res.* **7**, 1067 (1979).

[77] M. Dizdaroglu, and W. Hermes, *J. Chromatogr.* **171**, 321 (1979).

[78] H. Schott, *Nucleic Acids Symp. Ser. No. 7*, 203 (1980).

[79] H. Schott, and H. Schrade, *Nucleic Acids Symp. Ser. No. 9*, 187 (1981).

[80] H. Schott, *Nucleic Acids Res. Spec. Publ. No. 4*, 161 (1978).

[81] H. Schott, *J. Chromatogr.* **172**, 179 (1979).

[82] H. Schott, and H. Watzlawick, *J. Chromatogr.* **196**, 435 (1980).

[83] M. Dizdaroglu, W. Hermes, C. von Sonntag, and H. Schott, *J. Chromatogr.* **169**, 429 (1979).

[84] M. Dizdaroglu, M. G. Simic, and H. Schott, *J. Chromatogr.* **188**, 273 (1980).

[85] H. Eshaghpour, and D. M. Crothers, *Nucleic Acids Res.* **5**, 13 (1978).

[86] R. K. Patient, S. C. Hardies, J. E. Larson, R. B. Inman, L. E. Maquat, and R. D. Wells, *J. Biol. Chem.* **254**, 5548 (1979).

[87] D. A. Usher, *Nucleic Acids Res.* **6**, 2289 (1979).

[88] R. A. Baan, R. van Charldorp, E. van Leerdam, P. H. van Knippenberg, L. Bosch, J. F. M. De Rooij, and J. H. van Boom, *FEBS Lett.* **71**, 351 (1976).

[89] L. W. McLaughlin, F. Cramer, and M. Sprinzl, *Anal. Biochem.* **112**, 60 (1981).

[90] R. Dion, and R. J. Cedergren, *J. Chromatogr.* **152**, 131 (1978).

[91] J. H. van Boom, and J. F. M. De Rooij, *J. Chromatogr.* **131**, 169 (1977).

[92] S. Gillam, F. Rottman, and M. Smith, *Proc. Natl. Acad. Sci USA* **74**, 96 (1977).

[93] J. F. M. De Rooij, W. Bloemhoff, and J. H. van Boom, *J. Chromatogr.* **177**, 380 (1979).

[94] H. Komiya, K. Nishikawa, K. Ogawa, and S. Takemura, *J. Biochem.* **86**, 1081 (1979).

[95] H.-J. Fritz, R. Belagaje, E. R. Brown, H. R. Fritz, R. A. Jones, R. G. Lees, and H. G. Khorana, *Biochemistry* **17**, 1257 (1978).

[96] M. J. Gait, M. Singh, and R. C. Sheppard, *Nucleic Acids Res.* **8**, 1081 (1980).

[97] R. Crea, and T. Horn, *Nucleic Acids Res.* **8**, 2331 (1980).

[98] R. Téoule, R. Derbyshire, A. Guy, D. Molko, and A. Roget, *Nucleic Acids Symp. Ser. No.* **7**, 23 (1980).

[99] T. Horn, M. P. Vasser, M. E. Struble, and R. Crea, *Nucleic Acids Symp. Ser. No.* **7**, 225 (1980).

[100] K. E. Norris, F. Norris, and K. Brunfeldt, *Nucleic Acids Symp. Ser. No.* **7**, 233 (1980).

[101] M. J. Gait, S. G. Popov, M. Singh, and R. C. Titmas, *Nucleic Acids Symp. Ser. No.* **7**, 243 (1980).

[102] K. Miyoshi, and K. Itakura, *Nucleic Acids Symp. Ser. No.* **7**, 281 (1980).

[103] O. G. Chakhmakhcheva, V. A. Efimov, and Yu. A. Ovchinnikov, *Nucleic Acids Symp. Ser. No.* **7**, 345 (1980).

[104] K. Miyoshi, R. Arentzen, T. Huang, and K. Itakura, *Nucleic Acids Res.* **8**, 5507 (1980).

[105] K. Miyoshi, T. Miyake, T. Hozumi, and K. Itakura, *Nucleic Acids Res.* **8**, 5473 (1980).

[106] A. F. Markham, M. D. Edge, T. C. Atkinson, A. R. Greene, G. R. Heathcliffe, C. R. Newton, and D. Scanlon, *Nucleic Acids Res.* **8**, 5193 (1980).

[107] H. M. Hsiung, W. L. Sung, R. Broussean, R. Wu, and S. A. Narang, *Nucleic Acids Res.* **8**, 5753 (1980).

[108] R. Wetzel, H. L. Heyneker, D. V. Goeddel, P. Jhurani, J. Shapiro, R. Crea, T. L. K. Low, J. E. McClure, G. B. Thurman, and A. L. Goldstein, *Biochemistry* **19**, 6096 (1980).

[109] McC. M. I. Moseman, and R. I. Gumport, *Biochemistry* **19**, 635 (1980).

[110] M. D. Matteucci, and M. H., Caruthers, *Tetrahedron Lett.* **21**, 719 (1980).

[111] J. L. Fourrey, and D. J. Shire, *Tetrahedron Lett.* **22**, 729 (1981).

[112] E. Ohtsuka, H. Takashima, and M. Ikehara, *Tetrahedron Lett.* **22**, 765 (1981).

[113] S. Josephson, N. Balgobin, and J. B. Chattopadhyaya, *Nucleic Acids Symp. Ser. No.* **9**, 177 (1981).

[114] M. L. Duckworth, M. J. Gait, P. Goelet, G. F. Hong, M. Singh, and R. C. Titmas, *Nucleic Acids Res.* **9**, 1691 (1981).

[115] D. Molko, R. Derbyshire, A. Guy, A. Roget, and R. Téoule, *J. Chromatogr.* **206**, 493 (1981).

[116] L. W. McLaughlin, and J. U. Krusche, in: H. G. Gassen, and A. Lang (eds.): *Chemical and Enzymatic Synthesis of Gene Fragments*, p. 177. Verlag Chemie, Weinheim 1982.

10 Porphyrins

by *Hans Detlef Meyer*

10 Porphyrins

10.1 Introduction

The tetrapyrrolic porphyrin ring system (Figure 10-1) is involved in many biochemical processes. Therefore, porphyrins and their metalchelates are found ubiquitously in nature. Their best known and most important functions are the control of the biological oxidation reactions and oxygen transport; but it is interesting to note that porphyrins are also used for some other biological purposes, e. g. as colour in the feathers of turaco birds.

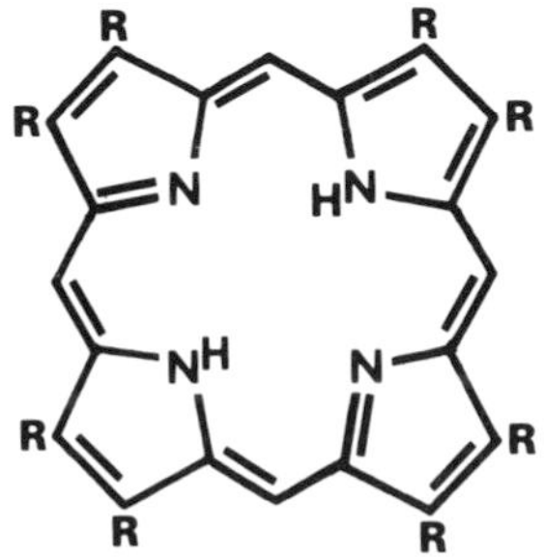

Figure 10-1. Porphyrin ring system.

The ring structure and the available ligand-binding groups allow porphyrins to bind many metals. The iron porphyrin complex, heme, usually together with a protein, is the central compound in biological oxidations. Chlorophyll, responsible for the photosynthesis in green plants, represents a magnesium containing complex, which is closely related to and derived from porphyrins.

10.1.1 Biosynthetic Pathway

The biosynthetic sequence of porphyrins is always achieved by individual organisms. The initial steps of the synthesis and the intermediates to be found are almost identical for different final compounds. The heme biosynthesis is demonstrated as an example in the following (Figure 10-2). Succinyl coenzyme A from citric acid cycle and glycine form the first precursor, δ-aminolevulinic acid. The condensation of two molecules of this compound leads to the monopyrrole porphobilinogen, the second precursor. Linking four porphobilinogens, followed by cyclization, produces a porphyrinogen. These labile intermediates are hexahydroporphyrins carrying four methylene bridges between the pyrrole rings. They can be oxidized very easily to the individual porphyrins. The first to be produced is uroporphyrinogen, with eight side chains consisting of four acetic and propionic acid groups, respectively. Four isomers are possible, but only two of them are physiological. These isomers I and III differ only in the position of the acid groups in ring D. The normal form is isomer III, which alone can be converted to heme in the

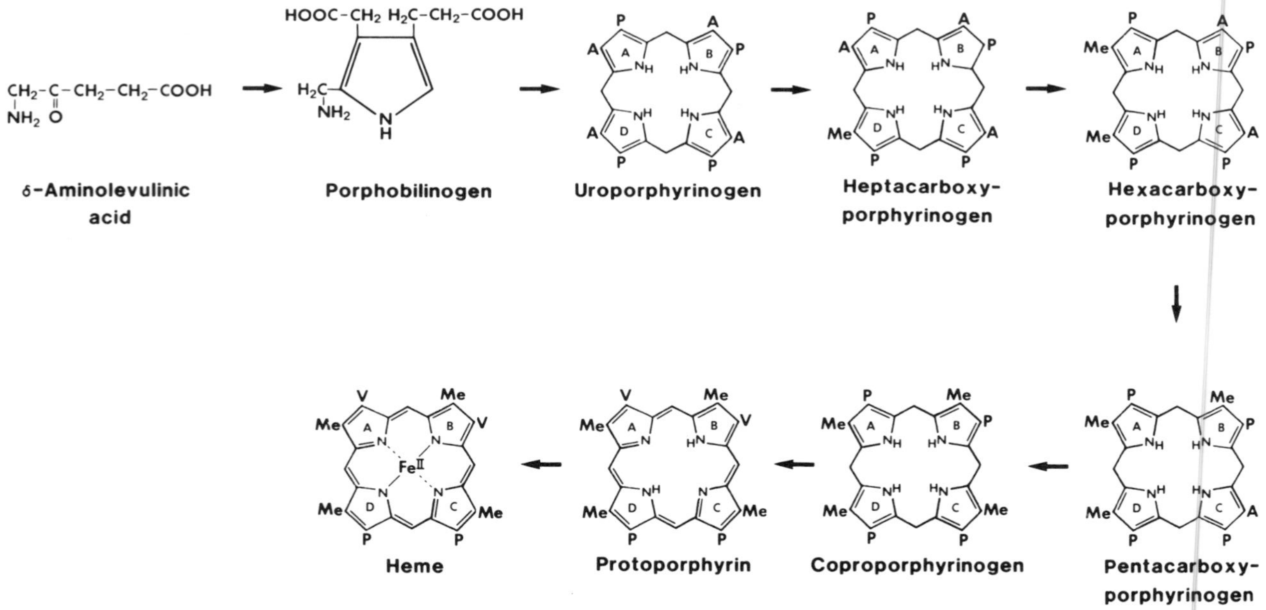

Figure 10-2. Pathway of heme biosynthesis.

following processes. A step-by-step decarboxylation of the acetic acid functions to methyl side chains is directed over the intermediates to coproporphyrinogen, containing further four propionic acid groups (Figure 10-2). Decarboxylation and a following oxidation of the resulting ethyl functions leads to the final vinyl groups in the positions 2 and 4 of protoporphyrinogen. Insertion of an iron-II ion into the oxidized form, protoporphyrin IX, finally gives heme.

All steps of this biosynthesis are controlled and catalyzed by different enzymes in mitochondria and cytoplasma. Disturbances of these processes, depending on hereditary or acquired enzyme defects, cause severe diseases, the *porphyrias*. Investigation into the nature of these diseases led to early studies of porphyrins. Another impetus for research in the porphyrin field was the interest in synthesis and biochemistry of chlorophyll. The analytical support of these works comprises nearly all chromatographic and physicochemical techniques.

10.1.2 Analytical Methods Others Than HPLC

In the epoch between Felix Hoppe-Seyler, who worked on chlorophyll in the 1870's [1], and Hans Fischer, who received the Nobel prize for his research on porphyrins in 1930 [2], analytical methods, including melting point, elemental analysis and spectrophotometry, measured manually point by point, had not changed in principle. Fractionation and quantitative determination of uro- and coproporphyrin from urine was developed by Rimington et al. [3]. Modified methods, measuring the absorption [4] or fluorescence [5], are still in practice today. The adsorption of porphyrins onto talc, introduced in 1945 by Grinstein et al. [6], was to be seen as an important step in further studies. The development of a thin-layer chromatographic method by With [7] was based on talc adsorption techniques. Separation of porphyrin derivatives, mostly methyl esters, on silica gel plates [8, 9] is the most widespread method as yet in many laboratories. Column and paper chromatographic techniques were employed in studies of porphyrins from porphyric patients in 1969 [10]. Electrophoresis [11] and counter current distribution [12] were also employed for separation of porphyrins from biological samples. In recent years, some modern analytical techniques were applied for the examination of porphyrins and metalloporphyrins, such as derivative spectrophotometry [13], nuclear magnetic resonance [14] and mass spectrometry [15].

10.1.3 Chemical and Physicochemical Properties

10.1.3.1 Solubility

The ampholytic character of porphyrins containing acid side-chains allows them to be dissolved in acids or bases. The porphyrins are least soluble in aqueous solutions of a pH-range about 4, depending on the isoelectric point of the individual porphyrin. Under those conditions therefore, they can easily be extracted by organic solvents. Diluted mineral acids re-extract porphyrins from ether or ethyl acetate. In the early 20th century, Willstätter and Fischer developed a fractionation method for porphyrins from ethereal solutions using increasing concentrations of hydrochloric acid [16]. Porphyrins with more acid groups are less soluble in organic solvents: uroporphyrin, for example, is insoluble in ether. Metal-chelates of porphyrins cannot be soluted in aqueous acids because they are unable to form cations. The metalloporphyrins lose their central metal-ion and are converted into the dications under the influence of strong mineral acids. Porphyrins with unsaturated side-chains have higher solubility in organic solvents than their saturated analogues. Mesoporphyrin with two ethyl groups is, therefore, less extractable from aqueous solutions than protoporphyrin containing two vinyl functions.

10.1.3.2 Spectroscopy

The planar and fully conjugated molecular structure of porphyrins explains well their spectroscopic behaviour. Detection of separated porphyrins is facilitated by their pronounced absorption and fluorescence spectra.

10.1.3.2.1 UV-VIS-Absorption

The characteristic absorption spectra show (besides some bands in the visible region) a sharp, strong band in the near-ultraviolet range, discovered by Soret in 1883 [17]. The wavelength of the Soret-bands and their molar-extinction coefficients depend on the nature of side-chains and vary with the solvent applied (Table 10-1). High molar-extinction coefficients of about $5 \cdot 10^5$ L/(mol cm) were found for some porphyrin dications.

10.1.3.2.2 Fluorescence

Irradiation of porphyrins with long-wave ultraviolet light causes an intensive red fluorescence, which shows higher values for acidic than for neutral or alkaline solutions. Differences in the side-chains and solute conditions affect both position and intensity of the fluorescence band (Table 10-1). Most metalloporphyrins found in biological samples show no fluorescence, except the zinc-complex, which emits light with a bathochromic shift compared to the free porphyrin

Table 10-1. Fluorescence Excitation (Soret-Band) and Emission Maxima of Porphyrins in Different Solvent Systems [41, 43].

	Solvent System	Excitation (nm)	Emission (nm)
Uroporphyrin	A	398	618
	B	405	598
Coproporphyrin	A	392	615
	B	400	589
Protoporphyrin IX	A	400	626
	B	408	604
Zinc protoporphyrin	A	414	586
Uroporphyrin octa-methyl ester	A	398	578

A 50 mmol/L aqueous tetrabutylammonium phosphate (pH 7.5)/acetonitrile (34/66)
B 1.5 mol/L hydrochloric acid

(Table 10-1). Fluorescence measurements of porphyrin concentrations are widely employed because of the higher sensitivity and greater selectivity of this technique, as compared to that of spectrophotometry.

10.2 Sample Preparation Procedures

In developing an analytical procedure, the practical purpose has to be kept in mind. A method for routine analysis should be as simple and rapid as possible, while giving reproducible and accurate results. Since HPLC has become a very sensitive and precise method, sample preparation is of increasing importance. These pre-chromatographic procedures include generally less accurate steps, which later influence the accuracy of the total method. Normally, the chromatographic determination of porphyrins from biological material requires a more or less complicated sample pre-treatment, depending on the material to be analyzed. The succeeding separation techniques determine the necessary sample preparation. Porphyrins can be isolated and analyzed either after converting them to esters, generally methyl esters, or directly in the naturally occurring form as free porphyrin carboxylic acids.

All manipulations done with samples to be analyzed for porphyrins should be carried out in the dark or under red light, to prevent decomposition of the porphyrins.

The most widely used methods are described first, in different sections.

10.2.1 Urine

10.2.1.1 Porphyrin Esters

Three steps characterize the techniques employed:

● isolation,
● esterification and
● concentration

of the porphyrins. Porphyrin esters, mostly methyl esters are used, have the advantage of greater solubility in organic solvents than free porphyrins, and therefore their extraction from biological material is facilitated. The scheme (Figure 10-3) is an excerpt of the methods most widely applied for analysis of urine and faeces [18 to 20].

10.2.1.1.1 Adsorption onto Talc

A portion of talc is added to an aliquot of urine sample adjusted to pH 4 (Figure 10-3). After stirring, the mixture is filtrated. The filtrate, which is discharged after adsorption of the porphyrins onto talc, should always be checked for remaining red fluorescence. This may occur when urines contain high amounts of porphyrins and, in which cases a further portion of talc has to be employed.

The following procedures to obtain samples ready for HPLC are shown in details in Figure 10-3.

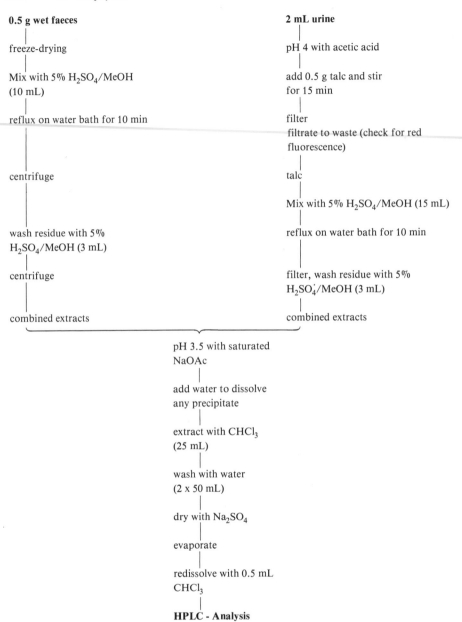

0.5 g wet faeces
|
freeze-drying
|
Mix with 5% H$_2$SO$_4$/MeOH
(10 mL)
|
reflux on water bath for 10 min
|
centrifuge
|
wash residue with 5%
H$_2$SO$_4$/MeOH (3 mL)
|
centrifuge
|
combined extracts

2 mL urine
|
pH 4 with acetic acid
|
add 0.5 g talc and stir
for 15 min
|
filter
filtrate to waste (check for red
fluorescence)
|
talc
|
Mix with 5% H$_2$SO$_4$/MeOH (15 mL)
|
reflux on water bath for 10 min
|
filter, wash residue with 5%
H$_2$SO$_4$/MeOH (3 mL)
|
combined extracts

pH 3.5 with saturated
NaOAc
|
add water to dissolve
any precipitate
|
extract with CHCl$_3$
(25 mL)
|
wash with water
(2 x 50 mL)
|
dry with Na$_2$SO$_4$
|
evaporate
|
redissolve with 0.5 mL
CHCl$_3$
|
HPLC - Analysis

Figure 10-3. Scheme for isolation and esterification of porphyrins from urine and faeces.

10.2.1.1.2 Solvent Extraction

Another method of porphyrin isolation is the extraction with organic solvents from urine acidified to pH 3.0 with concentrated hydrochloric acid [18, 21]. In the first extraction step, a mixture of ethyl acetate/n-butanol (1/1) is used, followed by several n-butanol extractions until the organic phase shows no further red fluorescence. After washing with water, the organic solvent is evaporated and the residue is esterified directly.

10.2.1.1.3 Pre-Separation on Polystyrene

Wilson et al. [22] employed a pre-separation on a polystyrene column (XAD-2). The loaded column is washed with 0.1 mol/L hydrochloric acid and then porphyrins are eluted with 2% hydrochloric acid in acetone. After evaporation of the solvent, the residue is processed in the manner described in next paragraph. Recoveries of 80 to 100% for urinary porphyrins are reported for this method.

10.2.1.1.4 Esterification

Esterification conditions described for urinary porphyrins adsorbed onto talc vary from 10 min under reflux with 5% sulfuric acid/methanol [19] to 16 h at 20 °C using a 10% sulfuric acid/methanol mixture [23]. For urine samples with high porphyrin concentrations, a direct esterification with sulfuric acid/methanol is possible [18, 21], but occasionally the presence of water may cause an incomplete esterification [24]. Other reagents used for esterification are 5% boron trifluoride in methanol [25, 26] and, less frequently, diazomethane [18].

10.2.1.1.5 Recovery

Applying the methods described above, using standard mixtures dissolved in urine, recoveries for the different porphyrins from about 75 to 80% are obtained [18]. Some other publications report recoveries up to 100% for porphyrins with saturated side-chains [27, 28]. Protoporphyrin containing vinyl groups shows significantly lower values, probably because of a slight decomposition due to the conditions employed [18].

Difficulties in quantitative determination of porphyrin esters are caused by incomplete esterification [18, 29] and the formation of mixed methyl ethyl esters resulting from chloroform stabilized with ethanol [30].

10.2.1.2 Free Porphyrins

HPLC analysis of free urinary porphyrins requires virtually no sample pre-treatment as compared to time-consuming esterification procedures.

10.2.1.2.1 Samples for Ion-Pair Technique

For ion-pair separation technique aliquots of urine can be injected directly onto the column [31]. Using the same separation technique, the author prefers, in contrast to reference [31], a preceding filtration of the urine specimen to remove particulate matter which can otherwise clog the column filters [32, 33].

Urines can contain extremely high amounts of porphyrins (>20 mg/L); such samples must be diluted, usually with the eluent [31, 33].

10.2.1.2.2 Samples for Other Techniques

Separation methods involving the trapping of porphyrins on a pre-column [34] or elution with acidic solvent systems [35] require urine samples to be acidified and centrifuged prior to injection.

Adams et al. [36] have dried small amounts of urine (50 to 100 µL) at 90 °C with a gentle stream of air and redissolved them in the eluent for injection. This procedure can possibly cause a decomposition of some porphyrins.

10.2.2 Faeces

Prior to the further processing of faeces samples, independently of the method applied, it is advisable to dry them for better and odourless handling. A complete deodoration is achieved by freeze-drying the stool specimen, which is then pulverized. Extraction of faeces with a large volume (50 mL/g) of ice-cold acetone also gives a dry, crumbly residue [26], but this technique is more time-consuming and complicated than freeze-drying.

10.2.2.1 Porphyrin Ester

10.2.2.1.1 Direct Esterification

In most work published so far, porphyrins in stool samples are esterified directly without preceding extraction [18, 20, 24]. Faeces specimens suspected of containing high amounts of porphyrins are treated with several portions of esterification reagent, which also serves as the extraction medium, until the filtrate shows no further red fluorescence [18] (Figure 10-3, Section 10.2.1.1.1). Esterification reagents and following procedures, shown in details in Figure 10-3, are almost the same as described for urine.

10.2.2.1.2 Purification of the Porphyrin Fraction

An additional clean-up step, using a separation on silicagel columns, was introduced by two different groups [25, 37]. In one case, the intention was to remove pigments of dietary origin [25]. However, since they do not interfere with porphyrins when using modern HPLC and detection techniques, it is superfluous to separate them prior to HPLC analysis. In the second case, the separation of the crude mixture of porphyrin esters resulted in two fractions containing proto- to uroporphyrin and a "sub-uroporphyrin-material" [37]. This fraction of red fluorescent compounds, which eluted later than uroporphyrin, consists mainly of incompletely esterified uroporphyrin [38].

10.2.2.2 Free Porphyrins

Faeces represent a very complex matrix. It is difficult to extract free porphyrin carboxylic acids completely from such samples. Several extraction methods have been applied and combined with spectroscopic determinations of the porphyrin fractions collected [20, 39]. However, employing these solvent mixtures as reported, we still had problems with the recovery of uroporphyrin. Application of a solution of tetrabutylammonium phosphate, a phase transfer agent, in methanol/water allows the extraction of a porphyrin standard mixture added to a stool specimen [40].

50 mg of dry pulverized stool are extracted with at least three portions (1 mL each) of a 60 mmol/L solution of tetrabutylammonium phosphate in methanol/water (80/20), until the liquid phase shows no red fluorescence under UV-light. The combined extracts are centrifuged and an aliquot of the supernatant can be injected directly (Figure 10-4).

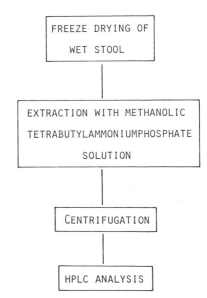

Figure 10-4. Sample preparation procedure for free prophyrins from stool.

10.2.3 Blood, Tissues and Other Materials

Analysis of porphyrins from whole blood and red blood cells is widely employed for the diagnosis of lead intoxication [41] and studies of porphyrin biosynthesis [42]. Only rarely is porphyrin determination from plasma or serum required [43].

Red blood cells are normally lysed by the solvents used for extraction and esterification. Tissues and bacteria have to be homogenized prior to isolation of porphyrins, on account of more stable cells.

Porphyrins are isolated from tissues mostly via formation of porphyrin esters, due to their facilitated extraction.

10.2.3.1 Porphyrin Esters

10.2.3.1.1 Solvent Extraction

Extraction prior to esterification is the technique customarily applied for cell and tissue samples [42, 44]. Cell homogenate is extracted twice with ethyl acetate/acetic acid (7/3). The combined supernatants are washed, first with 3% aqueous sodium acetate and then with water. After extraction of porphyrins from organic phase into hydrochloric acid, they are extracted back into ether. Following a washing with water, the ether is evaporated and the residue is treated with esterification reagents.

10.2.3.1.2 Adsorption onto Talc

Proteins from erythrocytes hemolysates are precipitated with perchloric acid in ethanol and then removed. The supernatant is adjusted to pH 3.5 and the porphyrins are adsorbed onto talc added to the solution [30]. The further processing corresponds to the procedure for faeces (Figure 10-3).

10.2.3.1.3 Esterification

10.2.3.1.3.1 Porphyrins

Another method is a direct esterification of homogenized material with previously described reagents, followed by a clean-up procedure similar to those used for faeces (Figure 10-3) [25, 45].

10.2.3.1.3.2 Porphyrin Chelates

Recently, a method for esterification of zinc- and magnesium-chelates of protoporphyrin IX was published, employed for studies of porphyrin complexation in cells [46]. The porphyrin chelates are purified with TLC and then converted to their methyl esters using diazomethane.

10.2.3.2 Free Porphyrins

Porphyrins in red blood cells consist mainly of zinc protoporphyrin IX [47]. Only some techniques enable the determination of zinc protoporphyrin [41, 48, 49], because metalloporphyrins decompose in strong acids.

10.2.3.2.1 Direct Injection of Hemolysate

Gotelli et al. [41] use for porphyrin analysis whole blood samples lysed with a mixture of Triton X-100 in 50 mmol/L tetrabutylammonium hydroxide in water (pH 7.5). An aliquot of centrifuged supernatant is injected directly.

10.2.3.2.2 Solvent Extraction

10.2.3.2.2.1 Blood

An extraction step with ethyl acetate/acetic acid (3/1) is involved in sample preparation described by two other groups [48, 49]. Part of the organic phase is then brought onto the column. Although samples injected still contain hemin and other related substances, interferences with interesting porphyrins can be avoided by selecting appropriate separation conditions. Removal of probably disturbing compounds is achieved by re-extraction of porphyrins from the organic solvent with hydrochloric acid [50, 51]. Neither injection of the hydrochloric acid solution directly [50] nor of a solution of porphyrins in the eluent, after inserting an additional extraction using ether [51], allows the determination of zinc protoporphyrin.

10.2.3.2.2.2 Plasma

For isolation of free porphyrin carboxylic acids, a similar extraction procedure is employed by Longas and Poh-Fitzpatrick [43].

10.2.3.2.2.3 Tissues

Analysis of free porphyrins from tissues of deep sea medusae was performed by Bonnett et al. [31]. Homogenized samples are extracted with the eluent consisting of aqueous 1 mmol/L tetrabutylammonium dihydrogen phosphate/ethanol (17/3). An aliquot of the filtrate is injected directly without further purification.

10.3 Separation Techniques

Separations of porphyrins have doubtlessly their greatest practical importance in the diagnosis of *porphyrias*. Hence, most papers published so far on determination of porphyrins with HPLC describe applications for clinical chemistry.

The diverse human materials analyzed for porphyrins show different porphyrin compositions. In urine the interesting compounds for diagnosis of *porphyrias* are the series uroporphyrin to coproporphyrin and isocoproporphyrin. For analysis of faeces in addition, the dicarboxylic porphyrins, mainly protoporphyrin IX and its metabolites, meso- and deuteroporphyrin, formed by bacterial conversion in the colon, have to be determined. Zinc protoporphyrin IX is found when examining porphyrins from erythrocytes. HPLC techniques used in clinical laboratory should allow the separation and identification of all these porphyrins.

Investigations of the biosynthesis of porphyrins is another field for HPLC analysis of these compounds, either of synthetic origin or isolated from different biological materials.

Separations of porphyrins can be achieved by using porphyrin esters or free porphyrin carboxylic acids. Even today many laboratories use HPLC of porphyrin esters on the polar silica gel columns customarily employed until recently. Reversed-phase materials, which are used for the most part today, allow the separation of free porphyrins, however.

10.3.1 Separation of Porphyrin Esters

In the early 1970's, HPLC columns were mostly packed with silica gel and then separations were run in adsorption mode. Therefore, the techniques of TLC, using porphyrin esters, could easily be transferred to HPLC. Some of the separation methods developed at that time are today only of historical value, because they are based on equipment or materials no longer available. In 1975, several groups independently presented methods employing HPLC for qualitative and quantitative analysis of porphyrin esters from human material [15, 28, 37, 52 to 54).

10.3.1.1 Flow Programming

For their studies of porphyrins from natural sources, Evans et al. [15, 53] employed HPLC and field desorption mass spectrometry. HPLC analysis of porphyrin methyl esters was readily performed on silica gel columns, the packing material being either of pellicular type (Corasil II) or the microparticulate type (LiChrosorb SI 60, 10 μm). A solvent mixture containing light petroleum/ethyl acetate (55/45) was pumped through the Corasil column using a flow programming mode. After elution of pentacarboxylic porphyrin, the flow-rate was increased from an initial 1 mL/min so as to elute the more polar compounds faster and in sharper peaks. Detection sensitivity, however, was correspondingly reduced. Furthermore, the retention time was found to be 26 min for uroporphyrin methyl ester and it was eluted in a relative broad peak.

Petryka and Watson [25] performed the separation of the porphyrin standards customarily used by increasing the flow-rate from 2 to 3 mL/min after the elution of pentacarboxylic porphyrin methyl ester. μ Porasil columns (30 cm × 0.4 cm) together with a mixture of benzene/ethyl acetate/chloroform (7/1/2) were employed. Despite the higher flow-rate for elution of the more polar components, uroporphyrin methyl ester peak showed a noticeable tailing.

10.3.1.2 Gradient Elution

Carlson and Dolphin [37, 52] were analysing porphyrin methyl ester mixtures isolated from faeces and urines. They investigated several columns (2 ft × 1/8 in o. d.) packed with diverse materials, especially Corasil II and Porasil T phases. Applying the latter one a superior resolution of the 2 to 8 carboxylic porphyrin esters was obtained. The solvent system consisted of a gradient from light petroleum/methylene dichloride (40/100), both containing 0.1% triethylamine, to light petroleum/methylene dichloride/n-propanol (15/100/50). The gradient was generated placing the less polar solvent in a loop between pump and column. Setting the flow-rate at 1 mL/min the more polar mixture reached the column after 12 min. The chromatograms obtained showed some broad peaks monitored at absorbance wavelength of 254 and 403.5 nm, respectively. Retention times ranged from about 4 min for protoporphyrin ester to nearly 20 min for uroporphyrin ester.

To achieve a better separation than obtained with flow programming, Evans et al. [15, 21] turned to gradient elution technique using a LiChrosorb Si 60 column (2 ft × 1/8 in o. d.) with an exponential gradient at a flow of 3 mL/min from hexane to 70% ethyl acetate in hexane. The method of generating the gradient in a glass mixing chamber is described in details in a later publication [21]. The gradient conditions decreased retention times significantly, e. g. for uroporphyrin methyl ester to just below 12 min. Coproporphyrin was detected down to 1 to 2 pmol by monitoring absorption at 400 nm. High reproducibility of retention data facilitated identification of peaks by comparison with standards. Quantitative analysis required an internal standard: in this case mesoporphyrin IX was an appropriate choice. It should be added to samples prior to esterification and extraction to monitor these procedures. Analyses were routinely carried out on 10 to 20 pmol of components and the collection of the material from a single peak generally gave a quantity sufficient for a field desorption mass spectrum. Structure and identity of porphyrin methyl esters eluted could be proven by this technique.

Very short separation times (<6 min) are possible with a LiChrosorb Si 100 column (25 cm × 0.2 cm) and a gradient elution [55]. Within 7 min the concentration of tetrahydrofuran in heptane was raised from 20 to 50% at a flow-rate of 2 mL/min. Porphyrin methyl esters from urine samples monitored at the Soret-band (400 nm) were baseline separated. Since porphyrin esters are poorly soluble in the eluent, they had to be dissolved in chloroform. For sufficient resolution, the injection volume was restricted to less than 50 μL.

10.3.1.3 Isocratic Elution

10.3.1.3.1 Porphyrin Methyl Esters

Profiles obtained from methyl esters of urinary porphyrins are presented in work from Evans et al. [18], which appeared later than the previously described methods published from this group. Separation of porphyrin methyl esters with 2 to 8 carboxylic groups was performed on a Partisil column (20 cm × 0.4 cm, 5 µm) in less than 10 min. At a flow-rate of 1.5 mL/min, ethyl acetate/cyclohexane (60/40) was used as the eluent in isocratic mode. Resolution in the region of dicarboxylic to pentacarboxylic porphyrin esters seems not to be sufficient for the quantitation of all porphyrins from some urine samples shown. Three different clean-up procedures were used for the analysis of the same urine samples. The results agree reasonably well.

In 1977, Gray et al. [19] published a report showing HPLC separations of urine and faeces samples from patients suffering from nearly all kinds of *porphyrias*. Separations were performed on µPorasil columns (30 × 0.4 cm) and isocratic elution with n-heptane/methyl acetate (3/2) at a flow-rate of 1.5 mL/min. The column effluent was monitored by measuring the absorbance at 404 nm. The porphyrin methyl esters were eluted in order of increasing polarity with good resolution. Retention times for meso- and uroporphyrin esters were between 4 and 16 min, respectively.

Two chromatograms are presented as examples, which show characteristic profiles for faecal porphyrins from a patient suffering from *hereditary coproporphyria* (Figure 10-5) and urinary porphyrins from a patient with *congenital erythropoietic porphyria* (Figure 10-6).

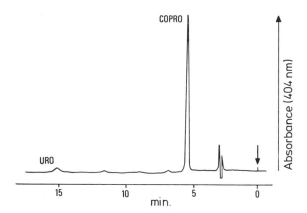

Figure 10-5. HPLC profile of urinary porphyrin methyl esters for *hereditary coproporphyria* (From reference [19]).

In two earlier papers, the same group has investigated different HPLC conditions, including flow and gradient programming [26, 54]. But the separation with isocratic elution showed a superior resolution of porphyrin methyl ester mixtures within a reasonable analysis time. Fractional hydrochloric acid/ether extraction and HPLC analysis of porphyrins from faeces were compared by Christensen and Romslo [20]. HPLC separation was carried out according to the procedure described by Gray et al. [19]. Deuteroporphyrin, as an internal standard, was added to the stool specimen prior to esterification. To rule out interference from endogenous deuteroporphyrin, the samples were processed in duplicates, with and without an internal standard.

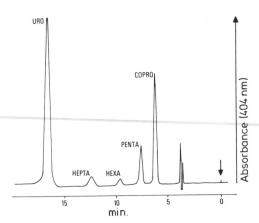

Figure 10-6. HPLC profile of porphyrin methyl esters for *congenital erythropoietic porphyria* (From reference [19]).

The solvent fractionation method was demonstrated to give falsely elevated values due to carry-over of protoporphyrin into the coproporphyrin fraction and vice versa. While HPLC analysis of the same stool samples showed no influence between the different porphyrins.

10.3.1.3.2 Cupric Chelates of Porphyrin Esters

Evans et al. [18], analyzing a standard mixture of porphyrin methyl esters kept for three days in diluted chloroform solution, observed additional peaks. They used the same separation conditions as for the porphyrin esters, a Partisil column together with ethyl acetate/cyclohexane. Field desorption mass spectrometry of these compounds showed that they were the corresponding cupric chelates of the porphyrin esters. Presumably, trace amounts of acid originating from chloroform might have caused dissolution of trace amounts of copper in flasks or the HPLC system. These copper(II)ions preferentially chelated those porphyrins containing less carboxylic side-chains. After a few hours, this complexation could already be observed. Porphyrin analysis of skin biopsies obtained from patients with *porphyria cutanea tarda* had been achieved by HPLC of the copper chelates of porphyrin methyl esters [45]. The porphyrins were converted after esterification into the corresponding complexes adding an excess of 0.1% copper(II)acetate in chloroform/methanol. The dried residue was redissolved in chloroform and an aliquot was injected onto a MicroPak CN column (25 cm × 0.2 cm) containing a bound alkyl nitrile phase. The compounds were eluted in isocratic mode with n-heptane/ethyl acetate isopropanol (60/40/0.5) and the individual fractions were detected by absorption at 400 nm. The chromatogram of cupric chelates obtained from biopsy material (Figure 10-7) shows a very

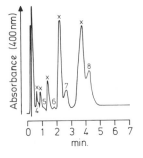

Figure 10-7. Chromatogram of porphyrin methyl esters and their copper chelates from skin extract 2 h after chelation with copper acetate. Peaks: 8 uroporphyrin; 7 heptacarboxylic porphyrin; 6 hexacarboxylic porphyrin; 5 pentacarboxylic porphyrin; 4 coproporphyrin. Peaks marked with an asterisk (X) on left side of numbered peaks refer to copper chelates (From reference [45]).

fast elution, but with unsatisfactory resolution of porphyrins with few carboxylic groups. In a subsequent publication [56], the same group demonstrated the enhanced sensitivity and a slightly better separation of the copper complexes.

10.3.1.3.3 Protoporphyrin Ester Chelates

HPLC separation of zinc and magnesium chelates of protoporphyrin IX methyl ester was performed in the course of studies of protoporphyrin complexation in etioplast preparations [46]. Esterified chelates purified by TLC were separated on a Brownlee LiChrosorb column (25 cm × 0.4 cm) with acetone/hexane (15/85) at a flow of 2 mL /min.

10.3.1.3.4 Mixed Methyl Ethyl Porphyrin Esters

Recently, Straka et al. [29] reported preparation and separation of mixed methyl ethyl esters of uroporphyrin, using a μPorasil column with ethyl acetate/n-heptane (55/45) as eluent. During the HPLC investigation of an assay of uroporphyrinogen decarboxylase from red cell hemolysates, unidentified peaks were observed in the chromatograms of porphyrins. One of these compounds was compared to synthetic methyl ethyl esters and it was determined to be uroporphyrin heptamethyl monoethyl ester.

10.3.1.4 Preparative Separation

Preparative HPLC was employed for isolation and purification of porphyrin esters obtained from the faeces of hexachlorobenzene-poisoned rats [15, 57]. The material was separated on a Porasil A (60) column (4 ft × 1 in o. d., 37 to 75 μm) with an exponential gradient from hexane to ethyl acetate during 3 h [15]. Although elution time was very long, the resolution was sufficient.

10.3.1.5 Separation of Isomers

The major chromatographic problem to be solved during the investigation of porphyrin biosynthesis is the separation of isomeric porphyrins.

10.3.1.5.1 Harderoporphyrin Esters

One of the first HPLC separations was performed by Cavaleiro et al. [44] in 1974. The separation of two isomers of harderoporphyrin tetramethyl ester, a precursor of protoporphyrin IX containing only one vinyl group, was achieved using a Corasil II column and a chloroform/cyclohexane-mixture as eluent.

A few years later, the separation of the same compounds and, in addition, protoporphyrin IX methyl ester under slightly modified conditions was reported [58]. The eluent consisted of cyclohexane/ethyl acetate (4/1) and detection wavelength was set at the Soret-band (402 nm).

10.3.1.5.2 Hexacarboxy Porphyrin Esters

Studying the decarboxylation mechanism from uroporphyrinogen to coproporphyrinogen, Jackson et al. [59] applied HPLC for the separation of isomeric hexacarboxy porphyrin hexamethyl esters. These porphyrins were produced by chicken red cell hemolysates incubated with the corresponding heptacarboxy porphyrins. HPLC analysis was carried out on a Partisil column (15 cm × 0.5 cm, 5 μm) with 1% acetone in chloroform at a flow of 1 mL/min.

10.3.1.5.3 Coproporphyrin Esters

Since methods previously used for porphyrin analysis, including HPLC, could not separate isomers of uroporphyrin, these compounds had to be decarboxylated in sealed tubes to corresponding coproporphyrins. After conversion into ethyl esters, separation of coproporphyrin isomers was performed on two μBondapak C_{18} columns (30 cm × 0.4 cm) with acetonitrile/water (7/3) as the eluent [60]. It required two recycles to obtain three fractions containing the isomers I, III/IV and II. The unresolved mixture of isomer III and IV was transesterified to methyl esters and rechromatographed on two Porasil columns with ether/heptane (2/3) at a flow of 2 mL/min. But to get a sufficient resolution of the components, which were measured at 380 nm, 10 to 12 recycling procedures had to be performed.

The same year, other groups had also succeeded in the separation of different coproporphyrin methyl esters [18, 26]. Using a mixture of ethyl acetate/cyclohexane (4/6) at a flow of 1.5 mL/min, Evans et al. [18] obtained on a Partisil column a baseline separation of copro- and isocoproporphyrin methyl esters. The application of μPorasil columns run with methyl acetate/isooctane (1/4) separated coproporphyrin methyl ester from deethyl- and isocoproporphyrin methyl esters. The latter were only partially resolved [26].

10.3.1.5.4 Uroporphyrin Esters

Most naturally occurring uroporphyrin is of type III isomer. Only trace amounts of uroporphyrin I are encountered under normal conditions in nature. However, in certain disease states, considerable quantities of uroporphyrin I are produced and excreted. In recent years, several methods have been published which render possible the separation of uroporphyrin ester isomers [61 to 63].

Bommer et al. [61] were the first to report HPLC determination of the isomers I and III on two μPorasil columns using n-heptane/acetic acid/acetone/water (90/60/30/0.05) at a flow of

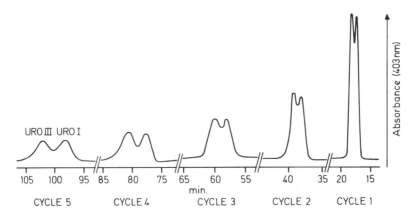

Figure 10-8. Separation of uroporphyrin octamethyl esters I and III using recycling mode (From reference [61]).

1.5 mL/min. After 5 recycling steps, an acceptable resolution was achieved (Figure 10-8). By using the two isomers labeled with ^3H (I) and ^{14}C (III), it was demonstrated that less than 2% cross-contamination occurred during the chromatographic procedure.

Nordlöv et al. [62] described a modification of the procedure mentioned above which uses n-heptane/acetic acid/acetone (6/3/2) as the eluent. At a flow-rate of 0.5 mL/min, a nearly complete separation of isomer I and III could be performed without recycling, but more than 3 h analysis time was needed. The two μPorasil columns hat to be equilibrated, with an eluent containing an additional one part water, for several hours. Employing the same system for separation of all four uroporphyrin octamethyl esters, three fractions, the isomers I, III/IV and II, were obtained. All efforts to resolve the two isomers III and IV had failed.

Recently, a method for the resolution of the uroporphyrin I and III methyl esters was published which shows a considerably reduced analysis time (20 min.) [63]. The column employed was an APS Hypersil (25 cm × 0.5 cm). Despite numerous attempts to improve the separation by modifying the eluent applied, hexane/ethyl acetate/butanol/acetic acid (85/12/3/0.1), no baseline resolution could be obtained. Nevertheless, for diagnostic applications, the method appears to be convenient.

10.3.2 Separation of Free Porphyrins

All methods reported above use porphyrin esters for separation, yet porphyrins occur as free carboxylic acids in nature. The intermediate esterification step, although simple enough in principle, may itself introduce problems, such as incomplete and differential esterification and reactions at vinyl groups. Moreover, esterification and the diverse extractions are laborious and time-consuming. Clearly it would be preferable if free porphyrin carboxylic acids from biological material could be examined directly or with very little sample pre-treatment.

Thus, reversed-phase columns, now in widespread use, are more suitable for the separation of many polar biological compounds. The separation techniques used for free porphyrins have to be adapted specifically to the material in which the porphyrins are to be determined since the matrix influences the separation decisively.

10.3.2.1 Ion-Pair Reversed-Phase Separations

Ion-pair chromatography is performed by adding a phase transfer agent to the mobile phase. These ion-pair reagents are ionic substances that are nonetheless soluble to some extent in nonpolar organic solvents. They facilitate both the extraction of ionic compounds and their separation on reversed-phase materials. To obtain "ion-pairs" with the acid functions of free porphyrins, several groups have chosen tetrabutylammonium phosphate as the counter-ion [31 to 33, 40 to 41].

10.3.2.1.1 Urine

Bonnett et al. [31] reported the first ion-pair HPLC of free porphyrins on reversed-phase columns (μBondapak C_{18}, 30 cm × 0.4 cm). The solvent systems used were all 1 mmol/L in tetrabutylammonium dihydrogen phosphate. Different mixtures of alcohol/water at flow-rates of 1 to 1.5 mL/min were applied, depending on the separation to be performed. Porphyrins from urine samples injected directly were eluted with 20% water in methanol and detected at 400 nm. However, other groups and the author could not reproduce the good resolution of the individual porphyrins obtained in 11 min.

In contrast to conditions previous reported [31], we found it necessary to employ a gradient elution for separation of free porphyrin carboxylic acids [32, 33, 40]. The individual porphyrins from uro- to mesoporphyrin were resolved well on a µBondapak C_{18} column using a multilinear gradient from 30 to 100% methanol in water, both containing 5 mmol/L tetrabutylammonium phosphate (pH 7.5) [32, 33] (Figure 10-9). The total analysis included reconditioning of the column with starting solvent conditions for 15 min takes 45 min. The pumps were set together at a flow-rate of 1 mL/min. The eluted porphyrins were monitored by a fluorescence detector specifically (excitation 399 nm, emission 615 nm). Starting conditions and the gradient profile had to be changed slightly from one column to the other, because of noticeable variations between the columns.

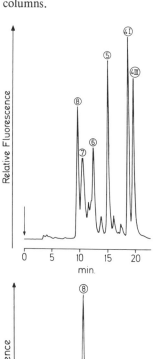

Figure 10-9. Ion-pair reversed-phase separation of porphyrin standards dissolved in urine. The numbers at the top of the peaks refer to the number of carboxylic groups in the different porphyrins. 4 I and 4 III coproporphyrin I and III.

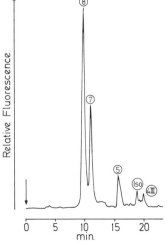

Figure 10-10. Ion-pair reversed-phase separation of free urinary porphyrins from a patient suffering from *porphyria cutanea tarda*. The numbers at the top of the peaks refer to the number of carboxylic groups. Iso isocoproporphyrin, 4 III coproporphyrin III.

Employing this HPLC technique, urine samples were injected, after a simple filtration, directly onto the column without the use of a guard column. Analysis of a urine sample from a patient with *porphyria cutanea tarda* resulted in a chromatogram showing the typical excretion pattern of porphyrins for this disease (Figure 10-10). Isocopro- and coproporphyrin III were separated from each other and from coproporphyrin I under the conditions applied. The detection limits of 0.2 ng for uro- and 0.1 ng for coproporphyrin are low enough to allow the analysis of normal urine specimens.

To identify and quantify the individual porphyrins, the method of standard additions [64] was applied by adding an appropriate amount of porphyrin standard mixture to the urine specimen. The urinary porphyrin profile of a patient suffering from *acute intermittent porphyria* shows two significant peaks, uro- and coproporphyrin (Figure 10-11 a). Comparison to the chromatogram of the same urine spiked with standard mixture (Figure 10-11 b) confirmed the coproporphyrin composition of 95% isomer III.

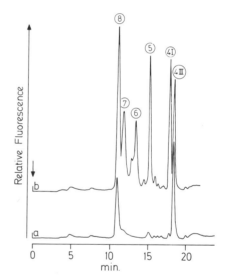

Figure 10-11. Porphyrin carboxylic acid profile of a patient with *acute intermittent porphyria* (a) 50 µL of patient urine; (b) 50 µL of patient urine spiked with porphyrin standard mixture. Peaks as in Figure 10-9.

10.3.2.1.2 Faeces

For the first time, we have demonstrated the separation of free porphyrin carboxylic acids from faeces employing similar HPLC conditions [40]. Generally, faeces contain detectable amounts only of porphyrins with fewer carboxylic groups. Therefore, the separation of stool porphyrins was performed with a multilinear gradient from 50 to 78% methanol within 17 min on the same type of µBondapak column used for urine analysis. A stool extract from a patient suffering from *erythrohepatic protoporphyria* was analyzed by this method (Figure 10-12).

A column combination consisting of a reversed-phase guard column (3 cm) together with a LiChrosorb RP 18 column (25 cm × 0.46 cm) was also employed for the separation of free stool porphyrins. But this combination required a gradient starting at 65% methanol and finishing after 12 min at 90% methanol in water. The chromatograms obtained with this system show considerable shorter retention times, compared to those from a µBondapak column, as demonstrated by a faecal porphyrin profile for *porphyria variegata* (Figure 10-13).

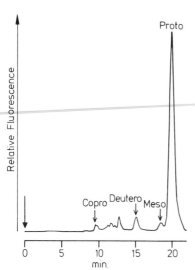

Figure 10-12. Separation of free porphyrins extracted from stool specimen from a patient with *erythrohepatic proto-porphyria* (μBondapak column).

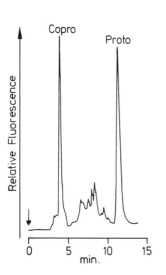

Figure 10-13. Faecal porphyrin profile for *porphyria variegata* (LiChrosorb column).

10.3.2.1.3 Blood

Gotelli et al [41] described ion-pair HPLC separations on reversed-phase columns (μBondapak C_{18}) of porphyrins from whole blood samples. The solvent, consisting of 50 mmol/L aqueous tetrabutylammonium hydroxide (pH 7.5 with phosphoric acid)/acetonitrile (34/66), was pumped at a flow of 2 mL/min. The column effluent was detected by a fluorometer (excitation 400 nm, emission > 560 nm). Thus, blood samples were injected directly after hemolysation of erythrocytes. The use of a guard column (3 cm) filled with pellicular C_{18}-material was required. The internal standard, uroporphyrin octamethyl ester, was dissolved in the lysing reagent.

The chromatogram obtained from pooled normal blood shows that zinc protoporphyrin IX, representing the main component, is well resolved from protoporphyrin IX (Figure 10-14).

Figure 10-14. Ion-pair reversed-phase separations of whole blood samples with uroporphyrin octamethyl ester (uro Me-ester) as internal standard. (A) Pooled normal blood; (B) blood from lead poisoning (From reference [41]).

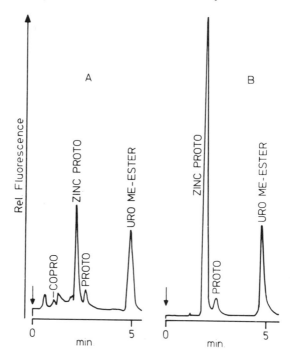

10.3.2.1.4 Other Materials

Employing in principle the same system used for urine samples, only changing the alcohol used, Bonnett et al. [31] were able to separate porphyrin mixtures from synthetic and natural sources. HPLC analysis of porphyrin extracts from deep sea medusae was performed with an ethanol/water-mixture (17/3) and resulted in the identification of major component as protoporphyrin. A solvent system consisting of 15% water in methanol allowed the separation of compounds from "haematoporphyrin derivative", a photosensitizer employed in clinical studies of cancer [65].

10.3.2.2 Other Reversed-Phase Separations

10.3.2.2.1 Urine

An HPLC technique for the determination of free urinary porphyrins was reported by Englert et al. [34] in 1979. They trapped the porphyrins on a pre-column and eluted nonporphyrin fluorescent compounds prior to the analytical separation of the porphyrins on the main column. The chromatography was carried out on a µBondapak C_{18} column equipped with a reversed-phase pre-column (5 cm × 0.46 cm). Acidified urine samples were brought onto the pre-column, which was then eluted first with 15% acetonitrile in 0.01 mol/L phosphoric acid and subsequently with the phosphoric acid alone. After equilibration with a 10 mmol/L phosphate buffer (pH 7.5) to pH 6 the pre-column was switched to the main column and separation was achieved by a 30 min gradient from 0 to 50% acetonitrile in phosphate buffer. All eluents were pumped with a flow of 1 mL/min. Separation of samples containing the series from uro- to coproporphyrin detected by fluorescence (excitation 400 nm, emission 650 nm) resulted in a chromatogram showing a sufficient resolution even of coproporphyrin isomers I and III. However, the method appears quite complex and time-consuming, because of the need for several eluents, precise valve switchings and a total analysis time of more than 100 min.

The same group had succeeded in a very fast separation of a synthetic mixture of free uroporphyrin isomers employing the same equipment [66]. The porphyrins were retained onto the pre-column as described in reference [34]. Applying a solvent mixture of 4% acetonitrile in 10 mmol/L phosphate buffer (pH 6.5), the isomers I to IV could be separated at a flow of 0.9 mL/min (Figure 10-15). The isomers II and IV were only partially resolved. The separation of the uroporphyrins I and III from urine samples was achieved by increasing acetonitrile to 5% and the flow to 1 mL/min. Within a very short analysis time of less than 15 min, the isomers are nearly baseline resolved.

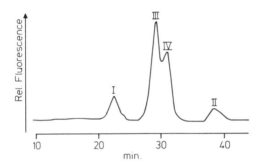

Figure 10-15. Chromatogram of a synthetic mixture of free uroporphyrin isomers I, II, III and IV (From reference [66]).

Bommer [67] modified the method from Wayne et al. [66] and employed it for routine analysis of uroporphyrin isomers I and III. The separation was performed with 5% acetonitrile in 10 mmol/L sodium phosphate (pH 6.85) on a μBondapak column at a flow-rate of 1 mL/min. The isomers, well resolved, were eluted within 10 min (Figure 10-16).

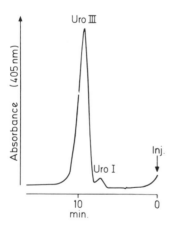

Figure 10-16. Rapid separation of uroporphyrin isomers I and III for routine use (From reference [67]).

For the determination of free urinary porphyrins, Ford et al. [35] applied reversed-phase columns (a μBondapak C_{18} together with a guard column (2.3 cm × 0.4 cm)). At a flow of 1 mL/min, a gradient from 55% methanol in 0.1 mol/L phosphate buffer (pH 3.5) to methanol was delivered by two pumps. Fluorescence detection of the sufficiently resolved porphyrins was carried out with excitation at 420 nm and emission at 510 nm, using a cut-off filter with a relatively low wavelength limit. The chromatograms of urine samples show a significant background signal and very large amounts of nonporphyrin fluorescent substances, clearly separated from the porphyrins.

Two abstracts reported reversed-phase separations of free urinary porphyrins [68, 69].

In 1976, the separation of free porphyrins on an ODS-Silex I column with 0.01% aqueous acetic acid/methanol (39/61) and fluorescence detection was described [68]. No detailed publication of this method followed. Free urinary porphyrins were separated on a μBondapak phenyl column using an eluent of 64% methanol in water (pH 2.1) which was 15.6 mmol/L of pentanesulfonic acid and 10 mmol/L tetrasodium ethylenediaminetetraacetate [69]. No further details, especially upon resolution achieved, are available.

10.3.2.2.2 Blood

In course of studies of acid hydrolysis of protoporphyrin IX dimethyl ester Culbreth et al. [50] developed an HPLC method for the separation of free porphyrins and methyl esters on reversed-phase columns (μBondapak C_{18}) which also allowed the determination of porphyrins from blood samples. The resolution of porphyrins with fewer carboxylic functions was achieved with a gradient elution, running from methanol/water/glacial acetic acid (6/4/1) to methanol/glacial acetic acid (10/1) at a flow of 2 mL/min. Final conditions were reached after 13.7 min when protoporphyrin IX was eluted. Fluorescence detection was carried out at the usual excitation wavelength (404 nm), using a sharp cut-off filter (595 nm) on the emission side. It was shown that hydrolysis of protoporphyrin dimethyl ester is complete after 2 to 3 h and that later decomposition of protoporphyrin occurs. That the HPLC separation of free porphyrins from blood extracts is possible was demonstrated in this paper.

Applying similar separation conditions, Salmi and Tenhunen [51] achieved the HPLC analysis of porphyrins from erythrocytes. Only proto- and coproporphyrin, but not zinc protoporphyrin, could be determined, because the sample clean-up used involved an extraction step with strong mineral acid. Fluorescein was employed for internal standardization. The same gradient reported in reference [50] was performed at a flow of 1 mL/min. After a gradient time of 10 min, the final conditions were held for 4 min. The chromatogram obtained from a standard mixture of uro- to mesoporphyrin shows a good resolution of the individual porphyrins measured by fluorescence.

Smith et al. [48] reported the HPLC determination of zinc proto- and protoporphyrin IX from extracts from whole blood samples. A μBondapak C_{18} column, eluted in isocratic mode with methanol/acetic acid/water (39/4/7) (pH 3.4) at a flow of 2 mL/min, provided a very short analysis time. The retention time for protoporphyrin was just below 5 min. The HPLC technique described was compared to several other methods for blood porphyrin analysis and a superior selectivity and sensitivity was demonstrated.

Recently, a μBondapak C_{18} column combined with a guard column filled with pellicular ODS-material was employed by Scoble et al. [49] for analysis of erythrocyte porphyrins. 8% of an aqueous KH_2PO_4-buffer (pH 3.4) in methanol was used at a flow of 2 mL/min for isocratic separation of meso-, proto-, copro- and zinc protoporphyrin detected with fluorimetry at the customarily used wavelengths. Good resolution of free carboxylic porphyrins was achieved in less than 6 min. Analytical recoveries for protoporphyrin and its zinc chelate better than 90%

were reported. Blood samples were processed using three different extraction procedures. HPLC, combined with an extraction with ethyl acetate/acetic acid (3/1), provided the best recoveries in comparison with the other methods applied.

10.3.2.3 Ion-Exchange Separation

One example of an ion-exchange separation of a mixture containing di-, tetra- and pentacarboxylic porphyrins (Figure 10-17) had been described by Evans et al. [15] in 1975. The column (3 ft × 1/8 in o. d.) was packed with a pellicular anion-exchanger (AS Pellionex SAX). The mobile phase, a gradient from 0 to 15% acetic acid in methanol for 11 min, was chosen to enable samples collected from HPLC to be easily evaporated for further mass spectrometric examination [21].

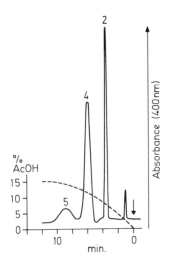

Figure 10-17. Ion-exchange separation of porphyrin di- (2), tetra- (4) and pentacarboxylic acids (5) by HPLC. The broken line shows the gradient profile (From reference [15]).

10.3.2.4 Separations on Silica Gel

10.3.2.4.1 Urine

In 1976, Adams et al. [36] reported the separation of free urinary porphyrins using a silica gel column (Silica A, 13 μm). The solvent system, consisting of 0.3% water in acetone adjusted at pH 7.6 with tributylamine, favoured a partition mechanism over adsorption. Isocratic elution at a flow of 2 mL/min allowed the resolution of the isomers I and III of copro- and uroporphyrin. The fluorescence detection with excitation at 403 nm and emission at 627 nm enabled the determination of coproporphyrin down to 30 pg. Despite the high sensivity of the technique, no other porphyrins, except uro-, coproporphyrin and small amounts of dicarboxylic porphyrins, were found in urine neither from healthy persons nor from porphyric patients. The chromatograms obtained from urine from patients with *porphyria cutanea tarda* show predominantly coproporphyrin III peaks.

Admittedly, *porphyria cutanea tarda* urine is known to contain high amounts of uro- and heptacarboxylic porphyrin.

10.3.2.4.2 Plasma

A similar system was used for separation of free plasma porphyrins by Longas and Poh-Fitzpatrick [43]. A solution of extracted porphyrins redissolved in acetone/0.1 mol/L hydrochloric acid was applied onto a Silica A column (25 cm × 0.3 cm). Elution was performed by a gradient from 2 to 90% of dilute acetic acid in acetone within 25 min at a flow-rate of 0.5 mL/min. The individual porphyrins eluted were detected by fluorescence (excitation 400 nm, emission 602 nm). The chromatogram of a commonly used standard mixture containing uro- to mesoporphyrin shows a rather poor resolution for the porphyrins with 8 to 6 carboxylic functions. The coproporphyrin isomers I and III were only slightly separated from each other (Figure 10-18).

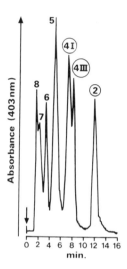

Figure 10-18. Separation of free porphyrin carboxylic acid standards on a silica gel column using a gradient of acetone/dilute acetic acid. Peaks as in Figure 10-9 (From reference [43]).

10.4 Detection

As mentioned in the introduction, porphyrins show very distinct spectroscopic properties. Therefore, nearly all analytical methods for qualitative and quantitative determination of porphyrins use spectrometry. Since variable UV- and fluorescence detectors are available, porphyrins separated by HPLC can be measured at their characteristic wavelengths.

10.4.1 UV-Absorption

The high molar extinction coefficients at the Soret-band of porphyrins enable a sensitive detection of the eluted components. Since, for the various porphyrins, the maxima of the Soret-band differ slightly (Table 10-1 Section 10.1.3.2.2), in practice a single intermediate wavelength, normally between 400 and 410 nm, is set on the detector, which provides an optimal sensitivity for all porphyrins to be analyzed. The detection limit can be improved when porphyrin copper-chelates, with their increased molar extinction coefficients, are used [56]. Porphyrin amounts in the lower ng-range (about 10 ng) are quantitated with this detection method [45]. Nonporphyrin compounds also absorbing in the wavelength range employed occasionally interfere with UV-detection of porphyrins.

10.4.2 Fluorescence

Fluorescence detection is more specific and sensitive than measurement of UV-absorption. This increased specificity depends on the fact that only a small number of substances fluoresce and that characteristic wavelengths for excitation and emission can be selected for one compound or a class of compounds [70]. Detection of porphyrins is mostly achieved by exciting at the wavelength of the Soret-region and measuring emission at 600 to 630 nm or by using a cut-off filter at about 580 or 600 nm. This arrangement allows the determination down to 30 pg of porphyrins in the column effluent [36]. Time-controlled changing of emission wavelength during a chromatogram provides an increase of selectivity and sensitivity for the detection of porphyrins differing significantly in their emission maxima, for example proto- and zinc protoporphyrin (Table 10-1) [71].

Fluorescence excitation and emission spectra obtained from eluted peaks, using a stop-flow technique, make possible an identification of the individual porphyrins [36].

10.4.2.1 Second-Derivative Fluorescence Detection

An interesting approach to introduce a new detection method is the development of second derivative fluorimetric monitoring of separated porphyrin esters by Zelt et al. [72]. This

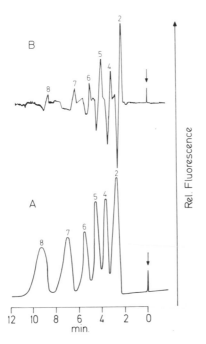

Figure 10-19. Separation of porphyrin methyl esters (2 to 8 carboxylic groups) monitored by fluorescence with zero order (A) and second derivative signal (B). Identification of peaks as in Figure 10-7 (from reference [72]).

technique was employed for determination of porphyrins isolated from cultures containing chick embryo liver cells. After separation of porphyrin esters on a Partisil 5 column, the effluent was monitored by fluorimetry (excitation 405 nm, emission 430 nm). The second derivative was electronically generated from zero order signal (Figure 10-19). The second derivative chromatogram, compared to the normal chromatogram, provides an increase in resolution and sensitivity, but the latter only for small and high peaks as shown for uroporphyrin methyl ester (Figure 10-19).

10.5 Application of HPLC for Diagnosis of *Porphyria*

Clinical symptoms allow only the tentative diagnosis of a *porphyria*, since for the individual forms there are no clear-cut manifestations, e. g. the different *acute hepatic porphyrias* may show similar symptoms and signs. Therapeutic reasons require the differentiation of several *porphyrias*, such as *porphyria cutanea tarda* and *porphyria variegata*, for example.

For further detailed information about *porphyrias*, please refer to the medical literature [73, 74].

10.5.1 Porphyrin Profiles in *Porphyria*

Porphyrias are caused by a decrease in activity of an enzyme or enzymes of the heme biosynthesis. This enzyme defect then leads to an increased synthesis of δ-aminolevulinic acid controlled by a negative feedback mechanism (Figure 10-20), resulting in an overproduction of porphyrin precursors and porphyrinogens situated in the pathway before the enzyme block. Accumulated porphyrinogens are excreted in urine and/or faeces and are oxidized to the corresponding porphyrins, while the porphyrin precursors are found only in urine.

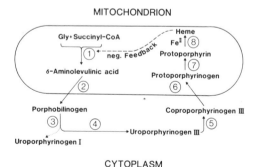

Figure 10-20. Heme biosynthetic pathway with participating enzymes. 1 δ-aminolevulinic acid synthase; 2 porphobilinogen synthase; 3 uro-porphyrinogen synthase; 4 uroporphyrinogen cosynthase; 5 uroporphyrinogen decarboxylase; 6 coproporphyrinogen oxidase; 7 protopor-phyrinogen oxidase; 8 ferrochelatase.

10.5.1.1 *Porphyria Cutanea Tarda*

Porphyria cutanea tarda represents more than half of all cases of *porphyria* and is induced by an inherited decrease of uroporphyrinogen decarboxylase activity in the liver cells (Table 10-2).

Due to the restriction in the synthetic pathway and the elevated synthesis before it, an increased urinary excretion of uro- and heptacarboxy porphyrin results, producing the characteristic profile of porphyrins in urine (Figure 10-10, 10-21).

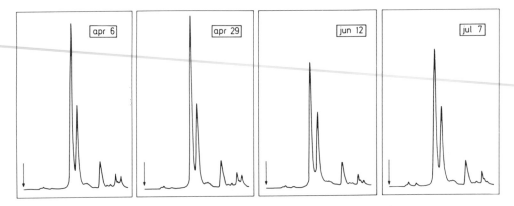

Figure 10-21. Porphyrin profiles of a 3 months surveillance of a patient with *porphyria cutanea tarda*.

The same porphyrins found in urine are observed in faeces, but the tetracarboxylic fraction is complex, containing excessive amounts of copro- and isocoproporphyrin (Figure 10-22). The latter is characteristic for this *porphyria*.

10.5.1.2 *Acute Intermittent Porphyria*

In *acute intermittent porphyria*, porphyrin levels are elevated mostly during acute attacks (Figure 10-11), whereas the faecal pattern remains almost normal. Increased urinary concentrations of the porphyrin precursors are excreted in acute phases and are an important diagnostic feature.

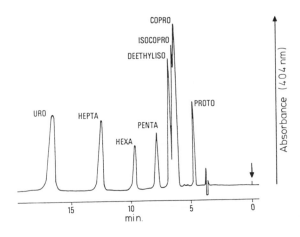

Figure 10-22. HPLC profile of porphyrin methyl esters from faeces from a patient with *porphyria cutanea tarda* (From reference [19]).

Table 10-2. Enzyme Defects in *Porphyria* and the Resulting Excretion Pattern of Porphyrins.

Porphyria	Enzyme Decreased in Activity	Precursors Elevated	Increased Porphyrins Urine	Faeces	Blood	Characteristical Profile (Fig.No.)
I. *Hepatic*						
p. cutanea tarda	uroporph. decarboxylase	n	+ - + +	+	n	10-10, 10-22
acute intermittent p.	uroporph. synthase	n- + +	n- +	n	n	10-11
p. variegata	protoporph. oxidase ferrochelatase	n- + +	n- +	+	n	10-13
hereditary copro-p.	coproporph. oxidase	n- + +	+	+	n	10-5
II. *Erythropoietic*						
congenital erythropoietic p. (M. Günther)	uroporph. cosynthase	n	+	+	+	10-6
erythrohepatic protop.	ferrochelatase	n	n	+	+	10-12
III. lead intoxication	ferrochelatase PBG-synthase	+	n- +	+	+	10-14

10.5.1.3 *Porphyria Variegata*

The rare *porphyria variegata* is characterized by a   considerable excess of proto- and coproporphyrin in the faeces with an excretion ratio of 2 to 1 (Figure 10-13). There is often an increased urinary coproporphyrin and, to a lesser extent, uroporphyrin in the quiescent phase. In acute attacks, large amounts of uroporphyrin are observed, partly due to non-enzymatic conversion of porphobilinogen.

10.5.1.4 *Hereditary Coproporphyria*

The least common of *acute hepatic porphyrias* is the *hereditary coproporphyria*, which shows increased concentrations of coproporphyrin, mostly isomer III, in urine (Figure 10-5) and faeces.

Accumulation of porphyrins in erythrocytes is observed for all *erythropoietic porphyrias* and for lead intoxication (Table 10-2).

10.5.1.5 *Congenital Erythropoietic Porphyria*

Congenital erythropoietic porphyria, also known as Morbus Günther, is a very rare disorder. Urinary porphyrin profile shows an excessive amount of uroporphyrin. However, coproporphyrin and the other porphyrins are also found in increased concentrations (Figure 10-6). Coproporphyrin is predominant in the faecal porphyrin pattern, but sometimes elevated uroporphyrin can also be determined. All porphyrins are mainly isomer I, mirroring the decreased activity of uroporphyrinogen cosynthase in this *porphyria*.

10.5.1.6 *Erythrohepatic Protoporphyria*

Extremely high amounts of protoporphyrin are excreted with faeces in *erythrohepatic protoporphyria* (Figure 10-12). High red cell concentration of this porphyrin is generally taken as an additional diagnostic feature (Figure 10-23). Urinary porphyrin composition usually remains normal, except when liver failure occurs as a terminal event. Then the urinary profile becomes similar to those for *porphyria cutanea tarda.*

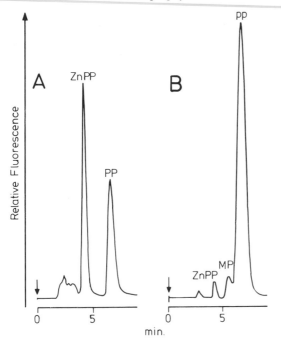

Figure 10-23. Ion-pair reversed-phase separations of porphyrins from red blood cells.
A: porphyrin standards added to red blood cell hemolysate.
B: blood specimen from a patient suffering from *erythrohepatic protoporphyria.*
Peaks: ZnPP zinc protoporphyrin, PP protoporphyrin, MP mesoporphyrin.

10.5.1.7 Lead Intoxication

Lead intoxication is characterized by a high increase of zinc protoporphyrin in red blood cells (Figure 10-14B), as well as slightly elevated amounts of copro- and protoporphyrin. The large amount of δ-aminolevulinic acid in urine is also very important for detection of lead intoxication.

10.5.2 Proceeding of Laboratory Diagnostic Procedure

Porphyrin analysis from human materials represents the decisive part in differential diagnosis of *porphyrias.* Because of the extraordinary variability of the clinical symptoms, a great number of requests for such analyses are demanded from the clinical chemist. HPLC analysis of all specimens is not recommended owing to the relatively high costs and the high frequency of negative results. Hence, we are proposing for diagnostic purposes the following stepwise proceeding:

- First screen patients' urine for elevated porphyrins and precursors by ion-exchange chromatography or by second-derivative UV spectroscopy at the Soret-band.
- In the second step, urines containing increased amounts of porphyrins are analyzed by HPLC. Porphyrins and precursors are quantitated.
- Porphyrin analysis from faeces or blood using HPLC methods represents the final step, which is only necessary to confirm a tentative diagnosis of some rare forms, such as *porphyria variegata* or *erythrohepatic protoporphyria*. Well-founded suspicion on lead intoxication requires the determination of erythrocyte porphyrins.

Besides the support of diagnostic procedure, the control of porphyric patients is an important task in clinical chemistry. The surveillance of a patient suffering from *porphyria cutanea tarda* is shown by the chromatograms from urine samples obtained over a period of three months (Figure 10-21). This patient remained out of therapy at his own will. The absolute amounts of the individual porphyrins varied depending on variations of daily urine volume and alterations of the porphyrin excretion. Despite everything the characteristic porphyrin profile was always the same.

Fortunately, for diagnosis of *porphyrias*, the porphyrin profile is the most important feature. Therefore, it is not necessary to determine the absolute amount of individual porphyrins excreted over 24 hours.

The determination of porphyrins form human excreta and biological samples by HPLC provides reproducible and accurate results. In the future, the progress in sample preparation and separation conditions, as well as a further improvement in columns and equipment for HPLC, will enable an expanded use of HPLC analysis of porphyrins in clinical chemistry and biochemistry.

10.6 References

[1] F. Hoppe-Seyler, *Hoppe-Seyler's Z. Physiol. Chem.* 4, 193 (1879).
[2] A. Treibs (ed.): *Das Leben und Wirken von Hans Fischer*. Hans Fischer Gesellschaft, München (1971).
[3] C. Rimington, G. C. S. Roets, and P. J. J. Fourie, *Onderstepoort J. Vet. Sci. Anim. Ind.* 10, 421 (1938).
[4] C. Rimington, and S. L. Sveinsson, *Scand. J. Clin. Lab. Invest.* 2, 209 (1950).
[5] S. Schwartz, L. Zieve, and C. J. Watson, *J. Lab. Clin. Med.* 37, 843 (1951).
[6] M. Grinstein, S. Schwartz, and C. J. Watson, *J. Biol. Chem.* 157, 323 (1945).
[7] T. K. With, *Clin. Biochem. (Montreal)* 1, 30 (1967).
[8] M. Doss, *Klin. Wochenschr.* 47, 1280 (1969).
[9] A. Seubert, S. Seubert, and H. Ippen, *Dtsch. Med. Wochenschr.* 104, 1459 (1979).
[10] S. Nacht, L. C. San Martin De Viale, and M. Grinstein, *Clin. Chim. Acta* 27, 445 (1970).
[11] W. H. Lockwood, and J. L. Davis, *Clin. Chim. Acta* 7, 301 (1962).
[12] J. E. Falk, and E. L. B. Dresel, *Biochim. Biophys. Acta* 39, 458 (1960).
[13] A. Schmitt, *J. Clin. Chem. Clin. Biochem.* 15, 303 (1977).
[14] H. Scheer, and J. J. Katz, in: K. M. Smith (ed.): *Porphyrins and Metalloporphyrins*, p. 399. Elsevier, Amsterdam 1975.
[15] N. Evans, D. E. Games, A. H. Jackson, and S. A. Matlin, *J. Chromatogr.* 115, 325 (1975).
[16] R. Willstätter, and M. Fischer, *Hoppe-Seyler's Z. Physiol. Chem.* 87, 423 (1913).
[17] J.-L. Soret, *Arch. Sci. Phys. Nat.* 10, 430 (1883).

[18] N. Evans, A. H. Jackson, S. A. Matlin, and R. Towill, *J. Chromatogr.* **125**, 345 (1976).

[19] C. H. Gray, C. K. Lim, and D. C. Nicholson, *Clin. Chim. Acta* **77**, 167 (1977).

[20] N. G. Christensen, and I. Romslo, *Scand. J. Clin. Lab. Invest.* **39**, 223 (1979).

[21] S. A. Matlin, A. H. Jackson, and N. Evans, in: E. Reid (ed.): *Methodological Development in Biochemistry*, Vol. **5**, p. 45. North Holland, Amsterdam 1976.

[22] J. H. P. Wilson, J. W. O. Van Den Berg, A. Edixhoven-Bosdijk, and L. H. M. Van Gastel-Quist, *Clin. Chim. Acta* **89**, 165 (1978).

[23] T. K. With, *Scand. J. Clin. Lab. Invest. Suppl.* **32**, 134 (1973).

[24] Z. J. Petryka, and C. A. Pierach, *J. Chromatogr. Sci.* **10**, 103 (1979).

[25] Z. J. Petryka, and C. J. Watson, *Anal. Biochem.* **84**, 173 (1978).

[26] C. K. Lim, C. H. Gray, and M. S. Stoll, in: M. Doss (ed.): *Porphyrins in Human Diseases*, p. 472. Karger, Basel 1976.

[27] T. Schoofs, K. Gossler, and K. H. Schaller, *GIT Fachz. Lab.* **22**, 610 (1978).

[28] G. H. Elder, *Clin. Haematol.* **9**, 371 (1980).

[29] J. G. Straka, J. P. Kushner, and B. F. Burnham, *Anal. Biochem.* **111**, 269 (1981).

[30] J. M. Fuhrhop, and K. M. Smith, in: K. M. Smith (ed.): *Porphyrins and Metalloporphyrins*,p. 835. Elsevier, Amsterdam 1975.

[31] R. Bonnett, A. A. Charalambides, K. Jones, I. A. Magnus, and R. J. Ridge, *Biochem. J.* **173**, 693 (1978).

[32] H. D. Meyer, K. Jacob, and W. Vogt, *J. High Resolut. Chromatogr. Chromatogr. Commun.* **3**, 85 (1980).

[33] H. D. Meyer, K. Jacob, W. Vogt, and M. Knedel, *J. Chromatogr.* **199**, 339 (1980).

[34] E. Englert Jr., A. W. Wayne, E. E. Wales Jr. and R. C. Straight, *J. High Resolut. Chromatogr. Chromatogr. Commun.* **2**, 570 (1979).

[35] R. E. Ford, C.-N. Ou, and R. D. Ellefson, *Clin. Chem.* **27**, 397 (1981).

[36] R. F. Adams, W. Slavin, and A. Rhys Williams, *Chromatogr. Newsl.* **4**, 24 (1976).

[37] R. E. Carlson, and D. Dolphin, in: P. E. Dixon, C. H. Gray, C. K. Lim, and M. S. Stoll (eds.): *HPLC in Clinical Chemistry*, p. 87. Academic Press, London 1976.

[38] C. Rimington, and T. K. With, *Enzyme* **7**, 17 (1974).

[39] T. K. With, *Scand. J. Clin. Lab. Invest.* **38**, 501 (1978).

[40] H. D. Meyer, K. Jacob, W. Vogt, and M. Knedel, *J. Chromatogr.* **217**, 473 (1981).

[41] G. R. Gotelli, J. H. Wall, P. M. Kabra, and L. J. Marton, *Clin. Chem.* **26**, 205 (1980).

[42] A. H. Jackson, D. M. Jones, G. Philip, T. D. Lash, A. M. Del C. Battle, and S. G. Smith, *J. Biochem.* **12**, 681 (1980).

[43] M. O. Longas, and M. B. Poh-Fitzpatrick, *Anal. Biochem.* **104**, 268 (1980).

[44] J. A. S. Cavaleiro, G. W. Kenner, and K. M. Smith, *J. Chem. Soc. Perkin Trans.* **I** 1974, 1188 (1974).

[45] L. Malina, V. Miller, and I. A. Magnus, *Clin. Chim. Acta* **83**, 55 (1978).

[46] M. L. Richter, and K. G. Rients, *FEBS Lett.* **116**, 211 (1980).

[47] A. A. Lamola, and T. Yamane, *Science* **186**, 936 (1974).

[48] R. M. Smith, D. Doran, M. Mazur, and B. Bush, *J. Chromatogr.* **181**, 319 (1980).

[49] H. A. Scoble, M. Mc Keag, P. R. Brown, and G. J. Kavarnos, *Clin. Chim. Acta* **113**, 253 (1981).

[50] P. Culbreth, G. Walter, R. Carter, and C. Burtis, *Clin. Chem.* **25**, 605 (1979).

[51] M. Salmi, and R. Tenhunen, *Clin. Chem.* **26**, 1832 (1980).

[52] R. E. Carlson, and D. Dolphin, in: M. Doss (ed.): *Porphyrins in Human Diseases*, p. 465. Karger, Basel 1976.

[53] N. Evans, A. H. Jackson, S. A. Matlin, and R. Towill, in: P. F. Dixon, C. H. Gray, C. K. Lim, and M. S. Stoll (eds.): *HPLC in Clinical Chemistry*, p. 71. Academic Press, London 1976.

[54] C. H. Gray, C. K. Lim, and D. C. Nicholson, in: P. F. Dixon, C. H. Gray, C. K. Lim, and M. S. Stoll (eds.): *HPLC in Clinical Chemistry*, p. 79. Academic Press, London 1976.

[55] P. Hörchner, and T. Rietveld, *J. Chromatogr.* **123**, 414 (1976).

[56] V. Miller, and L. Malina, *J. Chromatogr.* **145**, 290 (1978).

[57] A. H. Jackson, H. A. Sancovich, and A. M. Ferramola De Sancovich, *Bioorg. Chem.* **9**, 71 (1980).

[58] G. H. Elder, J. O. Evans, J. R. Jackson, and A. H. Jackson, *Biochem. J.* **169**, 215 (1978).

[59] A. H. Jackson, K. R. N. Rao, D. M. Supphayen, and S. G. Smith, *J. Chem. Soc. Chem. Commun.* 1977, 696 (1977).

[60] A. R. Battersby, D. G. Buckley, G. L. Hodgson, R. E. Markwell, and E. McDonald, in: P. F. Dixon, C. H. Gray, C. K. Lim, and M. S. Stoll (eds.): *HPLC in Clinical Chemistry*, p. 63. Academic Press, London 1976.

[61] J. C. Bommer, B. F. Burnham, R. E. Carlson, and D. Dolphin, *Anal. Biochem.* **95**, 444 (1979).

[62] H. Nordlöv, P. M. Jordan, G. Burton, and A. I. Scott, *J. Chromatogr.* **190**, 221 (1980).

[63] I. C. Walker, M. T. Gilbert, and K. Stubbs, *J. Chromatogr.* **202**, 491 (1980).

[64] J. P. Franke, and R. A. De Zeeuw, *Anal. Chem.* **50**, 1374 (1978).

[65] R. Bonnett, R. J. Ridge, P. A. Scourides, and M. C. Berenbaum, *J. Chem. Soc. Chem. Commun.* **1980**, 1198 (1980).

[66] A. W. Wayne, R. C. Straight, E. E. Wales Jr., and E. Englert Jr., *J. High Resolut. Chromatogr. Chromatogr. Commun.* **2**, 621 (1979).

[67] J. C. Bommer, Personal Communication (1982), unpublished data.

[68] R. F. Adams, and F. L. Vandemark, *Clin. Chem.* **22**, 1180 (1976).

[69] L. L. Needham, S. L. Sirmans, J. A. Liddle, and D. D. Bayse, *Clin. Chem.* **27**, 1099 (1981).

[70] W. Slavin, A. T. Rhys Williams, and R. F. Adams, *J. Chromatogr.* **134**, 121 (1977).

[71] H. D. Meyer, unpublished results.

[72] D. T. Zelt, J. A. Owen, and G. S. Mark, *J. Chromatogr.* **189**, 209 (1980).

[73] *Clin. Haematol.*, Vol. **9** (2), (1982) (special issue on porphyrias).

[74] K. Schreier (ed.): *Die angeborenen Stoffwechselanomalien*. Georg Thieme Verlag, Stuttgart 1979.

11 Steriod Hormones

by *Wolfgang Voelter*

11 Steroid Hormones

11.1 Introduction

Steroids are natural products with a perhydrocyclopentanophenantrene fused-ring system. Designation of rings (A, B, C, D) and the generally accepted numbering are seen from the formula of cholestane (Figure 11-1).

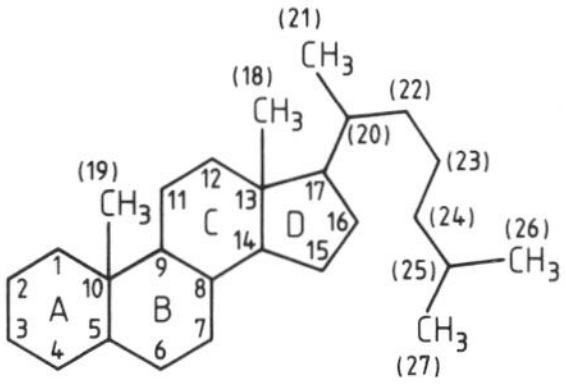

Figure 11-1. Structure of cholestane with generally accepted numbering of carbon atoms.

Ever since their discovery, chromatographic procedures like adsorption chromatography, column partition chromatography, paper chromatography, thin-layer chromatography and gas-liquid chromatography played an important role in steroid chemistry. Recently, because of several advantages, high performance column liquid chromatography has been applied to separate and identify steroids of different structure, using a variety of conditions. Several monographs give detailed information about the chemistry [1 to 4] and analysis [5 to 8] of steroids.

11.2 Androgens and Androstanes

Androgens are the male sexual hormones which all lack a side chain at position C_{17}. In Figure 11-2 the structures of some selected androgens and biologically occurring androstanes are given.

Using hydrophobic supports, coated with non-polar stationary phase material, Siggia and Dishman [9] separated androgens more than 10 years ago with fairly good resolution (Table 11-1).

Androgens have been analyzed using reversed-phase material of different structure and origin, including ODS Permaphase, Nucleosil CN, Nucleosil C_{18}, μBondapak, LiChrosorb RP-8 or LiChrosorb RP-18 [10 – 14]. Up to 1 ng of steroid is detectable by UV absorption at 254 nm.

The five major products of testosterone formed by hepatic microsomal monooxygenase can easily be separated by reversed-phase HPLC, as demonstrated by Figure 11-3 [15].

Reversed-phase HPLC (LiChrosorb RP-8) also separates androstane acetates with good resolutions, as is demonstrated in a communication by Higgins dealing with acetates of some 19-norsteroids [16]. Converting androstanes into benzoates, p-nitrobenzoates [17] or 2,4-dinitro-

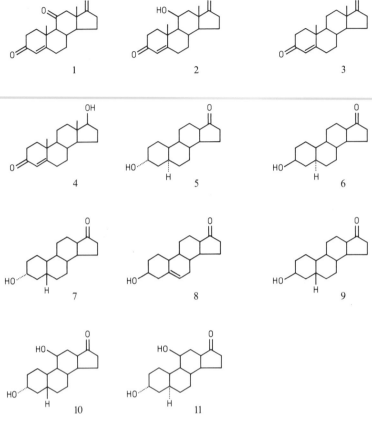

Figure 11-2. Structures of selected androstanes; **1**: 4-androstene-3,11-17-trione, **2**: 4-androstene-11β-ol-3,17-dione, **3**: 4-androstene-11,17-dione, **4**: testosterone, **5**: androsterone, **6**: epiandrosterone, **7**: etiocholanolone, **8**: dehydroepiandrosterone, **9**: epietiocholanolone, **10**: 11β-OH-etiocholanolone, **11**: 11β-OH-androsterone.

Table 11-1. Retention Data for Some Androgens, Separated on Amberlite LA-1 (n-dodecanal (trialkylmethyl)-amine). Chromatographic conditions: Column: 24% LA-1 on CTFE(terpolymer of trifluoroethylene, 325 mesh, 485 x 2 mm i. d.); mobile phase: water; flow-rate: 0.25 mL/min; detection: absorption at 250 nm [9].

Steroid	t_R,(min)	Relative t_R,	R
4-Androstene-3,11-17-trione	6.53	2.05	0.765
4-Androsten-11β-ol-3,17-dione	7.98	3.10	1.16
△-1,4-Androstadien-17β-ol-3-one	22.7	13.8	5.14
19-nor-4-Androstene-3,17-dione	26.9	16.8	6.27
19-nor-Testosterone	31.9	20.4	7.62
4-Androstene-3,17-dione	57.2	38.8	14.5
Testosterone	68.6	47.0	17.5

Figure 11-3. HPLC chromatogram of hydroxylated testosterones testosterone and androstenedione. Column: C_{18} reversed-phase (10 μm, 250 × 4.6 mm i. d.); mobile phase: the column was developed with methanol/water (55:45) followed by methanol/water/acetonitrile (55:35:10) initiated at the arrow; detection: absorption at 240 nm; injected sample volume: 10 μL; injection per steroid: 2β-hydroxytestosterone (2β-), 1.32 mmol/L, 6β-hydroxytestosterone (6β-) 0.33 mmol/L, 7α-hydroxytestosterone (7α-) 0.33 mmol/L, 16α-hydroxytestosterone (16α-) 0.37 mmol/L, testosterone (T) 0.33 mmol/L and androstenedione (A) 1.63 mmol/L (similar to reference [15]).

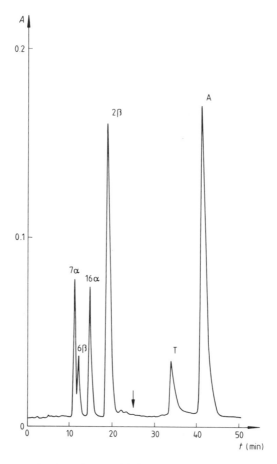

phenyl hydrazones [18] considerably increases the detection sensitivity by UV absorption. RI detection was also applied for the determination of androstanes, their sulfates and glucuronides, after separation by reversed-phase partition chromatography on a Micropak CH column using methanol/water mixtures as the eluents [19]. The elution order for the free and conjugated steroids is dehydroepiandrosterone, epiandrosterone, etiocholanolone and androsterone. Steroids with equatorially oriented hydroxyl groups are generally more polar than comparable ones with axial hydroxyl function.

Reversed-phase chromatography is also suitable for preparative separations of androstanes. A LiChrosorb RP-18 column has been applied recently for the successful isolation of 7α- and 7β-methyl derivatives of 17β-acetoxy-3-oxoandrost-4-ene and side-reaction products obtained by reaction of 17β-acetoxy-3-oxoandrosta-4,6-diene with lithium dimethylcuprate [14].

HPLC based on adsorption is also eminently suitable for the separation of androgens (Figure 11-4 [20]).

The Δ^4-3-ketones (III, VII and IX in Figure 11-4) show strong absorption at 254 nm and up to 30 ng of testosterone can be detected at that wavelength. 17-Ketosteroids are preferably detected at a wavelength of 280 nm; the sensitivity, however, is only about one-fiftieth of that for the Δ^4-3-ketones. Figure 11-4 demonstrates that the C_{19} steroids are eluted in three groups by adsorption

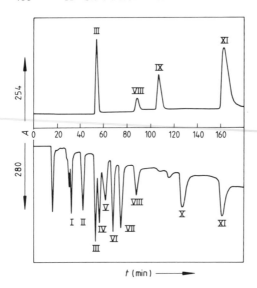

Figure 11-4. HPLC chromatogram of androgens. Column: Partisil 5 (two sections of 300 × 4.6 mm i. d.); mobile phase: dichloromethane/acetonitrile/2-propanol (179:20:1); flow-rate: 0.4 mL/min; detection: the effluent passed through two detectors in series, the first one set at 280 nm and the second one at 254 nm; sample: a mixture of 37 µg I (5 α-androstane-3,17-dione = androstanedione), 39 µg II (5 β-androstane-3,17-dione = etiocholanedione), 34 µg III (4-androstene-3,17-dione = androstenedione), 196 µg IV (3 β-hydroxy-5 β-androstan-17-one = epietiocholanolone), 188 µg V (3 β-hydroxy-5-androsten-17-one = dehydroepiandrosterone), 210 µg VI (3 β-hydroxy-5 α-androstan-17-one = epiandrosterone), 214 µg VII (3 α-hydroxy-5 α-androstan-17-one = androsterone), 6 µg VIII (1,4-androstadiene-3,17-dione = androstadienedione), 42 µg IX (17 β-hydroxy-4-androsten-3-one = testosterone), 297 µg X (3 α-hydroxy-5 β-androstan-17-one = ethiocholanolone) and 99 µg XI (17 α-hydroxy-4-androsten-3-one = epitestosterone) are applied by stop-flow to the column (similar to reference [20]).

chromatography: group 1: diketones (compounds I – III) is eluted first, followed by group 2: 3-hydroxy-17-ketones (compounds IV – VII) finally followed by group 3: 17-hydroxy-3-ketones (compounds IX and XI). Furthermore, the known fact that epimeric steroids are better resolved by adsorption than by reversed-phase partition chromatography, with the exception of 17-epimers [21], becomes obvious.

11.3 Estrogens

The estrogens are the female sexual hormones with an A ring of aromatic character. The structures of some selected estrogens are collected in Figure 11-5.

Because of their strong UV absorption, communications about the HPLC of estrogens appeared relatively early in the literature [22]. Estrogens and their derivatives have been separated by, both, adsorption (Zorbax BP-SIL, µPorasil, Corasil I, Partisil 5 [23 to 26] and reversed-phase (Zorbax BP-ODS, µBondapak C$_{18}$, LiChrosorb RP-8, Spherisorb S5-ODS [26

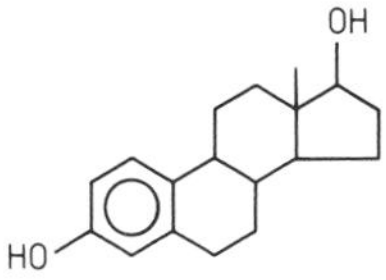

Figure 11-5. Structures of selected estrogens; 1: estradiol, 2: estrone, 3: estriol, 4: 16-epiestriol, 5: 16,17-epiestriol, 6: 6-ketoestradiol, 7: 2-hydroxyestriol, 8: 6α-hydroxyestriol.

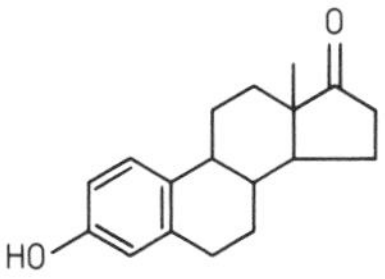

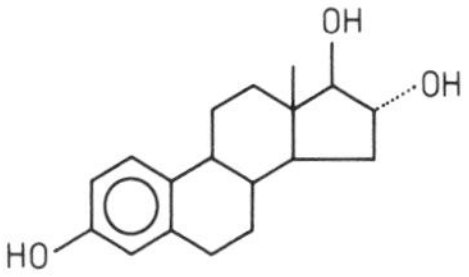

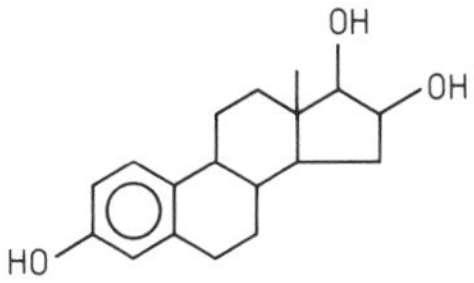

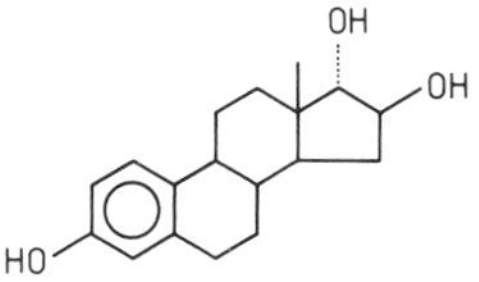

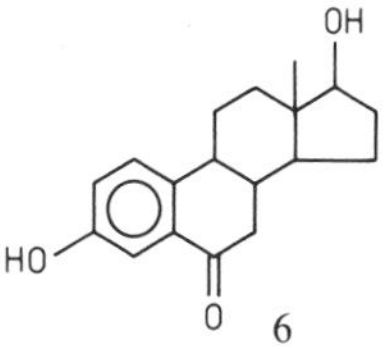

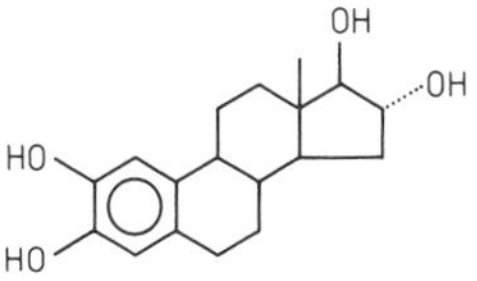

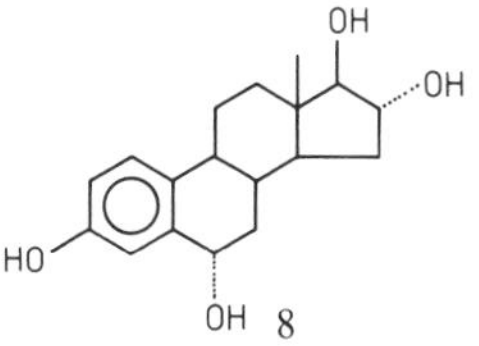

to 32]) chromatography. A comparison of the results received with adsorption and reversed-phase HPLC columns on naturally occurring estrogens is given in Table 11-2.

From Table 11-2 the following general conclusions can be made:

- Number and location of hydroxyl groups in estrogens play the most important role in their separation by HPLC.
- Addition of a keto group to an estrogen molecule does not increase the polarity in adsorption as much as in reversed-phase chromatography.
- Epimeric estrogens are better resolved in adsorption than in reversed-phase systems.
- The elution sequence of estrogens in reversed-phase is not exactly the reverse of that in adsorption chromatography; therefore both separations may give complementary information.
- The polarity of hydroxyl groups at C-16 and C-17 increases in the order of $17\alpha < 17\beta < 16\alpha < 16\beta$.
- 6-Ketoestradiol is more polar than 16-ketoestradiol in adsorption, but less polar in reversed-phase chromatography.

Several detailed studies on the HPLC separation of estrogen conjugates were performed using ion-exchange cellulose [33], μPartisil 10-SAX [34], LiChrospher Si-100 [35] or LiChrosorb RP-2 (RP-18) [36] columns. The most fundamental study on the application of ion-exchange celluloses for the separation of estrogen glucuronides, sulfates and phosphates was done by van der Wal and Huber [33]. The properties of selected ion-exchange celluloses are surveyed in Table 11-3.

Table 11-2. Retention Times (min) of Estrogens of Different HPLC Separations. – Chromatographic Conditions:

Condition 1: Column: Zorbax BP-SIL (7 to 8 µm, 250 × 4.6 mm i. d.); mobile phase: n-hexane/ethanol (9 : 1); flow-rate: 2 mL/min; detection: absorption at 280 nm; sample: between 1.5 and 10 µg of estrogen, dissolved in 50 µL eluent.

Condition 2: Column: Zorbax BP-SIL (7 to 8 µm, 250 × 4.6 mm i. d.); mobile phase: n-hexane/ethanol (97 : 3); flow-rate: 2 mL/min; detection: absorption at 280 nm; sample: between 1 and 10 µg of estrogen, dissolved in 50 µL eluent.

Condition 3: Column: Zorbax BP-ODS (7 to 8 µm; 250 × 4.6 mm i. d.); mobile phase: acetonitrile/water (35 : 65); flow-rate: 2 mL/min; detection: absorption at 280 nm; sample: between 1 and 3 µg estrogen, dissolved in 50 µL methanol.

Condition 4: Column: Zorbax BP-ODS (7 to 8 µm, 250 × 4.6 mm i. d.); mobile phase: acetonitrile/water (25 : 75); flow-rate: 2 mL/min; detection: absorption at 280 nm; sample between 1 and 5 µg estrogen, dissolved in 50 µL eluent [26].

Compounds	Conditions			
	1	2	3	4
Monools				
17-Deoxoestrone		3.25	>75	
Estrone		9.5	32	
6-Dehydroestrone		9.5	28.5	
Equilin		9.5	28.5	
Equilenin		10.5	25.5	
Diols				
Estradiol-17 α		16.25	25.5	
Estradiol-17 β	4.75	17.75	23	
2-Hydroxyestrone		19.5*)	16	
6-Dehydroestradiol		20.25	18.5	
17 α-Dihydroequilin		22.5	18.5	
3,16 α-Estradiol		22.5	21	
17 α-Dihydroequilenin		25.25	16	
16-Ketoestradiol		27.5	6.75	22.5
16 α-Hydroxyestrone		30.75	7.25	25.5
6-Ketoestradiol	6.75	32	7.25	25.5
Triols				
16-Epiestriol	8.25		9.25	
17-Epiestriol	8.25		13.5*)	
2-Hydroxyestradiol	8.25*)		13.5	
Estriol	11		4.25	13
6 α-Hydroxyestradiol	11		4.25	10
16,17-Epiestriol	12.75		4.25	13
6-Ketoestriol	16.75(15)**)		2.5	6.25
Tetraols				
2-Hydroxyestriol	19.25*)		3.5	7.75
6 α-Hydroxyestriol	28		2.5	4

*)   Broad peaks.
**)   Sample also gave a minor peak at 15 min.

Table 11-3. Particle Sizes and Ion-Exchange Capacities of Different Ion-Exchange Celluloses as Column Packings [33].

Anion-Exchanger	Particle Diameter Range, 10 to 90% µm	Mean Particle Diameter µm	Ion-Exchange Capacity mmol/g
Cellex PEI (polyethyleneimminecellulose)	7 to 17	11	0.21
Cellex AE (aminoethylcellulose)	10 to 19	14	0.29
Cellex T (triethylaminoethylcellulose)	11 to 19	14	0.15
Cellex GE (guanidoethylcellulose)	–	–	–
B 300 (ECTEOLA-cellulose)	12 to 27	19	0.27
	9 to 19	13	0.27
	8 to 16	11	0.15
ET 41 (ECTEOLA-cellulose)	6 to 16	11	0.15
Cellex E (ECTEOLA-cellulose)	7 to 16	11	0.17

The degree of chromatographic separation of two components is described by the resolution R which depends on the parameters given in equation (1):

$$R = (\alpha - 1) \cdot \frac{k}{1 + k} \cdot (n)^{\frac{1}{2}}$$

(1)

where

α selectivity;
k capacity ratio;
n number of theoretical plates;
l length of the column;
h theoretical plate height.

The capacity factor is calculated from the retention time t_R of the component and the retention time t_M of a nonretarded component (2):

$$k = \frac{t_R - t_M}{t_M} \cdot$$

(2)

The capacity ratio of a component can be determined from its distribution coefficient K and the phase ratio β (3):

$$k = K \cdot \beta \,.$$

(3)

The overall distribution coefficient K_x of the component X can be calculated from equation (4) for the ion-exchange equilibrium of the anion X^- and the dissociation equilibrium of the protonated form HX:

$$K_x = \frac{[X^-]_s}{[X^-]_m + [HX]_m} = \frac{K_1}{[A^-]_m (1 + K_2 [H^+]_m)} \qquad (4)$$

where

$[X^-]_s$ anion concentration of the sample component in the anion-exchanger;
$[X^-]_m$ anion concentration of the sample component in the mobile phase;
$[HX]_m$ concentration of the undissociated sample component in the mobile phase;
$[A^-]_m$ anion concentration of the counter-ion of the ion-exchanger in the mobile phase;
$[H^+]_m$ hydrogen ion concentration in the mobile phase;
K_1 ion-exchange equilibrium constant;
K_2 formation constant of HX.

From the equations 3 and 4 it follows that the capacity ratio depends on:

● The nature of the fixed ionogenic group.
● The ion-exchange capacity.
● The nature of the matrix of the ion-exchanger.
● The type and concentration of the eluent anion.
● The pH of the eluent.
● The temperature, for an anion to be separated.

In Figures 11-6, 11-7 and 11-8 chromatograms of the separations of estrogen conjugates with different ion-exchange celluloses are shown.

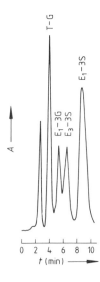

Figure 11-6. Chromatogram of the separation of estrogen conjugates. Column: Cellex T (14 μm, 250 × 3 mm i. d.); mobile phase: 0.25 mol/L perchlorate + 0.01 mol/L phosphate, pH 6.8); detection: absorption at 220 nm; temperature: 75 °C, samples: T-G: testosterone β-D-glucuronide, E_1-3 G: estrone β-D-glucuronide; E_3-3 S: estriol 3-sulfate, E_1-3 S: estrone 3-sulfate (similar to reference [33]).

Figure 11-7. Chromatogram of the separation of 17 α-estradiol 3-sulfate (17 αE$_2$-3 S) and 17 β-estradiol 17-sulfate (17 βE$_2$-17 S). Column: Cellex AE (14 μm, 250 × 3 mm i. D.); mobile phase: 0.025 mol/L perchlorate +0.01 mol/L phosphate pH 6.8); detection: absorption at 220 nm; temperature: 70 °C (similar to reference [33]).

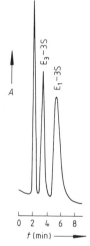

Figure 11-8: Chromatogram of the separation of estriol 3-sulfate (E$_3$-3 S) and estrone 3-sulfate (E$_1$-3 S). Column: Cellex PEI (11 μm, 250 ×3 mm i. d.); mobile phase: 0.25 mol/L perchlorate +0.01 mol/L phosphate, pH 8.5); detection: absorption at 220 nm; temperature: 50 °C (similar to reference [33]).

In Table 11-4 the influence of selected types of cellulose anion exchangers on the capacity ratios of estrogen conjugates is shown.

Table 11-4. Influence of Selected Types of Cellulose Anion Exchangers (see Table 11-3) on the Capacity Ratio of Estrogen Conjugates. – Chromatographic conditions: Column: 250 × 3 mm i. d., mobile phase: perchlorate + 0.01 mol/L phosphate, pH 6.8; detection: absorption at 220 nm [33].

ECTEOLA-Cellulose (0.025 mol/L ClO_4^-, 70 °C)		Polyethylene-iminecellulose (0.100 mol/L ClO_4^-, 50 °C)		Aminoethyl-cellulose (0.025 mol/L ClO_4^-, 70 °C)		Triethylamino-ethylcellulose (0.100 mol/L ClO_4^-, 70 °C)		Guanidoethyl-cellulose (0.250 mol/L ClO_4^-, 75 °C)	
Steroid conjugate	k	Steroid conjugate	k	Steroid conjugate	k	Steroid conjugate	k	Steroid conjugate	k
Testosterone β-D-glucuronide	0.54	Estriol 3-β-D-glucuronide	0.42	Testosterone β-D-glucuronide	0.55	Testosterone β-D-glucuronide	0.82	Estriol 3-β-D-glucuronide	1.75
Estriol 3-β-D-glucuronide	0.76	Testosterone β-D-glucuronide	0.46	Estriol 3-β-D-glucuronide	0.73	Estriol 3-β-D-glucuronide	1.01	Testosterone β-D-glucuronide	1.59
Estrone β-D-glucuronide	1.03	Estriol 17-β-D-glucuronide	1.03	Estrone β-D-glucuronide	0.75	Estrone β-D-glucuronide	1.49	Estrone β-D-glucuronide	2.09
Estrone 3-phosphate	1.24	Estriol 16-β-D-glucuronide	1.16	Testosterone sulfate	0.90	17 β-Estradiol 3-β-D-glucuronide	1.76	Estriol 17-β-D-glucuronide	2.40
Testosterone sulfate	1.57	Estrone β-D-glucuronide	1.18	17 β-Estradiol 3-β-D-glucuronide	1.05	Estrone 3-phosphate	1.94	Testosterone-sulfate	2.48
17 β-Estradiol 3-β-D-glucuronide	1.59	17 β-Estradiol 3-β-D-glucuronide	1.34	Estriol-3-sulfate	1.45	Estriol 17-β-D-glucuronide	2.05	17 β-Estradiol 3-β-glucuronide	2.60
17 β-Estradiol 3-phosphate	1.86	Estriol 3-sulfate	1.42	Estrone 3-sulfate	1.49	17 β-Estradiol 3.17-β-D-diglucuronide	2.16	Estriol 16-β-D-glucuronide	2.69
Estriol 17-β-D-glucuronide	1.98	Testosterone sulfate	1.69	Estriol 17-β-D-glucuronide	1.63	Estriol 16-β-D-glucuronide	2.17	Estriol 3-sulfate	3.09
Estriol 16-β-D-glucuronide	2.14	17 β-Estradiol 17-β-D-glucuronide	1.75	17 β-Estradiol 17-β-D-glucuronide	1.72	17 β-Estradiol 3, 17-diphosphate	2.31	17 β-Estradiol 17-β-D-glucuronide	3.43
17 β-Estradiol 3,-17-β-D-diglucuronide	2.39	17 β-Estradiol 3,-17-β-D-diglucuronide	1.85	17 α-Estradiol 3-sulfate	1.80	17 β-Estradiol 3-phosphate	2.32	Estrone 3-sulfate	3.92
17 β-Estradiol 17-β-D-glucuronide	2.68	Estrone 3-sulfate	4.65	Estriol 16-β-D-glucuronide	1.82	Testosterone sulfate	2.37	17α-Estradiol 3-sulfate	4.20

Table 11-4. (Continued).

ECTEOLA-Cellulose (0.025 mol/L ClO_4^-, 70°C)		Polyethylene-iminecellulose (0.100 mol/L ClO_4^-, 50°C)		Aminoethyl-cellulose (0.025 mol/L ClO_4^-, 70°C)		Triethylamino-ethylcellulose (0.100 mol/L ClO_4^-, 70°C)		Guanidoethyl-cellulose (0.250 mol/L ClO_4^-, 75°C)	
Steroid conjugate	k	Steroid conjugate	k	Steroid conjugate	k	Steroid conjugate	k	Steroid conjugate	k
Estriol 3-sulfate	3.13	Equilin 3-sulfate	4.85	Equilin 3-sulfate	1.90	17β-Estradiol 17-β-D-glucuronide	2.56	Equilin 3-sulfate	4.50
17β-Estradiol 17-phosphate	3.27	17α-Estradiol 3-sulfate	4.97	17β-Estradiol 3-sulfate	2.08	17β-Estradiol 17-phosphate	3.07	17β-Estradiol 3-sulfate	4.94
Estrone 3-sulfate	3.99	17β-Estradiol 3-sulfate-17-β-D-glucuronide	4.97	17α-Dihydroequilin 3-sulfate	2.49	Estriol 3-sulfate	3.84	17β-Estradiol 3,-17-β-D-diglucuronide	5.01
Equilin 3-sulfate	5.13	17β-Estradiol sulfate	5.26	17β-Estradiol 3,-17-β-D-diglucuronide	2.74	Estrone 3-sulfate	5.64	17α-Dihydroequilin 3-sulfate	5.32
17β-Estradiol 3,-17-diphosphate	5.20	17α-Dihydroequilin 3-sulfate	5.65	Equilenin 3 sulfate	2.94	17α-Estradiol 3-sulfate	6.02	17β-Estradiol 17-sulfate	5.70
17α-Estradiol 3-sulfate	5.53	17β-Estradiol 17-sulfate	6.04	17β-Estradiol 17-sulfate	3.04	17β-Estradiol 3-sulfate	6.77	Equilenin 3-sulfate	6.91
17β-Estradiol 3-sulfate	6.06	Estriol 3, 17-disulfate	6.70	17α-Dihydro-equilenin 3-sulfate	3.56	Equilin 3-sulfate	6.82	17α-Dihydro-equilenin 3-sulfate	7.88
17α-Dihydroequilin 3-sulfate	6.98	17β-Estradiol 17-phosphate	6.74	17β-Estradiol 3-sulfate-17-β-D-glucuronide	4.97	17β-Estradiol 17-sulfate	7.38	17β-Estradiol 3-sulfate-17-β-D-glucuronide	9.17
17β-Estradiol 17-sulfate	7.04	Estrone 3-phosphate	7.95	17β-Estradiol 17-phosphate	5.25	17β-Estradiol 3-sulfate-17-β-D-glucuronide	7.47	Estriol 3, 17-disulfate	9.86
17β-Estradiol 3-sulfate-17-β-D-glucuronide	7.09	17β-Estradiol 3,-17-diphosphate	9.04	Estrone 3-phosphate	6.46	17α-Dihydroequilin 3-sulfate	7.78	17β-Estradiol 3,-17-diphosphate	13.50
Equilenin 3-sulfate	9.04	17β-Estradiol 3-phosphate	9.17	Estriol 3, 17-disulfate	6.97	Equilenin 3-sulfate	12.40	Estriol 16, 17-disulfate	14.10
Estriol 3, 17-disulfate	10.90	Equilenin 3-sulfate	9.23	17β-Estradiol 3,-17-diphosphate	8.51	17β-Estriol 3, 17-disulfate	13.75	17β-Estradiol 3,-17-disulfate	14.35
17α-Dihydroequilenin 3-sulfate	13.25	17α-Dihydroequilenin 3-sulfate	10.75	17β-Estradiol 3,-17-disulfate	8.51	17α-Dihydroequilenin 3-sulfate	13.90	Estrone 3-phosphate	16.00

Table 11-4. (Continued).

ECTEOLA-Cellulose (0.025 mol/L ClO_4^-, 70 °C)		Polyethylene-iminecellulose (0.100 mol/L ClO_4^-, 50 °C)		Aminoethyl-cellulose (0.025 mol/L ClO_4^-, 70 °C)		Triethylamino-ethylcellulose (0.100 mol/L ClO_4^-, 70 °C)		Guanidoethyl-cellulose (0.250 mol/L ClO_4^-, 75 °C)	
Steroid conjugate	k	Steroid conjugate	k	Steroid conjugate	k	Steroid conjugate	k	Steroid conjugate	k
Estriol 16, 17-di-sulfate	16.30	17 β-Estradiol 3,-17-disulfate	12.90	17 β-Estradiol 3-phosphate	8.71	Estriol 16, 17-disulfate	18.10	17 β-Estradiol 3,-17-diphos-phate	19.20
17 β-Estradiol 3,-17-disulfate	16.80	Estriol 16,- 17-disulfate	16.15	Estriol 16,- 17-disulfate	13.00	17 β-Estradiol 3,-17-disulfate	20.65	17 β-Estradiol 3-phosphate	19.60

From Table 11-4 the following general conclusions can be drawn:

- The site of conjugation in the estrogen conjugates is more important than the type of steroid.
- Ring A conjugates are eluted before ring D conjugates.
- The elution order according to the type of steroid is estriol, estrone, equilin, estradiol, equilenin.
- Sulfates have the largest capacity ratios; glucuronides are usually eluted before the phosphates.

Contrary to variations of the anion-exchange cellulose material from batch to batch, their mean particle size $\bar{d}_p$ has only a relative slight effect on the capacity ratio (Table 11-5).

Table 11-5. Dependence of the Capacity Ratio k on the Batch and Particle Size of Different ECTEOLA-celluloses. – Chromatographic conditions: Column: 250 × 3 mm i. d.; mobile phase: 0.025 mol/L perchlorate + 0.0125 mol/L phosphate, pH 7.0; detection: absorbance at 220 nm; temperature 70 °C [33].

Steroid conjugate	ET 41 ($\bar{d}_p = 11$ μm)	Cellex E ($\bar{d}_p = 11$ μm)	B 300 ($\bar{d}_p = 11$ μm)	B 300 ($\bar{d}_p = 13$ μm)	B 300 ($\bar{d}_p = 19$ μm)
Testosterone β-D-glucuronide	1.58	1.09	0.47	0.41	0.45
Estriol β-D-glucuronide	2.46	1.71	0.67	0.51	0.67
Estrone β-D-glucuronide	3.20	2.43	0.92	0.65	0.84
Estrone 3-phosphate	3.90	4.44	1.00	0.85	0.88
17β-Estradiol 3,17-β-D-diglucuronide	10.00	4.15	1.33	1.13	1.24

Table 11-5. (Continued).

Steroid conjugate	ET 41 ($\bar{d}_p$ = 11 μm)	Cellex E ($\bar{d}_p$ = 11 μm)	B 300 ($\bar{d}_p$ = 11 μm)	B 300 ($\bar{d}_p$ = 13 μm)	B 300 ($\bar{d}_p$ = 19 μm)
17β-Estradiol 3-β-D-glucuronide	4.38	3.71	1.42	1.05	1.30
Testosterone sulfate	4.80	4.50	1.49	1.04	1.27
Estriol 17-β-D-glucuronide	5.07	4.65	1.74	1.28	1.68
17β-Estradiol 3-phosphate	4.76	6.44	1.47	1.27	1.32
Estriol 16-β-D-glucuronide	5.30	4.86	1.86	1.38	1.80
17β-Estradiol 17-β-D-glucuronide	6.49	6.29	2.44	1.74	2.24
Estriol 3-sulfate	9.90	8.62	2.89	1.77	2.56
17β-Estradiol 3,17-diphosphate	11.70	10.00	2.40	2.15	2.32
17β-Estradiol 17-phosphate	13.95	14.90	2.86	2.23	2.77
Estrone 3-sulfate	12.60	12.15	3.81	2.14	3.11
17β-Estradiol 3-sulfate	17.10	18.45	5.87	3.48	4.91
17β-Estradiol 17-sulfate	20.80	22.65	6.81	3.99	5.75
Estriol 3,17-disulfate	66.50	42.50	9.55	5.55	7.91
17β-Estradiol 3,17-disulfate	–	66.60	15.80	8.65	12.70

According to equations (I to IV) the capacity ratios are dependent on the eluent anion concentration [A⁻]. From a plot of the k-values of different estrogen conjugates versus the inverse of the anion concentration it is seen that:

- A great change in selectivity and even reversals of elution order occur.
- Glucuronides are generally eluted first, followed by phosphates and finally sulfates.
- At low ionic strength monoconjugates move faster than diconjugates.
- At high anion concentration the elution order may be reversed (Figure 11-9).

While the counter-ion concentration has a strong influence on the elution time of different types of estrogen conjugates, it alters only the absolute value of the capacity factors for a series of conjugates and does not influence the elution sequence. This statement becomes obvious from a plot of capacity ratios versus the inverse of the eluent anion concentration $[A^-]^{-1}$ for different estrogen sulfates in Figure 11-10.

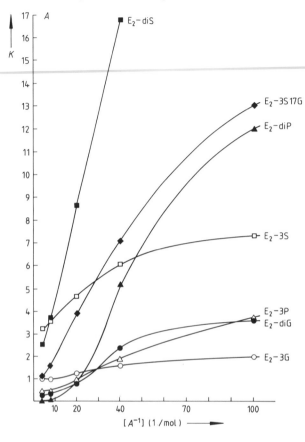

Figure 11-9. Dependence of the capacity ratio k of 17β-estradiol conjugates on the inverse of the eluent anion concentration $[A^-]^{-1}$. Column: ECTEOLA-cellulose B 300 (19 µm, 250 × 3 mm i. d.); mobile phase: perchlorate + 0.01 mol/L phosphate, pH 6.8; detection: absorption at 220 nm; temperature: 70 °C; samples (E_2-3G: 17β-estradiol 3β-D-glucuronide, E_2-diG: 17β-estradiol 3,17-β-D-glucuronide, E_2-3P: 17β-estradiol 3-phosphate, E_2-3S: 17β-estradiol 3-sulfate, E_2-diP: 17β-estradiol 3,17-diphosphate, E_2-3S17G: 17β-estradiol 3-sulfate-17-β-D-glucuronide, E_2-dis: 17β-estradiol 3,17-disulfate (similar to reference [33]).

The capacity ratios for estrogen conjugates by separation on ion-exchange celluloses is dependent on the eluent anion and cation; however, only minor selectivity changes are observed. Small capacity ratios are observed for estrogen phosphates if magnesium ions are used as eluent cation indicating complex formation (Table 11-6).

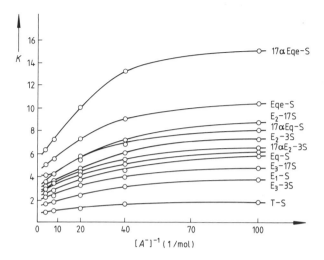

Figure 11-10. Dependence of the capacity ratios k of estrogen sulfates on the inverse of the eluent anion concentration $[A^-]^{-1}$. Column: ECTEOLA-cellulose B 300 (19 µm, 250 × 3 mm i.d.); mobile phase: perchlorate +0.01 mol/L phosphate, pH 6.8; detection: absorption at 220 nm; temperature: 70 °C; samples: T-S: testosterone sulfate, E_3-3S: estriol 3-sulfate, E_1-S: estrone 3-sulfate; E_3-17S: estriol 17-sulfate; Eq-S: equilin 3-sulfate; $17\alpha E_2$-3S: 17α-estradiol 3-sulfate; E_2-3S: 17β-estradiol 3-sulfate; 17α Eq-S: 17α-dihydroequilin 3-sulfate; E_2-17S: 17β-estradiol 17-sulfate; Eqe-S: equilenin 3-sulfate; 17α Eqe-S: 17α-dihydroequilenin 3-sulfate (similar to reference [33]).

Table 11-6. Influence of the Type of Eluent Anion and Cation on the Capacity Ratios k of Estrogen Conjugates. Chromatographic conditions: Column: ECTEOLA-cellulose B 300 (19 μm, 250 × 3 mm i. d.); mobile phase: 0.01 mol/L phosphate, pH 6.8; detection: absorption at 220 nm; temperature: 70 °C [33].

Steroid conjugate [ClO_4^-]	NaClO₄ 0.025	NaHSO₄ 0.100	NaNO₃ 0.100	NaCl 0.100	KCl 0.100	NH₄Cl 0.100	MgCl₂ 0.050	NH₄ phosphate 0.500	Na citrate 0.005	Na formate 0.100	Na acetate 0.100	Na propionate 0.125
Testosterone β-D-glucuronide	0.54	0.41	0.29	0.35	0.36	0.36	0.37	1.12	0.42	0.37	0.42	0.36
Estriol 3-β-D-glucuronide	0.76	0.63	0.50	0.58	0.62	0.60	0.63	1.27	0.68	0.61	0.68	0.58
Estrone β-D-glucuronide	1.03	0.74	0.59	0.67	0.71	0.69	0.72	1.72	0.74	0.68	0.77	0.67
Estrone 3-phosphate	1.24	0.67	0.64	0.75	0.84	0.79	0.49	0.93	1.34	0.87	1.04	0.77
Testosterone sulfate	1.57	1.17	0.94	1.03	1.08	1.07	1.25	3.01	1.07	1.07	1.14	1.01
17β-Estradiol 3-β-D-glucuronide	1.59	1.22	0.98	1.09	1.16	1.11	1.19	2.56	1.17	1.14	1.20	1.09
17β-Estradiol 3,17-β-D-diglucuronide	2.39	1.04	0.88	1.19	1.28	1.30	1.53	1.47	1.81	1.36	1.62	1.18
17β-Estradiol 3-phosphate	1.86	1.08	1.02	1.19	1.31	1.21	0.78	1.33	1.97	1.35	1.61	1.21
17β-Estradiol 3,17-diphosphate	5.20	1.28	1.55	1.18	1.31	1.21	0.76	0.59	1.97	2.76	3.62	2.14
Estriol 17-β-D-glucuronide	1.98	1.69	1.30	1.43	1.50	1.47	1.52	3.15	1.60	1.54	1.60	1.52
Estriol 16-β-D-glucuronide	2.14	1.78	1.42	1.55	1.61	1.51	1.54	3.38	1.72	1.59	1.71	1.56

17β-Estradiol 17-β-D-glucuronide	2.68	2.18	1.75	1.92	2.05	1.95	2.03	4.05	2.11	2.02	2.17	1.89
Estriol 3-sulfate	3.13	2.53	2.04	2.26	2.31	2.29	2.74	5.03	2.34	2.25	2.53	2.27
17β-Estradiol 17-phosphate	3.27	2.52	2.06	2.34	2.50	2.26	2.04	3.35	2.82	2.47	2.68	2.30
Estrone 3-sulfate	3.99	2.84	2.37	2.56	2.73	2.62	3.15	6.45	2.50	2.52	2.73	2.43
Equilin 3-sulfate	5.13	3.67	3.05	3.32	3.51	3.34	3.97	8.43	3.24	3.23	3.52	3.12
17α-Estradiol 3-sulfate	5.53	4.32	3.45	3.83	4.04	3.83	4.54	9.80	3.54	3.75	3.92	3.48
17β-Estradiol 3-sulfate	6.06	4.72	3.76	4.20	4.47	4.20	5.00	10.60	3.94	4.16	4.42	3.94
17α-Dihydroequilin 3-sulfate	6.98	5.40	4.50	5.03	5.15	4.95	5.83	12.00	4.69	4.74	5.23	4.54
17β-Estradiol 3-sulfate-17-β-D-glucuronide	7.09	4.08	3.50	4.80	5.34	4.96	6.76	6.29	5.57	4.95	5.98	4.42
17β-Estradiol 17-sulfate	7.04	5.72	4.53	5.07	5.34	4.91	5.72	11.95	4.95	4.93	5.36	4.68
Equilenin 3-sulfate	9.04	6.58	5.41	5.86	6.22	5.91	7.07	13.80	5.54	5.86	6.17	5.53
Estriol 3,17-disulfate	10.90	7.32	6.02	8.34	9.22	8.94	13.50	10.90	9.17	8.10	9.88	7.31
17α-Dihydroequilenin 3-sulfate	13.25	9.87	8.22	9.10	9.58	9.05	10.85	20.50	8.25	8.86	9.30	8.09
Estriol 16,17-disulfate	16.30	10.10	9.17	11.70	12.60	12.70	18.00	11.20	14.60	12.30	14.30	10.40
17β-Estradiol 3,17-disulfate	16.80	11.60	9.44	13.00	14.80	14.10	20.40	19.60	13.60	12.70	15.70	10.60

From Figure 11-11 the influence of the pH on the capacity ratio of estrogen conjugates for separations on ion-exchange celluloses becomes obvious and the following conclusions can be drawn:

- The elution order for estrogen conjugates is: glucuronides, phosphates, sulfates.
- Stronger retardation is observed at lower pH-values.
- For equivalent conjugates the elution order estriol, estrone, estradiol is observed.

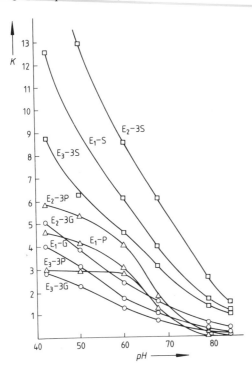

Figure 11-11. Influence of the pH of the eluent on the capacity ratio k of estrogen conjugates. Column: ECTEOLA-cellulose B 300 (19 μm, 250 × 3 mm i. d.); mobile phase: 0.025 mol/L perchlorate + 0.01 mol/L phosphate; detection: absorption at 220 nm; temperature 70 °C; samples: E_3-3G: estriol 3β-D-glucuronide, E_3-3P: estriol 3-phosphate, E_1-G: estrone β-D-glucuronide, E_1-P: estrone 3-phosphate, E_2-3G: 17β-estradiol 3-β-D-glucuronide, E_2-3P: 17β-estradiol 3-phosphate, E_3-3S: estriol 3-sulfate, E_1-S: estrone 3-sulfate, E_2-3S: 17β-estradiol 3-sulfate (similar to reference [33]).

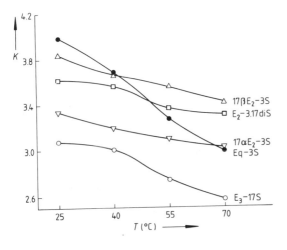

Figure 11-12. Dependence of the capacity ratio on the temperature for selected estrogen sulfates. Column: ECTEOLA-cellulose ET 41 (11 μm, 250 × 3 mm i. d.); mobile phase: 0.25 mol/L perchlorate + 0.01 mol/L phosphate, pH 8.5; detection: absorption at 220 nm; samples: E_3-17S: estriol 17-sulfate, Eq-3S: equilin 3-sulfate, 17α-E_2-3S: 17α-estradiol 3-sulfate, E_2-3,17diS: 17β-estradiol 3,17-disulfate, 17βE_2-3S: 17β-estradiol 3-sulfate (similar to reference [33]).

In principle, the capacity ratios of estrogen conjugates, separated on ion-exchange cellulose columns, decrease with increasing temperature; the size of decrease varies, however, from compound to compound, as demonstrated by Figure 11-12 for some estrogen sulfates.

A strong quaternary ammonium anion exchanger, chemically bonded to microparticulate silica, (LiChrosorb AN, 10 μm) has been used recently to separate estrogen conjugates [37]. Capacity factors of estrogen conjugates, separated on a LiChrosorb AN column with different mobile phases, are collected in Table 11-7. From Table 11-7 it becomes obvious that with decreasing methanol concentration and increasing pH-value the selectivity increases between the members of one type of conjugate. At high pH-values, changes of the LiChrosorb AN column material and peak broadening are observed. Compared to reversed-phase material considerably more peak dispersion may occur.

Table 11-7. Capacity Factors of Estrogen Conjugates Separated on a LiChrosorb AN (10 μm) Column. Chromatographic conditions: Column: 250 × 3 mm i. d.; detection: absorption at 220 nm; mobile phases: (A) 25% 1-propanol + 75% 0.01 mol/L phosphate, pH 9, 60 °C; (B) 50% ethanol + 50% 0.01 mol/L phosphate, pH 9, 70 °C; (C) 70% ethanol + 30% 0.01 mol/L phosphate, pH 9, 70 °C; (D) 80% methanol + 20% 0.01 mol/L phosphate, pH 9, 70 °C; (E) 80% methanol + 20% 0.01 mol/L phosphate, pH 6, 70 °C; (F) 60% methanol + 40% 0.01 mol/L phosphate, pH 9, 60 °C; (G) 60% methanol + 40% (1.0 mol/L NaClO$_4$ + 0.01 mol/L phosphate, pH 9), 70 °C; (H) 60% methanol + 40% (0.01 mol/L phosphate, pH 9, 0.2% propylamine), 70 °C; (I) 71% methanol + 9% acetonitrile + 20% 0.01 mol/L phosphate, pH 9, 60 °C; (K) 60% methanol + 20% acetonitrile + 20% 0.01 mol/L phosphate, pH 9, 60 °C; (L) 60% methanol + 20% acetonitrile + 20% 0.01 mol/L phosphate, pH 6, 70 °C; (M) 60% methanol + 20% acetonitrile + 20% 0.01 mol/L phosphate, pH 3, 70 °C; (N) 48% methanol + 24% acetonitrile + 24% 0.01 mol/L phosphate, pH 3, 70 °C [37].

Compound	A	B	C	D	E	F	G	H	I	K	L	M	N
Testosterone β-D-glucuronide	1.86	0.92	0.66	0.71	2.2	1.20	0.71	0.75	0.74	0.40	1.57	1.70	1.6
Estriol 3-β-D-glucuronide	1.31	0.92	0.96	0.99	2.7	1.02	0.11	0.66	1.04	0.53	2.0	2.4	2.7
17β-Estradiol 17β-D-glucuronide	3.3	1.55	1.09	1.31	3.1	2.4	0.28	1.35	1.24	0.72	2.2	2.0	1.8
Testosterone sulfate	5.8	2.1	1.12	1.22	3.3	2.5	0.30	1.55	1.42	0.63	2.0	12.7	8.0
Estriol 3-sulfate	6.8	2.8	1.89	1.88	4.3	3.1	0.24	1.75	1.66	0.88	2.5	15.5	9.0
17α-Dihydro-equilenin 3-sulfate	14.4	5.0	2.2	2.7	5.9	7.4	0.47	3.6	2.5	1.17	3.1	18.3	10.2
17β-Estradiol 3,17-β-D-diglucuronide	4.7	4.6	4.8	6.4	3.2	4.9	0.15	2.9	6.8	2.9		22.7	20.3
17β-Estradiol 17-phosphate	16.8	8.4	7.3	7.6	5.8	10.4	0.56	3.3	4.7	3.5	4.4	14.4	16.2
17β-Estradiol 3-phosphate	12.5	10.2	9.9	13.0	31.8	9.1	0.48	4.6	12.7	6.0	21.3	20.3	17.1
Estrone 3-phosphate	13.3	10.2	11.3	13.6	33.6	10.0	0.54	4.7	12.7	5.8	21.7	19.6	15.6

An anion exchanger, with a hydrocarbon matrix, is an excellent stationary phase for the separation of carbohydrates [38] and is also suitable for estrogen conjugates (Table 11-8).

However, for separations of estrogen conjugates on Aminex A-28 columns, long separation times are needed (Figure 11-13) [37]. Separations of estrogen glucuronides on superficially porous anion exchangers (Zipax SAX) or pellicular anion exchangers (AL Pellionex WAX) show low column efficiency and are therefore less suitable as stationary phases [37].

Table 11-8. Capacity Factors of Estrogen Glucuronides on Pellicular and Polystyrene Anion Exchangers. Chromatographic conditions: Column: 250 × 3 mm; detection at 220 or 275 nm; stationary and mobile phases: (A) Zipax SAX; 3.0 mol/L acetate, pH 4.0; 20 °C; (B) Zipax SAX; 2.0 mol/L acetate, pH 4.0; 20 °C; (C) Zipax SAX; 2.0 mol/L acetate, pH 4.0; 40 °C; (D) Zipax SAX; 2.0 mol/L acetate, pH 4.0; 60 °C; (E) Pellionex WAX; 0.005 mol/L perchlorate + 0.0002 mol/L phosphate, pH 4.0; 20 °C; (F) Pellionex WAX; 0.01 mol/L perchlorate + 0.0002 mol/L phosphate, pH 4.0; 20 °C; (G) Pellionex WAX; 0.01 mol/L perchlorate + 0.0002 mol/L phosphate, pH 4.0; 40 °C; (H) Pellionex WAX; 0.01 mol/L perchlorate + 0.0002 mol/L phosphate, pH 4.0; 60 °C; (I) Pellionex Wax; 0.1 mol/L acetate, pH 4.0; 20 °C; (K) Aminex A-28; 6.0 mol/L acetate, pH 4.0; 70 °C; (L) Aminex A-28; 8.3 mol/L acetate, pH 4.0; 70 °C; (M) Aminex A-28; 8.3 mol/L acetate, pH 4.0; 90 °C; (N) Aminex A-28; 8.3 mol/L acetate, pH 5.1; 90 °C; (P) Aminex A-28; 10.1 mol/L acetate, pH 4.0; 90 °C [37].

Compound	A	B	C	D	E	F	G	H	I	K	L	M	N	P
Testosterone β-D-glucuronide	0.00	1.19	0.94	0.60	1.37	0.78	0.77	0.76	0.86	4.8	1.61	1.51	1.75	0.65
Estriol 3-β-D-glucuronide	0.00	0.17	0.17	0.13	2.3	1.26	1.14	0.92	1.99	6.4	2.5	2.3	2.5	1.11
Estriol 17-β-D-glucuronide	0.26	1.57	1.15	0.76	3.5		1.72	1.47			7.0	5.9	6.2	2.8
Estriol 16-β-D-glucuronide	0.26	1.67	1.20	0.80	3.9	2.0	1.81	1.56	4.2		7.5	6.1	6.6	2.9
Estrone β-D-glucuronide	0.29	2.4	1.45	1.02	6.4	3.6	2.6	1.95	2.2		4.9	4.1	4.9	2.0
17β-Estradiol 3-β-D-glucuronide	0.42	2.7	1.79	1.20	5.5	2.9	2.6	1.84	4.1		7.2	6.1	7.3	2.9
17β-Estradiol 17-β-D-glucuronide	1.00	6.3	3.7	2.2	6.0	3.6	2.8	2.4	9.1		14.3	11.0	14.1	5.3

A fundamental investigation on the separation of estrogen conjugates on non-polar, chemically-bonded, stationary phases on silica was undertaken by van der Wal and Huber [37].

Table 11-9 surveys the results of the investigations on the dependence of the capacity factors of estrogen conjugates on pH, salt concentration and the presence of bases or acids in methanol buffer mobile phases.

Figure 11-13. Chromatogram of the separation of estrogen glucuronides. Column: Aminex A-28 (8 to 12 μm; 250 × 3 mm i. d.); mobile phase: 10.1 mol/L acetate, pH 4.0; detection: absorption at 275 nm; temperature: 90 °C; pressure: 90 bar; samples: CY: cytosine, TG: testosterone β-D-glucuronide, E$_3$-3G: estriol 3β-D-glucuronide, E$_1$-G: estrone β-D-glucuronide, E$_2$-3G: 17β-estradiol 3-β-D-glucuronide, E$_2$-17G: 17β-estradiol 17β-D-glucuronide. (Similar to reference [37]).

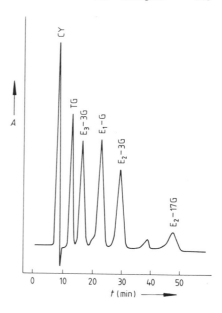

Table 11-9. Dependence of Capacity Factors of Estrogen Conjugates Separated on a RP 8 Column on the Composition of Methanol Buffer Mobile Phases. Chromatographic Conditions: Column: LiChrosorb RP 8 (5 μm, 250 × 3 mm i. d.); detection: absorption at 220 or 275 nm; temperature: 25 °C; mobile phases: (A) 40% methanol + 60% 0.08 mol/L phosphate, pH 4.5;(B) 40% methanol + 60% 0.05 mol/L phosphate, pH 7.7; (C) 40% methanol + 60% (0.05 mol/L phosphate, pH 7.7 + 0.5 mol/L NaClO$_4$); (D) 40% methanol + 60% (0.07 mol/L phosphate, pH 4.5 + 0.1 mol/L trimethylamine); (E) 40% methanol + 60% (0.07 mol/L phosphate, pH 4.5 + 0.1 mol/L trimethylamine + 0.05 mol/L pentanesulfonic acid); (F) 40% methanol + 60% (0.07 mol/L phosphate, pH 4.5 + 0.05 mol/L pentasulfonic acid) [37].

Compound	A	B	C	D	E	F
Estriol 3-β-D-glucuronide	0.75	0.45	0.45	0.55	0.25	0.2
Estriol 17-β-D-glucuronide	4.5	2.6	2.8	3.4	1.9	1.5
Estriol 16-β-D-glucuronide	4.6	2.8	2.9	3.7	1.9	1.55
Estrone β-D-glucuronide	6.4	3.8	3.7	5.1	2.8	2.2
17β-Estradiol 3-β-D-glucuronide	8.2	4.6	4.6	6.1	3.5	2.7
17β-Estradiol 17-β-D-glucuronide	11.8	6.2	6.5	8.6	4.6	3.7
Testosterone β-D-glucuronide	16.5	8.2	7.4	11.2	6.2	4.8
Estriol 3-sulfate	1.8	1.2	1.2	1.7	0.7	0.55
Estriol 17-sulfate	6.2	3.9	3.9	5.2	2.6	2.0
Equilenin 3-sulfate	9.5	5.5	5.2	7.5	3.8	2.9
17α-Dihydroequilenin-3-sulfate	10.5	6.2	6.1	8.4	4.4	3.4
Equilenin 3-sulfate	11.5	6.8	6.3	9.3	4.7	3.5
Estrone 3-sulfate	13.1	7.7	7.2	10.3	5.4	4.0
17α-Dihydroequilin-3-sulfate	13.1	7.7	7.9	10.5	5.7	4.3

Table 11-9. (Continued).

Compound	A	B	C	D	E	F
17β-Estradiol 3-sulfate	15.1	9.1	8.9	12.3	6.5	4.8
17β-Estradiol 17-sulfate	16.6	10.0	10.5	13.6	7.3	5.3
17α-Estradiol 3-sulfate	17.2	10.2	10.0	13.8	7.2	5.3
Testosterone sulfate	22.8	13.3	12.0	18.0	9.5	6.7

Table 11-10 and Figures 11-14 and 11-15 demonstrate that the influence of the nature of the organic modifier on the selectivity coefficients of estrogen conjugates for separations on non-polar chemically bonded stationary phases on silica may be considerable.

Table 11-10. Dependence of Capacity Factors of Estrogen Conjugates on the Organic Modifier of the Mobile Phase and the Temperature with Hydrophobic Adsorbents. Chromatographic Conditions: Column: 250 × 3 mm; detection: absorption at 220 or 275 nm; mobile phases: (A) to (K), LiChrosorb RP 2, 5μm. (A) 30% methanol + 70% 0.05 mol/L phosphate, pH 8.0, 25 °C; (B) 20% ethanol + 80% 0.05 mol/L phosphate, pH 8.0, 25 °C; (C) 12% 1-propanol + 88% 0.05 mol/L phosphate, pH 8.0, 25 °C; (D) 7% 1-butanol + 93% 0.05 mol/L phosphate, pH 8.0, 25 °C; (E) 15% acetonitrile + 85% 0.05 mol/L phosphate, pH 8.0, 25 °C; (F) 2% dichloromethane + 28% methanol + 70% 0.05 mol/L phosphate, pH 8.0, 25 °C; (G) 7% 1-butanol + 93% 0.05 mol/L phosphate, pH 8.0, 70 °C; (H) 15% acetonitrile + 85% 0.05 mol/L phosphate, pH 8.0, 70 °C; (I) 2% dichloromethane + 28% methanol + 70% 0.05 mol/L phosphate, pH 8.0, 70 °C; (K) 2% chloroform + 35% methanol + 63% 0.05 mol/L phosphate, pH 8.0, 70 °C. (L), LiChrosorb RP 8, 5μm; (L) 20% methanol + 20% acetonitrile + 60% 0.05 mol/L phosphate, pH 5.0 [37].

Compound	A	B	C	D	E	F	G	H	I	K	L 25 °C	L 50 °C	L 75 °C
Estriol 3-β-D-glucuronide	0.8	0.7	0.7	1.0	0.6	0.6	0.4	0.55	0.5	0.1	0.17	0.14	0.13
Estriol 17-β-D-glucuronide	3.0	3.5	3.4	4.3	2.7	2.7	1.8	2.4	1.8	0.7	1.28	1.12	0.86
Estriol 16-β-D-glucuronide	3.0	3.6	3.5	4.3	2.7	2.7	1.8	2.4	1.8	0.7	1.28	1.12	0.86
Estrone β-D-glucuronide	4.0	5.2	5.6	6.1	4.5	11.9	2.0	4.2	5.2	3.3	3.0	2.7	2.0
17β-Estradiol 3-β-D-glucuronide	4.5	5.7	6.4	8.2	3.5	5.3	2.8	3.4	4.5	1.5	2.1	1.89	1.47
17β-Estradiol 17-β-D-glucuronide	6.6	7.9	8.1	10.6	5.0	7.0	3.7	4.4	4.75	1.5	2.5	2.2	1.61
Testosterone β-D-glucuronide	9.0	10.4	9.5	7.9	6.8	16.7	2.6	6.1	8.1	4.2	4.0	3.5	2.7
Estriol 3-sulfate	2.3	2.6	2.2	2.3	2.5	2.0	1.2	2.1	1.25	0.4	1.32	1.14	0.90
Estriol 17-sulfate	5.8	6.9	6.0	7.3	6.3	5.8	3.4	5.0	3.1	1.1		3.2	2.4

Table 11-10. (Continued).

Compound	A	B	C	D	E	F	G	H	I	K	L 25°C	50°C	75°C
Equilenin 3-sulfate	9.4	12.0	10.7	11.9	16.9	19.2	4.5	11.9	8.1	5.1			
17α-Dihydroequilenin 3-sulfate	9.5	12.5	12.1	14.9	13.1	12.0	6.2	9.9	5.8	2.4			
Equilenin 3-sulfate	10.7	13.7	12.1	12.3	18.3	20.6	4.7	12.6	9.7	5.5			
Estrone 3-sulfate	11.8	15.4	13.5	15.5	21.4	38	5.5	15.2	12.5	7.2			
17β-Estradiol 3-sulfate	12.4	16.9	15.5	18.3	16.6	16.1	8.0	12.0	8.1	3.3			
17β-Estradiol 17-sulfate	13.7	18.6	17.3	19.9	15.6	15.7	8.9	10.8	7.6	2.9			
17α-Estradiol 3-sulfate	14.7	20.2	18.6	21.6	18.0	25.3	9.4	13.7	9.9	3.85			

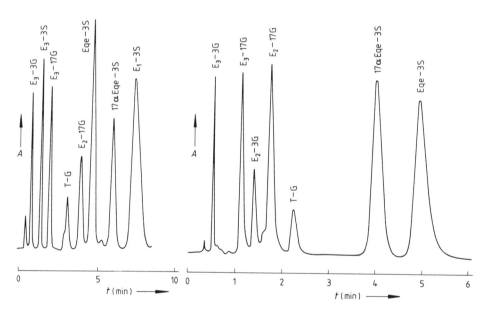

Figure 11-14. Chromatograms of estrogen conjugates run with different organic modifiers of the mobile phase. Column: LiChrosorb RP 2 (5 µm, 150 × 3 mm i. d.); detection: absorption at 220 nm; temperature: 70 °C; samples: E_3-3 G: 3-β-D-glucuronide, E_3-17 G: estriol 17-β-D-glucuronide, E_2-3 G: 17 β-estradiol 3-β-D-glucuronide, E_2-17 G: 17 β-estradiol 17-β-D-glucuronide, T-G: testosterone β-D-glucuronide, 17 α Eqe-3 S: 17 α-dihydroequilenin 3-sulfate, Eqe-3 S: equilenin 3-sulfate; E_3-3 S: estriol 3-sulfate, E_1-3 S: estrone 3-sulfate; mobile phases: chromatogram, to the left: 7% 1-butanol + 93% 0.05 mol/L phosphate, pH 8.0, chromatogram to the right: 15% acetonitrile + 85% 0.05 mol/L phosphate, pH 8.0 (similar to reference [37]).

11.4 Progestins

Progestins are C_{21} steroid hormones produced in the *adrenal cortex* of male and female mammals as well as in the *corpus luteum* during the menstrual cycle. Figure 11-15 shows the chemical structures of selected progestins.

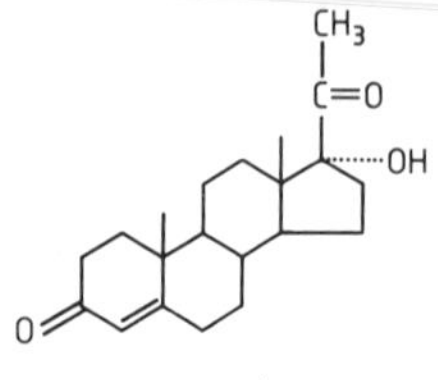

Figure 11-15. Structures of selected progestins; **1:** 17 α-hydroxyprogesterone, **2:** progesterone, **3:** 4-pregnene-20 β-ol-3-one, **4:** pregnenolone.

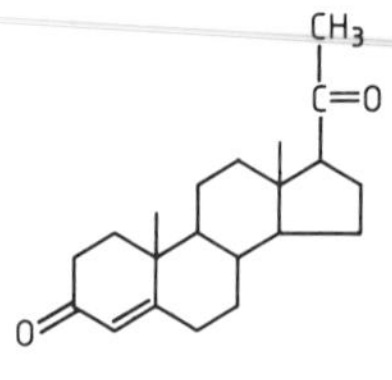

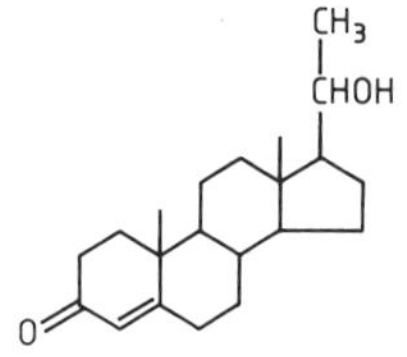

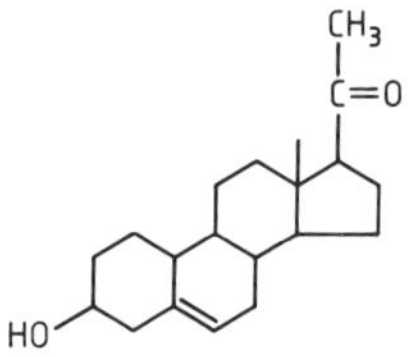

By combination of adsorption and reversed-phase HPLC it is possible to separate even complex mixtures of progesterone and its derivatives [39]. In Table 11-11 retention times of progesterone derivatives, separated by adsorption and reversed-phase HPLC are collected.

Table 11-11. Retention Times t_R of Progesterone Derivatives Determined by HPLC. – Chromatographic conditions:

Condition 1: Column: Partisil 5 (5 μm, 600 × 2 mm i. d.); mobile phase: 0.25% ethanol in dichloromethane, flow-rate: 1 mL/min; detection: absorption at 280 nm; samples: between 17 and 135 μg/steroid, dissolved in dichloromethane.

Condition 2: Column: Partisil: 5 (5 μm, 600 × 2 mm i. d.); mobile phase: hexane/isopropanol (97 : 3); flow-rate: 1 mL/min; detection: RI; samples: between 17 and 135 μg/steroid dissolved in the eluent.

Condition 3: Column: Zorbax BP-ODS (7 to 8 μm; 500 × 4 mm i. d.); mobile phase: acetonitrile/water (6 : 4); flow-rate: 1 mL/min; detection: RI; samples: 85 μg/steroid, dissolved in the eluent (similar to reference [39]).

Compounds	Conditions t_R (min)		
	1	2	3
Diones			
4-Pregnene-3,20-dione (progesterone)	44	–	40
5-Pregnene-3,20-dione	51	–	52
5 α-Pregnane-3,20-dione	18	–	62
5 β-Pregnane-3,20-dione	22	–	51

Table 11-11. (Continued).

Compounds	Conditions t_R (min)		
	1	2	3
Monohydroxymonoketones			
3 β-Hydroxy-5-pregnen-20-one (pregnenolone)	37	–	36
20 α-Hydroxy-4-pregnen-3-one	–	18	25
20 β-Hydroxy-4-pregnen-3-one	–	17	35
3 α-Hydroxy-5 α-pregnan-20-one	32	–	51
3 α-Hydroxy-5 β-pregnan-20-one	61	–	41
3 β-Hydroxy-5 α-pregnan-20-one	39	–	50
3 β-Hydroxy-5 β-pregnan-20-one	27	–	45
20 α-Hydroxy-5 α-pregnan-3-one	53	–	43
20 α-Hydroxy-5 β-pregnan-3-one	100	–	38
20 β-Hydroxy-5 α-pregnan-3-one	53	–	59
20 β-Hydroxy-5 β-pregnan-3-one	95	–	56
Diols			
5-Pregnene-3 β,20 α-diol	–	15	21
5-Pregnene-3 β,20 β-diol	–	15	27.5
5 α-Pregnane-3 α,20 α-diol	–	15	35
5 α-Pregnane-3 α,20 β-diol	–	16	44
5 α-Pregnane-3 β,20 α-diol	–	15	29
5 α-Pregnane-3 β,20 β-diol	–	13	38
5 β-Pregnane-3 α,20 α-diol	–	26	29
5 β-Pregnane-3 α,20 β-diol	–	22	38
5 β-Pregnane-3 β,20 α-diol	–	14.5	27
5 β-Pregnane-3 β,20 β-diol	–	14.5	38

From Table 11-11 the following conclusions can be drawn:

a) The more polar 5 β-pregnane-3,20-dione and 5-pregnene-3,20-dione are separated from the less polar 5 α-epimer respectively progesterone by adsorption chromatography.

b) The four diones of different structures are separable by adsorption but not partition chromatography.

c) The 20-epimers of monohydroxymonoketones are best separated by reversed-phase partition chromatography.

d) The biochemically important separation of progesterone from pregnenolone and 3 β-hydroxy-5 α-pregnan-20-one is difficult by adsorption but achievable by reversed-phase chromatography.

e) The separation of the most polar progesterone derivatives, the diols, can be achieved only by adsorption chromatography.

To improve the resolution in the HPLC of steroids, gradient elution may be advantageous, as was demonstrated recently by the separation of progesterone from its metabolites 17 α-hydroxy-progesterone, androsta-4-ene-3,17-dione and testosterone (Figure 11-16). HPLC of radiolabelled progesterone and its derivatives proves to be the most sensitive method for the determination of progestins [40].

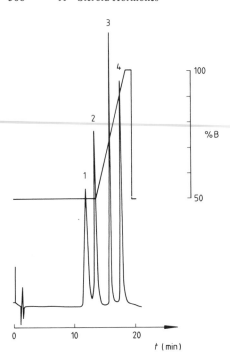

Figure 11-16. HPLC separation of androstenedione **(1)** from testosterone **(2)**, 17 α-hydroxyprogesterone **(3)** and progesterone **(4)**. Column: Partisil PXS 10 ODS-2 (250 × 4.6 mm i. d.); eluent: A water/tetrahydrofuran (99:1), B: water/tetrahydrofuran (1:1), 50% B for 9 min followed by an increase of 10% B/ min for 5 min then held at 100% B for 1 min; flow-rate: 2 mL/min; detection: absorption at 240 nm; samples: 24 µg of each steroid, dissolved in 6 µL solvent (similar to reference [41]).

11.5 Corticosteroids

Coprticosteroids are produced in the *adrenal cortex* and, according to their biological activity, are classified into mineralocorticoids (aldosterone, 11-deoxycortisone) and glucocorticoids (cortisone, cortisol). The structures of selected corticosteroids are seen in Figure 11-17.

In one of the earliest communications on HPLC investigations of corticosteroids, adsorption chromatography (Sil-X) was successfully used for the separations of cortisol from cortisone, substance S and androstenedione [42]. Since then several other laboratories have applied silica columns for HPLC of pregnane derivatives using dichloromethane/ethanol/water/methanol (963:20:12:5) [43], chloroform/methanol (197:3) [44], chloroform/methanol/water (983:150:2) [45], dichloromethane/ethanol/water (19:0.95:0.05) [46], dichloromethane/ethanol/water (948:35:17) [47 to 49] or chloroform/ethanol (97:3) [50] as mobile phases. Reversed-phase stationary phases in which alkylsilane, phenyl-, nitro-, cyanopropylsilane, cyanoethylsilane etc. groups are bound to silica are also successfully used for HPLC separations of pregnane derivatives [51 to 62]. Suitable organic modifiers are alkohols like methanol or 2-propanol or acetonitrile or tetrahydrofuran.

In a fundamental study O'Hare et al. [63] determined retention times for cortico- and many other steroids using reversed-phase packing material (Zorbax-ODS) and different mobile phases (Table 11-12, Figures 11-18 to 11-20).

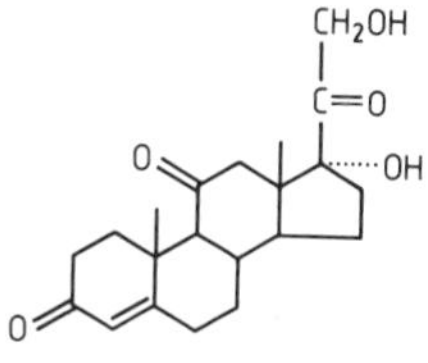

Figure 11-17. Structures of selected corticosteroids. 1: cortisone, 2: cortisol, 3: aldosterone, 4: corticosterone, 5: 11-dehydrocorticosterone, 6: 11-deoxycorticosterone, 7: 11-deoxycortisol, 8: 6-β-OH cortisol.

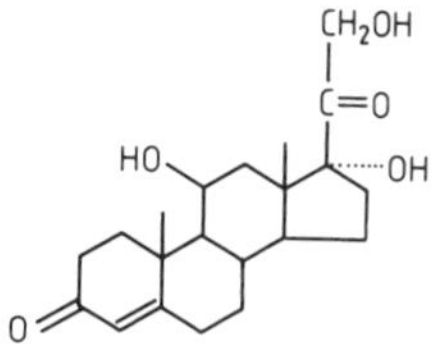

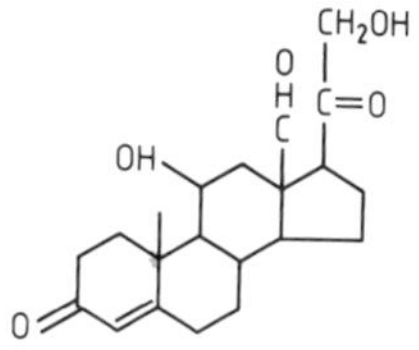

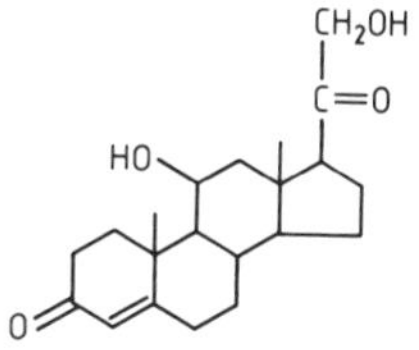

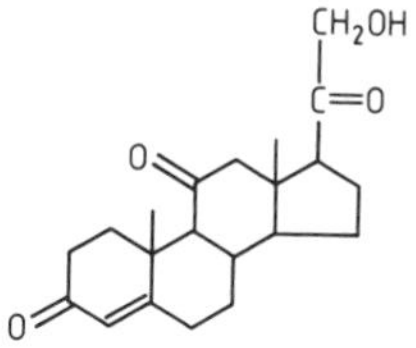

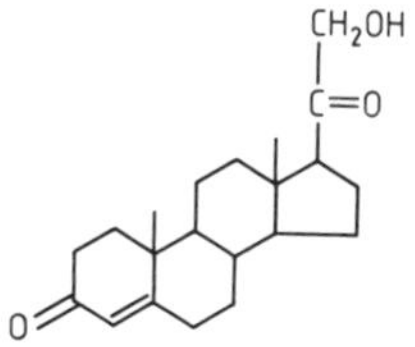

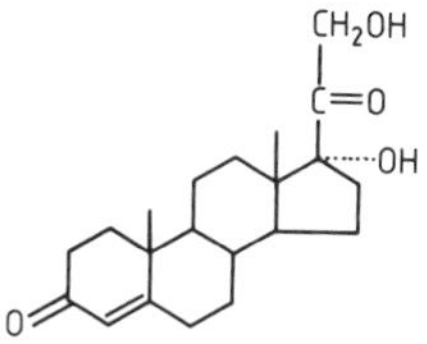

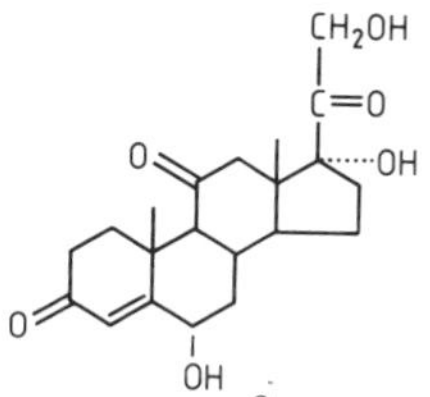

Table 11-12. Retention Times t_R of Steroids Including Corticosteroids Determined by HPLC Chromatography Using a Zorbax-ODS Column. – Chromatographic conditions:

Condition 1: Column: Zorbax-ODS (250 × 2.1 mm i. d.); mobile phase: gradient elution (Y = X²) starting with methanol/water (4:6) and ending with methanol (100%) in 50 min; fow-rate: 0.38 mL/min (start), 0.67 mL/min (end); detection: absorption at 240 nm.

Condition 2: Column: Zorbax-ODS (250 × 2.1 mm i. d.); mobile phase: gradient elution (Y – X²) starting with acetonitrile/water (8:25) and ending with acetonitrile (100%) in 50 min; flow-rate: 0.38 mL/min (start), 0.80 mL/min (end); detection: absorption at 240 nm.

Condition 3: Column: Zorbax-ODS (250 × 2.1 mm i. d.); mobile phase: gradient elution (Y = X²) starting with dioxane/water (1:4) and ending with dioxane (100%) in 50 min; flow-rate: 0.38 mL/min (start), 0.34 mL/min (end); detection: absorption at 254 nm [63].

Steroid	Conditions t_R (min)		
	1	2	3
6β-Hydroxycortisol (6β,11β,17α,21-tetrahydroxypregn-4-ene-3,20-dione)	3	3.5	4
11-Dehydroaldosterone (21-hydroxy-18-al-pregn-4-ene-3,11,20-trione)	8	5	15
17-Isoaldosterone (11β,21-dihydroxy-18-al-(17β)-pregn-4-ene-3,20-dione)	11	6	15

Table 11-12. (Continued).

Steroid	Conditions t_R (min)		
	1	2	3
18-Hydroxy-11-dehydrocorticosterone (18,21-dihydroxypregn-4-ene-3,11,20-trione)	11.5	6.5	17.5
Prednisone (17α,21-dihydroxypregna-1,4-diene-3,11,20-trione)	12	9	23
Aldosterone (11β,21-dihydroxy-18-al-pregn-4-ene-3,20-dione)	13.5	8	19
Estriol (estra-1,3,5(10)-triene-3,16α,17β-triol)	14	8	25
Cortisone (17α,21-dihydroxypregn-4-ene-3,11,20-trione)	14	9	25.5
19-Hydroxyandrostenedione (19-hydroxyandrost-4-ene-3,17-dione)	15	11.5	20
7α-Hydroxytestosterone (7α,17β-dihydroxyandrost-4-en-3-one)	15.5	9	19.5
18-Hydroxycorticosterone (11β,18,21-trihydroxy-pregn-4-ene-3,20-dione)	15.5	7	21
Prednisolone (11β,17α,21-trihydroxypregna-1,4-diene-3,20-dione)	15.5	9	26.5
Cortisol (11β,17α,21-trihydroxypregn-4-ene-3,20-dione)	16	9	27
Adrenosterone (androst-4-ene-3,11,17-trione)	18	17	28
19-Hydroxytestosterone (17β,19-dihydroxyandrost-4-en-3-one)	19	10	24
16α-Hydroxytestosterone (16α,17β-dihydroxyandrost-4-en-3-one)	21	11	27
11-Dehydrocorticosterone (21-hydroxypregn-4-ene-3,11,20-trione)	21.5	15	29.5
Dexamethasone (9-fluoro-16α-methyl-11β,17α,21-trihydroxypregna-1,4-diene-3,20-dione)	24	13	35
11β-Hydroxyandrostenedione (11β-hydroxyandrost-4-ene-3,17-dione)	24	17	32
21-Deoxycortisol (11β,17α-dihydroxypregn-4-ene-3,20-dione)	26.5	16	34.5
Corticosterone (11β,21-dihydroxypregn-4-ene-3,20-dione)	31	18	36
11β-Hydroxytestosterone (16β,17β-dihydroxyandrost-4-en-3-one)	31	15	33.5
18-Hydroxydeoxycorticosterone (18,21-dihydroxypregn-4-ene-3,20-dione)	31.5	16	34.5
11-Deoxycortisol (17α,21-dihydroxypregn-4-ene-3,20-dione)	33	20	37.5
6α-Hydroxyprogesterone (6α-hydroxypregn-4-en-3-one)	34	24.5	38.5
16α-Hydroxyprogesterone (16α-hydroxypregn-4-en-3-one)	35	24	38
11-Ketoprogesterone (pregn-4-ene-3,11,20-trione)	37	30	40
Estrone (3-hydroxyestra-1,3,5(10)-trien-17-one)	37	30.5	42.5
11β-Hydroxy-20α-dihydroprogesterone (11β,20α-dihydroxypregn-4-en-3-one)	38	26	49
Androstenedione (androst-4-ene-3,17-dione)	39	36	42
6β-Hydroxyprogesterone (6β-hydroxypregn-4-en-3-one)	39	30	41
Estradiol (estra-1,3,5(10)triene-3,17,β-diol)	40	29	43
11β-Hydroxyprogesterone (11β-hydroxypregn-4-en-3-one)	41	33	43
11-Deoxycorticosterone (21-hydroxypregn-4-ene-3,20-dione)	41	36	43.5
17α-Hydroxyprogesterone (17α-hydroxypregn-4-en-3-one)	41.5	38	45
Testosterone (17β-hydroxyandrost-4-en-3-one)	42	35	43.5
17α-Hydroxy-20α-dihydroprogesterone (17α,20α-dihydroxypregn-4-en-3-one)	42.5	32	42

Table 11-12. (Continued).

Steroid	Conditions t_R (min)		
	1	2	3
17 α-Hydroxy-20 β-dihydroprogesterone (17 α,20 β-dihydroxypregn-4-en-3-one)	43	32.5	43.5
Dehydroepiandrosterone (3 β-hydroxyandrost-5-en-17-one)	44	41	44
Androstenediol (androst-5-ene-3 β,17 β-diol)	45	38	–
17 α-Hydroxypregnenolone (3 β,17 α-dihydroxypregn-5-en-20-one)	45.5	39	–
5 α-Dihydrotestosterone (17 β-hydroxy-5 α-androstan-3-one)	46.5	42	–
Progesterone (pregn-4-ene-3,20-dione)	47	45	49
20 α-Dihydroprogesterone (20 α-hydroxypregn-4-en-3-one)	47.5	43.5	47.5
20 β-Dihydroprogesterone (20 β-hydroxypregn-4-en-3-one)	48.5	46	49.5
Pregnenolone (3 β-hydroxypregn-5-en-20-one)	48.5	47	50
Cholesterol (cholest-5-en-3 β-ol)	54	>60	–

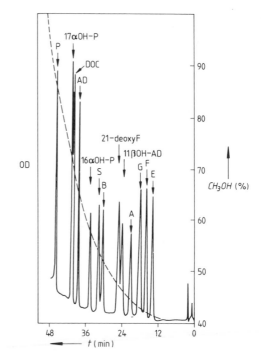

Figure 11-18. HPLC separation of adrenal steroids. Column: Zorbax-ODS (250 × 2.1 mm i. d.), mobile phase: gradient elution (---) starting with methanol/water (4:6) and ending with methanol (100%) in 50 min.; flow-rate: 0.38 mL/min (start), 0.67 mL/min (end); detection: absorption at 240 nm; samples (210 to 440 ng/steroid): P: progesterone, 17 α OH-P: 17 α-hydroxyprogesterone, DOC: 11-deoxycorticosterone, AD: androstenedione, 16 α OH-P: 16 α-hydroxyprogesterone, S: 11-deoxycortisol, B: corticosterone, 21-deoxyF: 21-deoxycortisol, 11 β OH-AD: 11 β-hydroxyandrostenedione, A: 11-dehydrocorticosterone, G: adrenosterone, F: cortisol, E: cortisone (similar to reference [63]).

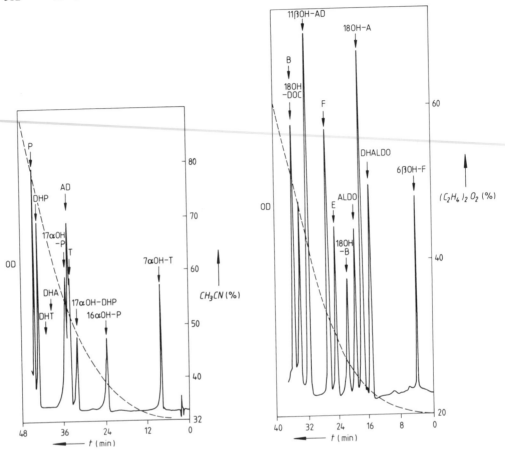

Figure 11-19. HPLC separation of testis steroids. Column: Zorbax-ODS (250 × 2.1 mm i. d.); mobile phase: gradient elution (---) starting with acetonitrile/water (8:25) and ending with acetonitrile (100%) in 50 min; flow-rate: 0.38 mL/min (start), 0.80 mL/min (end); detection: absorption at 240 nm; samples: 330 to 750 ng/steroid: P: progesterone, DHP: 20α-dihydroprogesterone, DHT: 5α-dihydrotestosterone, DHA: dehydroepiandrosterone, 17α OH-P: 17α-hydroxyprogesterone, AD: androstenedione, T: testosterone, 17α OH-DHP: 17α-hydroxy-20α-dihydroprogesterone, 16α OH-P: 16α-hydroxyprogesterone, 7α OH-T: 7α-hydroxytestosterone (similar to reference [63].

Figure 11-20. HPLC separation of polar adrenal steroids. Column: Zorbax-ODS (250 × 2.1 mm i. d.); mobile phase: gradient elution (- - - -) starting with dioxane/water (1:4) and ending with dioxane (100%) in 50 min; flow-rate: 0.38 mL/min (start), 0.34 mL/min (end); detection: absorption at 254 nm; samples: 250 to 750 ng/steroid: B: corticosterone, 18 OH-DOC: 18-hydroxy-11-deoxycorticosterone, 11 β OH-AD: 11 β-hydroxyandrostenedione, F: cortisol, E: cortisone, 18 OH-B: 18-hydroxycortisterone, ALDO: aldosterone, 18 OH-A: 18-hydroxy-11-dehydrocorticosterone, DHALDO: 11-dehydroaldosterone, 6 β OH-F: 6 β-hydroxycortisol (similar to reference [63]).

11.6 Determination of Steroid Hormones in Biological Fluids

Numerous publications deal with HPLC determinations of corticosteroids [64 to 71], testosterone [72], estrogenic steroids [25, 27, 73] or steroid drugs [74 to 76] in biological fluids. Stationary phases of reversed-phase packing material like Sil-X-RP [64], Hypersil ODS [66], RP-8 [70, 76], μBondapak C_{18} [72, 73], Partisil-10 ODS [27], LiChrosorb C_2 [73], LiChrosorb RP-18 [73], silica [25, 27, 65, 67, 69, 70, 74, 75] or polar coated silica [68, 71, 73] have been in use.

Before the HPLC analysis of steroids in biological fluids is performed, the perhydrocyclopentanophenanthrene derivatives are usually extracted by an organic solvent e. g. methylene chloride [64, 67, 69, 76], diethyl ether [25, 27] etc.

A typical extraction method, used for the determination of corticosteroids from plasma (5 mL), is shown in Figure 11-21.

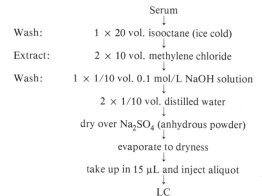

Figure 11-21. Method for extraction of corticosteroids [64].

Estrogenic steroid concentrations in human urine during pregnancy are important parameters for the gynecologist. Recently HPLC methods were developed to determine urinary estrogens [25, 27, 73]. HPLC chromatograms of extracts of pregnancy urine using liquid-solid and reversed-phase stationary phase material are shown in Figures 11-22 and 11-23; the calculated estrogen levels in the pregnancy urine with relative standard deviations are surveyed in Table 11-13.

Table 11-13. Calculated Estrogen Levels in the Pregnancy Urine with Relative Standard Deviations (RSD, see Figures 11-22, 11-23), [27].

Compound	Concentration in the Urine (g/L)	
	Partisil-5 Column	Partisil-10 ODS Column
Estrone	–	$7.3 \cdot 10^{-3}$ (RSD 18%)
Estradiol	$1.8 \cdot 10^{-3}$ (RSD 18%)	$2.5 \cdot 10^{-3}$ (RSD 18%)
Estriol	$33 \cdot 10^{-3}$ (RSD 15%)	$30 \cdot 10^{-3}$ (RSD 9%)

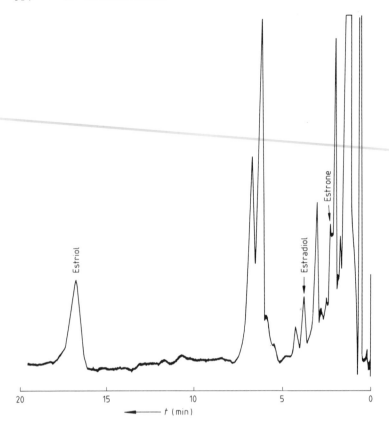

Figure 11-22. Chromatogram of an extract of pregnancy urine (40 mL hydrolyzed with concentrated hydrochloric acid and extracted into diethyl ether). Column: Partisil-5 (7 µm, 150 × 4.9 mm i. d.); mobile phase: ethanol/n-hexane (5:95); flow-rate: 5 mL/min; detection: absorption at 280 nm (similar to reference [27]).

HPLC is also suitable for a quantitative assay of plasma 11-deoxycorticol and cortisol in the metyrapone test [69]. The conditions for HPLC determination of 11-deoxycortisol and cortisol in plasma are described in the legends of Figures 11-24 and 11-25. To 0.6 mol/L plasma 0.05 mL 3 mol/L sodium hydroxide solution and 100 ng prednisone resp. prednisolone are added. Then 4 mL dichloromethane are added for 5 min and after centrifugation the organic layer is washed with 0.1 mol/L hydrochloric acid and water. 3 mL of the extract are evaporated to dryness and dissolved in 50 µL of chloroform. 20 µL are used for the HPLC separation (Figures 11-24 and 11-25).

Using a microparticulate silica gel column and methanol/methylene chloride (3:97) as mobile phase, prednisone, dexamethasone, cortisol and prednisolone, extracted from a biological fluid, are separable in a single run by HPLC. 1 mL biological fluid is extracted with 10 mL methylene chloride, washed with sodium hydroxide and then water before HPLC separation (Figure 11-26) [67].

Figure 11-23. Chromatogram of an extract of pregnancy urine (40 mL hydrolyzed with concentrated hydrochloric acid and extracted into diethyl ether, the etheral phase was evaporated to dryness and redissolved in 1 mL of a 55:45 (v/v) mixture of methanol/0.1% ammonium carbonate for HPLC separation). Column: Partisil-10 ODS (10 µm, 250 × 4.6 mm i. D.); mobile phase: methanol/0.1% aqueous ammonium carbonate (55:45); flow-rate: 2 mL/min; detection: absorption at 280 nm (similar to reference [27]).

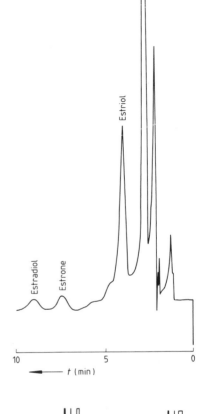

Figure 11-24. HPLC chromatograms of plasma extracts before (left side) and after (right side) administration of metyrapone (30 mg/kg body weight, plasma taken after 8^h of the administration of metyrapone, for preparation of the plasma samples see text). Column: SI-10 (10 µm, 250 × 3mm i. d.); mobile phase: chloroform/isooctane/methanol/water (4 .5:48.5:2.9:0.12); flow-rate: 65 mL/h; detection: absorption at 254 nm; sample identification: S: 11-deoxycortisol, P$_1$: prednisone (internal standard, see text, similar to reference [69]).

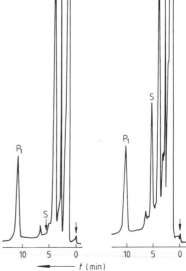

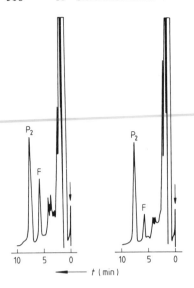

Figure 11-25. HPLC chromatograms of plasma extracts before (left side) and after (right side) administration of metyrapone (30 mg/kg body weight, plasma taken after 8 h of administration, for preparation of the plasma sample see text). Column: SI-10 (10 µm, 250 × 3 mm i. d.); mobile phase: chloroform/isooctane/methanol/water (71:25:3.75:0.25); flow-rate: 65 mL/h; detection: absorption at 254 nm; sample identification: F: cortisol, P_2: prednisolone (internal standard, see text, similar to reference [69]).

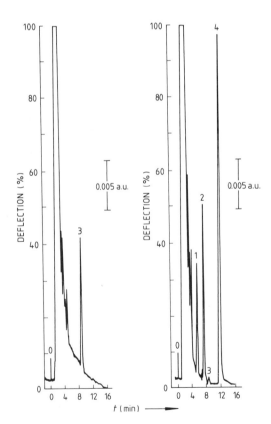

Figure 11-26. HPLC chromatograms of plasma extracts before (left side) and after (right side) administration of prednisone (plasma taken 3 hours after a single oral dosage of 50 mg prednisone, for preparation of the plasma sample see text). Column: Zorbax™ SIL (5 to 6 µm, 250 × 4.6 mm i. d.); mobile phase: methanol/methylene chloride (3:97); flow-rate: 2 mL/min; detection: absorption at 254 nm; sample identification: 1: prednisone, 2: dexamethasone (internal standard), 3: cortisol, 4: prednisolone, (similar to reference [67]).

11.7 HPLC Investigations of Steroid Drugs

HPLC has become one of the most important methods for the analysis of synthetic steroid drugs. For example, silica columns were successfully applied for the separation of prednisone and prednisolone [75, 77], dexamethasone [77, 78] or triamcinolone acetonide [79]. Numerous HPLC investigations on steroid drugs using reversed-phase packing material have appeared in the literature, e. g. on prednisolone [80, 81], methylprednisolone [45, 82], triamcinolone acetonide [83], fludrocortisone acetate [84], ethynodiol diacetate [85], betamethasone 17-valerate, clobetasol 17-propionate, clobetasone 17-butyrate, beclomethasone dipropionate, betamethasone 21-disodiumphosphate, betamethasone [86], budesonide and related corticosteroids [53], 21-dehydroprednisolone [87] or testolactone [88].

In a fundamental study of S. Hara and S. Hayashi [65] a systematization of the correlation between chemical structures of solutes and retention behaviour of steroidal pharmaceuticals on silica and bonded reversed-phase columns was undertaken.

For comparing the retention behaviours of all steroids relative retention volumes are calculated using testosterone as a standard. The relative retention value $V_R (A)_T$ is calculated acording to equation (5):

$$\log V_R (A)_T = \log \frac{V_R (A)}{V_R (T)} \ , \tag{5}$$

where

$V_R (A)$ is the net retention volume of sample A, and

$V_R (T)$ is the net retention volume of testosterone.

The relative retention value $\log V_R (A)_1$ of a sample A can be obtained directly by comparison with the value of testosterone if injected simultaneously for the Corasil II-ethylacetate/n-hexane (1 : 4) system. If the same solvent system with different proportions is applied (e. g. ethylacetate/n-hexane (1 : 9)) the relative retention value of sample B may be calculated from the value of sample 30 according to equation (6):

$$\log [V_R (B)/ V_R (T)] = \log \frac{V_R (B)/ V_R (30) \text{ [ethyl acetate/n-hexane} (1:9)]}{V_R (30)/ V_R (T) \text{ [ethyl acetate/n-hexane} (1:4)]} \ . \tag{6}$$

If the ethyl acetate/n-hexane ratio is changed to e. g. 1 : 19 repeated extrapolation of sample 4 is required to obtain the retention value of sample C (7):

$$\log [V_R (C)/ V_R (T)] = \log \frac{V_R (C)/ V_R (4) \text{ [ethyl acetate/n-hexane} (1:19)]}{V_R (4)/ V_R (30) \text{ [ethyl acetate/n-hexane} (1:9)]}$$

$$\cdot \frac{1}{V_R (30)/ V_R (T) \text{ [ethyl acetate/n-hexane} (1:4)]} \ . \tag{7}$$

For a pair of compounds P and Q with similar structures but differing in a functional group the difference in relative retention volumes $\Delta \log V_R$ is (8):

$$\Delta \log V_R = \log V_R(Q) - \log V_R(P) = \log k(Q) - \log k(P) ,$$

(8)

where

$V_R(Q)$, $V_R(P)$ are retention volumes of samples Q and P, and

$k(Q)$, $k(P)$ are capacity factors of samples Q and P .

$\Delta \log V_R$ can also be calculated from the relative retention values $\log V_R/V_R(T)$ using testosterone as standard.

In Table 11-14 retention volumes of steroids in one adsorption and two reversed-phase systems are collected.

For a correlation between elution behaviours and the chemical structures of steroids, relative retention volumes for two reversed- and three polar phase elutions of pairs of steroids having the same basic structure but differing in one functional group were compared (Figure 11-27).

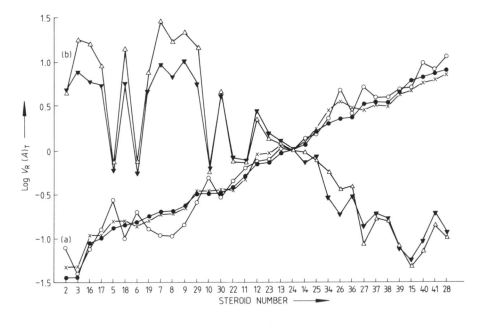

Figure 11-27. Relative retention volumes of steroidal pharmaceuticals.

a) Column: Corasil II (600 × 2.3 mm i. d.), mobile phases: .-.-. (n-hexane/ethyl acetate), x-x-x (n-hexane/diethyl ether), o-o-o n-hexane/2-propanol; flow-rate: 1.0 mL/min.
b) Column: Bondapak C_{18}/Corasil (600 × 2.3 mm i. d.), mobile phases: ▼-▼-▼ (methanol/water), Δ-Δ-Δ (acetonitrile/water); flow-rate: 1.5 mL/min.

Detection: absorption at 254 nm or R. I.; samples: 2: 3-methoxy-17α-ethynyl-estrane-1,3,5 (10)-trien-17β-ol, 3: 17β-valeryloxy-estrane-1,3,5 (10)-trien-3-ol, 16: 17β-propionyloxy-4-chloro-androstan-4-en-3-one, 17: 17β-acetoxy-4-chloro-androstan-4-en-3-one, 5: 17α-ethynyl-estrane-1,3,5(10)-triene-3,17β-diol, 18: 17β-propionyloxy-androstan-4-en-3-one, 6: 3-hydroxy-estrane-1,3,5(10)-trien-17-one (estrone), 19: 17β-acetoxy-androstan-4-en-3-one, 7: 17β [β-(phenyl-propionyloxy)]-estran-4-en-3-one, 8: 17β-[β-(2-furylpropionyloxy)]-estran-4-en-3-one, 9: 3-benzoyloxy-estrane-1,3,5 (10)-trien-17β-ol, 29: 17α-caproyl-oxy-pregnan-4-ene-3,20-dione, 10: estrane-1,3,5(10)-triene-3,17β-diol (estradiol), 30: pregnan-4-ene-3,20-dione (progesterone), 22: 17β-hydroxy-17α-ethynyl-androstan-4-en-3-one, 11: 17β-hydroxy-17α-ethynyl-estran-4-en-3-one, 12: 17β-hydroxy-17α-ethyl-estran-4-en-3-one, 23: 17β-hydroxy-17-methyl-androstan-4-en-3-one, 13: 17β-hydroxy-17α-methyl-estran-4-en-3-one, 24: 17β-hydroxy-androstan-4-en-3-one (testosterone), 14: 17β-hydroxy-estran-4-en-3-one (19-nortestosterone), 25: 17β-hydroxy-17α-methyl-androstan-1,4-dien-3-one, 34: 17α-hydroxy-21-acetoxy-pregnan-4-ene-3,11,20-trione (cortisone acetate), 26: 14α-hydroxy-androstan-4-ene-3,17-dione, 36: 11β, 17α-dihydroxy-21-acetoxy-pregnan-4-ene-3,20-dione (hydrocortisone acetate), 27: 6β, 17β-dihydroxy-androstan-4-en-3-one, 37: 11β, 17α, 21-triydroxy-16α-methyl-9α-fluoro-pregnane-1,4-diene-3,20-dione, 38: 11β, 17α, 21-trihydroxy-16β-methyl-9α-fluoro-pregnane-1,4-diene-3,20-dione, 39: 17α, 21-dihydroxy-pregnan-4-ene-3,11,20-trione (cortisone), 15: estrane-1,3,5 (10)-triene-3, 16α, 17β-triol (estriol), 40: 11β, 17α, 21-trihydroxy-pregnan-4-ene-3,20-dione (hydrocortisone), 41: 11β, 17α, 21-trihydroxy-6β-methyl-pregnane-1,4-diene-3,20-dione, 28: 14α,17β-dihydroxy-androstan-4-en-3-one, 42: 11β,17α,21-trihydroxy-pregnane-1,4-diene-3,20-dione (prednisolone) (similar to reference [65]).

From Figure 11-27 the following conclusions can be drawn:

a) Elution sequences are mainly dependent on the stationary and not the mobile phase.

b) The elution sequences in the reversed-phase separations are generally opposite to those in adsorption chromatography.

c) The difference in retention sequences with different mobile phases is relatively small for reversed-phase separations.

d) With reversed-phase separations methanol/water and acetonitrile/water systems gave parallel retention values.

e) For separations on silica columns stronger differences in retention sequences with different solvent systems are observed.

Determined or calculated retention parameters for changing functional groups are collected in Tables 11-14 and 11-15.

From Tables 11-15 and 11-16 the following facts become obvious:

a) The 6β, 14α-and 16α-hydroxyl groups afford large absolute values of the parameters for both stationary phases.

b) Acylation of alcoholic hydroxyl groups also affords large absolute values for both stationary phases.

c) Alkylation and acylation of a phenolic hydroxyl group affords extremely large positive values in reversed-phase systems.

d) Introduction of an alkyl group into 17α-position of a steroid with a β-hydroxyl group affords positive parameters which increase from methyl to ethyl in the reversed-phase system.

e) Reduction of C-11 and C-17 carbonyl to β-hydroxyl groups affords small parameters in the reversed-phase, but larger ones in the polar phase systems.

f) Introduction of chlorine into position 4 of 3-oxo-4-ene steroids affords positive and negative values in the reversed- and polar phase systems, respectively.

g) Introduction of a methyl group at position 6β and 10β affords positive and negative parameters in the reversed- and polar phase systems, respectively.

Table 11-14. Retention Volumes of Steroidal Pharmaceuticals. – Chromatographic conditions: Columns: 600 × 2.3 mm i.d.; detection: absorption at 254 nm or RI [65].

Steroid	Silica (Corasil II) Packing n-Hexane/Ethyl Acetate (v/v)				Steroid	Reversed-Phase (Bondapak C_{18}/Corasil) Packing Methanol/Water (v/v)			Acetonitrile/Water (v/v)				
	19:1	9:1	4:1	3:2		2:3	1:1	4:1	1:9	1:4	3:7	2:3	1:1
3,17β-Dipropionyloxy-estrane-1,3,5(10)-triene	0.85	0.26			11β,16α,17α,21-Tetrahydroxy-9α-fluoro-pregnane-1,4-diene-3,20-dione	0.60			1.50	0.60			
3-Methoxy-17α-ethynyl-estrane-1,3,5(10)-trien-17β-ol	2.79	0.78			Estrane-1,3,5(10)-triene-3,16α,17β-triol(estriol)	1.40			4.65	1.65			
17β-Valeryloxy-estrane-1,3,5(10)-trien-3-ol	2.79	0.82			17α,21-Dihydroxy-pregnan-4-ene-3,11,20-trione(cortisone)	2.00*)			7.10*)	2.70*)			
17β-Propionyloxy-4-chloro-androstan-4-en-3-one	6.83	1.87			11β,17α,21-Trihydroxy-pregnane-1,4-diene-3,20-dione(prednisolone)	2.20			6.30	2.20			
3-Benzyloxy-16α-17β-diacetoxy-estrane-1,3,5(10)-triene	7.30*)	2.00*)	0.39		11β,17α,21-Trihydroxy-pregnan-4-ene-3,20-dione(hydrocortisone)	2.30			6.80	2.30			
17β-Acetoxy-4-chloro-androstan-4-en-3-one	8.95	2.31	0.55		14α,17β-Dihydroxy-androstan-4-en-3-one	3.10				3.50			
17α-Ethyl-estrane-1,3,5(10)-triene-3,17β-diol	9.98	2.77	0.69		6β,17β-Dihydroxy-androstan-4-en-3-one	3.40				2.90			
17β-Propionyloxy-androstan-4-en-3-one	10.83	3.00	0.80		11β,17α,21-Trihydroxy-16β-methyl-9α-fluoro-pregnane-1,4-diene-3,20-dione	4.30				5.30			
3-Hydroxy-estrane-1,3,5-(10)-trien-17-one(estrone)	11.84	3.23	0.92		11β,17α,21-Trihydroxy-16α-methyl-9α-fluoro-pregnane-1,4-diene-3,20-dione	4.60				5.60			
17β-Acetoxy-androstan-4-en-3-one		3.70	0.96		14α-Hydroxy-androstan-4-ene-3,17-dione	4.60				12.10			
17β-Acetoxy-1-methyl-androstan-1-en-3-one		3.71	0.96		11β,17α,21-Trihydroxy-6β,methyl-pregnane-1,4-diene-3,20-dione	4.90				4.80			
17β-[β-(Phenylpropionyloxy)]-estran-4-en-3-one		4.21	1.12		17α-Hydroxy-21-acetoxy-pregnan-4-ene-3,11,20-trione (cortisone acetate)	7.40	2.20			19.40	3.65		
17β-[β-(2-Furylpropionyloxy)]-estran-4-en-3-one		4.21	1.12		11β,17α-Dihydroxy-21-acetoxy-pregnan-4-ene-3,20-dione(hydrocortisone acetate)	7.80*)	2.30*)			13.20*)	2.50*)		
3-Benzoyloxy-estrane-1,3,5(10)-trien-17β-ol		4.58	1.28		3-Hydroxy-estrane-1,3,5(10)-trien-17-one(estrone)		3.90				4.80		
17β-Hydroxy-6α-methyl-17α-(1-propynyl)-androstan-4-en-3-one		6.85	1.52		17α-Ethynyl-estrane-1,3,5(10)-triene-3,17β-diol		4.00				4.60		
17α-Caproyloxy-pregnan-4-ene-3,20-dione		6.85	1.53		11β,17α-Dihydroxy-21-acetoxy-16α-methyl-6α,9α-difluoro-pregnane-1,4-diene-3,20-dione		4.10			22.40	4.18		
Estrane-1,3,5(10)-triene-3,17β-diol(estradiol)		6.88	1.57		Estrane-1,3,5(10)-triene-3,17β-diol(estradiol)		4.40			18.60	3.40		

Table 11-14.(Continued).

Steroid	Silica (Corasil II) Packing n-Hexane/Ethyl Acetate (v/v)			
	19:1	9:1	4:1	3:2
Pregnane-4-ene-3,20-dione (progesterone)		7.00*)	1.73*)	
17β-Hydroxy-17α-ethynyl-androstan-4-en-3-one		8.13	2.00	
17β-Hydroxy-17α-ethynyl-estran-4-en-3-one		10.25	2.60	
9β,10α-Pregnane-4,6-diene-3,20-dione		10.25	2.60	
17α-Acetoxy-6-methyl-pregnane-4,6-diene-3,20-dione			3.30	
17β-Hydroxy-17α-ethyl-estran-4-en-3-one			3.77	
17β-Hydroxy-17α-methyl-androstan-4-en-3-one			3.92	
17βHydroxy-17α-methyl-estran-4-en-3-one			5.10	0.96
17α-Acetoxy-6-chloro-pregnane-4,6-diene-3,20-dione			5.10	1.02
17β-Hydroxy-androstan-4-en-3-one(testosterone)			5.20*)	1.10*)
17β-Hydroxy-estran-4-en-3-one (19-nortestosterone)			6.20	1.15
17β-Hydroxy-17α-methyl-androstane-1,4-dien-3-one			8.10	1.68
17α-Hydroxy-21-acetoxy-pregnan-4-ene-3,11,20-trione (cortisone acetate)				2.20
17β,17α-Dihydroxy-21-acetoxy-16α-methyl-6α,9α-diofluoro-pregnane-1,4-diene-3,20-dione				2.45
14α-Hydroxy-androstan-4-ene-3,17-dione				2.45
11β,17α-Dihydroxy-21-acetoxy-pregnan-4-ene-3,20-dione (hydrocortisone acetate)				2.50

Steroid	Reversed-Phase (Bondapak C$_{18}$/Corasil) Packing							
	Methanol/Water (v/v)			Acetonitrile/Water (v/v)				
	2:3	1:1	4:1	1:9	1:4	3:7	2:3	1:1
17β-Hydroxy-estran-4-en-3-one(19-nortestosterone)		5.45					1.65	
17β-Hydroxy-17α-ethynyl-estran-4-en-3-one		5.50				4.80*)	1.25*)	
17β-Hydroxy-17α-ethynyl-androstan-4-en-3-one		6.00					1.30	
17β-Hydroxy-17α-methyl-androstan-1,4-dien-3-one		6.00					1.35	
17β-Hydroxy-androstan-4-en-3-one (testosterone)		7.40*)					1.70	0.75
17β-Hydroxy-17α-methyl-estran-4-en-3-one		9.50					2.02	0.95
17β-Hydroxy-17α-methyl-androstan-4-en-3-one		11.50					2.30	1.02
17β-Hydroxy-6α-methyl-17α-(1-propynyl)-androstan-4-en-3-one		20.40					4.70	1.60
17β-Hydroxy-17α-ethyl-estran-4-en-3-one		20.80					4.00	1.35
9β,10α-Pregnane-4,6-diene-3,20-dione		22.10					5.00	1.65
17α-Acetoxy-6-methyl-pregnane-4,6-diene-3,20-dione		24.60					5.60	1.70
17α-Acetoxy-6-chloro-pregnane-4,6-diene-3,20-dione		27.80*)	1.15*)				5.73*)	1.75*)
Pregnan-4-ene-3,20-dione (progesterone)			1.25					2.58
17β-Acetoxy-androstan-4-en-3-one			1.40					4.00
3-Methoxy-17α-ethynyl-estrane-1,3,5(10)-trien-17β-ol			1.50					2.20
17β-Acetoxy-4-chloro-androstan-4-en-3-one			1.55					4.90

Compound	
6β,17β-Dihydroxy-androstan-4-en-3-one	3.55
11β,17α,21-Trihydroxy-16α-methyl-9α-fluoro-pregnane-1,4-diene-3,20-dione	3.65
11β,17α,21-Trihydroxy-16β-methyl-9α-fluoro-pregnane-1,4-diene-3,20-dione	3.65
17α,21-Dihydroxy-pregnan-4-ene-3,11,20-trione (cortisone)	4.71*)
Estrane-1,3,5(10)-triene-3,16α,17β-triol (estriol)	6.60
11β,17α,21-Trihydroxy-pregnan-4-ene-3,20-dione(hydrocortisone)	6.90
11β,17α,21-Trihydroxy-6β-methyl-pregnane-1,4-diene-3,20-dione	7.80
14α,17β-Dihydroxy-androstan-4-en-3-one	8.20
11β,17α,21-Trihydroxy-pregnane-1,4-diene-3,20-dione(prednisolone)	8.70
11β,16α,17α,21-Tetrahydroxy-9α-fluoro-pregnane-1,4-diene-3,20-dione	9.05

Compound		
17α-Caproyloxy-pregnan-4-ene-3,20-dione	1.65	8.10
17β-Acetoxy-1-methyl-androstan-1-en-3-one	1.70	5.10
17β-Propionyloxy-androstan-4-en-3-one	1.75	7.60
17β-Propionyloxy-4-chloro-androstan-4-en-3-one	1.85	8.30
17β-[β-(2-Furylpropionyloxy)]-estran-4-en-3-one	2.00	8.52
17β-Valeryloxy-estrane-1,3,5(10)-trien-3-ol	2.35	9.35
17β-[β-(Phenylpropionyloxy)]-estran-4-en-3-one	2.95	15.30
3-Benzoyloxy-estrane-1,3,5(10)-trien-17β-ol	3.10	11.15
3-Benzoyloxy-16α,17β-diacetoxy-estrane-1,3,5(10)-triene	3.30	14.92
3,17β-Dipropionyloxy-estrane-1,3,5(10)-triene	3.50	19.27

*) Internal standards

Table 11-15. Retention Parameters of Converted Functional Groups Δ LOG V_R of Steroids Determined Respectively Calculated for a Bondapak C_{18}/Corasil Column (600 × 2.3 mm i.d.) – Chromatographic Conditions: Flow-rate: 1.5 mL/min; detection: absorption at 254 nm or RI [65].

Functional Group		Steroid		Methanol/Water (v/v) (in Parentheses)			Acetonitrile/Water (v/v) (in Parentheses)		
From P	To Q	From	To	Δ log V_R	Retention Volume (mL) P	Q	Δ log V_R	Retention Volume (mL) P	Q
6β-H	OH	17β-Hydroxy-androstan-4-en-3-one (testosterone)	6β, 17β-Dihydroxy-andro-stan-4-en-3-one	−0.83 (1:1)	7.40	1.10	−1.08 (calcd.)	1.70 (2:3)	2.90 (1:4)
14α-H	OH	17β-Hydroxy-androstan-4-en-3-one (testosterone)	14α, 17β-Dihydroxy-an-drostan-4-en-3-one	−0.91 (calcd.)	7.40 (1:1)	3.10 (2:3)	−0.99 (calcd.)	1.70 (2:3)	3.50 (1:4)
16α-H	OH	Estrane-1,3,5(10)-triene-3,17β-diol (estradiol)	Estrane-1,3,5(10)-triene-3,16α, 17β-triol (estriol)	−1.03 (calcd.)	4.40 (1:1)	1.40 (2:3)	−1.05 (1:4)	18.60	1.65
17β-OH	OCOMe	17β-Hydroxy-androstan-4-en-3-one (testosterone)	17β-Acetoxy-androstan-4-en-3-one	0.66 (calcd.)	7.40 (1:1)	1.40 (4:1)	0.69 (2:3)	1.70	8.40
17β-OH	OCOEt	17β-Hydroxy-androstan-4-en-3-one (testosterone)	17β-Propionyloxy-andro-stan-4-en-3-one	0.76 (calcd.)	7.40 (1:1)	1.75 (4:1)	1.01 (1:1)	0.75	7.60
17β-OH	OCO-(CH₂)₃CH₃	Estrane-1,3,5(10)-triene-3, 17β-diol (estradiol)	17β-Valeryloxy-estrane-1,3,5(10)-trien-3-ol	1.11 (calcd.)	4.40 (1:1)	2.35 (4:1)	1.54 (calcd.)	3.40 (3:7)	9.35 (1:1)
17β-OH	OCO(CH₂)₂-C₆H₅	17β-Hydroxy-estrane-4-en-3-one(19-nortestoste-rone)	17β-[β-(Phenylpropio-nyloxy)]-estrane-4-en-3-one	1.12 (calcd.)	5.45 (1:1)	2.95 (4:1)	1.48 (calcd.)	1.65 (2:3)	15.30 (1:1)
17β-OH	OCO(CH₂)₂-C₄H₄O	17β-Hydroxy-estrane-4-en-3-one (19-nortestoste-rone)	17β-[β-(2-Furylpropionyl-oxy)]-estran-4-en-3-one	0.95 (calcd.)	5.45 (1:1)	2.00 (4:1)	1.23 (calcd.)	1.65 (2:3)	8.52 (1:1)
21-OH	OCOMe	17α, 21-Dihydroxy-preg-nan-4-ene-3,11,20-trione (cortisone)	17α-Hydroxy-21-ace-toxy-pregnan-4-ene-3,11,-20-trione (cortisone acetate)	0.57 (calcd.)	2.00 (2:3)	2.20 (1:1)	0.86 (1:4)	2.70	19.40
21-OH	OCOMe	11β, 17α, 21-Trihydro-xy-pregnan-4-ene-3,20-di-one (hydrocortisone)	11β, 17α-Dihydroxy-21-acetoxy-pregnan-4-ene-3,20-dione (hydrocor-tisone acetate)	0.53 (2:3)	2.30	7.80	0.76 (1:4)	2.30	13.20
17β-OH	COMe	17β-Hydroxy-androstan-4-en-3-one (testosterone)	Pregnan-4-ene-3,20-dione (progesterone)	0.61 (calcd.)	7.40 (1:1)	1.25 (4:1)	0.54 (1:1)	0.75	2.58
3-OH	OMe	17α-Ethynylestrane-1,3,-5(10)-triene-3, 17β-diol	3-Methoxy-17α-ethynyl-estrane-1,3,5(10)-trien-17β-ol	0.96 (calcd.)	4.00 (1:1)	1.50 (4:1)	0.78 (calcd.)	4.60 (3:7)	2.20 (1:1)

				1.23 (calcd.)	4.40 (1:1)	3.10 (4:1)	1.62 (calcd.)	3.40 (3:7)	11.15 (1:1)
3-OH	$OCOC_6H_5$	Estrane-1,3,5(10)-triene-3,17β-diol (estradiol)	3-Benzoyloxy-estrane-1,3,5(10)-trien-17β-ol						
17α-H	Me	17β-Hydroxy-androstan-4-en-3-one (testosterone)	17β-Hydroxy-17α-methyl-androstan-4-en-3-one	0.19 (1:1)	7.40	11.50	0.13 (2:3)	1.70	2.30
17α-H	Me	17β-Hydroxy-estran-4-en-3-one(19-nortestosterone)	17β-Hydroxy-17α-methyl-estran-4-en-3-one	0.24 (1:1)	5.45	9.50	0.09 (2:3)	1.65	2.02
17α-H	Et	17β-Hydroxy-estran-4-en-3-one(19-nor-testosterone)	17β-Hydroxy-17α-ethylestran-4-en-3-one	0.58 (1:1)	5.45	20.80	0.39 (2:3)	1.65	4.00
17α-H	Ethynyl	Estrane-1,3,5(10)-triene-3,17β-diol (estradiol)	17α-Ethynylestran-1,3,5(10)-triene-3,17β-diol	-0.04 (1:1)	4.40	4.00	0.13 (3:7)	3.40	4.60
17α-H	Ethynyl	17β-Hydroxy-androstan-4-en-3-one (testosterone)	17β-Hydroxy-17α-ethynylandrostan-4-en-3-one	-0.09 (1:1)	7.40	6.00	-0.12 (2:3)	1.70	1.30
17α-H	Ethynyl	17β-Hydroxy-estran-4-en-3-one(19-nortestosterone)	17β-Hydroxy-17α-ethynylestran-4-en-3-one	0.00 (1:1)	5.45	5.50	-0.12 (2:3)	1.65	1.25
17α-H	$OCO(CH_2)_4CH_3$	Pregnan-4-ene-3,20-dione(progesterone)	17α-Caproyloxy-pregnan-4-ene-3,20-dione	0.12 (4:1)	1.25	1.65	0.50 (1:1)	2.58	8.10
17α-Ethynyl	Et.	17β-Hydroxy-17α-ethynyl-estran-4-en-3-one	17β-Hydroxy-17α-ethyl-estran-4-en-3-one	0.58 (1:1)	5.50	20.80	0.51 (2:3)	1.25	4.00
$C_{11}=O$	11β-OH	17α,21-Dihydroxy-pregnan-4-ene-3,11,20-trione (cortisone)	11β,17α,21-Trihydroxy-pregnan-4-ene-3,20-dione (hydrocortisone)	0.06 (2:3)	2.00	2.30	-0.07 (1:4)	2.70	2.30
$C_{11}=O$	11β-OH	17α-Hydroxy-21-acetoxy-pregnan-4-ene-3,11,20-trione(cortisone acetate)	11β,17α-Dihydroxy-21-acetoxy-pregnan-4-ene-3,20-dione(hydrocortisone acetate)	0.02 (1:1)	2.20	2.30	-0.17 (1:4)	19.40	13.20
$C_{17}=O$	17β-OH	3-Hydroxy-estrane-1,3,5(10)-trien-17-one (estrone)	Estrane-1,3,5(10)-triene-3,17β-diol (estradiol)	0.05 (1:1)	3.90	4.40	-0.15 (3:7)	4.80	3.40
$C_{17}=O$	17β-OH	14α-Hydroxy-androstan-4-ene-3,17-dione	14α,17β-Dihydroxy-androstan-4-en-3-one	-0.17 (2:3)	4.60	3.10	-0.54 (1:4)	12.10	3.50
4-H	Cl	17β-Acetoxy-androstan-4-en-3-one	17β-Acetoxy-4-chloro-androstan-4-en-3-one	0.04 (4:1)	1.40	1.55	0.09 (1:1)	4.00	4.90
4-H	Cl	17β-Propionyloxy-androstan-4-en-3-one	17β-Propionyloxy-4-chloro-androstan-4-en-3-one	0.02 (4:1)	1.75	1.85	0.04 (1:1)	7.60	8.30
Sat.^{1,2}	$\Delta^{1,2}$	17β-Hydroxy-17α-methyl-androstan-4-en-3-one	17β-Hydroxy-17α-methyl-androstane-1,4-dien-3-one	-0.28 (1:1)	11.50	6.00	-0.23 (2:3)	2.30	1.35
Sat.^{1,2}	$\Delta^{1,2}$	11β,17α,21-Trihydroxy-pregnane-4-ene-3,20-dione(hydrocortisone)	11β,17α,21-Trihydroxy-pregnane-1,4-diene-3,20-dione(prednisolone)	-0.02 (2:3)	2.30	2.20	-0.02 (1:4)	2.30	2.20

Table 11-15. (Continued).

Functional Group		Steroid		Methanol/Water (v/v) (in Parentheses)			Acetonitrile/Water (v/v) (in Parentheses)		
					Retention Volume (mL)			Retention Volume (mL)	
From	To	From	To	$\Delta \log V_R$			$\Delta \log V_R$		
P	Q	P	Q		P	Q		P	Q
6β-H	Me	11β,17α-Trihydroxy-pregnane-1,4-diene-3,20-dione(prednisolone)	11β,17α,21-Trihydroxy-6β-methyl-pregnane-1,4-diene-3,20-dione	0.35 (2:3)	2.20	4.90	0.34 (1:4)	2.20	4.80
10β-H	Me	17β-Hydroxy-estran-4-en-3-one(19-nor-testosterone)	17β-Hydroxy-androstan-4-en-3-one(testosterone)	0.13 (1:1)	5.45	7.40	0.01 (2:3)	1.65	1.70
10β-H	Me	17β-Hydroxy-17α-methyl-estran-4-en-3-one	17β-Hydroxy-17α-methyl-androstan-4-en-3-one	0.08 (1:1)	9.50	11.50	0.03 (1:1)	0.95	1.02
10β-H	Me	17β-Hydroxy-17α-ethynyl-estran-4-en-3-one	17β-Hydroxy-17α-ethynyl-androstan-4-en-3-one	0.04 (1:1)	5.50	6.00	0.02 (2:3)	1.25	1.30
16α-Me	β-Me	11β,17α,21-Trihydroxy-16α-methyl-9α-fluoro-pregnane-1,4-diene-3,20-dione	11β,17α,21-Trihydroxy-16β-methyl-9α-fluoro-pregnane-1,4-diene-3,20-dione	−0.03 (2:3)	4.60	4.30	−0.02 (1:4)	5.60	5.30

Table 11-16. Retention Parameters of Converted Functional Groups Δlog V_R of Steroids Determined Respectively Calculated for a Corasil II Column (600 × 2.3 nm i.d.) – Chromatographic conditions: Flow-rate: 1.0 mL/min; detection: absorption at 254 nm or RI [65].

Functional Group From P	To Q	Steroid From P	To Q	n-Hexane/Ethyl Acetate (v/v) (in Parentheses) Δlog V_R	Retention Volume (mL) P	Q	n-Hexane/Diethylether (v/v) (in Parentheses) Δlog V_R	Retention Volume (mL) P	Q	n-Hexane/2-Propanol (v/v) (in Parentheses) Δlog V_R	Retention Volume (mL) P	Q
6β-H	OH	17β-Hydroxy-androstan-4-en-3-one (testosterone)	6β,17β-Dihydroxy-androstan-4-en-3-one	0.51 (3:2)	1.10	3.55	0.44 (1:1)	2.10 (3:2)	5.78	0.73 (15:1)	0.62	3.29
14α-H	OH	17β-Hydroxy-androstan-4-en-3-one (testosterone)	14α,17β-Dihydroxy-androstan-4-en-3-one	0.87 (3:2)	1.10	8.20	0.87 (0:1)	0.35	2.60	1.06 (15:1)	0.62	7.10
16α-H	OH	Estrane-1,3,5(10)-triene-3,17β-diol (estradiol)	Estrane-1,3,5(10)-triene-3,16α,17β-triol (estriol)	1.30 (calcd)	1.57 (4:1)	6.60 (3:2)	1.21 (1:1)	1.06 (3:2)	9.55 (1:1)	0.85 (15:1)	0.50	3.50
17β-OH	OCOMe	17β-Hydroxy-androstan-4-en-3-one (testosterone)	17β-Acetoxy-androstan-4-en-3-one	-0.73 (4:1)	5.20	0.96	-0.72 (calcd)	3.78 (3:2)	1.67 (4:1)	-0.89 (50:1)	6.99	0.90
17β-OH	OCOEt	17β-Hydroxy-androstan-4-en-3-one (testosterone)	17β-Propionyloxy-androstan-4-en-3-one	-0.81 (4:1)	5.20	0.80	-0.79 (calcd)	3.78 (3:2)	1.63 (4:1)	-1.00 (50:1)	6.99	0.70
17β-OH	OCO(CH₂)₃-CH₃	Estrane-1,3,5(10)-triene-3,17β-diol (estradiol)	17β-Valeryloxy-estrane-1,3,5(10)-trien-3-ol	-0.92 (9:1)	6.88	0.82	-0.87 (4:1)	3.10	0.42	-1.08 (50:1)	3.40	0.28
17β-OH	OCO-(CH₂)₂C₆H₅	17β-Hydroxy-estran-4-en-3-one (19-nortestosterone)	17β-[β-(Phenylpropionyloxy)]-estran-4-en-3-one	-0.74 (4:1)	6.20	1.12	-0.82 (3:2)	4.80	0.73	-1.06 (50:1)	9.15	0.80
17β-OH	OCO(CH₂)₂-C₄H₄O	17β-Hydroxy-estran-4-en-3-one(19-nortestosterone)	17β-[β-(2-Furylpropionyloxy)]-estran-4-en-3-one	-0.74 (4:1)	6.20	1.12	-0.82 (3:2)	4.80	0.73	-1.06 (50:1)	9.15	0.80
21-OH	OCOMe	17α, 21-Dihydroxy-pregnan-4-ene-3,-11,20-trione (cortisone)	17α-Hydroxy-21-acetoxypregnan-4-ene-3,-11,20-trione (cortisone acetate)	-0.33 (3:2)	4.71	2.20	-0.40 (1:3)	9.10	3.60	-0.36 (15:1)	3.10	1.35
21-OH	OCOMe	11β,17α,21-Trihydroxy-pregnan-4-ene-3,20-dione (hydrocortisone)	11β,17α-Dihydroxy-21-acetoxy-pregnan-4-ene-3,20-dione (hydrocortisone acetate)	-0.44 (3:2)	6.90	2.50	-0.49 (1:3)	11.90	3.85	-0.62 (15:1)	6.10	1.45
17β-OH	COMe	17β-Hydroxy-androstan-4-en-3-one (testosterone)	Pregnan-4-ene-3,20-dione (progesterone)	-0.48 (4:1)	5.20	1.73	-0.45 (3:2)	3.78	1.35	-0.52 (50:1)	6.99	2.10

Table 11-16. (Continued).

Functional Group		Steroid		n-Hexane/Ethyl Acetate (v/v) (in Parentheses)			n-Hexane/Diethylether (v/v) (in Parentheses)			n-Hexane/2-Propanol (v/v) (in Parentheses)		
					Retention Volume (mL)			Retention Volume (mL)			Retention Volume (mL)	
From P	To Q	From	To	$\Delta\log V_R$	P	Q	$\Delta\log V_R$	P	Q	$\Delta\log V_R$	P	Q
3-OH	OMe	17α-Ethynyl-estrane-1,3,5(10)-triene-3,17β-ol	3-Methoxy-17α-ethynyl-estrane-1,3,5(10)-trien-17β-ol	−0.55 (9:1)	2.77	0.78	−0.51 (4:1)	1.35	0.42	−0.42 (50:1)	1.50	0.57
3-OH	OCOC₆H₅	Estrane-1,3,5(10-triene-3,17β-diol (estradiol)	3-Benzoyloxy-estrane-1,3,5(10)-trien-17β-ol	−0.18 (9:1)	6.88	4.58	−0.21 (4:1)	3.10	1.91	−0.53 (50:1)	3.40	1.00
17α-H	Me	17β-Hydroxy-androstan-4-en-3-one (testosterone)	17β-Hydroxy-17α-methylandrostan-4-en-3-one	−0.12 (4:1)	5.20	3.92	−0.03 (1:1)	2.10	1.96	−0.12 (50:1)	6.99	5.37
17α-H	Me	17β-Hydroxyestran-4-en-3-one (19-nortestosterone)	17β-Hydroxy-17α-methylestran-4-en-3-one	−0.09 (4:1)	6.20	5.10	−0.01 (1:1)	2.50	2.47	−0.10 (50:1)	9.15	7.32
17α-H	Ethyl	17β-Hydroxyestran-4-en-3-one (19-nortestosterone)	17β-Hydroxy-17α-ethylestran-4-en-3-one	−0.22 (4:1)	6.20	3.77	−0.15 (3:2)	4.80	3.44	−0.25 (50:1)	9.15	5.19
17α-H	Ethynyl	Estrane-1,3,5(10)-triene-3,17β-diol (estradiol)	17α-Ethynylestrane-1,3,5(10)-triene-3,17β-diol	−0.40 (9:1)	6.88	2.77	−0.36 (4:1)	3.10	1.35	−0.24 (50:1)	3.40	1.96
17α-H	Ethynyl	17β-Hydroxy-androstan-4-en-3-one (testosterone)	17β-Hydroxy-17α-ethynylandrostan-4-en-3-one	−0.42 (4:1)	5.20	2.00	−0.42 (1:1)	2.10	0.80	−0.35 (50:1)	6.99	3.12
17α-H	Ethynyl	17β-Hydroxyestran-4-en-3-one (19-nortestosterone)	17β-Hydroxy-17α-ethynylestran-4-en-3-one	−0.38 (4:1)	6.20	2.60	−0.44 (3:2)	4.80	1.76	−0.31 (50:1)	9.15	4.50
17α-H	OCO-(CH₂)₄CH₃	Pregnan-4-ene-3,20-dione (progesterone)	17α-Caproyloxy-pregnan-4-ene-3,20-dione	−0.05 (4:1)	1.73	1.53	−0.02 (3:2)	1.35	1.30	−0.06 (50:1)	2.10	1.84
17α-Ethynyl	Ethyl	17β-Hydroxy-17α-ethynylestran-4-en-3-one	17β-Hydroxy-17α-ethylestran-4-en-3-one	0.16 (4:1)	2.60	3.77	0.29 (3:2)	1.75	3.44	0.06 (50:1)	4.50	5.19
C₁₁=O	11β-OH	17α,21-Dihydroxy-pregnan-4-ene-3,11,20-trione (cortisone)	11β,17α,21-Trihydroxypregnan-4-ene-3,20-dione (hydrocortisone)	0.17 (3:2)	4.71	6.90	0.12 (1:3)	9.10	11.90	0.29 (15:1)	3.10	6.10
C₁₁=O	11β-OH	17α-Hydroxy-21-acetoxy-pregnan-4-ene-	11β,17α-Dihydroxy-21-acetoxy-pregnan-4-ene-	0.06 (3:2)	2.20	2.50	0.03 (1:3)	3.60	3.85	0.03 (15:1)	1.35	1.45

Structure	Substituent	Compound 1	Compound 2									
C$_{17}$=O	17β-OH	3,11,20-trione (cortisone acetate)	3,20-dione (hydrocortisone acetate)	0.33 (9:1)	3.23	6.88	0.39 (4:1)	1.27	3.10	0.39 (50:1)	1.40	3.40
C$_{17}$=O	17β-OH	3-Hydroxyestrane-1,3,5(10)-trien-17-one (estrone)	Estrane-1,3,5(10)-triene-3,17β-diol (estradiol)	0.53 (3:2)	2.45	8.20	0.39 (0:1)	1.05	2.60	0.38 (15:1)	2.95	7.12
4-H	Cl	17β-Acetoxy-androstan-4-en-3-one	17β-Acetoxy-4-chloro-androstan-4-en-3-one	−0.21 (9:1)	3.70	2.31	−0.22 (4:1)	1.67	1.00	−0.11 (50:1)	0.90	0.70
4-H	Cl	17β-Propionyloxy-androstan-4-en-3-one	17β-Propionyloxy-4-chloro-androstan-4-en-3-one	−0.21 (9:1)	3.00	1.87	−0.20 (4:1)	1.63	1.03	−0.11 (50:1)	0.70	0.54
Sat.^{1,2}	Δ^{1,2}	17β-Hydroxy-17α-methylandrostan-4-en-3-one	17β-Hydroxy-17α-methylandrostan-1,4-dien-3-one	0.32 (4:1)	3.92	8.10	0.26 (1:1)	1.96	3.53	0.34 (50:1)	5.37	11.69
Sat.^{1,2}	Δ^{1,2}	11β,17α,21-Trihydroxy-pregnan-4-ene-3,20-dione (hydrocortisone)	11β,17α,21-Trihydroxy-pregnane-1,4-diene-3,20-dione (prednisolone)	0.12 (3:2) / 0.12 (3:2)	6.90 / 6.90	8.70 / 8.70	0.17 (0:1) / 0.17 (0:1)	1.38 / 1.38	2.05 / 2.05	−0.08 (15:1) / −0.08 (15:1)	6.10 / 6.10	5.10 / 5.10
6β-H	Me	11β,17α,21-Trihydroxy-pregnane-1,4-diene-3,20-dione (prednisolone)	11β,17α,21-Trihydroxy-6β-methylpregnane-1,4-diene-3,20-dione	−0.05 (3:2)	8.70	7.80	−0.04 (0:1)	2.05	1.86	0.00 (15:1)	5.10	5.10
10β-H	Me	17β-Hydroxy-estran-4-en-3-one (19-nortestosterone)	17β-Hydroxyandrostan-4-en-3-one (testosterone)	−0.08 (4:1)	6.20	5.20	−0.10 (3:2)	4.80	3.78	−0.12 (50:1)	9.10	6.99
10β-H	Me	17β-Hydroxy-17α-methylestran-4-en-3-one	17β-Hydroxy-17α-methylandrostan-4-en-3-one	−0.11 (4:1)	5.10	3.92	−0.10 (1:1)	2.47	1.96	−0.14 (50:1)	7.36	5.39
10β-H	Me	17β-Hydroxy-17α-ethynylestran-4-en-3-one	17β-Hydroxy-17α-ethynylandrostan-4-en-3-one	−0.11 (4:1)	2.60	2.00	−0.13 (3:2)	1.76	1.31	−0.16 (50:1)	4.50	3.12
16-Me	β-Me	11β,17α,21-Trihydroxy-16α-methyl-9α-fluoro-pregnane-1,4-diene-3,20-dione	11β,17α,21-Trihydroxy-16β-methyl-9α-fluoro-pregnane-1,4-diene-3,20-dione	0.00 (3:2)	3.65	3.65	0.00 (0:1)	0.96	0.96	0.00 (15:1)	2.17	2.17

11.8 References

[1] L. Fieser, and M. Fieser: *Steroids*. Van Nostrand-Reinhold, Princeton, New Jersey 1959.
[2] C. W. Shoppee: *Chemistry of the Steroids*. Butterworth, London 1964.
[3] W. Klyne: *The Chemistry of the Steroids*. Wiley, New York 1957.
[4] E. Heftman: *Biochemistry of Steroids*. Van Nostrand-Reinhold, Princeton, New Jersey 1960.
[5] H. Carstensen: *Steroid Hormone Analysis*. Marcel Dekker, New York 1967.
[6] J. E. Bush: *The Chromatography of Steroids*. Pergamon, Oxford 1961.
[7] R. Neher: *Steroid Chromatography*. Elsevier, Amsterdam 1964.
[8] R. Neher, in: J. C. Giddings, and R. A. Keller (eds.): *Advances in Chemistry*, Vol. 4 Marcel Dekker, New York 1967.
[9] S. Siggia, and R. A. Dishman, *Anal. Chem.* **42**, 1223 (1970).
[10] R. E. Huettemann, and A. P. Shroff, *J. Chromatogr. Sci.* **13**, 357 (1975).
[11] C. G. B. Frischkorn, and H. E. Frischkorn, *J. Chromatogr.* **151**, 331 (1978).
[12] C. G. B. Frischkorn, and H. W. Dürbeck, *Fresenius' Z. Anal. Chem.* **290**, 160 (1978).
[13] H. W. Dürbeck, C. G. B. Frischkorn, and H. E. Frischkorn, *Deutsch. Z. Sportmed.* **29**, 97 (1978).
[14] F. Gasparrini, S. Cacchi, L. Caglioti, D. Misiti, and M. Giovannoli, *J. Chromatogr.* **194**, 239 (1980).
[15] T. A. van der Hoeven, *J. Chromatogr.* **196**, 494 (1980).
[16] J. E. Higgins, *J. Chromatogr.* **148**, 335 (1978).
[17] F. A. Fitzpatrick, and S. Siggia, *Anal. Chem.* **45**, 2310 (1973).
[18] F. A. Fitzpatrick, S. Siggia, and J. Dingman, *Anal. Chem.* **44**, 2211 (1972).
[19] M. Lafosse, G. Kéravis, and M. H. Durand, *J. Chromatogr.* **118**, 283 (1976).
[20] I. R. Hunter, M. K. Walden, and E. Heftmann, *J. Chromatogr.* **176**, 485 (1979).
[21] W. Voelter, and T. Kronbach, unpublished results.
[22] J. F. K. Huber, and J. A. R. J. Hulsman, *J. Chromatogr.* **62**, 79 (1971).
[23] A. G. Butterfield, B. A. Lodge, and N. J. Pound, *J. Chromatogr. Sci.* **11**, 401 (1973).
[24] D. Maysinger, C. S. Marcus, W. Wolf, M. Tarle, and J. Casanova, *J. Chromatogr.* **130**, 129 (1977).
[25] R. J. Dolphin, *J. Chromatogr.* **83**, 421 (1973).
[26] J.-T. Lin, and E. Heftmann, *J. Chromatogr.* **212**, 239 (1981).
[27] R. J. Dolphin, and P. J. Pergande, *J. Chromatogr.* **143**, 267 (1977).
[28] H. Fukuchi, S. Tsukiai, and M. Inoue, *Yakuzaigaku* **38**, 102 (1978).
[29] G. Kéravis, M. Lafosse, and M. H. Durand, *Chromatographia* **10**, 678 (1977).
[30] P. Helboe, and M. Thomsen, *Arch. Phar. Chemi Sci. Ed.* **6**, 397 (1978).
[31] K. R. Bagon, and E. W. Hammond, *Analyst (London)* **103**, 156 (1978).
[32] L. F. Krzeminski, B. L. Cox, and G. H. Dunn, III, *J. Agr. Food Chem.* **26**, 891 (1978).
[33] S. van der Wal, and J. F. K. Huber, *J. Chromatogr.* **135**, 305 (1977).
[34] P. I. Musey, D. C. Collins, and J. R. Preedy, *Steroids* **31**, 583 (1978).
[35] B. Fransson, K.-G. Wahlund, I. M. Johansson, and G. Schill, *J. Chromatogr.* **125**, 327 (1976).
[36] J. Hermansson, *J. Chromatogr.* **152**, 437 (1978).
[37] S. van der Wal, and J. F. K. Huber, *J. Chromatogr.* **149**, 431 (1978).
[38] H. Bauer, and W. Voelter, Chap. 8 of this monograph.
[39] J.-T. Lin, E. Heftmann, and I. R. Hunter, *J. Chromatogr.* **190**, 169 (1980).
[40] S. Allenmark, A. A. son Berg, M. Hammar, and E. Lindström, *J. Chromatogr.* **224**, 399 (1981).
[41] D. G. Walters, P. M. D. Foster, and R. C. Cottrell, *J. Chromatogr.* **219**, 152 (1981).
[42] J. C. Touchstone, and W. Wortmann, *J. Chromatogr.* **76**, 244 (1973).
[43] T. Matsuzawa, M. Kato, M. Sekiguchi, and I. Ishiguro, *Rinsho Kugaku* **5**, 239 (1977).
[44] C. P. de Vries, C. Popp-Snijders, W. de Kieviet, and A. C. Akkerman-Faber, *J. Chromatogr.* **143**, 624 (1977).
[45] G. Schwedt, H. H. Bussemas, and Ch. Lippmann, *J. Chromatogr.* **143**, 259 (1977).
[46] E. Gaetani, and C. F. Laureri, *Farmaco Ed. Prat.* **29**, 110 (1974).
[47] C. Hesse, K. Pietrizik, and D. Hötzel, *Z. Klin. Chem. Klin. Biochem.* **12**, 193 (1974).
[48] F. K. Trefz, D. J. Byrd, and W. Kochen, *J. Chromatogr.* **107**, 181 (1975).
[49] T. Matsunaga, *Nagoya Shiritsu Daigaku Igakkai Zasshi* **26**, 330 (1975).
[50] I. I. Frolov, R. G. Vorobyoeva, I. V. Mironova, A. Z. Chernov, and Ya. I. Yashin, *J. Chromatogr.* **80**, 167 (1973).

[51] J. A. Mollica, and R. F. Strusz, *J. Pharm. Sci.* **61**, 444 (1972).

[52] W. C. Landgraf, and E. C. Jennings, *J. Pharm. Sci.* **62**, 278 (1973).

[53] A. Wikby, A. Thalén, and G. Oresten, *J. Chromatogr.* **157**, 65 (1978).

[54] M. C. Olson, *J. Pharm. Sci.* **62**, 2001 (1973).

[55] R. H. King, L. T. Grady, and J. T. Reamer, *J. Pharm. Sci.* **63**, 1591 (1974).

[56] J. Butler, V. Fantl, and C. K. Lim, in: P. F. Dixon, C. H. Gray, and C. K. Lim (eds.): *High-Pressure Liquid Chromatrography in Clinical Chemistry* Proc. of a Symposium 1975. Academic Press, London 1976, p. 59.

[57] D. C. Garg, J. W. Ayres, and J. G. Wagner, *Res. Commun. Chem. Pathol. Pharmacol.* **18**, 137 (1977).

[58] J. H. van den Berg, C. R. Mol, R. S. Deelder, and J. H. Thijssen, *Clin. Chim. Acta* **78**, 165 (1977).

[59] N. W. Tymes, *J. Chromatogr. Sci.* **15**, 151 (1977).

[60] G. Gordon, and P. R. Wood, *Proc. Anal. Div. Chem. Soc.* **14**, 30 (1977).

[61] S. Gallant, S. M. Bruckheimer, and A. C. Brownie, *Anal. Biochem.* **89**, 196 (1978).

[62] V. Das Gupta, and A. G. Ghanekar, *J. Pharm. Sci.* **67**, 889 (1978).

[63] M. J. O'Hare, E. C. Nice, R. Magee-Brown, and H. Bullmann, *J. Chromatogr.* **125**, 357 (1976).

[64] W. Wortmann, C. Schnabel, and J. C. Touchstone, *J. Chromatogr.* **84**, 396 (1973).

[65] S. Hara, and S. Hayashi, *J. Chromatogr.* **142**, 689 (1977).

[66] N. R. Scott, and P. F. Dixon, *J. Chromatogr.* **164**, 29 (1979).

[67] J. Q. Rose, and W. J. Jusko, *J. Chromatogr.* **162**, 273 (1979).

[68] M. Schöneshöfer, and H. J. Dulce, *J. Chromatogr.* **164**, 17 (1979).

[69] C. P. de Vries, M. Lomecky-Janousek, and C. Popp-Snijders, *J. Chromatogr.* **183**, 87 (1980).

[70] R. Ballerini, and M. Chinol, *J. Chromatogr.* **193**, 413 (1980).

[71] M. Schöneshöfer, R. Skobolo, and H. J. Dulce, *J. Chromatogr.* **222**, 478 (1981).

[72] R. C. Cochran, K. J. Darney jr., and L. L. Ewing, *J. Chromatogr.* **173**, 349 (1979).

[73] W. Slikker jr., G. W. Lipe, and G. D. Newport, *J. Chromatogr.* **224**, 205 (1981).

[74] J.J. de Ridder, P. C. J. M. Koppens, and H. J. M. van Hal, *J. Chromatogr.* **143**, 281 (1977).

[75] J. C. K. Loo, A. G. Butterfield, J. Moffatt, and N. Jordan, *J. Chromatogr.* **143**, 275 (1977).

[76] M. C. Petersen, R. L. Nation, and J. J. Ashley, *J. Chromatogr.* **183**, 131 (1980).

[77] J. C. K. Loo, and N. Jordan, *J. Chromatogr.* **143**, 314 (1977).

[78] S. E. Tsuei, J. J. Ashley, R. G. Moore, and W. G. McBride, *J. Chromatogr.* **145**, 213 (1978).

[79] J. W. Higgins, *J. Chromatogr.* **115**, 232 (1975).

[80] D. Wang, P. Chung, and J. Lai, *T'ai-wan Yao Hsueh Tsa Chih* **28**, 11 (1977).

[81] K. H. Mueller, and B. Stuber, *Pharm. Acta Helv.* **53**, 124 (1978).

[82] M. D. Smith, and D. J. Hoffman, *J. Chromatogr.* **168**, 163 (1979).

[83] G. Gordon, and P. R. Wood, *Analyst (London)* **101**, 876 (1976).

[84] H. M. Abdou, T. M. Ast, and F. J. Cioffi, *J. Pharm. Sci.* **67**, 1397 (1978).

[85] S. Görög, and B. Herényi, *J. Chromatogr.* **152**, 240 (1978).

[86] C. Burgess, *J. Chromatogr.* **149**, 233 (1978).

[87] D. Dekker, and J. H. Beijnen, *J. Chromatogr.* **193**, 480 (1980).

[88] G. Carignan, B. A. Lodge, and W. Skakum, *J. Chromatogr.* **206**, 174 (1981).

12 Vitamins

by *Thomas Kronbach und Wolfgang Voelter*

12 Vitamins

12.1 The Fat-Soluble Vitamins A, D, E and K

Biological assays for the determination of some vitamins are very sensitive and may be used for samples of low vitamin content. However, such assays suffer from low accuracy, are time-consuming and therefore not suited to routine analysis.

Physical and chemical methods generally work faster and are more reproducible than biological assays. Normally, quantitative analyses are carried out by colorimetry, spectrophotometry or fluorimetry. Prior to analysis, interfering substances have to be removed which is not always entirely possible. Determination of provitamin A content in tomatoes, for example, leads to erroneously high values because of high contents in lycopene, which is biologically completely inactive [1]. Gas-liquid chromatography (GLC) may be applied in some special cases but is generally not suitable for thermally unstable vitamins such as A and D.

For liquid-chromatographic methods, no elevated temperature and only minimum sample purification is required. Column chromatography has therefore been widely used for sample preparation and, due to the availability of efficient and stable columns and sensitive detectors, HPLC has become the fastest and most accurate method for the analysis of the fat-soluble vitamins, their esters, isomers, and other related compounds.

12.1.1 Vitamin A (Retinol)

The carotinoid Vitamin A has the following structure:

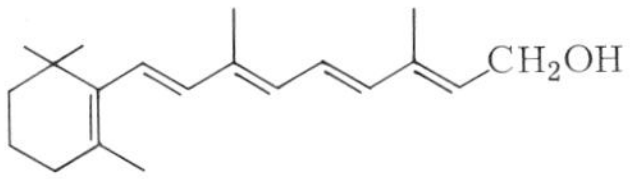

Vitamin A (retinol, λ_{max} = 325 nm, ε = 5200 [2]) is involved in the visual process in its alcohol, aldehyde, and ester forms and isomerisation of rhodopsin (retinal bound to opsin via a schiff base) plays a central role. The photolability and sensitivity against heat and oxidation of vitamin A and its derivatives causes problems for the analytical chemist. Therefore, sample preparation has to be carried out very carefully to prevent degradation. Due to the fact that retinol is the most lipophilic vitamin, interfering lipid material has to be removed prior to analysis, generally by saponification and/or precipitation.

These procedures, however, require long reaction times or elevated temperatures and suitable conditions have to be worked out carefully.

Gel permeation chromatography (GPC) is an excellent method of circumventing chemical pretreatment steps and was applied successfully to the determination of vitamin A in cod liver oil by Williams et al. [3] and for isolation and identification of vitamin A metabolites in intestinal mucosa [4].

As can be seen from Table 12-1, investigations concerning retinol are carried out either to detect different vitamin A-related compounds or for simultaneous determination with other vitamins. In the latter case, reversed-phase HPLC is used, due to the greater polarity range of investigated compounds (Figure 12-1). Whereas in the former case adsorption chromatography is preferred, as it is well-known to be advantageous in separating closely related compounds like isomers.

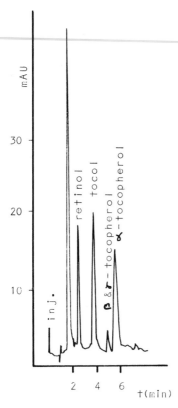

Figure 12-1. Reversed-phase separation of retinol, tocopherols and the internal standard tocol from a serum extract. Column: 4.6 × 250 mm RSIL-C$_{18}$ (10 μm); eluent: methanol; flow: 2 mL/min; temperature: 40 °C; detection: UV at 292 nm. According to de Leenheer et al. [10].

Table 12.1. Survey of HPLC Separations of All-trans-retinol (Vitamin A).

Investigated Compounds[*])	Stationary Phase[**])	Eluent	Application	Ref.
All-trans-retinol 13-cis-retinol	R	Methanol/10 mmol/L sodium acetate (80:20)	Standard solutions	[5]
11-Cis,13-cis,9-cis-retinol all-trans-retinol	S	5% Dioxane in n-hexane	Visual pigments	[6]
13-Cis-retinoic acid, all-trans-retinol, all-trans-retinyl acetate (internal standard)	R	1% Ammonium acetate in H$_2$O/acetonitrile (20:80)	Plasma	[7]
Vitamins K, A acetate, D$_2$, E, E acetate, A	R	H$_2$O/methanol gradient elution	Standard solutions	[3]

Table 12.1. (Continued).

Investigated Compounds[*)	Stationary Phase[**)	Eluent	Application	Ref.
Different retinyl esters	R	Methanol with different contents of Ag^+	Serum and chromatographic aspects	[8]
Retinoic acid, retinol, retinyl palmitate	R	10 mmol/L sodium acetate in H_2O/methanol (20:80)	Standard solutions	[4, 5]
Vitamins A acetate, D_2, E acetate	R	H_2O/methanol (1:9)	Multivitamin tablets	[9]
Pyrene (internal standard), vitamin D_2, vitamin E acetate, vitamin A	R	H_2O/methanol (gradient elution	Vitamin capsule extract	[3]
Retinol, vitamin E	R	Methanol	Serum	[10]
Vitamins B_1, B_{12}, K_3, C, D_2, E, A	R	H_2O/methanol (gradient elution)	Standard solutions	[11]
Retinol	R	Methanol/H_2O (92:8)	Cod liver oil after purification by GPC	[3]

*) Compounds matched with "&" are not resolved. Names occur in order of elution.
**) S: straight-phase HPLC on silica support.
   R: reversed-phase HPLC on chemically bound octadecyl support (on glass or silica)

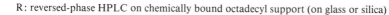

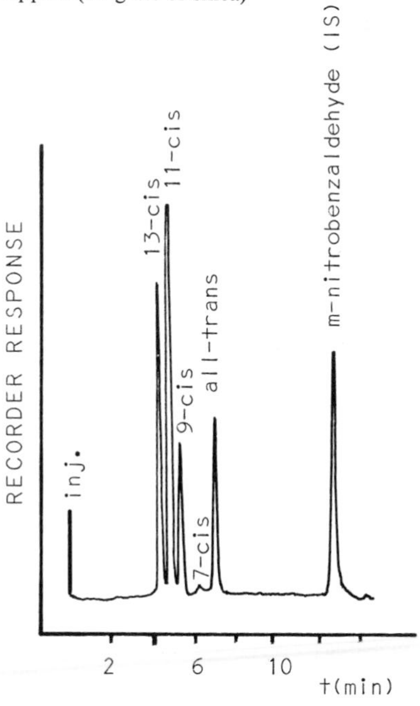

Figure 12-2. Separation of isomeric retinals. Column 4 × 300 mm μ-Porasil; eluent: 12% diethyl ether in n-hexane; pressure: 34 bar; temperature: ambient; detection: UV at 254 nm. According to Tsukida et al. [15].

The advantageous use of adsorption chromatography for separation of isomers is also documented in Table 12-2, in which data from HPLC separations of retinal are collected. All-trans-retinal has the following structure:

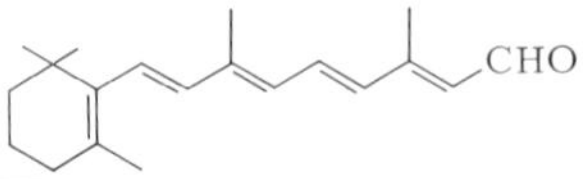

Of all vitamin A compounds, retinal is the only one possessing biopotency in the cis form. HPLC brought a real breakthrough in the investigation of cis-trans isomerisation of retinoids, identification of cis-trans retinals in biological samples, and purification of isomers (Figure 12-2).

Table 12-2. Survey of HPLC Separations of All-trans-retinal.

Separated Compounds*)	Stationary Phase**)	Eluent	Application	Ref.
13-Cis,11-cis-,9-cis-retinal all-trans-retinal	S	5% Dioxane in n-hexane	Rod outer segments extract and preparative HPLC	[6]
13-Cis,11-cis,9-cis,7-cis, all-trans-retinal	S	12% Diethyl ether in n-hexane	Preparative HPLC of retinal isomers	[12]
13-Cis-,11-cis,9-cis, all-trans-retinal	S		Visual pigments	[6]
	CN-modified silica	1% Diethyl ether in n-hexane		[13]
	S	12% Diethyl ether in n-hexane	Aprotic solvent effects on cis-trans-isomerisation	[14]
13-Cis, 11-cis retinal, 13-cis, 11-cis-dehydroretinal, 9-cis-retinal, 9-cis-dehydroretinal, 7-cis-retional, 7-cis-dehydro-retional, all-trans-retinal, all-trans-dehydroretinal, m-nitrobenzaldehyde (internal standard)	S	6% Diethyl ether in n-hexane	Photoisomerisation of retinals and dehydroretinals	[15]

*)   Compounds matched with "&" are not resolved. Names occur in order of elution.
**) S: straight-phase HPLC on silica support.
R: reversed-phase HPLC on chemically bound octadecyl support (on glass or silica).

Applications of HPLC for the resolution of all-trans-retionic acid and retinyl esters are shown in Tables 2-3 and 12-4. The separation of these compounds is of importance for synthesis and product control, structure elucidation and determination in biological material.

Table 12-3. Survey of HPLC Separations of All-Trans Retionic Acid.

Separated Compounds*)	Stationary Phase**)	Eluent	Application	Ref.
13-Cis-retionic acid	R	10 mmol/L Sodium acetate/ methanol (25:75)	Standard solutions	[5]
4-Ketoretionic acid 4-Hydroxyretinoic acid	R	10 mmol/L Sodium acetate/ methanol (35:65)	Standard solutions	[5]
Aromatic retinoids	S	n-Hexane/THF/acetic acid (98:1.5:0.6) or n-hexane/methyl-benzoate/propionic acid (87.5:12.5:0.35)	Plasma	[16]
Aromatic retinoic acid analogs	S	Dichloromethane/methanol (99.5:0.5)	Biological fluids	[17]
5,6-Epoxyretinoic acid	R	10 mmol/L Ammonium acetate in methanol/H_2O (60:40)	Vitamin A metabolites in tissues after GPC	[4]

*) Compounds matched with "&" are not resolved. Names occur in order of elution.
**) S: straight-phase HPLC on silica support.
R: reversed-phase HPLC on chemically bound octadecyl support (on glass or silica).

Table 12-4. Survey of HPLC Separations of Retinyl Esters.

Separated Compounds*)	Stationary Phase**)	Eluent	Application	Ref.
All-trans-retinyl acetate and 10 isomers	R	Methanol/H_2O (90:10)	^{1}H-NMR of isomers for structure elucidation	[18]
Retinyl acetate, vitamin D_2, vitamin E acetate	R	Methanol/H_2O (98:2)	Multivitamin tablets	[19]
Methyl retionate, methyl-4-hydroxyre-tinoate, methyl-4-ketoretinoate	S	THF/n-hexane (7.5:92.5)	Standard solutions	[5]
Methyl-4-ketoretinoate methyl retinoate	R	Methanol/H_2O (85:15)	Standard solutions	[5]
Vitamin A acetate & vitamin E acetate, vitamin D_2	S	1.25% Isopropanol in cyclo-hexane	Multivitamin tablets	[9]
Ethyl benzoate (internal standard) 13-cis-retinyl acetate all-trans-retinyl acetate	S	0.1% Dioxan in n-hexane	Synthesis and product control	[20]

Table 12-4. (Continued).

Separated Compounds[*]	Stationary Phase[**]	Eluent	Application	Ref.
Naphthalene (internal standard), 13-cis,9-cis, all-trans-retinyl acetate	Al_2O_3	1% Diethylether in n-hexane	Synthesis and product control	[20]
Retinyl acetate vitamin D_2, vitamin E succinate	Zipax HCP	Methanol/0.1% H_3PO_4 in H_2O (77:23)	Vitamin tablet extract	[3]
11-Cis,9-cis-all-trans-retinyl palmitate	S	0.1% Dioxan in n-hexane	Retinal pigment epithelium extract	[6]
Retinyl palmitate	R	Isopropanol/H_2O (85:15)	Standard solutions	[3]

[*]   Compounds matched with "&" are not resolved. Names occur in order of elution.
[**] S: normal-phase HPLC on silica support.
R: reversed-phase HPLC on chemically bound octadexyl support (on glass or silica).

12.1.2 Vitamin D and Related Compounds

Vitamin D analysis concentrates mainly on two topics. The first is concerned with the separation from other fat-soluble vitamins or from vitamin D isomers to control their concentrations in bulk products, pharmaceutical dosage forms, biological samples, and animal-feed. The second is the investigation of the metabolism of vitamin D_2 and D_3, in which the role of some less bioactive metabolites is still not well understood.

Group separations of fat soluble vitamins were carried out in both, normal and reversed-phase mode. In an early report a Vydac column was used to separate vitamin D_3 and previtamin D_3 from some vitamin A compounds [23]. Tomkins and Tscherne [21] developed a Zorbax Sil column with moist hexane/dichloromethane/ethylacetate (84:12:4) to separate vitamin A acetate, vitamin D_2 and p-nitrophenylacetonitrile (internal standard) from gelatine protected vitamin A acetate/vitamin D_2 beadlets. Tartivita et al. [22] used chloroform/n-hexane/tetra-hydrofuran (70:3:1) with a μ-Porasil column and obtained the following elution order: 2-p-dimethylaminobenzaldehyde (internal standard); tachysterol₃ and vitamin D_3 (Fig. 12-4). Williams et al. separated: chrysene (internal standard); vitamin A acetate; vitamin D_2; and vitamin E succinate on a Zipax HCP column with methanol/water (77:23) and 0.14% phosphoric acid as the eluent [3]. Reversed-phase techniques were also used by the same authors on a Permaphase ODS column with a gradient from water to methanol at 5%/minute to separate: vitamin K; vitamin A acetate; vitamin D_2; vitamin E; vitamin E acetate; and vitamin A (in elution order). Earlier, the vitamins B_2, B_{12}, K_3, C, D_2, E, and A were separated in the same laboratory [11] using the same conditions but with a gradient at 3%/minute. Erikson et al. [19] determined vitamin A acetate, vitamin D_2 and vitamin E acetate in multiplex tablets using a C_{18}-column and 2% water in methanol as the eluent. Burns and Mackay [9] compared reversed-phase and adsorption modes

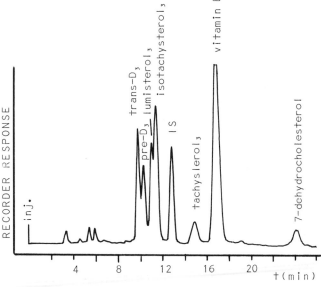

vitamin D₂ R =

vitamin D₃ R =

vitamin D

pre-vitamin D

tachysterol

lumisterol (9β, 10α)

ergosterol (9α, 10β)

vitamin D metabolites:
25-hydroxyvitamin D (25-OH-D)
1,25-dihydroxyvitamin D (1,25-(OH)₂-D)
24,25-dihydroxyvitamin D (24,25-(OH)₂-D)
25,26-dihydroxyvitamin D (25,26-(OH)₂-D)
1,24,25-trihydroxyvitamin D (1,24,25-(OH)₃-D)

Figure 12-3. Structures of vitamin D and related compounds.

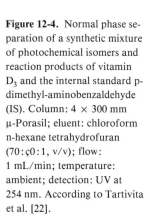

Figure 12-4. Normal phase separation of a synthetic mixture of photochemical isomers and reaction products of vitamin D₃ and the internal standard p-dimethyl-aminobenzaldehyde (IS). Column: 4 × 300 mm μ-Porasil; eluent: chloroform n-hexane tetrahydrofuran (70:ç0:1, v/v); flow: 1 mL/min; temperature: ambient; detection: UV at 254 nm. According to Tartivita et al. [22].

for the assay of fat-soluble vitamins in multivitamin tablets and suggest a combination of both methods for the separation and quantification of vitamin A, A acetate, D_2, E, and E acetate.

Table 12-5 summarizes the HPLC separation conditions for vitamin D and structurally related compounds, excluding the D metabolites which are discussed below.

Table 12-5. Survey of HPLC Separations of D Vitamins and Structurally Related Compounds.

Separated Compounds*)	Stationary Phase**)	Eluent	Application	Ref.
D_3	S	n-Hexane/iso-propanol (99.5:0.5)	Rat skin	[24]
D_3	S	Isooctane/isopropanol (99.5:0.5) (analytical) chloroform/iso-octane/methanol (75:25:1) (preparative)	Food ingre-dients after purification by preparative HPLC	[25]
D_3	S	n-Hexane/chloroform (70:30)	Feed	[26]
D_2 & D_3	R	Methanol/H_2* (95:5)	Standard solutions	[27]
D_2, D_3	R	Methanol/H_2O (95:5) + varying amounts of silver nitrate	Standard solutions	[27]
Pre-D_2, tachysterol, D_2	S	Chloroform/ag.sat.n-hexane/dry-n-hexane/THF/Acetic acid (60:15:25:1.5:0.4)	Raw materials and pharma-ceutical pre-parations	[28]
Trans D_3, pre D_3, lumisterol$_3$, isotachy-sterol$_3$, tachysterol$_3$, D_3, 9,7-dehydrochole-sterol	S	Chloroform/n-hexane/THF (70:30:1)	Synthesis control	[22]
Pre-D_2 & pre-D_3, lumisterol$_3$, D_2 & D_3, tachysterol$_3$, pro D_2 & pro-D_3	S	Light petroleum/1.2-dichloro-ethane/dioxane (90:8:2)	Raw materials and pharma-ceuticals	[29]
D_2 & D_3, pre-D_2 & pre-D_3, pro-D_2 & pro-D_3	S	n-Hexane/2-propanol (96:4)	Fish products	[30]
	R	Methanol/H_2O (95:5)		
Pre-D_2 & pre-D_3, lumisterol$_3$, D_2 & D_3 & tachysterol, pro-D_2 & pro-D_3	S	Light petroleum/1,2-dichlor-ethane/THF (85:8:7)	Standard solutions	[29]
Pre-D_3, trans D_3, lumisterol$_3$, isotachy-sterol$_3$, D_3, tachysterol, 4,6-cholestadienol, 7-dehydro-cholesterol	S	0.3% n-Pentanol in n-hexane	Resins oils, aqueous dispersions	[31]

Table 12-5. (Continued).

Separated Compounds*)	Stationary Phase**)	Eluent	Application	Ref.
Trans-D_3, isotadysterol, pre-D_3, tachysterol, D_3, lumisterol$_3$, 7-dehydro-cholesterol	R	Acetonitrile/pro-pionitrile/H_2O (79:15:6)	Resins, oils and aqueous dispersions	[31]
Cis-D_3 tachysterol$_3$, lumisterol$_3$, trans-D_3, pre-D_3	S	isooctane/ethanol (99:1:0.9)	Resins, oils	[32]

*)   Compounds matched with "&" are not resolved. Names occur in order of elution.
**) S: straight-phase HPLC on silica support.
R: reversed-phase HPLC on chemically bound octadecyl support (on glass or silica).

Vitamin D_3 is hydroxylated in the liver to 25-OH-D_3 and to 1.25-$(OH)_2$-D_3 (see Figure 12-3) derivatives in the kidney before it becomes active in the intestinal absorption of calcium and phosphorus and in the mobilization of these compounds from previously formed bone. Some further metabolites have been identified, namely the 24,25-$(OH)_2$-D_3, 25,26-$(OH)_2$-D_3 and 1,24,25-$(OH)_3$-D_3 derivatives which show less bioactivity and their functions are not so well understood. The developments in the isolation of these metabolites have been reviewed [33 to 37]. Vitamin D_2 is metabolized in a similar manner.

Table 12-6 summarizes the application of HPLC for the investigation of the vitamin D metabolism.

Table 12-6. Applications of HPLC on the Investigation of Vitamin D Metabolites and Related Compounds.

Separated Compounds*)	Stationary Phase**)	Eluent	Application	Ref.
D_3 and numerous hydroxylated metabolites (1, 24, 25)	S	Dichloromethane/methanol gradient from 0.02 to 6% methanol	Standard solutions	[38]
D_3 and numerous hydroxylated metabolites (1, 24, 25)	S	Dichloromethanol (98:2)	Standard solutions	[38]
25-OH-D_2, 25-OH-D_3	S	n-Hexane/2-propanol (97.5:2.5)	Plasma	[39]
1 α-OH-D_3	S	Light petroleum/dichloroethane/ THF/n-propanol (50:25:24:5)	Pharmaceutical preparations	[40]
25-OH-D_3	S	Light petroleum/dichloroethane/ THF/n-propanol (40:5:15:0.6)	Pharmaceutical preparations	[40]

Table 12-6. (Continued).

Separated Compounds[*]	Stationary Phase[**]	Eluent	Application	Ref.
25-OH-pre-D$_{3'}$ 25-OH-D$_3$	S	Light petroleum/dichloroethane/ THF/n-propanol (40:5:15:0.6)	Standard solutions	[40]
1α-OH-D$_{3'}$ 1α-OH-pre-D$_3$	S	Light petroleum/dichloroethane/ THF/n-propanol (50:25:24:5)	Standard solutions	[40]
D$_2$ & D$_{3'}$ 24-OH-D$_{2'}$ 24-OH-D$_{3'}$ 25-OH-D$_{2'}$ 25-OH-D$_3$	S	Skellysolve B/2-propanol (97.5:2.5)	Standard solutions	[41]
D$_{2'}$ D$_3$ 25-OH-D$_{2'}$ 25-OH-D$_3$	S & R combined method	S: n-Hexane/2-propanol (94.5:5.5), R: methanol/H$_2$O various	Plasma	[42]
25-OH-D$_2$	different S & R combined method	S: n-Hexane/2-propanol (94.5:5.5), R: methanol/2-propanol/H$_2$O (70:18:12)	Semipreparative isolation and purification of 25-OH-D$_2$ from plasma	[43]
25-OH-D$_3$	S (preparative) R (analytical)	S: n-Hexane/2-propanol (94:5:5.5), R: methanol/2-propanol/H$_2$O (70:18:12)	Plasma investigations after purification by prep. HPLC	[44]
25-OH-D$_{3'}$ 24,25-(OH)$_2$-D$_{3'}$ 25,26 (OH)$_2$-D$_{3'}$ 1α, 25-(OH)$_2$-D$_3$	S	Dichloromethane/methanol (97:3)	Plasma	[45]
25-OH-D$_{3'}$ 1α-OH-D$_{3'}$ 1α, 25-(OH)$_2$-D$_3$	S	Light petroleum/dichlorethane/ THF/n-propanol (50:25:24:5)	Standard solutions	[40]
D$_{2'}$ 25-OH-D$_{2'}$ 24,25-(OH)$_2$-D$_{2'}$ 1α-OH-D$_{2'}$ 1,25-(OH)$_2$-D$_2$	S	Skellysolve B/2-propanol (90:10)	Plasma	[41, 54]
D$_{3'}$25-OH-D$_{3'}$ 24,25-(OH)$_2$-D$_{3'}$ 1α-OH-D$_3$ 25,26-(OH)$_2$-D$_{3'}$ 1,25-(OH)$_2$-D$_3$	S	Skellysolve B/2-propanol (90:10)	Plasma	[41, 54]
25-OH-D$_{2'}$ 25-OH-D$_{3'}$ 24,25-(OH)$_2$-D$_3$	S	n-Hexane/ethanol (95:5)	Serum	[46]

Table 12-6. (Continued).

Separated Compounds*)	Stationary Phase**)	Eluent	Application	Ref.
1 α, 25-(OH)$_2$-D$_3$, 25-OH-D$_3$ 1 α-OH-D$_3$	R	94% Ethanol/H$_2$O (80:20)	Standard solutions	[40]
1 α, 25-(OH)$_2$-D$_3$	S	Light petroleum/dichloro- ethane/THF/n-propanol (50:25:24:5)	Standard solutions	[40]
24-S, 25-(OH)$_2$-D$_3$-tri- TMS, 24-R, 25-(OH)$_2$- D$_3$-tri-TMS	S	n-Hexane/dichloromethane (98:2)	Standard solutions	[38]
1 α, 25-(OH)$_2$-D$_3$, 1 α, 25-(OH)$_2$-pre-D$_3$	S	Light petroleum/dichloroethane/ THF/n-propanol (50:25:24:5)	Standard solutions	[40]
24,25-(OH)$_2$-D$_2$, 24,25-(OH)$_2$-D$_3$	S	Skellysolve B/2-propanol (90:10)	Plasma	[41, 54]
1 α, 24 R, 25-(OH)$_3$-D$_3$, 1 α, 24 S, 25-(OH)$_3$-D$_3$	S	Dichloromethane/methanol (96.5:3.5)	Standard solutions	[38]

*) Compounds matched with "&" are not resolved. Names occur in order of elution for abbreviations see Figure 12-1.
**) S: straight-phase HPLC on silica support.
  R: reversed-phase HPLC on chemically bound octadecyl support.

  Due to the discussed lability of vitamin D solutions, *sample pretreatment* steps should be carried out with care to prevent isomerization or degradation. Normally, rinsing the glass ware with different solvents is sufficient but surface deactivation by silanization has also been described. Investigations of biological matrices affords some *prefractionation* to remove the large excess of by-products (e. g. proteins and/or lipids) as well as to preconcentrate the sample because of the low concentrations of the compounds of interest. Usually, the first step is extraction with organic solvents, followed by further prepurification on Sephadex LH 20 [e. g. 47, 99, 48], hydroxyalkoxypropyl Sephadex [49], Celite 545 (80% aq. methanol stationary, n-pentane eluent) [50], or low-pressure [e. g. 45] as well as high-pressure chromatography [51, 47] on silica. These procedures are exemplified in Figure 12-5 based on the "multiple assay" method of Shepard and DeLuca [47].
  Although the vitamin 1,25-(OH)$_2$-D derivative is the most biopotent form of vitamin D, its quantification in biological samples is difficult. Whereas the vitamins D$_2$, D$_3$ and their corresponding 25-OH-D and 24,25-(OH)$_2$-D metabolites occour in normal human plasma at concentrations of about 1 to 30 µg/L, 1,25-(OH)$_2$-D has an average value of 31 ng/L [44]. This leads to severe detection problems, due to the limited amount of biological sample when spectrophotometric detection is carried out. Since competitive protein-binding assays are very sensitive, they can be used as an alternative to detect the extremely low amounts of 1,25-(OH)$_2$-D in biological material. Normally separation of vitamin D$_2$ and D$_3$ is not achieved in both, normal and reversed-phase mode. The addition of silver ions to the mobile phase, however, results in the

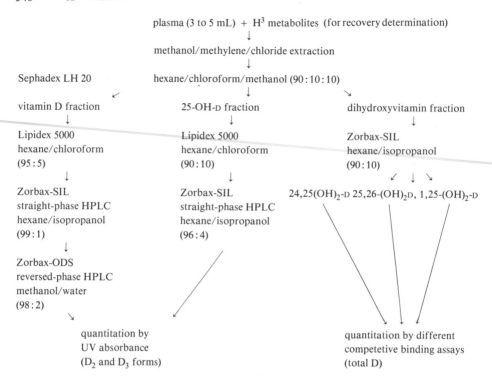

plasma (3 to 5 mL) + H³ metabolites (for recovery determination)
↓
methanol/methylene/chloride extraction
↓

Sephadex LH 20   hexane/chloroform/methanol (90:10:10)
                                              ↓

vitamin D fraction   25-OH-D fraction   dihydroxyvitamin fraction
        ↓   ↓   ↓
Lipidex 5000   Lipidex 5000   Zorbax-SIL
hexane/chloroform   hexane/chloroform   hexane/isopropanol
(95:5)   (90:10)   (90:10)
        ↓   ↓
Zorbax-SIL   Zorbax-SIL   24,25(OH)₂-D 25,26-(OH)₂D, 1,25-(OH)₂-D
straight-phase HPLC   straight-phase HPLC
hexane/isopropanol   hexane/isopropanol
(99:1)   (96:4)
        ↓
Zorbax-ODS
reversed-phase HPLC
methanol/water
(98:2)

        quantitation by   quantitation by different
        UV absorbance   competetive binding assays
        (D₂ and D₃ forms)   (total D)

Figure 12-5. Schematic diagram of the determination of vitamin D metabolites by the "multiple assay" procedure according to [47].

formation of different π-complexes and, therefore, a greater increase of polarity for vitamin D_2 than for D_3, and baseline separation is possible [26]. Unfortunately, this method was only used for D_2 and D_3 itself but application to similar problems should be possible.

Internal standardization is desirable to correct sample loss during sample preparation and besides radiolabelled vitamins [eg. 52, 47] a considerable number of reference substances were used which include progesterone [28], p-cresol, α-naphthol [53] and p-nitrophenylacetonitrile [21]. Recovery rates are normally better than 80 percent.

12.1.3 Vitamin E (Tocopherols and Tocotrienols)

Eight different compounds contribute to the biological activity of vitamin E to a different extent: α, β-, γ- and δ-tocopherol and their corresponding tocotrienols (containing three unsaturated bonds in the side chain).

The structures of the different tocopherols are surveyed in Table 12-7.

α-Tocopherol is considered to be the biologically most active compound but other tocopherols and tocotrienols may also contribute, to some extent, to the biological activity. Due to the relatively poor absorption of α-tocopherol (λ_{max} = 292 nm, $E^1_{1\,cm}$ = 72 [55]), the detection

Table 12-7. Structures of Tocopherols.

Compound	Structure		

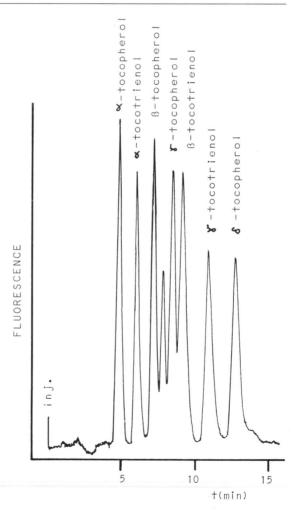

	R^1	R^2	R^3
α-tocopherol	CH_3	CH_3	CH_3
β-tocopherol	CH_3	H	CH_3
γ-tocopherol	H	CH_3	CH_3
δ-tocopherol	H	H	CH_3
tocol	H	H	H

Figure 12-6. Separation of vitamin E compounds. Column: 3.2 × 250 mm LiChrosorb Si 60 (5 µm); eluent: 5% diethyl ether in moist hexane; flow: 2 mL/min; fluorescence detection with excitation at 290 nm and emission at 330 nm. According to Thompson and Hatina [56].

limits are not as good as for the other fat-soluble vitamins using UV absorption spectroscopy. By fluorescence detection, however, the sinsitivity is increased about tenfold if an excitation wavelength at 290 nm, which can be extrapolated from the results of Thompson and Hatina [56], is used. A further twentifold increase in sensitivity can be obtained by shifting the excitation wavelength to 205 nm in accordance with the fluorescence excitation spectrum of α-tocopherol published by Hatam and Kayden [57]. As it can be seen from Table 12-8 the HPLC separations are carried out in normal and reversed-phase mode. The former method seems to be more suitable for the analysis of the different members of the vitamin E group, as documented by the excellent paper of Thomson and Hatina [56], whereas reversed-phase HPLC (especially with gradient elution) is more efficient in separating α-tocopherol from other vitamins (Figure 12-6).

Table 12-8. Survey of HPLC Separation of Tocopherols.

Separated Compounds	Stationary Phase	Eluent	Application	Ref.
α-,β-,γ-,δ-Tocopherols	Silica	0.2% Isopropanol or 5% diethyl ether in n-hexane	Foods, tissues	[56]
α-,β-,γ-Tocotrienols	Silica	5% Diethyl ether in hexane	Preparative HPLC	[56]
Vitamin A, tocol, α-Tocopherol	Reversed-phase (C_{18})	Methanol	Serum	[10]
α-,β-,γ-,δ-Tocopherols, tocol	Silica	n-Hexane (diisopropyl ether) (92:8)	Serum	[58]
α-,β-,γ-Tocopherols	Amine phase	n-Hexane/isopropanol (98:2)	Serum	[58]
α-,β-,γ-Tocopherols	Reversed-phase (C_{18})	Methanol/H_2O (95:5)	Plasma cellular elements of blood	[57]
α-Tocopherol	Reversed-phase (C_{18})	Methanol/H_2O (97:3)	Plasma	[59]
α-Tocopherol	Reversed-phase (C_{18})	Methanol	Serum	[60]
Carotinoids, vitamin K, α-Tocopheryl acetate	Silica	n-Hexane/diisopropyl-ether (96:4)	Plasma	[61]
α-Tocopherol	Reversed-phase (C_{18})	Methanol/H_2O (95:5)	Animal feedstuffs	[62]
α-Tocopheryl acetate, vitamins A and D_2	Reversed-phase (C_{18})	Methanol/H_2O (9:1)	Multivitamin tablets	[9]

Table 12-8. (Continued).

Separated Compounds	Stationary Phase	Eluent	Application	Ref.
α-Tocopherol, α-Tocopheryl acetate, vitamin A, vitamin A acetate, vitamins D_2 and K	Reversed-phase (C_{18})	H_2O/methanol gradient elution	Standard solutions	[3]
Vitamins A,B_1,B_{12},K_3, C,D_2 and E	Reversed-phase (C_{18})	H_2O/methanol gradient elution	Standard solutions	[11]
α-,β-,γ-,δ-Tocopherols	Various straight & reversed-phase	Various	Standard solutions	[63]

12.1.4 Vitamin K

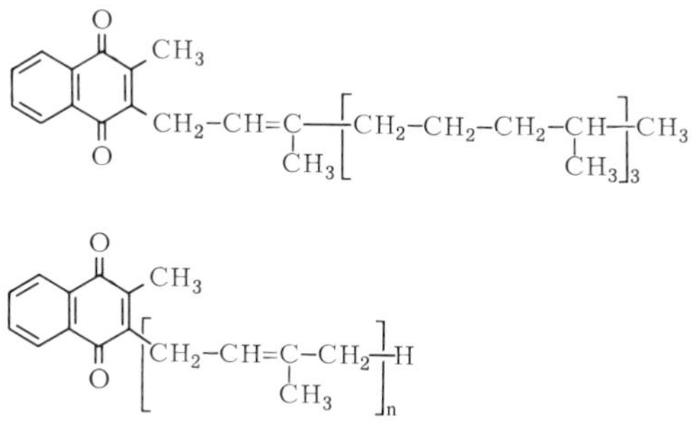

Phylloqinone (vitamin K_1)

Menaquinone-n (Mk-n) (vitamin K_2)

Figure 12-7. Structures of vitamin K compounds.

Vitamin K (see Figure 12-7) is essential for the formation of prothrombin and other blood-clotting proteins by the liver [64]. Therefore, there is growing interest in the metabolism and biochemical function of vitamin K in man, but only a few communications deal with the analysis of K vitamins, their analogs, and metabolites. Since natural vitamin K_1 occurs only in the trans-form, whilst synthetic products contain cis- and trans-isomers [65, 66] preparative separation is required for studying biological activity of these isomers [67 to 69] or their metabolites [70]. Purification of cis-trans isomers by TLC and conventional LC lead to conflicting results about their biopotency due to different purities of separated fractions. Matschiner et al. found the metabolic interconversion of phylloquinone and phylloquinone-2,3-epoxide [71] which lead to the development of several aqueous reversed-phase HPLC systems for these substances [72 to 74]. Non-aqueous reversed-phase HPLC [75] resulted in high column efficiency, enhanced solubility of the sample, lower operating pressures and extended column life, as demonstrated, for example, by Haroon et al. in their resolution of vitamin K_1 epoxide, a chlorinated analog of K_1 (chloro-K_1) and vitamin K_1 on Zorbax ODS with 30% dichloromethane in acetonitrile [76].

The same authors also used normal phase HPLC to separate 2′,3′-cis-chloro vitamin K_1, trans-chloro-K_1, 2′,3′-cis-K_1, 2′,3′-cis-K_1 epoxide, trans K_1 epoxide, and trans K_1 on Spherisorb-5 with 25% dry dichloromethane in hexane [76]. They found that the order of elution of vitamin K_1 and K_1 epoxide in normal phase systems is dependent on the moderator employed; an effect which occurs in varying degrees on different silica supports. Earlier developments of reversed-phase techniques made possible the separation of menaquinones [77 to 79], which are formed by bacteria whereas phylloquinone is a plant product. Menadione, menaquinone-3, 2,3-epoxy-menaquinone-4, 2-demethylmenaquinone-4, and menaquinone-4 were separated in that order on Partisil 10 ODS with acetonitrile/water (66:33) by Donnahey et al. [74]. It was found, however, that it is necessary to use different eluting solvents for phylloquinone and the epoxy derivative on the one hand and MK-4, MK-3 and their epoxy derivatives on the other. TLC was found by the same workers to be a good tool for sample preparation to remove interfering compounds from crude lipid fractions [74]. This problem was circumvented by Lefevere et al. [80] with a combined adsorption and reversed-phase HPLC procedure to detect endogenous vitamin K_1 levels in serum. The deproteinized serum was extracted with n-hexane, the hexane fraction was evaporated to dryness and the residue was dissolved in the eluent for normal phase HPLC (silica, 0.2% acetonitrile in n-hexane). This prefractionation yielded three fractions, of which one, containing vitamin K_1 was collected, evaporated and redissolved in the eluent for reversed-phase HPLC (low-load octadecyl; 8% dichloromethane in acetonitrile). This procedure gives extraction recoveries of more than 90% and a total recovery of 60 to 89% using vitamin trans-(^{3}H)-K_1 as the internal standard. Furthermore, a cyano-bonded phase was found to separate in the order: vitamin K_1, K_1-epoxide, MK-4 and MK-9 (RSil CN, 0.05% acetonitrile in n-hexane). Acetonitrile was found to be superior to dichloromethane due to an increase in column selectivity. Under physiological conditions, vitamin K_1 levels in human serum were found to be in the range of 5 to 30 ng/mL and the detection limit of the method is 500 pg/mL, which demonstrates the excellent applicability of HPLC to determine vitamin K in biological fluids.

12.2 Water-soluble Vitamins

The water-soluble vitamins offer a wide range of approaches for their chromatographic resolution and quantification due to the presence of ionic functions in these molecules. A considerable number of investigations on lipid-soluble vitamins are carried out by adsorption HPLC but this method is rarely used for the water-soluble vitamins. Reversed-phase, ion-exchange, and ion-pairing techniques are dominant. Figure 12-8 shows the reversed phase separation of various water soluble vitamins. The detectability is also extended to methods sensitive to ionic functions. Therefore, electrochemical detection is now used with advantage to detect the water-soluble vitamins.

Some water-soluble vitamins – biotin, pantothenic acid and vitamin B_{12} – had to be excluded from our survey because no reports have appeared so far. This is mainly due to the aliphatic structures of biotin and pantothenic acid which are insensitive in UV detection and also to the complex structure of vitamin B_{12}.

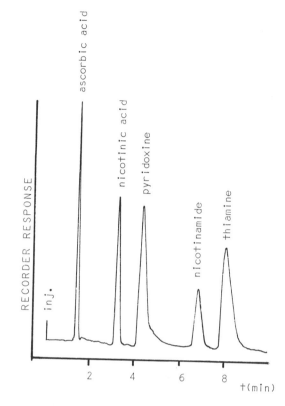

Figure 12-8. Reversed-phase separation of water soluble vitamins with high salt concentrations in the mobile phase. Column: 4.2 × 300 mm C$_{18}$ (10 µm); eluent 500 mmol/L Li$_2$SO$_4$ in methanol water (5:95); flow: 1.5 mL/min; detection: UV at 254 nm. According to Jandera and Churácek [88].

12.2.1 Vitamin B$_1$ (Thiamine)

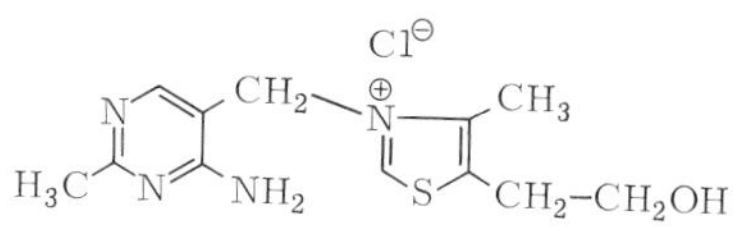

Figure 12-9. Structure of Thiamine.

Thiamine (Figure 12-9) is involved as a co-factor in the intermediate carbohydrate metabolism and plays a physiological role in the nerve excitation process [81 to 83]. The classical determination uses the thiochrome reaction during which the fluorescent thiochrome is formed in alkaline media.

Determination of thiamine by HPLC can be carried out in a number of different modes, namely cation-exchange, anion-exchange, reversed-phase (C-2, C-8, C-18), amino bonded-phase and ion-pair chromatography. Either direct analysis of thiamine is performed with subsequent UV-detection, or thiamine is converted to thiochrome by post-column-derivatization, or it is converted to thiochrome prior to HPLC. Each of these different methods has its own advantages, and their use depends on the specific problem of investigation. Since thiamine is a quarternary amine at acidic or neutral pH, its resolution is greatly dependent on the pH and the ionic strength of the eluent. This is demonstrated by the work of Williams et al. [84], who could elute thiamine only at basic pH by cation-exchange on Zipax SCX (0.05 mol/L NaH_2PO_4 at pH 9 and 0.8 mol/L $NaClO_4$). Wills et al. [85] studied systematically the retention of water-soluble vitamins – including thiamine – using different modes of HPLC namely reversed-phase HPLC on C-18 columns, paired-ion chromatography on C-18-columns and on amino-bonded phases. In all these procedures retention depended, to a considerable extent, on the pH used. Water-soluble vitamins cover a wide range of polarity; therefore gradient elution is often helpful for their analysis, which is documented in the results of Vandemark [86].

Table 12-9 gives a comprehensive review of HPLC investigations concerned with the analysis of thiamine in different matrices.

Table 12-9. Survey of HPLC Investigations in the Field of Vitamin B_1.

Investigated Compounds	Stationary Phase*)	Eluent	Application	Ref.
Niacin, vitamin B_2, B_6, folic acid, vitamin B_1	-NH_2	1 mmol/L NaH_2PO_4/acetonitrile (80:20)	Pharmaceutical preparations	[86]
Vitamin C and folic acid, vitamin B_6, niacin, vitamin B_1, B_2	RP-8	A: 1% Ammoniumcarbonate, B: methanol; from A to B in 4%/min	Pharmaceutical preparations	[86]
Niacin, vitamin B_6, B_1, B_2, C, folic acid	RP-2	A: 0.5% Hexadecyl-trimethyl-ammonium bromide, B: methanol, gradient from 5% B to 60% B in 3%/min	Pharmaceutical preparations	[86]
Niacin, niacinamide, pyridoxine, thiamine, riboflavin	RP-18	5 mmol/L Sodium hexa-multi-vitamin sulfonate in blends 1% acetic acid/methanol (75:25)	Multivitamin blends	[87]
Ascorbic acid, niacin, pyridoxine, niacinamide, thiamine	RP-18	0.5 mol/L Li_2SO_4 in methanol/water (5:95)	Standard solutions	[88]
Vitamin B_6, nicinamide and vitamin B_2 phosphate, metagin, propagin, thiamine	Strong cation-exchange	0.1 mol/L Phosphate buffer, pH 8	Veterinary tablet extracts	[89]
Thiamine-HCl, thiamine monophosphate, thiamine diphosphate, thiamine triphosphate	Anion exchange	A: 1 mmol/L KH_2PO_4, pH 6.0; B: 0.5 mol/LKH_2PO_4, pH 6.0; gradient from 0 to 70% B after 4 min. at 5% B/min.	Standard solutions	[90]
Oxythiamine, thiamine	RP-18 (PIC)	Water/methanol (3:1) plus 1% acetic acid and 1 mmol/L heptane/sulfonic acid	Standard solutions	[90]

Table 12-9. (Continued)

Investigated Compounds	Stationary Phase*)	Eluent	Application	Ref.
Thiamine, thiamine monophosphate, thiamine diphosphate	RP-18 (PIC)	50 mmol/L Tetrabutyl-ammoniumhydroxyde and 1% acetic acid (pH 4.3)	Standard solutions	[90]
Thiamine as thio-chrome	S	Methanol/diethylether (22:88)	Urine	[91]
Ascorbic acid, niacin, niacinamide, folic acid, thiamine, riboflavin, vitamin B_{12}	RP-18 (PIC)	Tetrabutylammonium phosphate in water/methanol (70:30)	Standard solutions	[85]
Ascorbic acid, niacin, folic acid, pyridoxin, riboflavin, vitamin B_{12}, niacinamide, thiamine	Various: RP,-NH_2, RP-PIC	Water/methanol with addition of salts or PIC-reagents	Systematic approach to analysis of water-soluble vitamins	[85]
Thiamine	Strong cation exchange	50 mmol/L Na_2HPO_4 (pH 9), 0.8 mol/L $NaClO_4$	Tablet extract	[84]
Thiamine, riboflavin, niacin	Strong anion ex hange	10 mmol/L $NaNO_3$	Tablet extract	[84]
Thiamine, thiamine monophosphate, thiamine diphosphate, thiamine triphosphate	Amino column	90 mmol/L Potassium phosphate buffer pH 8.4/acetonitrile (40:60)	Rat tissues	[93]

*) S: straight-phase HPLC on silica support.
RP: reversed phase HPLC on chemically bound alkyl support with indicated chain length.
-NH_2: amino bonded phase.
PIC: paired ion chromatography.

12.2.2 Vitamin B_2 (Riboflavin)

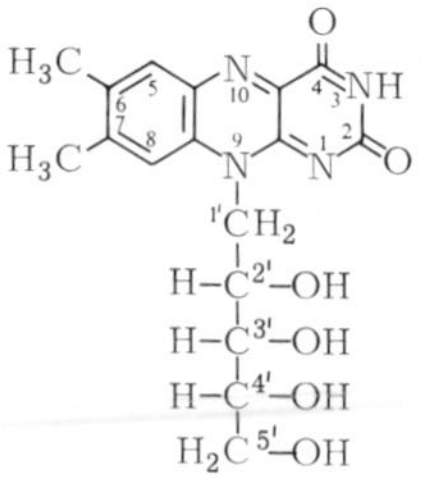

Figure 12-10. Structure of riboflavin.

Riboflavin (Figure 12-10) is normally assayed by fluorimetric methods which are quantified by comparing the fluorescence of the sample in the oxidized state (fluorescing form) with the reduced state (leuko form) [94, 95]. For riboflavin determination in biological fluids, several other methods have been described: thin-layer chromatographic [96], microbiological [97] and protozoological methods [98]. As for the other water-soluble vitamins, a number of HPLC modes can be applied for identification and quantitation of riboflavin. Due to the growing interest in quantitation of water-soluble vitamins in pharmaceutical preparations, group separations of these compounds are often carried out and some of them are quoted in Table 12-9. In addition, Knox and Pryde [99] described the application of a SAS (short alkyl-bonded chains on silica support) column for the separation of caffeine, and the vitamins B_2, B_3 and B_6 by Jurand [100], who used methanol/water/ammonia (85 : 15 : 25) containing 0.1% sodium lauryl sulphate as eluent. This separation could be carried out in less than ten minutes, with baseline separation for all components.

Riboflavin, amino acids, vitamin B_6, C and niacinamide were separated on an amino-bonded phase [101]. This mixture could be separated quantitatively in less than 30 minutes using an acetonitrile/phosphate buffer gradient.

Riboflavin is excreted in human urine only as free riboflavin [102, 103], which was also confirmed by HPLC [104, 105]. Furthermore, the later investigations could point out clearly that results in vitamin analysis are mostly more reliable and more specific using HPLC because of good separation from interfering substances, which might lead to confusing results using fluorometric assays. Since centrifugation is the only required sample preparation for riboflavin determination in urine and the time for analysis is in the range of 5 minutes, this method is best suited for routine analysis.

12.2.3 Vitamin B_6 (Pyridoxine group)

Six molecular species – pyridoxol, pyridoxal and pyridoxamine (see Figure 12-11) – and their corresponding phosphates – possess vitamin B_6 activity, although pyridoxol is the form commonly used in pharmaceutical formulations.

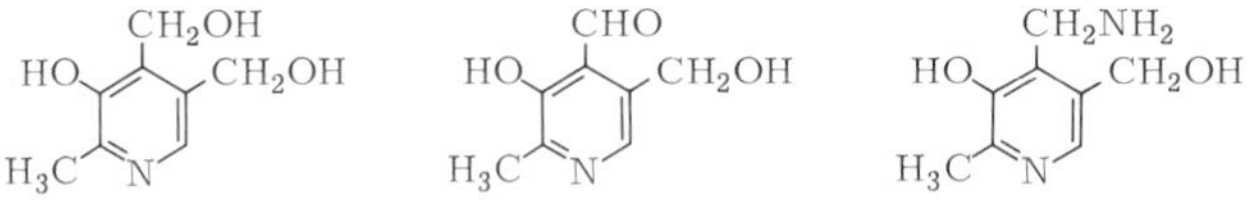

Figure 12-11. Some structures of pyridoxines possessing vitamine B_6 biopotency.

For vitamin B_6 detemination in food and body fluids, many earlier methods were tedious, costly and often lacked precision [106 to 109]. Therefore, HPLC brought a breakthrough in the rapid, precise and selective determination of different vitamin B_6 species. So is it possible today to determine all the vitamins at plasma concentration levels [110]. In group separations of the B_6 vitamins or the water-soluble vitamins mostly pyridoxol itself is determined, due to the aim of investigating pharmaceutical preparations. For pharmacologic and metabolic studies, however, the distinct determination of different forms of vitamin B_6 is necessary. Table 12-10 gives brief review on studies on vitamin B_6.

Table 12-10. Survey on HPLC Investigations Concerning Pyridoxine, Pyridoxal and Pyridoxamine.

Investigated Compounds	Stationary Phase	Mobile Phase	Application	Ref.
Pyridoxamine phosphate, pyridoxamine, pyridoxol phosphate, pyridoxol, pyridoxal phosphate, pyridoxal	Animex A-25	0.4 mol/L NaCl 10 mmol/L glycine 5 mmol/L semicarbazide pH 10 (NaOH)	Tablets and plasma	[110]
Pyridoxamine phosphate, pyridoxamine, pyridoxol phosphate, pyridoxol, 3-hydroxy-pyridine, pyridoxal, pyridoxic acid	Animex A-25	0.4 mol/L NaCl 10 mmol/L glycine pH 10 and 2.5 (stepwise gradient)	Multivitamin preparations	[111]
Pyridoxal, pyridoxamine	RP-18	67 mmol/L KH_2PO_4 pH 2.6 (H_3PO_4)	Plasma, urine, pharmaco-kinetics	[112]
Pyridoxamine, pyridoxal, pyridoxol,	RP-18	33 mmol/L KH_2PO_4 pH 2.2 (H_3PO_4)/acetonitrile (99:1)	Milk extract	[113]
Pyridoxal, pyridoxol, pyridoxamine	cation exchange (Animex A-5)	0.7 mol/L Ammonium formate buffer (isocratic) 10 mmol/L (pH 6.5) to 1 mol/L (pH 6.6) ammonium formate buffer (gradient)	Standard solutions	[114]
Pyridoxal, pyridoxol, pyridoxamine	PIC RP-18	Heptanesulfonate/2-propanol	Standard solutions	[114]

*) Names occur in order of elution.

For further investigations – especially for vitamin B group separations – refer also to references [84, 85, 87 to 89].

12.2.4 Vitamin C (Ascorbic Acid)

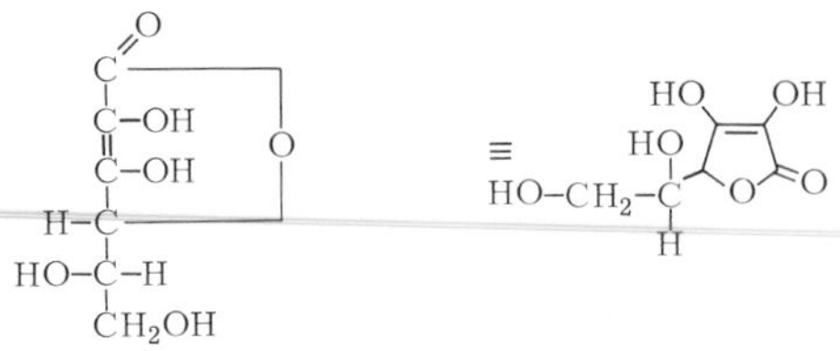

Figure 12-12. Structure of ascorbic acid.

Ascorbic acid is determined classically by 2,6-dichlorophenolindephenol visual titration [116], microfluorimetry [117], or colorimetry of the 2,4-dinitrophenylhydrazone derivative of dehydroascorbid acid [118]. Other techniques like electrochemical [119, 120], turbidimetric [121] and gaschromatographic [122] procedures were also developed. However, these assays are mostly time-consuming and are often limited by a number of interfering substances [123 to 125] found in the natural matrices. This leads to the evaluation of HPLC systems, which were performed by either ion-exchange, paired ion or reversed phase mode.

Ascorbic acid analysis is complicated by certain compounds such as dehydroascorbic acid which possesses bioactivity but is very poorly absorbed [126]. Therefore, dehydroascorbic acid should be included in *in vivo* investigations but should be excluded from ascorbate analysis in foods and pharmaceuticals. Moreover, care must be taken not to oxidize the strong UV-absorbing ascorbic acid to the non-absorbing dehydroascorbic acid during sample pretreatment or by ionic modifiers during chromatography.

Isoascorbic acid (D-ascorbic acid) is not found in natural products. Its biological activity is 20 times less than that of ascorbic acid but it is cheaper than L-ascorbic acid and is used by some manufacturers to supplement foods or drinks like orange juice. Bui-Nguyên separated isoascorbic acid from ascorbic acid with 75% acetonitrile in 5 mmol/L potassium dihydrogen phosphate solution (pH 4.4 to 4.7) on an amino bonded phase [127] and was able to determine levels of isoascorbic acid in orange juices. Orange juice was also subject to the investigations of Williams et al. [84] who used a strong anion-exchange column (Zipax SAX) eluted with 5 mmol/L sodium dihydrogen phosphate.

Pharmaceutical preparations and/or foods were investigated by a number of analysts. Wils et al. [85] were able to separate ascorbic acid, niacin, niacinamide, folic acid, vitamin B12, riboflavin and thiamine on μ Bondapac C_{18} with PIC reagent A in water/methanol (70:30). Pyridoxine, niacinamide, riboflavin, vitamin B12, ascorbic acid and niacin were separated in the same laboratory [85] on μ Bondapak NH_2 with 0.125% citrate/methanol (20:80). Vandemark [86] studied the retention behaviour of water-soluble vitamins including ascorbic acid on different stationary phases (e. g. amino, RP-8, RP-2 columns). The amino column separated riboflavin, pyridoxine, ascorbic acid, folic acid and thiamine with acetonitrile/ 1 mmol/L disodium hydrogen phosphate (pH 3) (80:20). The RP-8 column did not separate ascorbic acid from folic acid with a 4% per min gradient from 1% ammonium carbonate in water to methanol. However, good results were obtained with RP-2 material (niacin, pyridoxine, thiamin, riboflavin, ascorbic acid, folic acid in elution order) with gradient elution at 3.8% per min 5 to 60% methanol in 0.5% hexadecyltrimethyl ammonium bromide in water.

Besides amino acids and carbohydrates (xylitol, inositol, sorbitol) intravenous solutions may contain watersoluble vitamins (B_2, B_6, C, niacinamide) and were analyzed by Schuster [101] applying a stepwise gradient, with 10 mmol/L postassium dihydrogen phosphate (pH 4.3)/ acetonitrile on an amino-bonded phase.

Reversed-phase ion-pair chromatography with 1 mmol/L tridecylammonium formate in 50% methanol/water and a μ Bondapak C-18 column was used to detect ascorbic acid in multivitamin products and selected foods (e. g. tomatoe juice) by Sood et al. [128]. So far, reports on investigations of ascorbic acid in *biological samples* are not numerous but with the availability of various specific detection systems (e. g. electrochemical detection) an increase in such reports can be assumed for the future. Urine samples were analyzed by Wagner et al. [129] with 0.8% metaphosphoric acid on μ Bondapak C_{18} to examine the role of the absorption of ascorbic acid above the 500 mg dosage, following oral and intravenous application of vitamin C. Rege and Nahrwold [130] determined ascorbic acid and dehydroascorbic acid in a variety of biological samples eluting an amino-bonded column 2.5 mmol/L potassium dihydrogen phosphate/acetonitrile (50:50) and using dual wavelength UV detection. The advantageous use of electrochemical detection for ascorbic acid determination in brain tissue was described by Thrivikraman et al. [131] eluting a strong anion-exchange column with 10 mmol/L sodium dihydrogenphosphate. Pachla and Kissinger [132] extended the applications of electrochemical detection of ascorbic acid to a variety of samples like baby food, fruit juices, artificial fruit drinks, fruits, fortified cereals, milk products, urine, multivitamin formulations and others

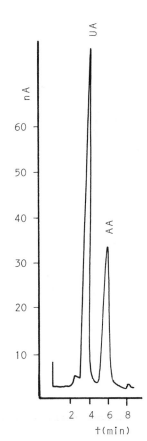

Figure 12-13. Analysis of ascorbic acid (AA, 19 ng) and uric acid (UA) in human urine (diluted 1:100) with anion-exchange chromatography and electrochemical detection. Column: 2.1 × 500 mm (glass) Zipax SAX; eluent: 50 mmol/L acetate buffer, pH 4.75; temperature 25 °C; flow: 0.33 mL/min; detector potential 700 mV vs. Ag/AgCl. According to Pachla and Kissinger [132].

(Figure 12-13). They used a thin-layer amperometric detector with a carbon paste eletrode and various strong anion-exchange columns eluted with 3% methaphosphoric acid/8% acetic acid. This demonstrates the advantage of specific and sensitive detectors in investigating single compounds in complex matrices.

Electrochemical detection was also used by Carr and Neff [133] to determine ascorbic acid in marine animals by anion-exchange column chromatography. An interesting chromatographic approach was made by Jandera and Churacek [88] replacing organic ion pairing substances by high concentrations of inorganic ions. Ascorbic acid, niacin, pyridoxine, niacinamide and thiamine were eluted with 500 mmol/L lithium sulfate in water/methanol (95:5) from an octadecyl silica column (Figure 12-8).

12.2.5 Nicotinic Acid

Figure 12-14. Structures of Nicotinic acid and Nicotinamide.

Nicotinic acid and its amide were included in a number of publications concerning the group separation of water-soluble vitamins which are discussed elsewhere in this chapter [84 to 86, 88, 101). However, there are only a few publications of HPLC methods for the determination of these compounds in biological matrices such as food, body fluids or tissue. All published HPLC procedures suffer from low sensitivity, so that only food samples with a content of 10 mg/L or more can be analysed [134]. In other cases, less selective but more sensitive procedures like GLC [135 to 137] are applied.

12.2.6 Folic Acid

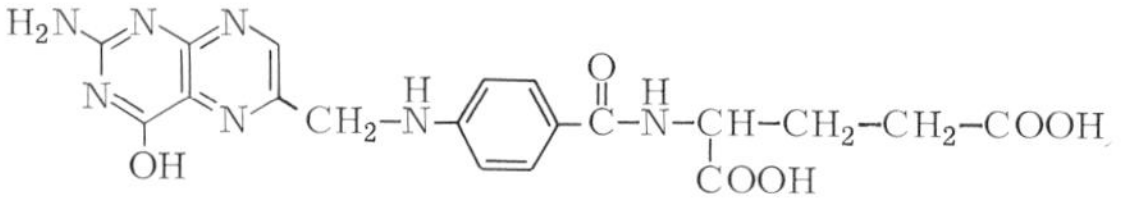

Figure 12-15. Structure of folic acid.

Naturally occuring derivatives of folic acid consist of a family of compounds differing in the oxidation state of the pteridine ring, in the number of glutamate residues and in the state of substitution with one carbon unit at positions N-5 or N-10.

Normally analysis of the various polyglutamate derivatives is performed after hydrolysis to the corresponding monoglutamate species by conventional ion-exchange chromatography on derivatized cellulose. These procedures are time consuming and suffer from a lack of sensitivity and reproducibility. Therefore, a number of HPLC methods were developed to circumvent these disadvantages.

Figure 12-16. Paired ion chromatographic separation of the three oxidation states of folic acid and N-(p-aminobenoyl)-L-glutamic acid. Column: 4 × 300 mm µBondapak C$_{18}$ (10 µm); eluent: 35% methanol water with 5 mmol/L tetrabutyl-ammonium phosphate; flow 1 mL/min; temperature: ambient; detection: UV at 254 nm. ME: 2-mercaptoethanol; PABG: N-(p-aminobenzoyl)-L-glutamic acid; FH$_4$: 5,6,7,8-tetrahydrofolic acid; FH$_2$: 7,8-dihydrofolic acid; F: folic acid. According to Brantman and McComish [140].

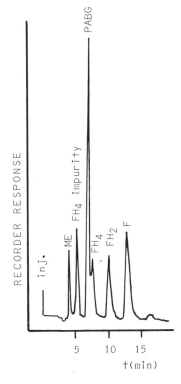

Table 12-11 gives a brief survey of folic acid investigations.

Table 12-11. Survey of Investigations of Folic Acid and its Related Derivatives.

Investigated Compounds*)	Stationary Phase**)	Mobile Phase	Application	Ref.
Nicotinic acid, riboflavin monophosphate, folic acid	Anion-exchange	Concave exponential gradient from 4 mmol/L to 200 mmol/L NaH$_2$PO$_4$ (pH 4.4) at 10%/min	Standard solutions	[84]
Ascorbic acid, nicotinic acid, nicotinic acid amide, folic acid, vitamin B$_{12}$, riboflavin, thiamine	RP-18	PIC A in water/methanol (70:30)	Standard solutions	[85]
Nicotinic acid, vitamins B$_6$, B$_2$, C, folic acid, thiamine	Amino column	1 mmol/L Na$_2$HPO$_4$ (pH 3.0)/ acetonitrile (20:80)	Standard solutions	[86]
Nicotinic acid, vitamins B$_6$, B$_1$, B$_2$, C, folic acid	RP-2	A: 0.5% Hexadecyltrimethyl ammonium bromide B: methanol gradient from 5 to 60% B at 3.8%/min	Standard solutions	[86]

Table 12-11. (Continued).

Investigated Compounds*)	Stationary Phase**)	Mobile Phase	Application	Ref.
Folic acid and 9 derivatives	Strong anion-exchange	Gradient elution	Standard solutions	[138]
p-Aminobenzoyl-glutamate, 5, 6, 7, 8-tetrahydrofolic acid, folic acid, 7, 8-dihydrofolic acid	Weak anion-exchange	25 mmol/L NaH_2PO_4	Standard solutions	[139]
N-(p-Aminobenzoyl)-L-glutamic acid, 5, 6, 7, 8-tetrahydrofolic acid, 7, 8-dihydrofolic acid, folic acid	RP-18 PIC	35% Methanol/water/tetra-butylammonium phosphate	Standard solutions	[140]
N^5-Formyltetrahydro-folic acid, N^5-methylte-trahydrofolic acid, folic acid	Anion exchange	0 to 6 mmol/L Potassium perchlorate gradient at 1%/min	Serum after folate treatment	[141]
Dihydrofolic acid, N^5-formyltetrahydrofolic acid, folic acid & N^5-methyltetrahydrofolic acid	RP-18 PIC	5 mmol/L Tetrabutylammonium phosphate in methanol/water (30:70)	Serum after folate treatment	[141]
p-Aminobenzoylgluta-mate, 5, 6, 7, 8-tetrahy-drofolic acid, folic acid, 7, 8-dihydrofolic acid, 5-methyltetrahy-drofolic acid	RP-Phenyl PIC	36 mmol/L $NaClO_4$ 130 mmol/L KH_2PO_4 0.9 mmol/L KOH 0.5% methanol after pre-equili-bration with tetrabutylamonium phosphate buffer	Foods, purifi-cation by for-mation of ion pairs	[142]
p-Aminobenzoylgluta-mate, 5-formyltetrahy-drofolic acid, dihydro-folic acid, 5-methylte-trahydrofolic acid, folic acid	RP-18 PIC	5 mmol/L Tetrabutylammonium phosphate gradient to methanol	Standard solutions	[143]
5-Methyltetrahydro-folic acid	Strong anion exchange and RP-8	50 mmol/L Sodium phosphate buffer pH 4.95/methanol (4:1)	Plasma and spinal fluid with electro chemical de-tection after column pre-concentration	[144]

Table 12-11. (Continued).

Investigated Compounds*)	Stationary Phase**)	Mobile Phase	Application	Ref.
p-Aminobenzoyl-glutamate, 10-formyl-tetrahydrofolic acid, tetrahydrofolic acid, 5-formyltetrahydrofolic acid, dihydrofolic acid, 5-methyltetrahydrofolic acid, folic acid, and various decomposition products	RP-18 PIC	A: 10 mmol/L tetrabutyl ammonium phosphate in water B: 10 mmol/L tetrabutyl ammonium phosphate in 50% methanol concave gradient from 15 to 25% B	Standard solutions	[145]

*) Compounds matched with "&" are not resolved. Names occur in order of elution.

**) RP: Reversed phase HPLC on chemically bound àlkyl support with indicated chain length.

12.3 Investigation of Vitamins in Biological Matrices

Although most of the vitamins could be separated quantitatively in the early seventies from standard solutions, determination of vitamins and related compounds in biological matrices is still a severe problem for the analytical chemist or biochemist today. Three main avenues to solve these problems can be seen.

Sample preparation has to remove the excess of organic and inorganic compounds as well as to pre-concentrate the vitamins to enhance the minimum detectable level. This is, according to classical methods, carried out by extraction and evaporation, which is not only tedious and lacks reproducibility (which can be corrected by internal standardization) but these procedures are often the source of artifacts produced by heat, light or chemicals (e. g. photoisomerization of retinals [15] or oxidation of ascorbic acid [130].

To circumvent these problems, two systematic approaches can be kept in mind. The first is sample prefractionation by size exclusion what enables the separation from high molecular weight substances (e. g. proteins) and salts [3, 4, 47]. The second approach is the on-line pre-purification and pre-concentration using a pre-column. This method enables separation from highly polar components such as salts and proteins, whereas the sample is enriched on the pre-column. However, these recently developed methods [146, 147] have not yet been applied to the analysis of vitamins but an easy adaption to these problems should be possible.

Selective separation conditions can give a further increase removing interfering by-products, as documented by Reingold et al. [142] who trapped folate derivatives on the column by the *in situ* generation of ion-pairs until interfering substances from food are eluted from the column.

Enhancing *selectivity of detection* is the third possibility to improve the analysis of vitamins in biological matrices. A simple approach is the choice of detection wavelengths which have minimum response to by-products. This procedure, however, is limited by the broad UV absorption of the interfering compounds. Fluorescence detection is the method of choice for analyzing tocopherols, resulting in a tremendous increase in sensitivity [e. g. 56, 57].

Electrochemical detection is best suited for the analysis of water-soluble vitamins like ascorbic acid or folic acid to increase selectivity. This was well documented for ascorbic acid determination in a variety of matrices by Pachla and Kissinger [132].

However, in the analysis of vitamins in biological matrices, most attention should be paid to sample preparation because the contamination of the columns with biological constituents can result in a loss of column efficiency and a drastically reduced lifetime of the column.

12.4 References

[1] M. Zakaria, and K. Simpson, *J. Chromatogr.* **176**, 109 (1979).
[2] H. R. Cama, F. D. Collins, and R. A. Morton, *Biochem. J.* **50**, 48 (1951).
[3] R. C. Williams, J. A. Schmit, and R. A. Henry, *J. Chromatogr. Sci.* **10**, 494 (1972).
[4] A. M. McMormick, J. L. Napoli, and H. F. DeLuca, *Meth. Enzymol.* **67**, 220 (1980).
[5] A. M. McMormick, J. L. Napoli, and H. F. DeLuca, *Anal. Biochem.* **86** 25 (1978).
[6] J. E. Paanakker, and G. W. T. Groenedijk, *J. Chromatogr.* **168**, 125 (1979).
[7] J.-G. Besner, R. Leclaire, and P. R. Band, *J. Chromatogr.* **183**, 346 (1980).
[8] M. G. M. de Ruyter, and A. P. de Leenheer, *Anal. Chem.* **51**, 43 (1979).
[9] D. T. Burns, and C. Mackay, *J. Chromatogr.* **200**, 300 (1980).
[10] A. P. de Leenheer, V. O. R. C. De Bevere, M. G. M. de Ruyter, and A. E. Claeys, *J. Chromatogr.* **162**, 408 (1979).
[11] J. A. Schmit, R. A. Henry, R. C. Williams, and J. F. Dieckman, *J. Chromatogr. Sci.* **9**, 645 (1971).
[12] K. Tsukida, A. Kodama, and M. Ho, *J. Nutr. Sci. Vitaminol.* **24**, 593 (1978).
[13] F. G. Pilkiewicz, M. J. Pettei, A. P. Yudd, and K. Nakanishi, *Exp. Eye Res.* **24**, 421 (1977).
[14] K. Tsukida, A. Kodama, and M. Ito, *J. Chromatogr.* **134**, 331 (1977).
[15] K. Tsukida, R. Masahara, and M. Ito, *J. Chromatogr.* **192**, 395 (1980).
[16] R. Hänni, D. Hervouet, and A. Busslinger, *J. Chromatogr.* **162**, 615 (1979).
[17] C. V. Puglisi, and J. A. F. de Silva, *J. Chromatogr.* **152**, 421 (1978).
[18] B. A. Halley, and E. C. Nelson, *J. Chromatogr.* **175**, 113 (1979).
[19] M. Eriksson, T. Eriksson, and B. Sörensen, *Acta Pharm. Suec.* **15**, 274 (1978).
[20] M. Vecchi, J. Vesely, and G. Oesterhelt, *J. Chromatogr.* **83**, 447 (1973).
[21] D. F. Tomkins, and R. J. Tscherne, *Anal. Chem.* **46**, 1602 (1974).
[22] K. A. Tartivita, J.P. Sciarello, and B. C. Rudy, *J. Pharm. Soc.* **65**, 1024 (1976).
[23] G. J. Krol, C. A. Mannan, F. Q. Gemmill, Jr., G. E. Hicks, and B. T. Kho, *J. Chromatogr.* **74**, 43 (1972).
[24] K. Takada, T. Okano, Y. Tamura, S. Matsui, and T. Kobayashi, *J. Nutr. Sci. Vitaminol.* **25**, 385 (1979).
[25] R. K. D. Tiebach, and M. Schramm, *Chromatographia* **13**, 403 (1980).
[26] H. Cohen, and M. Lapointe, *J. Chromatogr. Sci.* **17**, 510 (1979).
[27] R. J. Tscherne, and G. Capitano, *J. Chromatogr.* **136**, 337 (1977).
[28] G. A. Walker, B. E. Carpenter, and D. L. Tuescher, *J. Pharm. Sci.* **69**, 846 (1980).
[29] R. Vanhaelen-Fastré, and M. Vanhaelen, *J. Chromatogr.* **153**, 219 (1978).
[30] E. Egaas, and G. Lambertsen, *Internat. J. Vit. Nutr. Res.* **49**, 35 (1979).
[31] E. J. De Vries, J. Zeeman, R. J. E. Esser, B. Borsje, and F. J. Mulder, *J. Assoc. Off. Anal. Chem.* **62**, 129 (1979).
[32] H. Hofsass, N. J. Alicino, A. L. Hirsch, L. Ameika, and L. D. Smith, *J. Assoc. Off. Anal. Chem.* **61**, 735 (1978).
[33] H. F. DeLuca, *N. Engl. J. Med.* **289**, 359 (1973).
[34] H. F. DeLuca, *Fed. Proc., Fed. Am. Soc. Exp. Biol.* **33**, 2211 (1974).
[35] D. R. Fraser, *Proc. Nutr. Soc.* **34**, 139 (1975).
[36] H. F. DeLuca, *Clin. Endocrinol.* **5**, Suppl. 979 (1976).
[37] H. F. DeLuca, *Biochem. Pharmacol.* **26**, 563 (1977).

[38] N. Ikekawa, and N. Koizumi, *J. Chromatogr.* **119**, 227 (1976).

[39] J. A. Eisman, R. M. Shepard, and H. F. DeLuca, *Anal. Biochem.* **80**, 298 (1977).

[40] R. Vanhaelen-Fastré, and M. Vanhaelen, *J. Chromatogr.* **179**, 131 (1979).

[41] G. Jones, and H. F. DeLuca, *J. Lipid. Res.* **16**, 448 (1975).

[42] G. Jones, *Clin. Chem.* **24**, 287 (1978).

[43] T. Okano, N. Matsuyama, T. Kobayashi, E. Kurado, S. Kodama, and T. Matsuo, *J. Nutr. Sci. Vitaminol.* **25**, 479 (1979).

[44] N. Matsuayama, T. Okano, K. Takada, T. Takao, Y. Terao, N. Hashimoto, and T. Kobauashi, *J. Nutr. Sci. Vitaminol.* **25**, 469 (1979).

[45] B. Pelc, and A. L. Holmes, *J. Chromatogr.* **173**, 403 (1979).

[46] T. J. Gilbertson, and R. P. Stryd, *Clin. Chem.* **23**, 1700 (1977).

[47] R. M. Shepard, and H. F. DeLuca, *Meth. Enzymol.* **67**, 393 (1980).

[48] P. C. Schaefer, and R. S. Goldsmith, *J. Lab. Clin. Med.* **91**, 104 (1978).

[49] J. N. Thompson, W. B. Maxwell, and M. L.'Abbé, *J. Assoc. Off. Anal. Chem.* **60**, 998 (1977).

[50] K. T. Koshy, and A. L. Van Der Slik, *Anal. Biochem.* **85**, 283 (1978).

[51] A. C. Ray, J. N. Dwyer, and J. C. Reagov, *J. Assoc. Off. Anal. Chem.,* **60**, 1296 (1977).

[52] K. T. Koshy, *Meth. Enzymol.* **67**, 357 (1980).

[53] K. Tsukida, *Meth. Enzymol.* **67**, 326 (1980).

[54] Y. Tanaka, H. F. DeLuca, and N. Ikekawa, *Meth. Enzymol.* **67**, 370 (1980).

[55] J. G. Baxter, C. D. Robeson, J. D. Taylor, and R. W. Lehman, *J. Am. Chem. Soc.* **65**, 918 (1943).

[56] J. N. Thompson, and G. Hatina, *J. Liq. Chromatogr.* **2**, 327 (1979).

[57] L. J. Hatam, and H. J. Kayden, *J. Lipid. Res.* **20**, 639 (1979).

[58] L. Jansson, B. Nilsson, and R. Lindgreen, *J. Chromatogr.* **181**, 242 (1980).

[59] C. H. McMurray, and W. Blanchflower, *J. Chromatogr.* **178**, 525 (1979).

[60] A. P. De Leenheer, V. O. De Bevere, A. A. Cruyl, and A. E. Claeys, *Clin. Chem.* **24**, 585 (1978).

[61] B. Nilsson, B. Johansson, L. Jansson, and L. Holmberg, *J. Chromatogr.* **145**, 169 (1978).

[62] C. H. McMurray, and W. J. Blanchflower, *J. Chromatogr.* **176**, 488 (1979).

[63] G. T. Vatassery, V. R. Maynard, and D. F. Hagen, *J. Chromatogr.* **161**, 299 (1978).

[64] C. T. Emson, J. A. Sadowski, and J. W. Suttie, *J. Biol. Chem.* **250**, 4744 (1975).

[65] H. Mayer, U. Gloor, O. Isler, R. Rüegg, and O. Wiss, Helv. *Chim. Acta* **47**, 221 (1964).

[66] L. M. Jackman, R. Rüegg, G. Ryser, C. von Planta, U. Gloor, H. Mayer, P. Schudel, M. Kofler, and O. Isler, *Helv. Chim. Acta* **48**, 1382 (1965).

[67] J. T. Matschiner, and R. G. Bell, *J. Nutr.* **102**, 625 (1972).

[68] T. E. Khaner, C. Siegfried, A. K. Willingham, and J. T. Matschiner, *J. Nutr.* **105**, 1519 (1975).

[69] J. Lowenthal, and G. M. V. Rivera, *J. Pharmacol. Exp. Ther.* **209**, 330 (1979).

[70] M. J. Thierry-Palmer, M. S. Stern, C. A. Kost, and J. C. Montgomery, in: J. W. Suttle (ed.): *Proc. 8th Steenbock Symposium Vitamin K Metabolism and Vitamin K-Dependent Proteins Madison, Wisconsin, June 10–13, 1979,* p. 333. University Park Press, Baltimore 1980.

[71] J. T. Matschiner, R. G. Bell, J. M. Amelotti, and T. E. Knauer, *Biochim. Biophys. Acta* **201**, 309 (1970).

[72] G. R. Elliot, E. M. Odam, and M. G. Townsend, *Biochem. Soc. Trans.* **4**, 615 (1976).

[73] T. D. Bjornsson, S. E. Swezey, P. J. Mettin, and T. F. Blaschke, *Thromb. Hamostas.* **39**, 466 (1978).

[74] P. L. Domahey, V. T. Burt, H. H. Rees, and J. F. Pennock, *J. Chromatogr.* **170**, 272 (1979).

[75] M. J. Shearer, V. Allan, Y. Haroon, and P. Barkham, in: J. W. Suttie (ed.): *Proc. 8th Steenbock Symposium Vitamin K Metabolism and Vitamin K-Dependent Proteins, Madison, Wisconsin, June 10–13, 1979,* p. 317. University Park Press, Baltimore 1980.

[76] Y. Harron, M. J. Shearer, and P. Barkham, *J. Chromatogr.* **200**, 293 (1980).

[77] J. T. Matschiner, and W. V. Taggart, *Anal. Biochem.* **18**, 88 (1967).

[78] H. R. Bollinger, in: E. Stahl (ed.): *Thin Layer Chromatography,* 2nd Engl. Ed., p. 259. Springer, Berlin-Heidelberg-New York 1969.

[79] J. T. Matschiner, and J. M. Ameotti, *J. Lipid. Res.* **9**, 176 (1968).

[80] M. F. Lefevere, A. P. De Leenheer, and A. E. Claeys, *J. Chromatogr.* **186**, 749 (1979).

[81] A. von Muralt, *Vitamin. Horm. (N.Y.)* **5**, 93 (1941).

[82] Y. Hokawa, and J. R. Cooper, *Science* **166**, 759 (1969).

[83] Y. Hokawa, *J. Appl. Nutr.* **29**, 5 (1977).

[84] R. C. Williams, D. R. Baker, and J. A. Schmit, *J. Chromatogr. Sci.* **11**, 618 (1973).

[85] R. B. H. Wills, C. G. Shaw, and W. R. Day, *J. Chromatogr. Sci.* **15**, 262 (1977).

[86] F. L. Vandemark, *Chromatogr. Newsl.* **8**, 27 (1980).

[87] R. C. Kirchmeier, and R. P. Upton, *J. Pharm. Sci.* **67**, 1444 (1978).

[88] P. Jandera, and J. Charachek, *J. Chromatogr.* **197**, 181 (1980).

[89] K. Callmer, and L. Davies, *Chromatographia* **7**, 644 (1974).

[90] C. J. Gubler, and B. C. Hemming, *Meth. Enzymol.* **62**, 63 (1979).

[91] R. L. Roser, A. H. Andrist, W. H. Harrington, H. K. Naito, and D. Lonsdale, *J. Chromatogr.* **146**, 43 (1978).

[92] K. Ishi, K. Sarai, H. Sanemori, and T. Kawasaki, *J. Nutr. Sci. Vitaminol.* **25**, 517 (1979).

[93] K. Ishi, K. Sarai, H. Sanemori, and T. Kawasaki, *Anal. Biochem.* **97**, 191 (1979).

[94] *United States Pharmacopeia,* p. 627. 19th rev. Mack Publishing Co., Easton, P. A. 1975.

[95] N. P. Mellor, and A. R. Maass: *Advances in Automated Analysis,* Vol. 9, p. 67. Mediad. Tarrytown, N.Y. 1973.

[96] C. Haworth, R. Oliver, and R. Swaile, *Analyst (London)* **96**, 432 (1971).

[97] M. Telegdy-Konats, and M. Heqedus, *Elelmez. Ipar.* **24**, 358 (1970).

[98] H. Baker, O. Frank, S. Feingold, R. Gellene, C. Leevy, and S. H. Hunter, *Am. J. Clin. Nutr.* **19**, 17 (1966).

[99] J. H. Knox, and A. Pryde, *J. Chromatogr.* **112**, 171 (1975).

[100] J. Jurand, unpublished results.

[101] R. Schuster, *Anal. Chem.* **52**, 617 (1980).

[102] W. J. Jusko, and G. Levy, *J. Pharm. Sci.* **56**, 58 (1967).

[103] B. Stripp, *Acta Pharmacol. Toxicol.* **22**, 353 (1965).

[104] A. R. Williams, and W. Slavin, *Chromatogr. Newsl.* **5**, 9 (1977).

[105] M. D. Smith, *J. Chromatogr.* **182**, 285 (1980).

[106] K. K. Steward, in: H. S. Hertz, and S. N. Chester (eds.): *National Bureau of Standards: Proc. Ninth Materials Research Symposium, April 1979,* p. 249.

[107] C. A. Storvick, E. M. Benson, M. A. Edwards, and M. G. Woodring, *Meth. Biochem. Anal.* **12**, 183 (1964).

[108] E. W. Toepfer, and M. M. Polansky, in: R. S. Harris, I. G. Wool, and J. A. Loraine (eds.): *Vitamins and Hormones,* Vol. 22, p. 825. Academic Press, New York.

[109] Y. H. Loo, and W. M. Cort, *Meth. Neurochem.,* **2**, 169 (1972).

[110] J. T. Vanderslice, and C. E. Maire, *J. Chromatogr.* **196**, 176 (1980).

[111] J. T. Vanderslice, K. K. Stewart, and M. M. Yarmas, *J. Chromatogr.* **176**, 280 (1979).

[112] W. J. O'Reilly, P. J. M. Guele, M. J. A. Hoes, and E. van der Kleyn, *J. Chromatogr.* **183**, 492 (1980).

[113] K. L. Lim, R. W. Young, and J. A. Driksel, *J. Chromatogr.* **188**, 285 (1980).

[114] A. K. Williams, *Meth. Enzymol.* **62**, 415 (1979).

[115] *The United States Pharmacopeia,* p. 120. 19th Revise, Mack Publishing Co., Easton, Pa. 1975.

[116] M. Z. Barakat, S. K. Shebab, N. Darwish, and A. El-Zoheiry, *Anal. Biochem.* **53**, 245 (1973).

[117] M. J. Deutsch, and C. E. Weeks, *J. Assoc. Off. Agric. Chem.* **48**, 1248 (1965).

[118] J. H. Roe, M. B. Mills, M. J. Oesterling, and C. M. Damron, *J. Biol. Chem.* **174**, 201 (1948).

[119] J. Lindquist, and S. M. Farroha, *Analyst. (London)* **100**, 377 (1975).

[120] J. Lindquist, *Analyst (London)* **100**, 339 (1975).

[121] J. W. Ralls, *J. Agric. Food. Chem.* **23**, 609 (1975).

[122] J. E. Schlack, *J. Assoc. Off. Anal. Chem.* **57**, 1346 (1974).

[123] M. Zobel, *Ernährungsforschung* **16**, 257 (1971).

[124] P. R. Beljaars, W. V. S. Horrocks, and T. M. N. Rondags, *J. Assoc. Off. Anal. Chem.* **57**, 65 (1974).

[125] F. De Fabrizio, *J. Pharm. Sci.* **63**, 91 (1974).

[126] M. H. Hashmi, A. A. Ayaz, A. Viegas, and A. S. Adil, *Microchem. J.* **16**, 645 (1971).

[127] M. H. Bui-Nguyên, *J. Chromatogr.* **196**, 163 (1980).

[128] S. P. Sood, L. E. Sartori, D. P. Wittmer, and W. G. Hamey, *Anal. Chem.* **48**, 796 (1976).

[129] E. S. Wagner, B. Lindley, and R. D. Coffin, *J. Chromatogr.* **163**, 225 (1979).

[130] R. C. Rose, and D. L. Nahrworld, *Anal. Biochem.* **114**, 140 (1981).

[131] K. V. Thrivikraman, C. Refshauge, and R. N. Adams, *Life Sci.* **15**, 1355 (1974).

[132] L. A. Pachla, and P. T. Kissinger, *Anal. Chem.* **48**, 364 (1976).

[133] R. S. Carr, and J. M. Neff, *Anal. Chem.* **52**, 2428 (1980).

[134] D. P. Witmer, and W. G. Haney, Jr., in: K. Tsuji (ed.): *GLC and HPLC Determination of Therapeutic Agents,* p. 1243. Marcel Dekker, New York-Basel.

[135] A. R. Prosser, and A. J. Sheppard, *J. Chromatogr. Sci.* **57**, 1004 (1968).

[136] J. D. Ashby, and J. C. Deavin, *J. Pharm. Pharmacol.* **21**, 525 (1969).

[137] J. Vessman, and S. Stromberg, *J. Chromatogr. Sci.* **64**, 311 (1975).

[138] R. W. Stout, A. R. Cashmore, J. K. Coward, C. G. Horvath, and J. R. Bertino, *Anal. Biochem.* **71**, 119 (1976).

[139] L. L. Reed, and M. C. Archer, *J. Chromatogr.* **121**, 100 (1976).

[140] A. R. Brantman, and M. McComish, *J. Chromatogr.* **151**, 87 (1978).

[141] S. K. Chapman, B. C. Greene, and R. R. Streiff, *J. Chromatogr.* **145**, 302 (1978).

[142] R. N. Reingold, M. F. Picciamo, and E. G. Perkins, *J. Chromatogr.* **190**, 237 (1980).

[143] B. A. Allen, and R. A. Newman, *J. Chromatogr.* **190**, 241 (1980).

[144] J. Lankelma, E. von der Kleijn, and M. J. T. Jansen, *J. Chromatogr.* **182**, 35 (1980).

[145] D. W. Horne, W. T. Briggs, and C. Wagner, *Anal. Biochem.* **116**, 393 (1981).

[146] W. Voelter, T. Kronbach, K. Zech, and R. Huber, *J. Chromatogr.* **239**, 475 (1982).

[147] W. Roth, K. Beschke, R. Jauch, A. Zimmer, and F. W. Koss, *J. Chromatogr.* **222**, 13 (1981).

13 Organic Acids in Humans

by *Hartmut Liebich*

13 Organic Acids in Humans

13.1 Introduction and Clinical Relevance

The class of organic acids in serum and in urine consists of a heterogeneous multitude of components, originating from very different biochemical pathways. Their main sources are

(a) the degradation of the branched-chain amino acids valine, leucine and isoleucine;
(b) the metabolism of the aromatic amino acids phenylalanine, tyrosine, tryptophan and histidine;
(c) the metabolism of biogenic amines;
(d) β- and ω-oxidation of fatty acids;
(e) ketogenesis;
(f) biosynthesis of fatty acids;
(g) the metabolism of monosaccharides.

In addition to these main sources, organic acids are formed by some other known reaction pathways as well as by mechanisms which are not yet clarified.

According to their chemical properties, most of the organic acids can be classified into:

- fatty acids;
- aliphatic dicarboxylic acids;
- aliphatic oxocarboxylic acids;
- aliphatic hydroxycarboxylic acids;
- phenols;
- aromatic acids;
- furancarboxylic acids;
- nitrogen-containing aliphatic and aromatic acids;
- acid conjugates.

The analysis of the organic acids is meaningful for answering questions from two standpoints, from the standpoint of pure biochemistry and from the standpoint of applied biochemistry and clinical chemistry. For the first viewpoint, the objective will be, for example, the investigation of degradation processes such as the ω-oxidation in the fatty acid metabolism, or the study of bio-synthesis pathways such as the formation of regular ketone bodies and higher-molecular-weight ketone bodies. For the second viewpoint, the goal will be a diagnostic answer based on abnormal concentrations of certain organic acids in serum or urine, such as elevated amounts of phenyl-pyruvic acid in urine in case of *phenylketonuria* on the basis of an inherited deficiency in the activity of the enzyme phenylalanine-4-hydroxylase, or elevated amounts of vanillylmandelic acid in urine in case of a tumor such as a *phaeochromocytoma* or a *neuroblastoma*. In this article, the second viewpoint, i. e., the role of the organic acids as diagnostic markers, will be emphasized.

13.2 Methodical Aspects

13.2.1 Isolation of the Organic Components

In some cases, single organic acids can be detected and quantitatively determined directly in the biological fluid on the basis of specific reactions. Lactic acid is measured by an enzymatic reaction using lactate dehydrogenase [1], acetoacetic acid by an enzymatic reaction using β-hydroxybutyrate dehydrogenase [2], uric acid by a colorimetric reaction [3] or an enzymatic reaction [4], phenylpyruvic acid by a colorimetric reaction [5]. Some acids can be determined by HPLC using the non-pretreated biological sample, e. g. hippuric acid in urine [6], 5-hydroxyindole-3-acetic acid in urine [7] and cerebrospinal fluid [8] and homovanillic acid in urine [9] and in cerebrospinal fluid [8]. Direct injection of urine is also applied in HPLC analysis of profiles of organic acids [10, 11].

In most cases, the organic acids have to be isolated from the biological material prior to analysis. This holds true for both of the two main analytical separation techniques, i. e., GC and HPLC. Two principal methods are used for the isolation of the acidic components, solvent extraction and isolation by anion-exchange chromatography.

In solvent extraction, acceptable results are obtained using diethyl ether [12 to 15] or ethyl acetate [16 to 24] or a mixture of these solvents [25, 26], for example in the ratio of 1 : 1. Other solvents, such as dichloromethane [27], dichloromethane/tert-amyl alcohol (2:1) [28], dichloromethane/isopropanol (9:1) [29], benzene/ethyl acetate (1:1) [30], are less frequently used. To improve the extraction, the urine or serum sample can be saturated with salts, e. g. sodium chloride. The methods are not time-consuming, since normally they are carried out batchwise rather than continuously. However, for many organic acids, especially polyhydroxycarboxylic acids and other very polar acids, the procedure is not quantitative. Protein-containing fluids, especially serum, have to be deproteinized prior to the extraction. The removal of the proteins can be achieved either by dialysis or by precipitation. Since protein-bound organic acids are partially lost using the dialysis procedure, the precipitation of the proteins is mostly preferable. However, some organic acids may co-precipitate with the proteins.

Isolation of the organic acids by anion-exchange chromatography is widely used, especially when acid profiles are to be studied. DEAE-Sephadex [31 to 34], Dowex [35], Amberlyst A-26 [36, 37] and other anion-exchange resins are employed. Isolation by anion-exchange is more laborious than solvent extraction procedures. Anion-exchange is, however, more quantitative, and it is chosen when detailed profiles of various classes of organic acids, including the hydroxycarboxylic acids, are investigated, and when, in comparative studies, small changes in the profiles need to be detected. The improvement in the isolation of polyhydroxycarboxylic acids using DEAE-Sephadex instead of diethyl ether/ethyl acetate has been described [38]. Good results for profiles are also obtained using Extrelut ^{R} columns in the isolation procedure [39].

13.2.2 Derivatization of the Acids

The separation of the organic acids by HPLC does not require a derivatization to increase the volatility and the thermostability of the acids, as is necessary in GC. Therefore, in many cases the isolated acids are immediately subjected to HPLC analysis. For HPLC a derivatization can be useful to facilitate the detection of the acids. Phenylpyruvic acid is reacted with 4'-hydrazino-2-stilbazole in aqueous methanol to give the corresponding fluorescent hydrazone [30], or determined by UV detection after derivatization with 2,3-diaminonaphthalene on a pre-column [40]. 2-Oxocarboxylic acids are separated and detected as 2,4-dinitrophenylhydrazones [41], or as quinoxalinols after reaction with o-phenylenediamine [42]. Free fatty acids from serum are measured by fluorescence labelling with 4-bromomethyl-7-methoxycoumarin [29, 43].

For the separation of the organic acids by GC, derivatization is the rule. In the majority of the cases the carboxyl functions of the acids are transformed either into the trimethylsilyl esters or into the methyl esters. Trimethylsilylation is usually achieved with bis(trimethylsilyl)trifluoro-acetamide (BSTFA) [25, 33, 44 to 49] or bis(trimethylsilyl)acetamide (BSA) [22 to 24, 32, 32, 50 to 53]. For the methylation of the organic acids most laboratories use the reaction with diazomethane [13, 26, 36, 37, 39, 54 to 59].

Both, the trimethylsilyl esters and the methyl esters, have advantages and limitations. Often the methyl esters have better chromatographic properties. Working with GC-MS to identify the acids, the mass spectra of the methyl esters are easier to interpret than the spectra of the tri-methylsilyl esters, since the fragmentation of the methyl esters is often simpler and more predictable. When the necessary working precautions are followed, methylation with diazomethane is very simple and rapid. However, the procedure also has some disadvantages. Since the hydroxyl groups of phenolic acids are methylated as well, it is not possible to distinguish between originally present aromatic OH-groups and OCH_3-groups. Another disadvantage is a possible reaction of diazomethane with double bonds of unsaturated dicarboxylic acids, e. g. fumaric acid, to produce artifacts. Both of these drawbacks are not encountered when working with trimethylsilyl esters. Further derivatives of the carboxyl group, especially when using electron capture detection, are hexafluoroisopropyl esters [60, 61] and pentafluorobenzyl esters [62].

In addition to the carboxyl group, other functional groups in organic acids are derivatized. Whereas the hydroxyl groups of hydroxycarboxylic acids are transformed into the trimethylsilyl ethers, when the organic acids are trimethylsilylated, they are usually left underivatized, when the organic acids are methylated.

The carbonyl groups of oxocarboxylic acids are transformed into oximes [23, 24, 53, 63], O-methyloximes [36], O-ethyloximes [31, 46] or O-trimethylsilylquinoxalinols [64, 65]. Without derivatization of the carbonyl groups, many oxocarboxylic acids are not stable for GC analysis. Phenolic OH-groups are derivatized with trifluoroacetic anhydride [60, 61] or heptafluoro-butyric anhydride [62] allowing electron capture detection.

13.2.3 Pre-Fractionation

Because of the high complexity of the mixture of organic acids in serum and in urine, a pre-fractionation of the total mixture is essential, when constituents of low concentrations shall be studied. Pre-fractionation is effectively achieved either by preparative TLC [36, 55] and by HPLC [55]. An example of a pre-fractionation by preparative TLC is included in Schemes 13-1 and 13-2, which illustrate the analytical procedures for GC analyses of the organic acids in general (Scheme 13-1) and for the oxocarboxylic acids in particular, requiring special protective measures at the carbonyl group (Scheme 13-2).

The pre-fractionation procedure is as follows. The mixture of the acid methyl esters or the O-methyloximated acid methyl esters of the isolated constituents is separated into four fractions

Analytical procedure for the organic
acids (including pre-fractionation)

Scheme 13-1. Analytical procedure for the
organic acids (including pre-fractionation).

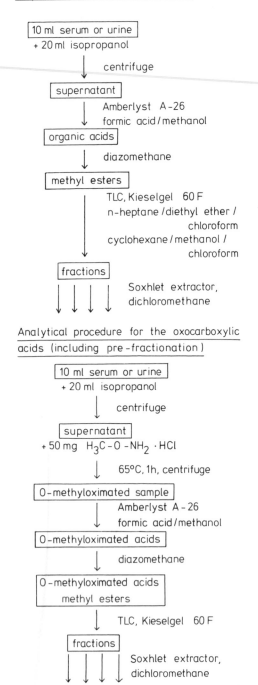

Analytical procedure for the oxocarboxylic
acids (including pre-fractionation)

Scheme 13-2. Analytical procedure for the
oxocarboxylic acid (including pre-fractionation).

(further sub-fractions are also possible) using 20 × 20 cm thin-layer plates (Kieselgel 60 F$_{254}$). The sample is applied to the left side of the plate as a band 13 cm in length. On the right side, a mixture of the reference substances (i. e. methyl stearate, methyl phenylacetate, methyl indole-butyrate and dimethyl tartrate) is applied. The plate is developed with two solvent mixtures in succession. The first solvent mixture (n-heptane/diethyl ether/chloroform, 40:30:30) is allowed to run to the upper edge of the plate. After marking the position of methyl indolebuty-rate under a UV lamp (254 nm), the plate is developed with the second solvent mixture (cyclo-hexane/chloroform/methanol, 40:55:5) up to the marked position of methyl indolebutyrate. While the left side of the plate is covered, the right side is treated with a 2,7-dichlorofluorescein spray in order to make the reference substances visible at 366 nm.

With the aid of the reference substances, the left side of the thin-layer plate is divided into four zones: fraction 1, the zone between methyl stearate and methyl phenylacetate; fraction 2, the zone between methyl phenylacetate and methyl indolebutyrate; fraction 3, the zone between methyl indolebutyrate and dimethyl tartrate; and fraction 4, the zone between dimethyl tartrate and starting line. The four fractions are scraped off separately and extracted from the silica gel with dichloromethane continuously over 12 h in a Soxhlet extractor. Fraction 1 contains mainly fatty acids, fraction 2, dicarboxylic acids, the derivatized oxocarboxylic acids and aromatic acids, fraction 3, hydroxycarboxylic acids, aromatic acids, nitrogen-containing acids and acid conjugates, and fraction 4, additional acid conjugates.

13.2.4 Separation and Detection

As mentioned above, there are essentially two techniques available for the analysis of organic acids, i. e., HPLC and GC. When we select the method, we have to consider several criteria. HPLC analysis of the acids is in most cases less laborious and less time-consuming than GC, because the sample preparation is simpler. Usually a derivatization step can be omitted, and a pre-fractionation may be not necessary, since the detection is inherently more specific for certain classes of acids than it normally is in GC. Quantitation of the acids by HPLC is quite precise. As a result of these facts, HPLC lends itself very suitable for quantitative routine analyses of a number of organic acids, and for the analysis of higher-boiling acids which are precluded from GC analysis.

GC analysis of the acids has the advantage that it permits the analysis of a much more complete spectrum of organic acids, including those which cannot be easily detected by HPLC. On the other hand, specificity of the HPLC detectors is their limitation. The separating efficiency of the GC capillary columns used for the analysis of the acids is usually better than can be reached by HPLC columns. Coupling with mass spectrometry is much more established for GC than it is for HPLC. For these reasons, GC is used when detailed profile studies of organic acids not detectable by HPLC are required, and when organic acids are to be identified by mass spectrometry. The lower specificity of the regular GC analysis, as compared with the HPLC analysis, can be overcome by more specific detectors, e. g. the thermionic specific detector for nitrogen-containing substances, or by using mass spectrometers in the mode of mass fragmento-graphy.

For HPLC separations of organic acids, reversed-phase systems are most frequently chosen. Usually, the analyses are concerned with the determination of a single acid or a small number of different acids. Good results are achieved in the separation and quantitation of metabolites of biogenic amines in urine and cerebrospinal fluid, especially 5-hydroxyindole-3-acetic acid [7, 16, 20, 28, 66, 67], vanillylmandelic acid [17, 67, 68], vanillic acid [67, 69], homovanillic acid [9, 17, 67, 70] and 3,4-dihydroxyphenylacetic acid [19]. In some instances, the amino acids and amines themselves or the glycolic metabolites, e. g. 3-methoxy-4-hydroxyphenylglycol are measured together with the acids [8, 19, 69, 71 to 73]. By measuring the conversion of tyrosine in dihydroxyphenylalanine, the activity of the enzyme tyrosine hydroxylase is determined [74].

Other acids or groups of acids separated and determined by HPLC are hippuric acid [6], uric acid [75], quinolinic acid [35], urocanic acid [76], aliphatic and aromatic oxocarboxylic acids [27, 40, 41, 30] and fatty acids [29]. An example of fatty acid separation is given in Figure 13-1.

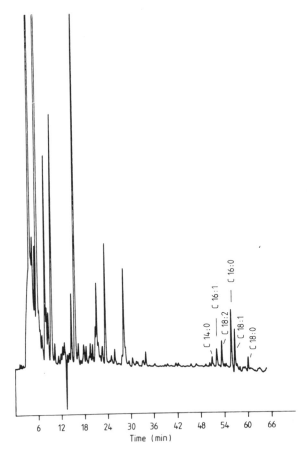

Figure 13-1. HPLC chromatogram of an extract of serum from dog, derivatized with 4-bromomethyl-7-coumarin. Column: 250 mm × 4 mm i. d. RP-8, 5 μm according to reference [29].

In some instances, the investigation of profiles by HPLC has been described, using reversed-phase columns [18, 77] or anion-exchange columns [10, 11]. Such a profile is illustrated in Figure 13-2. It is obvious that in these instances very good separating efficiency is reached.

The detectors used in the described HPLC analyses of organic acids are UV, electrochemical and fluorescence detectors.

For the GC analysis of organic acids, the formerly used packed columns have usually been replaced by glass and, more recently, by fused-silica capillary columns. Suitable phases for

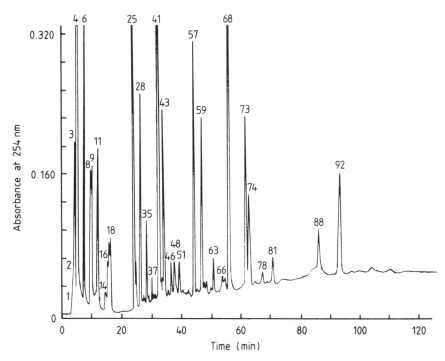

Figure 13-2. HPLC chromatogram of human urine from a normal male subject. Column: 500 mm × 4 mm i. d. Diaion CDR-10. Peaks: 1: trigonelline, 3: creatin + creatinine, 6: pseudouridine, 9: pyridoxine, 11: uracil, 18: hypoxanthine, 25: xanthine, 35: urocanic acid, 41: uric acid, 43: 2-amino-3-hydroxybenzoylglycine, 48: dimethyluric acid, 51: 5-hydroxymethyl-2-furoylglycine, 57: 2-furoylglycine, 59: 5-hydroxymethyl-2-furoic acid, 66: 3-methoxy-4-hydroxyphenylacetic acid, 68: hippuric acid, 73: quinaldic acid, 74: 3-hydroxybenzoylglycine, 88: benzoic acid, 92: indoleacetic acid; according to reference [10].

organic acids are OV-17, OV-101 and SE-30. For detection, the flame ionization detector is most widely used.

It must be pointed out that every investigator of organic acids must be aware of possible artifacts as a source of error. These artifacts may be produced at any step of the sample preparation procedure and during the separation. Because of the high temperature, the risk of producing artifacts during the separation is higher for the GC than for the HPLC analysis. Other sources of errors are interferences from drugs and medications. Some examples of artifacts and other interferences are described within a review on profiling of human body fluids [78]. Many other observations are reported [e. g. 52, 79, 80].

13.3 Organic Acids as Markers for Metabolic Disorders

More than 250 organic acids have been described in the literature. In addition to these, at least the same number of so far unidentified acids has been detected. All of these acids occur in serum and/or urine of healthy individuals, however, in a very wide range of concentrations. Physiological abnormalities, such as inborn errors of metabolism, endocrinological defects, certain tumors, diseases of the liver and the kidneys, lead to sometimes very drastic shifts in the concentration of an acid or of one or several classes of acids.

There is a vast number of publications on organic acids. Most of them deal in each case with a very limited number or a certain functional class of acids, usually in conjunction with a metabolic abnormality. Some publications are concerned with a broader spectrum of organic acids, and give detailed data on healthy individuals [25, 26, 33, 34, 37, 45, 81] and patients with metabolic and other diseases [39, 82, 83], and on the effect of dietary variations on the acids [84]. In most cases, the acids are analyzed in urine.

Organic acids are probably the class of low-molecular-weight biological substances in which chromatographic methods have contributed most to complement our knowledge of metabolic pathways and to aid, in some cases to make possible, the clinical diagnosis of a metabolic disease. In the following, examples of metabolic disorders will be given, leading to characteristic alterations of the concentrations and the profiles of organic acids.

13.3.1 Inborn Errors of Metabolism

An inborn error of metabolism is a congenital defect in the metabolism, often in the metabolism of amino acids, caused by an insufficient enzyme activity at a certain step of the biochemical pathway. Quite often such a defect leads to severe abnormalities in the development of a person, usually a child, and to mental retardation. Since by giving a patient suffering from such a defect a special diet, the abnormal development can be prevented, it is essential to detect and to specify the enzyme defect. Many of these defects cause specific organic *acidemias* and/or *acidurias,* in some cases in conjunction with amino *acidemias* and amino *acidurias.*

13.3.1.1 Phenylketonuria

Phenylketonuria is the most common disorder in the group of organic acidurias due to an inborn error, and has a frequency in the general population of about 1 per 10 000 live-born infants [85]. Untreated patients suffer from severe mental retardation. In a group of 1778 mentally retarded patients, 1% suffered from *phenylketonuria* and approximately 5% had some form of abnormal organic *aciduria* [86]. The disorder is caused by a deficiency in the activity of phenyl-alanine-4-hydroxylase (Scheme 13-3). The normal conversion of phenylalanine to tyrosine is prevented, and the alternative pathway to phenylpyruvic acid and its metabolites is utilized, leading to elevated levels of phenylalanine in blood and high excretions of phenylpyruvic acid (substance **6** in Scheme 13-3), phenyllactic acid (substance **7**) and 2-hydroxyphenylacetic acid (substance **8**) in urine. In addition to these acids, an increase of 4-hydroxyphenylpyruvic acid and 4-hydroxyphenyllactic acid is observed [24, 87], probably due to an inhibition of 4-hydroxy-phenylpyruvate oxidase in *phenylketonuria* [87].

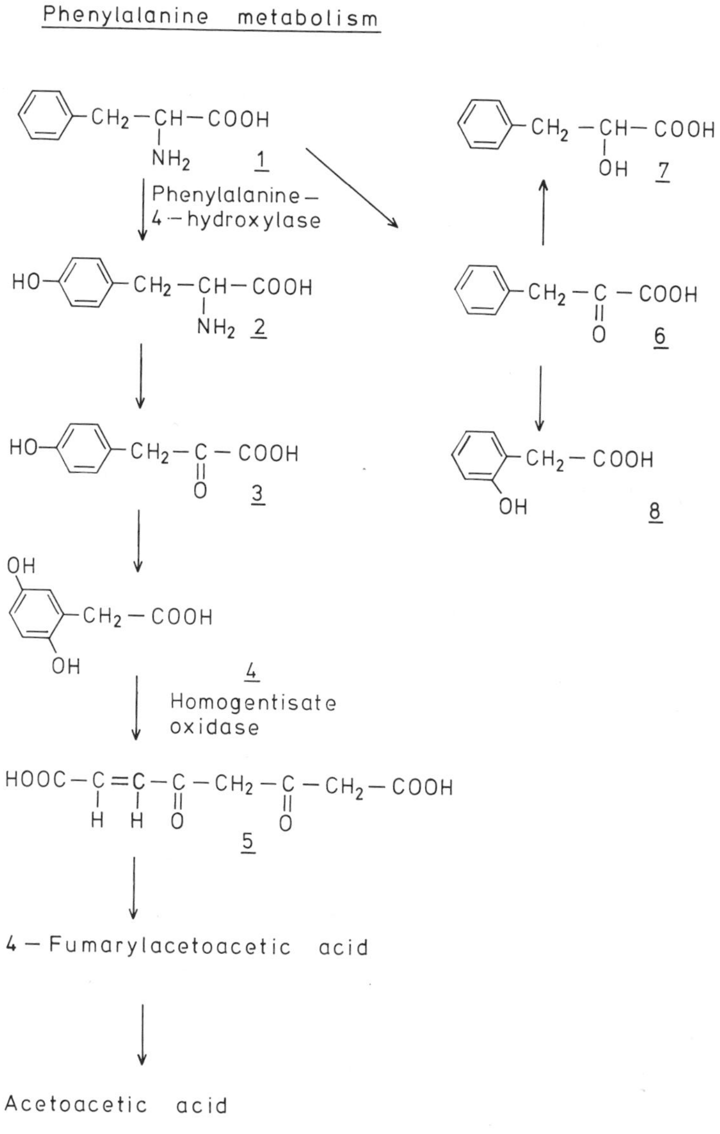

Phenylalanine   metabolism

Scheme 13-3. Phenylalanine metabolism. − **1**: phenylalanine, **2**: tyrosine, **3**: 4-hydroxyphenylpyruvic acid, **4**: homogentisic acid, **5**: 4-maleylacetoacetic acid, **6**: phenylpyruvic acid, **7**: phenyllactic acid, **8**: 2-hydroxyphenylacetic acid.

13.3.1.2 Alkaptonuria

Another disorder within the line of the phenylalanine metabolism is the *alkaptonuria* with a frequency of 1 per 100 000. The defect does not lead to mental retardation. It is caused by a deficiency in the activity of homogentisate oxidase (Scheme 13-3) and is recognized by a high excretion of homogentisic acid in urine. An abnormal amino *acidemia* is not observed.

13.3.1.3 Maple Syrup Urine Disease

Maple syrup urine disease or branched-chain *ketoaciduria* is another defect in the amino acid metabolism leading to cerebral degenerations and mental retardation. It is caused by a deficiency in the activity of the enzyme which catalyzes the oxidative decarboxylation of the 2-oxocarboxylic acids in the metabolism of valine (Scheme 13-4), leucine (Scheme 13-5) and isoleucine (Scheme 13-6). Consequently, the excretion of the 2-oxocarboxylic acids and their corresponding reduction products is increased in urine, i.e., 2-oxoisovaleric acid and 2-hydroxyisovaleric acid (substances **2** and **9** in Scheme 13-4), 2-oxoisocaproic acid and 2-hydroxyisocaproic acid (substances **2** and **9** in Scheme 13-5), and 2-oxo-3-methylvaleric acid and 2-hydroxy-3-methylvaleric acid (substances **2** and **8** in Scheme 13-6). The amino acids valine, leucine and isoleucine are elevated in blood and in urine. In addition to the substances which can be directly explained with the enzyme defect, a number of acidic metabolites are excreted in urine which are found in patients with *ketoacidosis* in general [44].

13.3.1.4 3-Methylcrotonylglycinuria

Besides maple syrup urine disease, there are several more disorders in the metabolism of the branched-chain amino acids. They lead to *3-methylcrotonylglycinuria, propionic acidemia* or *methylmalonic aciduria,* in some cases to combinations of two or all three of these defects. All three disorders may cause mental retardation.

3-Methylcrotonylglycinuria exists in at least two types. Type I, which is biotin-unresponsive, is caused by a deficiency in the activity of methylcrotonyl-CoA carboxylase [78, 88] in the leucine metabolism (Scheme 13-5). Due to this enzyme block, 3-methylcrotonyl-CoA (substance **4** in Scheme 13-5) is conjugated with glycine to form 3-methylcrotonylglycine (formula **7** in Formula table 13-1). 3-Methylcrotonylglycine is an acid conjugate. In urine, essentially two series of aliphatic and aromatic acid conjugates are found, the glycine series (examples are given in Formula table 13-1) and the glutaminic acid series (examples are given in Formula table 13-2). Besides 3-methylcrotonylglycine, an additional typical acid is increased as a result of the described enzyme block, i.e., 3-hydroxyisovaleric acid (substance **11** in Scheme 13-5).

3-Methylcrotonylglycinuria type II, which is biotin-responsive [78], is usually associated with *propionic acidemia* [32, 89], and both may have a common cause. Since 3-methylcrotonyl-CoA carboxylase and propionyl-CoA carboxylase both contain biotin as cofactor, and since a clinical response to biotin is observed, it is assumed that the two enzymes are not primarily insufficient, but that the activity of the holocarboxylase synthetase, which activates biotin, is defective [89].

13.3.1.5 Propionic Acidemia

Propionic acidemia is caused by an insufficient activity of propionyl-CoA carboxylase (Scheme 13-7), leading to a block in the transformation of propionyl-CoA (substance **1** in Scheme 13-7), which stems e.g. from the valine and isoleucine metabolism, into methylmalonyl-CoA (substance **2** in Scheme 13-7). In serum and urine, mostly elevated levels of propionic acid are

Acid conjugates of the glycine series

$H_3C-CH_2-\overset{\displaystyle C=O}{C}-NH-CH_2-COOH$

5

$H_3C-CH-CH_2-\overset{\displaystyle C=O}{C}-NH-CH_2-COOH$
$\quad\quad\;\, |$
$\quad\quad\; CH_3$

6

$H_3C-\overset{\displaystyle |}{C}=CH-\overset{\displaystyle C=O}{C}-NH-CH_2-COOH$
$\quad\;\; CH_3$

7

$H_3C-CH=\overset{\displaystyle |}{C}-\overset{\displaystyle C=O}{C}-NH-CH_2-COOH$
$\quad\quad\quad CH_3$

8

$\langle\text{phenyl}\rangle-\overset{\displaystyle C=O}{C}-NH-CH_2-COOH$

1

$\langle\text{o-OH-phenyl}\rangle-\overset{\displaystyle C=O}{C}-NH-CH_2-COOH$

2

$\langle\text{m-HO-phenyl}\rangle-\overset{\displaystyle C=O}{C}-NH-CH_2-COOH$

3

$\langle\text{p-HO-phenyl}\rangle-\overset{\displaystyle C=O}{C}-NH-CH_2-COOH$

4

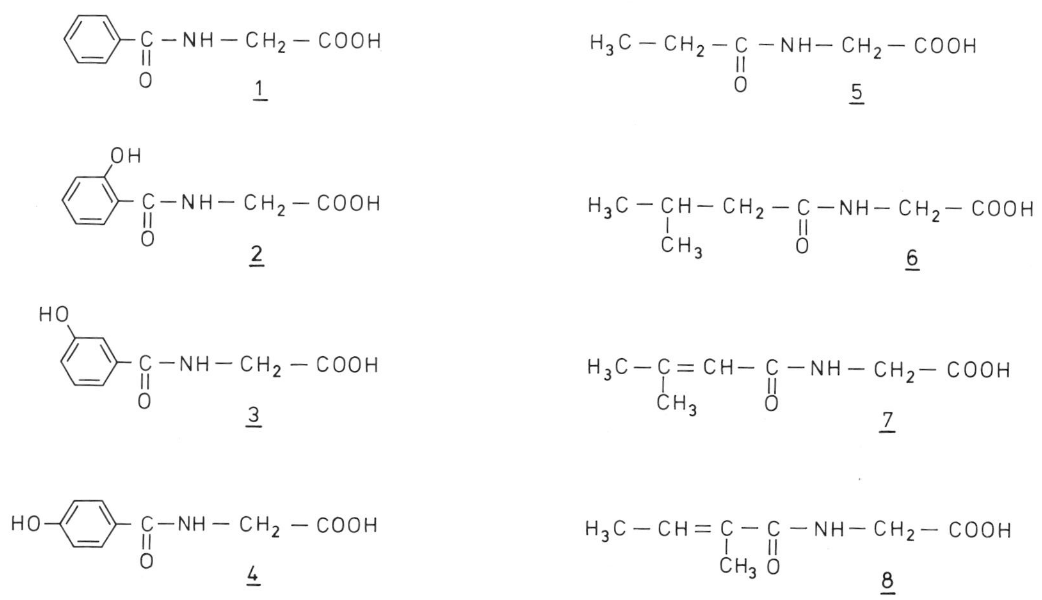

Formula Table 13-1. Acid conjugates of the glycine series. – **1**: hippuric acid, **2**: 2-hydroxyhippuric acid, **3**: 3-hydroxyhippuric acid, **4**: 4-hydroxyhippuric acid, **5**: propionylglycine, **6**: isovalerylglycine, **7**: 3-methylcrotonylglycine, **8**: tiglylglycine.

Acid conjugates of the glutaminic acid series

COOH
|
⟨benzene⟩—CH₂—C—NH—CH
           ‖ |
           O   CH₂
                    |
           1   CH₂
                    |
                    COOH

           COOH
           |
H₃C—CH—CH₂—C—NH—CH
    | ‖ |
    CH₃   O   CH₂
                     |
           2   CH₂
                     |
                     COOH

COOH
|
⟨benzene⟩—CH₂—C—NH—CH
           ‖ |
           O   CH₂
                    |
           3   CH₂
                    |
                    C=O
                    |
                    NH₂

⟨benzene⟩—CH₂—C—NH—⟨glutarimide ring⟩N—H
           ‖
           O
           4

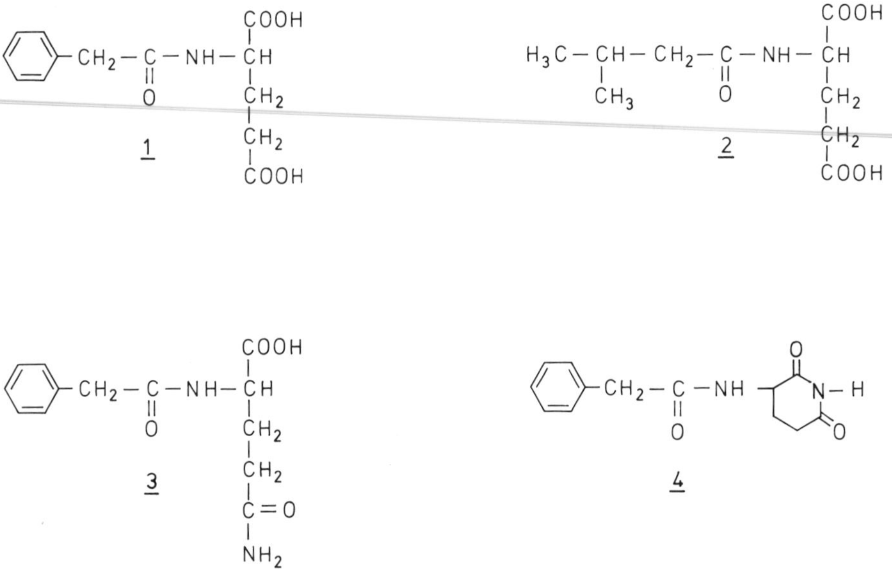

Formula Table 13-2. Acid conjugates of the glutaminic acid series. — **1:** N-phenylacetylglutaminic acid, **2:** N-isovalerylglutaminic acid, **3:** N-phenylacetylglutamine, **4:** N-phenylacetylglutaminimide.

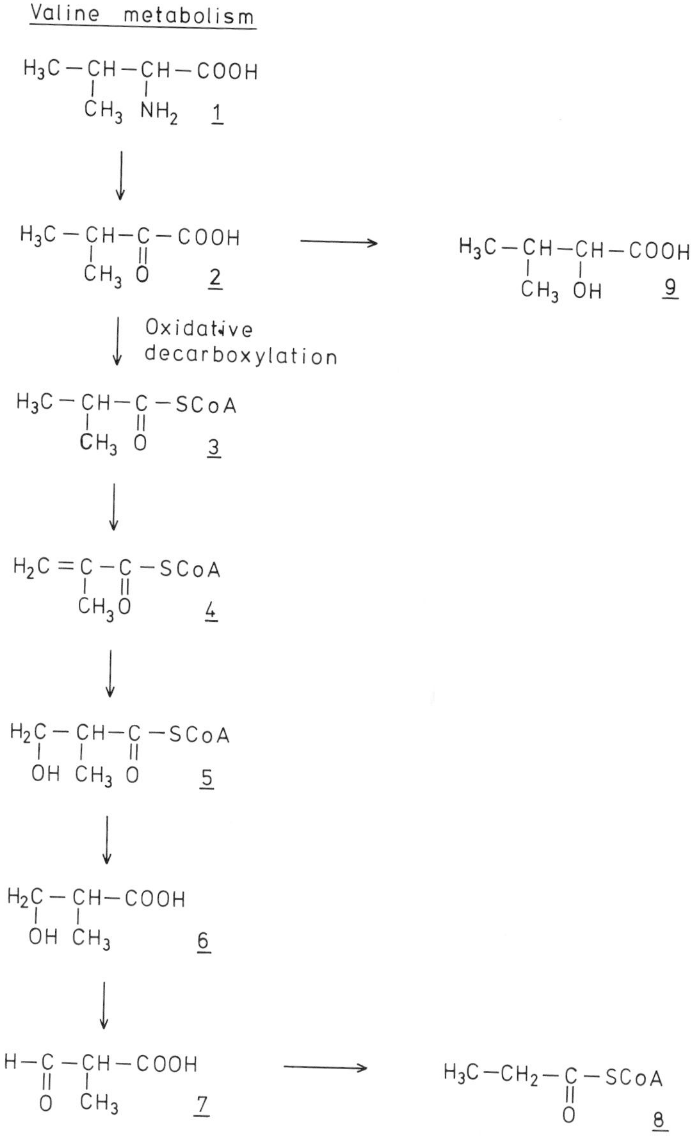

Valine metabolism

$$H_3C-CH-CH-COOH$$
$$\underset{CH_3}{|} \quad \underset{NH_2}{|} \quad \underline{1}$$

↓

$$H_3C-CH-\underset{O}{\overset{}{C}}-COOH$$
$$\underset{CH_3}{|} \quad \quad \underline{2}$$ ⟶ $$H_3C-CH-CH-COOH$$
$$\underset{CH_3}{|} \quad \underset{OH}{|} \quad \underline{9}$$

↓ Oxidative decarboxylation

$$H_3C-CH-\overset{}{C}-SCoA$$
$$\underset{CH_3}{|} \quad \underset{O}{\overset{||}{}} \quad \underline{3}$$

↓

$$H_2C=\overset{}{C}-\overset{}{C}-SCoA$$
$$\underset{CH_3}{|} \quad \underset{O}{\overset{||}{}} \quad \underline{4}$$

↓

$$H_2C-CH-\overset{}{C}-SCoA$$
$$\underset{OH}{|} \quad \underset{CH_3}{|} \quad \underset{O}{\overset{||}{}} \quad \underline{5}$$

↓

$$H_2C-CH-COOH$$
$$\underset{OH}{|} \quad \underset{CH_3}{|} \quad \underline{6}$$

↓

$$H-\overset{}{C}-CH-COOH$$
$$\underset{O}{\overset{||}{}} \quad \underset{CH_3}{|} \quad \underline{7}$$ ⟶ $$H_3C-CH_2-\overset{}{C}-SCoA$$
$$\underset{O}{\overset{||}{}} \quad \underline{8}$$

Scheme 13-4. Valine metabolism. – **1**: valine, **2**: 2-oxoisovaleric acid, **3**: isobutyryl-CoA, **4**: methyl-acrylyl-CoA, **5**: 3-hydroxyisobutyryl-CoA, **6**: 3-hydroxyisobutyric acid, **7**: methylmalonic acid semial-dehyde, **8**: propionyl-CoA, **9**: 2-hydroxyisovaleric acid.

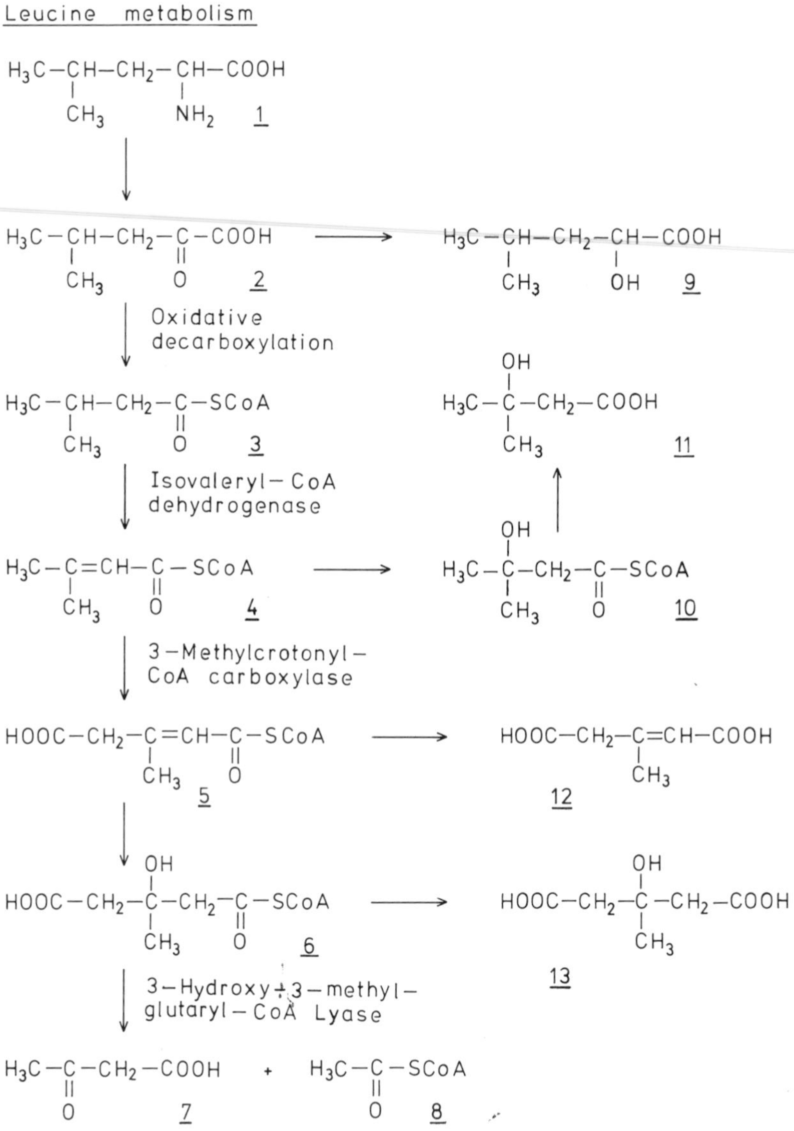

Leucine   metabolism

$$H_3C-CH-CH_2-CH-COOH$$
$$\overset{|}{CH_3} \qquad \overset{|}{NH_2} \quad \underline{1}$$

↓

$$H_3C-CH-CH_2-\overset{O}{\overset{||}{C}}-COOH \longrightarrow H_3C-CH-CH_2-CH-COOH$$
$$\overset{|}{CH_3} \qquad \underline{2} \qquad\qquad \overset{|}{CH_3} \qquad \overset{|}{OH} \quad \underline{9}$$

│ Oxidative
↓ decarboxylation

$$H_3C-CH-CH_2-\overset{O}{\overset{||}{C}}-SCoA \qquad\qquad H_3C-\overset{OH}{\overset{|}{C}}-CH_2-COOH$$
$$\overset{|}{CH_3} \qquad \underline{3} \qquad\qquad\qquad \overset{|}{CH_3} \qquad \underline{11}$$

│ Isovaleryl−CoA
↓ dehydrogenase   ↑

$$H_3C-\overset{}{C}=CH-\overset{O}{\overset{||}{C}}-SCoA \longrightarrow H_3C-\overset{OH}{\overset{|}{C}}-CH_2-\overset{O}{\overset{||}{C}}-SCoA$$
$$\overset{|}{CH_3} \qquad \underline{4} \qquad\qquad\qquad \overset{|}{CH_3} \qquad \underline{10}$$

│ 3−Methylcrotonyl−
↓ CoA carboxylase

$$HOOC-CH_2-\overset{}{C}=CH-\overset{O}{\overset{||}{C}}-SCoA \longrightarrow HOOC-CH_2-\overset{}{C}=CH-COOH$$
$$\overset{|}{CH_3} \qquad \underline{5} \qquad\qquad\qquad\qquad \overset{|}{CH_3}$$
$$\underline{12}$$

↓ OH

$$HOOC-CH_2-\overset{OH}{\overset{|}{C}}-CH_2-\overset{O}{\overset{||}{C}}-SCoA \longrightarrow HOOC-CH_2-\overset{OH}{\overset{|}{C}}-CH_2-COOH$$
$$\overset{|}{CH_3} \qquad \underline{6} \qquad\qquad\qquad\qquad \overset{|}{CH_3}$$
$$\underline{13}$$

│ 3−Hydroxy−3−methyl−
↓ glutaryl−CoA Lyase

$$H_3C-\overset{O}{\overset{||}{C}}-CH_2-COOH \quad + \quad H_3C-\overset{O}{\overset{||}{C}}-SCoA$$
$$\qquad \underline{7} \qquad\qquad\qquad\qquad \underline{8}$$

Scheme 13-5. Leucine metabolism. − **1**: leucine, **2**: 2-oxoisocaproic acid, **3**: isovaleryl-CoA, **4**: 3-methyl-crotonyl-CoA, **5**: 3-methylglutaconyl-CoA, **6**: 3-hydroxy-3-methylglutaryl-CoA, **7**: acetoacetic acid, **8**: acetyl-CoA, **9**: 2-hydroxyisocaproic acid, **10**: 3-hydroxyisovaleryl-CoA, **11**: 3-hydroxyisovaleric acid, **12**: 3-methylglutaconic acid, **13**: 3-hydroxy-3-methylglutaric acid.

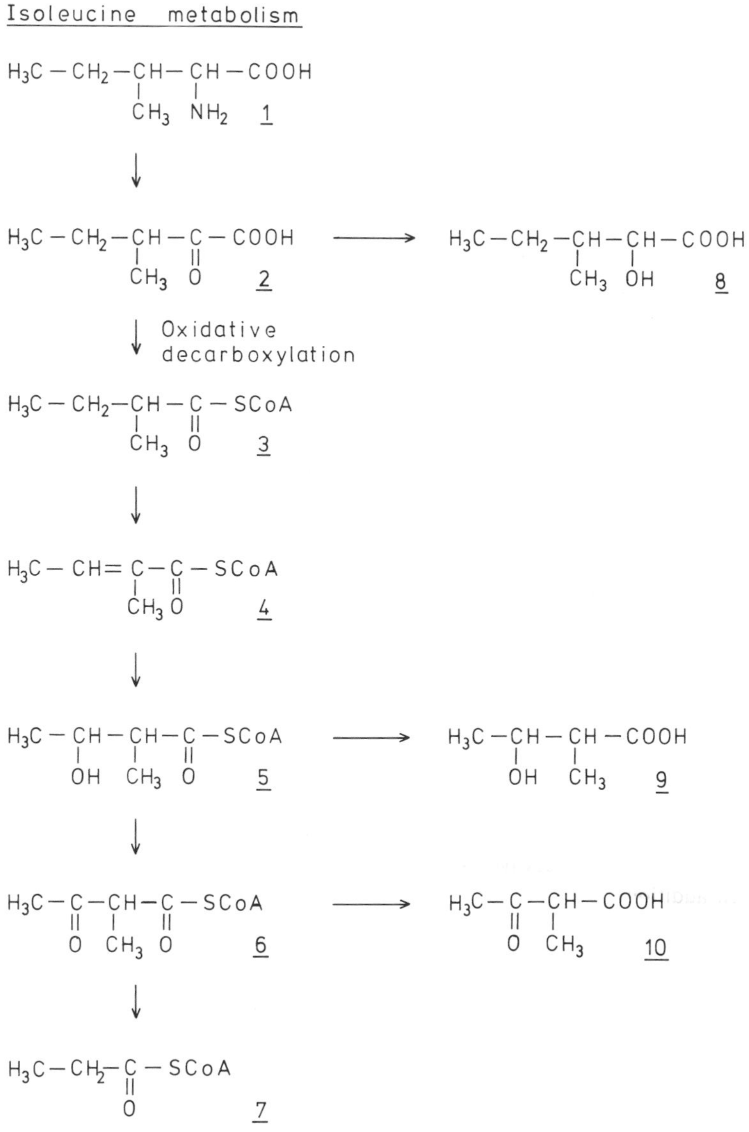

Isoleucine   metabolism

$H_3C - CH_2 - CH - CH - COOH$
$\qquad\qquad | \qquad |$
$\qquad\qquad CH_3 \quad NH_2 \quad \underline{1}$

$\downarrow$

$H_3C - CH_2 - CH - C - COOH \qquad\longrightarrow\qquad H_3C - CH_2 - CH - CH - COOH$
$\qquad\qquad | \qquad \|$
$\qquad\qquad CH_3 \quad O \qquad \underline{2}$
$\qquad\qquad\qquad\qquad\qquad\qquad\qquad\qquad\qquad\qquad\qquad\qquad CH_3 \quad OH \qquad \underline{8}$

$\quad\downarrow$ Oxidative
$\qquad$ decarboxylation

$H_3C - CH_2 - CH - C - SCoA$
$\qquad\qquad | \qquad \|$
$\qquad\qquad CH_3 \quad O \qquad \underline{3}$

$\downarrow$

$H_3C - CH = C - C - SCoA$
$\qquad\qquad\qquad | \quad \|$
$\qquad\qquad\quad CH_3 \; O \qquad \underline{4}$

$\downarrow$

$H_3C - CH - CH - C - SCoA \qquad\longrightarrow\qquad H_3C - CH - CH - COOH$
$\qquad\quad | \qquad | \quad \|$
$\qquad\quad OH \quad CH_3 \; O \qquad \underline{5}$
$\qquad\qquad\qquad\qquad\qquad\qquad\qquad\qquad\qquad\qquad\qquad\quad OH \quad CH_3 \qquad \underline{9}$

$\downarrow$

$H_3C - C - CH - C - SCoA \qquad\longrightarrow\qquad H_3C - C - CH - COOH$
$\qquad\;\; \| \quad | \quad \|$
$\qquad\;\; O \; CH_3 \; O \qquad \underline{6}$
$\qquad\qquad\qquad\qquad\qquad\qquad\qquad\qquad\qquad\qquad\quad O \; CH_3 \qquad \underline{10}$

$\downarrow$

$H_3C - CH_2 - C - SCoA$
$\qquad\qquad\qquad \|$
$\qquad\qquad\qquad O \qquad\qquad \underline{7}$

Scheme 13-6. Isoleucine metabolism. − **1**: isoleucine, **2**: 2-oxo-3-methylvaleric acid, **3**: 2-methylbutyryl-CoA, **4**: tiglyl-CoA, **5**: 3-hydroxy-2-methylbutyryl-CoA, **6**: 2-methylacetoacetyl-CoA, **7**: propionyl-CoA, **8**: 2-hydroxy-3-methylvaleric acid, **9**: 3-hydroxy-2-methylbutyric acid, **10**: 2-methylacetoacetic acid.

found. Characteristic metabolites are propionylglycine, 3-hydroxypropionic acid and several condensation products from acetyl-CoA and propionyl-CoA, i.e., 3-oxovaleric acid, 3-hydroxyvaleric acid, 3-oxo-2-methylbutyric acid, 3-hydroxy-2-methylbutyric acid, and 3-oxo-2-methylvaleric acid [90, 91]. A further condensation product, probably between propionyl-CoA and oxaloacetic acid, is methylcitric acid [32].

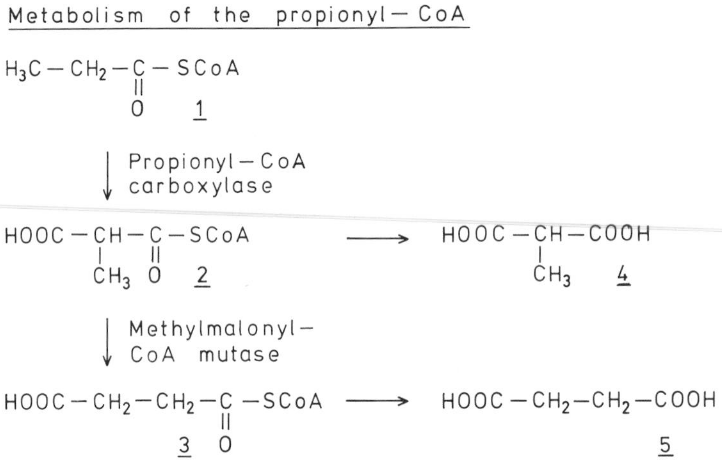

Metabolism of the propionyl— CoA

$H_3C - CH_2 - C - SCoA$
            $\underset{0}{\overset{\|}{}}$ $\underline{1}$

↓ Propionyl—CoA
    carboxylase

$HOOC - CH - C - SCoA$ $\longrightarrow$ $HOOC - CH - COOH$
       $\underset{CH_3}{|}$ $\underset{O}{\overset{\|}{}}$ $\underline{2}$ $\underset{CH_3}{|}$ $\underline{4}$

↓ Methylmalonyl—
    CoA mutase

$HOOC - CH_2 - CH_2 - C - SCoA$ $\longrightarrow$ $HOOC - CH_2 - CH_2 - COOH$
                   $\underline{3}$ $\overset{\|}{O}$ $\underline{5}$

Scheme 13-7. Metabolism of the propionyl-CoA. – **1**: propionyl-CoA, **2**: methylmalonyl-CoA, **3**: succinyl-CoA, **4**: methylmalonic acid, **5**: succinic acid.

13.3.1.6 Methylmalonic Aciduria

The defect of this abnormality lies in the block of the conversion of methylmalonyl-CoA into succinyl-CoA (Scheme 13-7) which is mediated by the enzyme methylmalonyl-CoA mutase.

This enzyme requires coenzyme B_{12} (adenosylcobalamin), which is derived from vitamin B_{12}. Vitamin B_{12} deficiency leads to a *methylmalonic aciduria,* but is a reversible biochemical disturbance. On the other hand, *methylmalonic aciduria* can be observed in newborn infants and young children with severe metabolic *acidosis* who are not vitamin B_{12} deficient [92, 93]. This inborn error is very severe and is not vitamin B_{12} dependent. Both forms of *methylmalonic aciduria* are characterized by excessive amounts of methylmalonic acid in urine (substance **4** in Scheme 13-7). In addition, much smaller amounts of 3-hydroxyvaleric acid and methylcitric acid may be detected.

13.3.1.7 Isovaleric Acidemia

Isovaleric acidemia is a recessively inherited defect in the metabolization pathway of leucine, and is caused by a deficiency of isovaleryl-CoA dehydrogenase activity (Scheme 13-5). Isovaleryl-CoA accumulates and is transformed in isovaleric acid, isovalerylglycine (substance **6** in Formula table 13-1), N-isovalerylglutaminic acid (substance **2** in Formula table 13-2), 3-hydroxyisovaleric acid, 4-hydroxyisovaleric acid, and 3-hydroxyisoheptanoic acid [94, 95].

13.3.1.8 3-Hydroxy-3-methylglutaric Aciduria

This disorder results from an enzymic defect in the last step of leucine degradation. The condition is characterized by a deficiency of 3-hydroxy-3-methylglutaryl-CoA lyase activity (Scheme 13-5). It leads to the urinary excretion of large amounts of 3-hydroxy-3-methylglutaric acid (substance **13** in Scheme 13-5), 3-methylglutaconic acid (substance **12** in Scheme 13-5), 3-methyl-glutaric acid and 3-hydroxyisovaleric acid (substance **11** in Scheme 13-5) [96, 97].

13.3.1.9 Congenital Lactic Acidosis

Some cases have been reported in which this clinical condition occured in neonates and was fatal. Several enzyme deficiencies have been made responsible for *congenital lactic acidosis*. A defect in the normal β-oxidation of fatty acids, probably at the acyl-CoA dehydrogenase step, results in a variety of saturated and unsaturated C_6 to C_{14} dicarboxylic acids in urine, together with a high lactic acid excretion [54, 58]. Another form of *congenital lactic acidosis* is assigned to a deficiency in the pyruvate dehydrogenase complex and in the pyruvate decarboxylase activity [46]. Besides greatly increased levels of lactic acid and pyruvic acid, elevated levels of 2-oxo-glutaric, 2-hydroxyglutaric, malic, fumaric, succinic, glyceric and isocitric acids are observed. Further enzyme defects leading to *lactic acidosis* are related to fructose-1,6-diphosphatase, glucose-6-phosphatase and cytochrome c oxidase [46]. Whereas the normal lactic acid, produced in the human body, has the L-configuration, D-lactic acid has been found in urine and cere-brospinal fluid of a mentally retarded patient [98].

13.3.2 Diabetic Ketoacidosis

Whereas inborn errors of metabolism are defects which occur infrequently in the normal population, *diabetes mellitus* is a chronic metabolic disease with the very high frequency of 1.5 to 2.5% in the western hemispere [99]. In periods of decompensation of the *diabetes,* the patients may develop a *ketoacidosis.* During *ketoacidosis,* one encounters very drastic changes in the concentrations of organic acids in serum and in urine.

From the different classes of organic acids, four groups are affected: fatty acids, aliphatic dicarboxylic acids, aliphatic oxocarboxylic acids and aliphatic hydroxycarboxylic acids.

13.3.2.1 Fatty Acids

The concentrations of the whole spectrum of free fatty acids are elevated in serum and urine. This is due to the increased lipolysis caused by the low insulin activity during *ketoacidosis.*

13.3.2.2 Aliphatic Dicarboxylic Acids

Of the aliphatic dicarboxylic acids in urine and in serum, it is mainly the saturated acids with even-numbered carbon chains which are elevated, especially succinic acid (C_4), adipic acid (C_6), suberic acid (C_8) and sebacic acid (C_{10}). They are formed from long-chain monocarboxylic acids by ω-oxidation followed by β-oxidation (Scheme 13-8). The possibility of oxidation at the last carbon atom of long-chain fatty acids has been known for a long time and was called ω-oxida-tion in 1934 [100]. The mechanism of the formation of the medium-chain dicarboxylic acids has been proven by feeding ketotic rats with ^{14}C-labeled palmitic acid [101]. The proportion of ω-ox-idation in fatty acid metabolism in normal individuals is small. It gains importance during *ketoacidosis,* apparently according to a back-up mechanism. It has been found in experiments with ketotic rats that between 5 and 20% of the fatty acids are metabolized by initial ω-oxidation [102, 103].

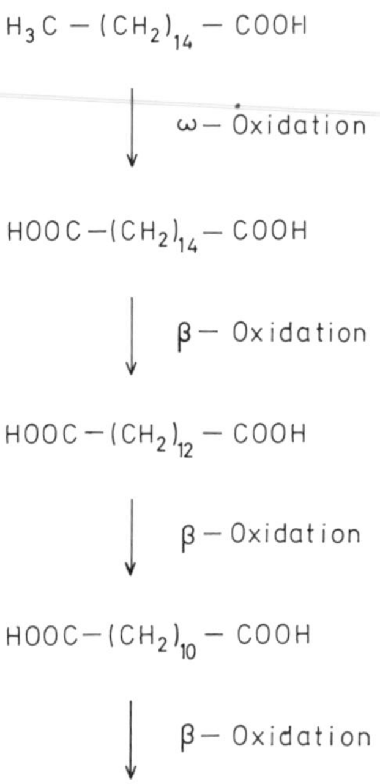

$$H_3C - (CH_2)_{14} - COOH$$

$$\downarrow \quad \omega - \dot{O}xidation$$

$$HOOC - (CH_2)_{14} - COOH$$

$$\downarrow \quad \beta - Oxidation$$

$$HOOC - (CH_2)_{12} - COOH$$

$$\downarrow \quad \beta - Oxidation$$

$$HOOC - (CH_2)_{10} - COOH$$

$$\downarrow \quad \beta - Oxidation$$

Scheme 13-8. ω-Oxidation of fatty acids.

Methyl-branched dicarboxylic acids, e. g., methylsuccinic, methylglutaric, methyladipic, methylpimelic, methylsuberic, and also some ethyl-branched dicarboxylic acids, are very little affected by *acidosis.* It has been supposed that they are formed by ω-oxidation of 3-methyl- or ante-iso-methyl-branched monocarboxylic acids by the microflora of the intestinal tract [104].

The unsaturated dicarboxylic acids, especially mesaconic acid (trans-methylbutenedioic acid), citraconic acid (cis-methylbutenedioic acid) and the two cis-trans isomers of 3-methylglutaconic acid [26] are also very little affected by *ketoacidosis.*

An observation regarding succinic acid is that it reaches its maximum of excretion 2 to 4 days later than the other saturated dicarboxylic acids. For that reason it must be assumed that succinic acid is predominantly formed, not from the long-chain even-numbered fatty acids, but more from propionyl-CoA (Scheme 13-7), which itself originates from odd-numbered fatty acids and from the amino acids valine and isoleucine.

In serum, the same saturated and unsaturated dicarboxylic acids are found as in urine, however in much smaller concentrations (Figures 13-3 and 13-4).

13.3.2.3 Aliphatic Oxocarboxylic Acids

Oxocarboxylic acids are formed by ketogenesis or by transamination of amino acids. During ketoacidosis, ketogenesis (Scheme 13-9) is a strongly enhanced process. On the other hand, as a result of elevated levels of the amino acids valine, leucine and isoleucine in case of diabetes [105,

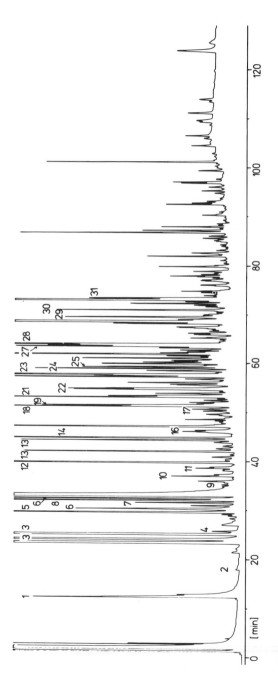

Figure 13-3. Gas chromatogram of fraction 2 of the organic acids in urine of a ketoacidotic patient, 25 m glass capillary column, coated with OV-17. The substances are identified by mass spectrometry. Peaks: 1: 3-hydroxybutyric acid, 2: pyruvic acid, 3: 3-oxobutyric acid, 4: 2-oxoisovaleric acid, 5: succinic acid, 6: 2-oxoisocaproic acid, 7: 2-oxo-3-methylvaleric acid, 8: methylsuccinic acid, 9: citraconic acid, 10: glutaric acid, 11: 3-methylglutaric acid, 12: phenylacetic acid, 13: 3-methylglutaconic acid, 14: adipic acid, 15: phenylpropionic acid, 16: 3-methyladipic acid, 17: heptenedioic acid, 18: heptenedioic acid, 19: pimelic acid, 20: hydroxybenzoic acid, 21: anthranilic acid, 22: hydroxybenzoic acid, 23: suberic acid, 24: hydroxyphenylacetic acid, 25: 3-methylsuberic acid, 26: dihydroxybenzoic acid, 27: phenylpyruvic acid, 28: azelaic acid, 29: sebacic acid, 30: dihydroxybenzoic acid, 31: 3-carboxy-4-methyl-5-propyl-2-furanpropionic acid.

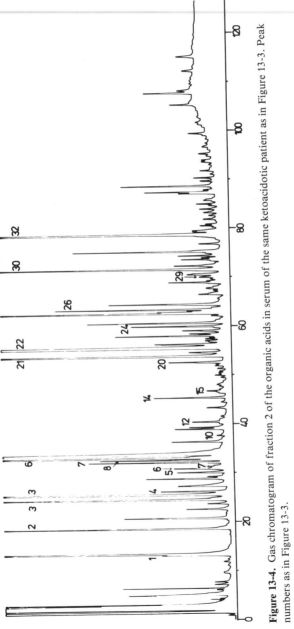

Figure 13-4. Gas chromatogram of fraction 2 of the organic acids in serum of the same ketoacidotic patient as in Figure 13-3. Peak numbers as in Figure 13-3.

106], especially in case of *ketoacidosis,* the formation of the amino acid metabolites is favored. This leads to sometimes drastically elevated levels of acetoacetic acid in serum and in urine and to elevated levels of 2-oxoisovaleric acid (substance **2** in Scheme 13-4), 2-oxoisocaproic acid (substance **2** in Scheme 13-5), and 2-oxo-3-methylvaleric acid (substance **2** in Scheme 13-6).

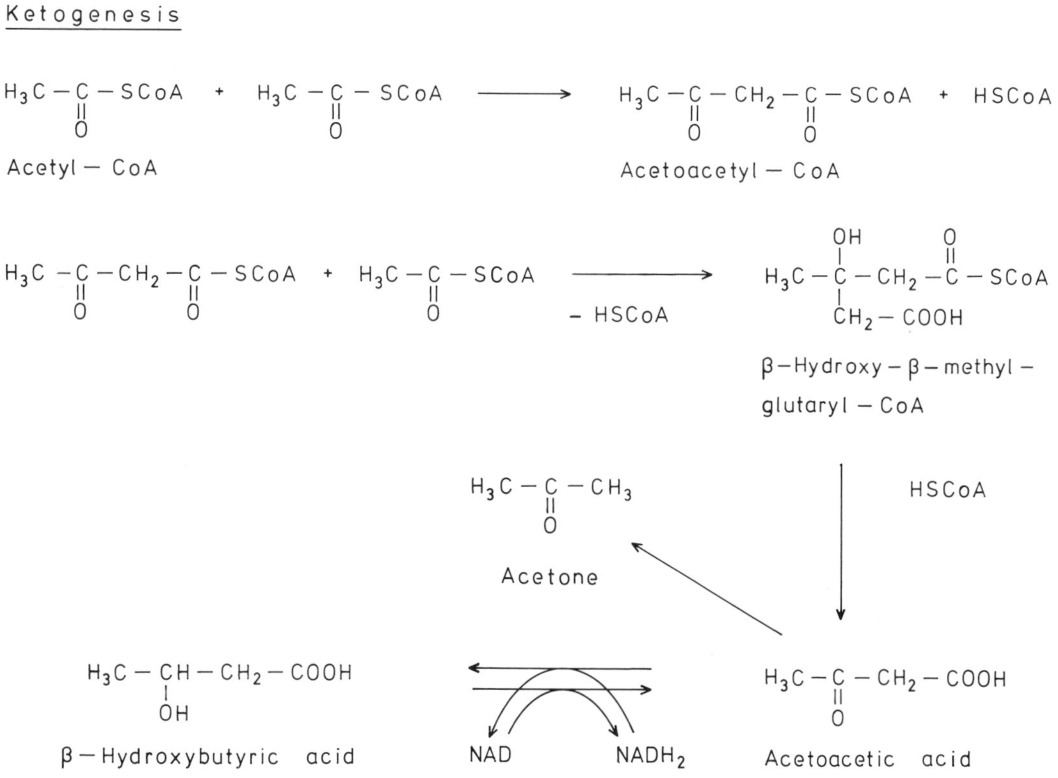

Ketogenesis

$$H_3C - \underset{\underset{O}{\|}}{C} - SCoA \quad + \quad H_3C - \underset{\underset{O}{\|}}{C} - SCoA \quad \longrightarrow \quad H_3C - \underset{\underset{O}{\|}}{C} - CH_2 - \underset{\underset{O}{\|}}{C} - SCoA \quad + \quad HSCoA$$

Acetyl − CoA   Acetoacetyl − CoA

$$H_3C - \underset{\underset{O}{\|}}{C} - CH_2 - \underset{\underset{O}{\|}}{C} - SCoA \quad + \quad H_3C - \underset{\underset{O}{\|}}{C} - SCoA \quad \xrightarrow{\quad - HSCoA \quad} \quad H_3C - \underset{\underset{CH_2 - COOH}{|}}{\overset{\overset{OH}{|}}{C}} - CH_2 - \overset{\overset{O}{\|}}{C} - SCoA$$

β−Hydroxy − β − methyl − glutaryl − CoA

$$H_3C - \underset{\underset{O}{\|}}{C} - CH_3$$

Acetone   HSCoA

$$H_3C - \underset{\underset{OH}{|}}{C}H - CH_2 - COOH$$ NAD   NADH_2 $$H_3C - \underset{\underset{O}{\|}}{C} - CH_2 - COOH$$

β − Hydroxybutyric   acid   Acetoacetic   acid

Scheme 13-9. Ketogenesis.

When then oxocarboxylic acids are analyzed in the form of their O-methyloximated acid methyl esters, which contain nitrogen, they can be selectively monitored with the nitrogen-specific detector, i.e. the thermionic specific detector (Figure 13-5). Depending on the steric conditions, the O-methyloximes of the oxocarboxylic acid methyl esters may form syn-anti isomers. The profiles of the oxocarboxylic acids in serum and in urine of normal individuals, diabetic patients under good therapeutical control, and patients with *ketoacidosis* have been described [36].

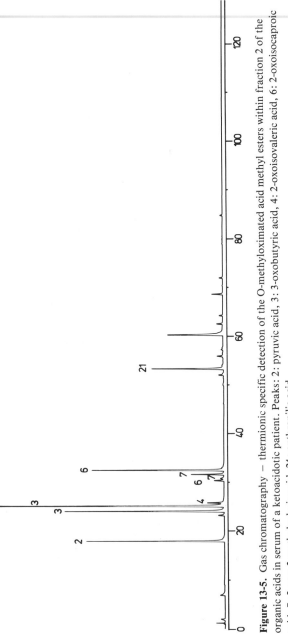

Figure 13-5. Gas chromatography – thermionic specific detection of the O-methyloximated acid methyl esters within fraction 2 of the organic acids in serum of a ketoacidotic patient. Peaks: 2: pyruvic acid, 3: 3-oxobutyric acid, 4: 2-oxoisovaleric acid, 6: 2-oxoisocaproic acid, 7: 2-oxo-3-methylvaleric acid, 21: anthranilic acid.

13.3.2.4 Aliphatic Hydroxycarboxylic Acids

As pointed out above, during *ketoacidosis* there is an increased production of metabolites of the branched-chain amino acids. From the valine degradation 3-hydroxyisobutyric acid and 2-hydroxyisovaleris acid are formed (substances **6** and **9** in Scheme 13-4), from leucine 3-hydroxyisovaleric acid and 2-hydroxyisocaproic acid (substances **11** and **9** in Scheme 13-5), and from isoleucine 3-hydroxy-2-methylbutyric acid and 2-hydroxy-3-methylvaleric acid (substances **9** and **8** in Scheme 13-6). These acids are found elevated in most cases of *ketoacidosis* [56, 107, 108]. The hydroxycarboxylic acid which is most drastically increased during *ketoacidosis,* is 3-hydroxybutyric acid, which is formed by reduction of acetoacetic acid in the course of *ketogenesis* (Scheme 13-9). Besides the described acids, a number of 3-hydroxydicarboxylic acids, probably formed by a combination of ω-oxidation and incomplete β-oxidation, have been found in urine [21].

13.3.3 Diseases Related to Catecholamines, Serotonin and their Metabolites

A number of diseases of very different character are related to catecholamines, serotonin and their metabolites. Changes in the concentrations of the substances are indicative for these diseases and can be used for their diagnosis. Catecholamines are biochemically synthesized from L-tyrosine in peripheral and central adrenergic neurons and in the chromaffin cells of the *adrenal medulla.* Serotonin is found in the argentaffin cells of the intestines and in platelets. Both, catecholamines and serotonin have multiple biochemical functions, one of which is their function as neurotransmitters.

The determination of the biogenic amines and their metabolites (Schemes 13-10 and 13-11) is useful for diagnostic purposes in several depressive, psychotic and neurological disorders. It has also been reported that serotonin and its metabolite, 5-hydroxyindole-3-acetic acid (substance **5** in Scheme 13-11) is elevated in blood of autistic and retarded children [109]. In addition, catecholamines and their metabolites are very important to diagnose catecholamine-secreting tumors, such as *phaeochromocytoma,* as a result of which hypertension occurs. Urinary elevations of 5-hydroxyindole-3-acetic acid are indicative for carcinoid tumors.

The acidic catecholamine metabolites most often measured for diagnostic purposes are vanillylmandelic acid (VMA, substance **14** in Scheme 13-10), vanillic acid (VA, substance **16** in Scheme 13-10), homovanillic acid (HVA, substance **19** in Scheme 13-10) and 3,4-dihydroxyphenylacetic acid (DOPAC, substance **9** in Scheme 13-10). The non-acidic catecholamine metabolite most often determined is 3-methoxy-4-hydroxyphenylglycol (MHPG, substance **15** in Scheme 13-10) [8, 17, 19, 48, 67 to 69, 71, 110]. The determinations are carried out either by HPLC methods (Figure 13-6) or by GC separation and mass fragmentographic detection and quantitation.

The biogenic amines themselves, or their precursing amino acids can be determined together with the acids, especially when HPLC methods are applied. Of the serotonin metabolites, 5-hydroxyindole-3-acetic acid is usually measured, sometimes together with serotonin [7, 20, 66, 72, 109].

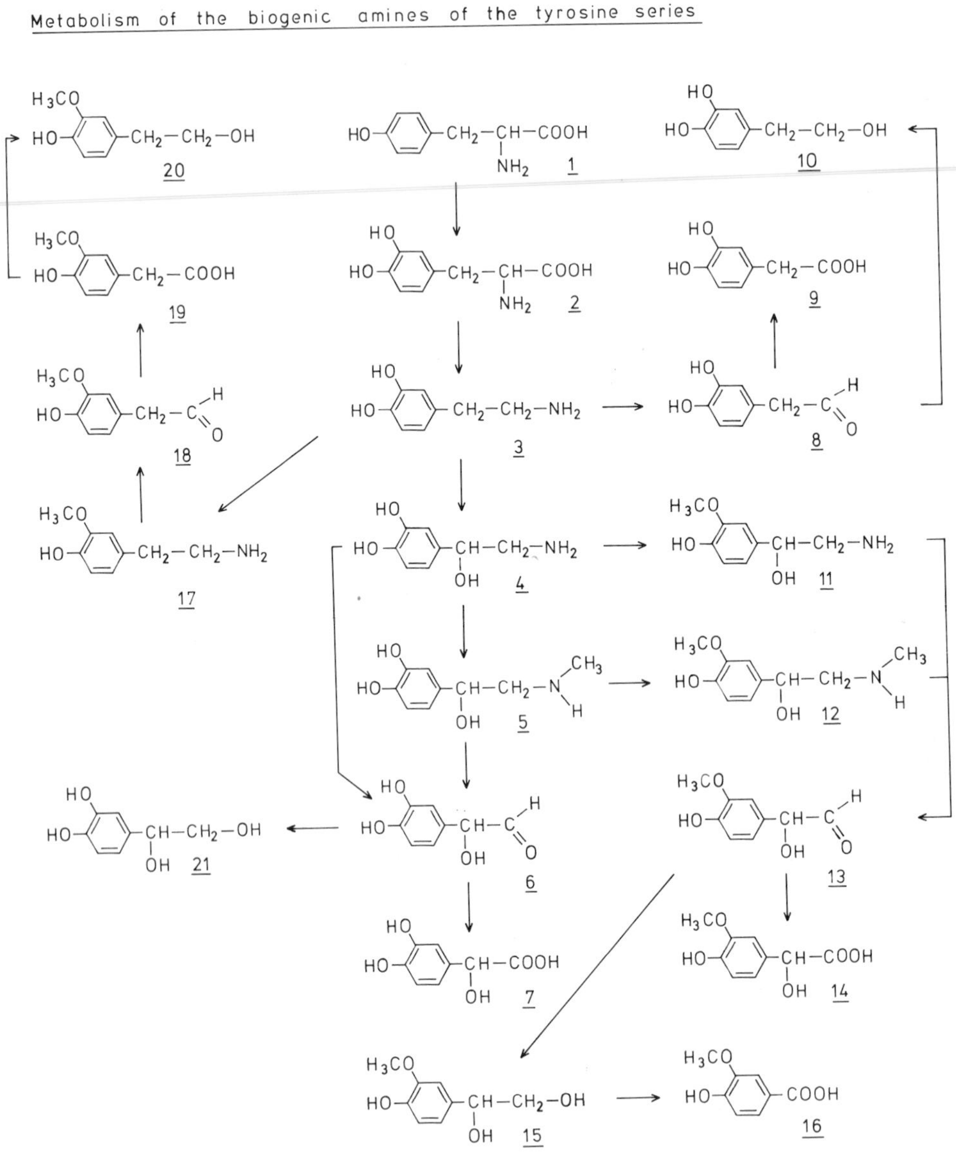

Metabolism of the biogenic amines of the tyrosine series

Scheme 13-10. Metabolism of the biogenic amines of the tyrosine series. – 1: tyrosine, 2: 3,4-dihydroxy-phenylalanine (DOPA), 3: dopamine, 4: noradrenalin, 5: adrenalin, 6: 3,4-dihydroxyphenylglycolalde-hyde, 7: 3,4-dihydroxymandelic acid, 8: 3,4-dihydroxyphenylacetaldehyde, 9: 3,4-dihydroxyphenylacetic acid, 10: 3,4-dihydroxyphenylethanol, 11: normetanephrin, 12: metanephrin, 13: 3-methoxy-4-hydroxy-phenylglycolaldehyde. 14: 3-methoxy-4-hydroxymandelic acid (vanillylmandelic acid), 15: 3-methoxy-4-hydroxyphenylglycol, 16: vanillic acid, 17: methoxytyramin, 18: 3-methoxy-4-hydroxyphenylacetalde-hyde, 19: 3-methoxy-4-hydroxyphenylacetic acid (homovanillic acid), 20: 3-methoxy-4-hydroxyphenyl-ethanol, 21: 3,4-dihydroxyphenylglycol.

Metabolism of the biogenic amines
of the tryptophan series

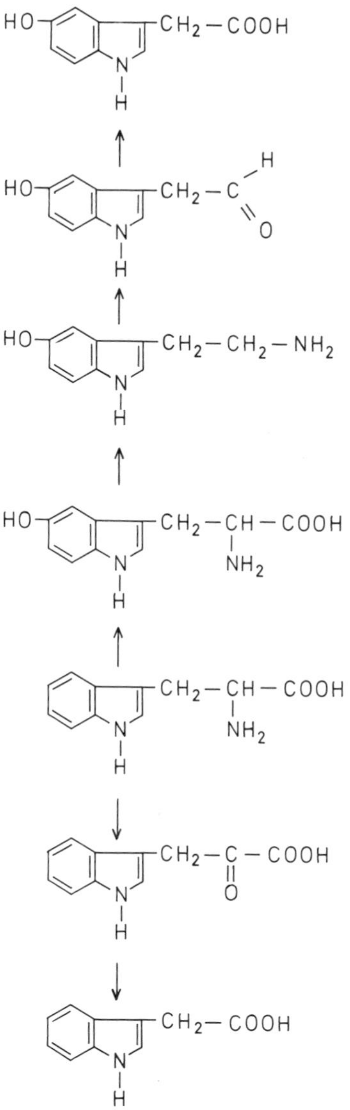

$$HO-\!\!\langle\!\langle \rangle\!\rangle\text{-}CH_2-COOH \qquad \underline{5}$$

↑

$$HO-\!\!\langle\!\langle \rangle\!\rangle\text{-}CH_2-C\overset{H}{\underset{O}{\diagdown}} \qquad \underline{4}$$

↑

$$HO-\!\!\langle\!\langle \rangle\!\rangle\text{-}CH_2-CH_2-NH_2 \qquad \underline{3}$$

↑

$$HO-\!\!\langle\!\langle \rangle\!\rangle\text{-}CH_2-\underset{NH_2}{CH}-COOH \qquad \underline{2}$$

↑

$$\langle\!\langle \rangle\!\rangle\text{-}CH_2-\underset{NH_2}{CH}-COOH \qquad \underline{1}$$

↓

$$\langle\!\langle \rangle\!\rangle\text{-}CH_2-\underset{O}{\overset{\|}{C}}-COOH \qquad \underline{6}$$

↓

$$\langle\!\langle \rangle\!\rangle\text{-}CH_2-COOH \qquad \underline{7}$$

Scheme 13-11. Metabolism of the biogenic amines of the tryptophan series. – **1:** tryptophan, **2:** 5-hydroxytryptophan, **3:** 5-hydroxytryptamin (serotonin), **4:** 5-hydroxyindole-3-acetaldehyde, **5:** 5-hydroxyindole-3-acetic acid, **6:** indole-3-pyruvic acid, **7:** indole-3-acetic acid.

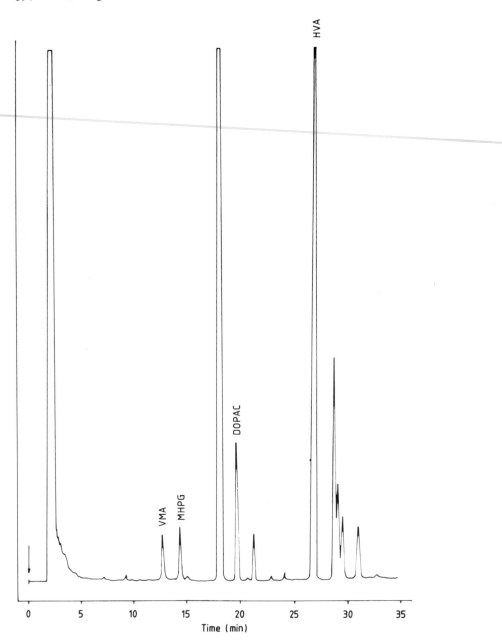

Figure 13-6. HPLC chromatogram of an ethyl acetate extract of a sample of human lumbar cerebrospinal fluid. Column: 250 mm × 4.6 mm i. d. Ultraspere ODS, 5 μm; according to reference [71].

13.4 References

[1] K. Gawehn, and H. U. Bergmeyer, in: H. U. Bergmeyer (ed.): *Methoden der enzymatischen Analyse*, p. 1538. Verlag Chemie, Weinheim 1974.

[2] D. H. Williamson, J. Mellanby, and H. A. Krebs, *Biochem. J.* **82**, 90 (1962).

[3] E. W. Rice, and B. S. Gorgan, *Clin. Chem.* **8**, 181 (1962).

[4] N. Kageyama, *Clin. Chim. Acta* **31**, 421 (1971).

[5] H. Bickel, *Dtsch. med. Wschr.* **88**, 1850 (1963).

[6] A. Astier, and A. M. Deutsch, *J. Chromatogr.* **182**, 88 (1980).

[7] K.-G. Wahlund, and B. Edlen, *Clin. Chim. Acta* **110**, 71 (1981).

[8] G. M. Anderson, J. G. Young, and D. J. Cohen, *J. Chromatogr.* **164**, 501 (1979).

[9] T. R. Rosano, H. H. Brown, and J. M. Meola, *Clin. Chem.* **27**, 228 (1981).

[10] K. Seta, M. Washitake, T. Anmo, N. Takai, and T. Okuyama, *J. Chromatogr.* **181**, 311 (1980).

[11] K. Seta, M. Washitake, I. Tanaka, N. Takai, and T. Okuyama, *J. Chromatogr.* **221**, 215 (1980).

[12] P. S. Draganac, S. J. Steindel, and W. G. Trawick, *Clin. Chem.* **26**, 910 (1980).

[13] J. E. Pettersen, E. Jellum, and L. Eldjarn, *Clin. Chim. Acta* **38**, 17 (1972).

[14] J. E. Pettersen, and E. Jellum, *Clin. Chim. Acta* **41**, 199 (1972).

[15] E. Jellum, O. Stokke, and L. Eldjarn, *Clin. Chem.* **18**, 800 (1972).

[16] P. P. Tracy, L. E. Wold, J. D. Jones, and M. F. Burritt, *Clin. Chem.* **27**, 160 (1981).

[17] A. Yoshida, M. Yoshioka, T. Sakai, and Z. Tamura, *J. Chromatogr.* **227**, 162 (1982).

[18] I. Molnar, and C. Horvath, *J. Chromatogr.* **143**, 391 (1977).

[19] M. H. Joseph, B. V. Kadam, and D. Risby, *J. Chromatogr.* **226**, 361 (1981).

[20] O. Beck, G. Palmskog, and E. Hultman, *Clin. Chim. Acta* **79**, 149 (1977).

[21] J. Greter, S. Lindstedt, H. Seeman, and G. Steen, *Clin. Chem.* **26**, 261 (1980).

[22] T. Niwa, T. Ohki, K. Maeda, A. Saito, and K. Kobayashi, *Clin. Chim. Acta* **99**, 71 (1979).

[23] H. J. Sternowsky, J. Roboz, F. Hutterer, and G. Gaull, *Clin. Chim. Acta* **47**, 371 (1973).

[24] K. Tanaka, A. West-Dull, D. G. Hine, T. B. Lynn, and T. Lowe, *Clin. Chem.* **26**, 1847 (1980).

[25] W. L. Fitch, P. J. Anderson, and D. H. Smith, *J. Chromatogr.* **162**, 249 (1979).

[26] H. M. Liebich, A. Pickert, U. Stierle, and J. Wöll, *J. Chromatogr.* **199**, 181 (1980).

[27] S. N. Nissen, C. van Huysen, and M. W. Haymond, *J. Chromatogr.* **232**, 170 (1982).

[28] Z. K. Shihabi, and J. Scako, *Clin. Chem.* **26**, 907 (1980).

[29] W. Voelter, R. Huber, and K. Zech, in: A. Zlatkis, R. Segura, and L. S. Ettre (eds.): *Advances in Chromatography 1981*, p. 529. Elsevier Scientific Publishing Company 1981.

[30] T. Hirata, M. Kai, K. Kohashi, and Y. Ohkura, *J. Chromatogr.* **226**, 25 (1981).

[31] R. A. Chalmers, and R. W. E. Watts, *Analyst* **97**, 958 (1972).

[32] R. A. Chalmers, A. M. Lawson, and R. W. E. Watts, *Clin. Chim. Acta* **52**, 43 (1974).

[33] S. C. Gates, N. Dendramis, and C. C. Sweeley, *Clin. Chem.* **24**, 1674 (1978).

[34] A. M. Lawson, R. A. Chalmers, and R. W. Watts, *Clin. Chem.* **22**, 1283 (1976).

[35] J. I. Patterson, and R. P. Brown, *J. Chromatogr.* **182**, 425 (1980).

[36] H. M. Liebich, A. Pickert, and J. Wöll, *J. Chromatogr.* **217**, 255 (1981).

[37] M. Spiteller, and G. Spiteller, *J. Chromatogr.* **164**, 253 (1979).

[38] P. Sims, R. Truscott, and B. Halpern, *J. Chromatogr.* **222**, 337 (1981).

[39] D. Pinkston, G. Spiteller, H. von Henning, and D. Matthaei, *J. Chromatogr.* **223**, 1 (1981).

[40] T. Hayashi, T. Sugiura, H. Tereda, S. Kawai, and T. Ohno, *J. Chromatogr.* **118**, 403 (1976).

[41] H. Tereda, T. Hayashi, S. Kawai, and T. Ohno, *J. Chromatogr.* **130**, 281 (1977).

[42] T. Hayashi, H. Todoriki, and H. Naruse, *J. Chromatogr.* **224**, 197 (1981).

[43] W. Dünges, *Anal. Chem.* **49**, 442 (1977).

[44] C. Jakobs, E. Solem, J. Ek, K. Halvorsen, and E. Jellum, *J. Chromatogr.* **143**, 31 (1977).

[45] L. Björkman, C. McLean, and G. Steen, *Clin. Chem.* **22**, 49 (1976).

[46] R. A. Chalmers, A. M. Lawson, and O. Borud, *Clin. Chim. Acta* **77**, 117 (1977).

[47] J. Greter, S. Lindstedt, H. Seeman, and G. Steen, *Clin. Chem.* **26**, 261 (1980).

[48] N. Narasimhachari, K. Leiner, and C. Brown, *Clin. Chim. Acta* **62**, 245 (1975).

[49] T. Niwa, K. Maeda, T. Ohki, and J. Sakakibara, *J. Chromatogr.* **228**, 59 (1982).

[50] F. W. Bultitude, and S. L. Newham, *Clin. Chem.* **21**, 1329 (1975).

[51] J. Dosman, L. C. Crawhall, G. A. Klassen, O. A. Mamer, and P. Neumann, *Clin. Chim. Acta* **51**, 93 (1974).

[52] M. Duran, D. Ketting, S. K. Wadman, C. Jakobs, R. B. H. Schutgens, and H. A. Veder, *Clin. Chim. Acta* **90**, 187 (1978).

[53] K. Tanaka, D. G. Hine, A. West-Dull, and T. B. Lynn, *Clin. Chem.* **26**, 1839 (1980).

[54] L. Borg, S. Lindstedt, and G. Steen, Clin. Chim. Acta **41**, 363 (1972).

[55] A. Grupe, and G. Spiteller, *J. Chromatogr.* **226**, 301 (1981).

[56] S. Landaas, *Clin. Chim. Acta* **54**, 39 (1974).

[57] W. Lehnert, L. Schuchmann, R. Urbanek, H. Niederhoff, and N. Böhm, *Eur. J. Pediatr.* **128**, 197 (1978).

[58] S. Lindstedt, K. Norberg, G. Steen, and E. Wahl, *Clin. Chem.* **22**, 1330 (1976).

[59] B. Sjöquist, B. Lindström, and E. Änggard, *Life Sci.* **13**, 1655 (1973).

[60] J. Chauhan, and A. Darbre, *J. Chromatogr.* **183**, 391 (1980).

[61] S. Takahashi, M. Yoshioka, S. Yoshiue, and Z. Tamura, *J. Chromatogr.* **145**, 1 (1978).

[62] B. A. Davis, and A. A. Boulton, *J. Chromatogr.* **222**, 161 (1981).

[63] R. A. Chalmers, R. W. E. Watts, *Analyst* **97**, 951 (1972).

[64] U. Langenbeck, A. Hoinowski, K. Mantel, and H.-U. Möhring, *J. Chromatogr.* **143**, 39 (1977).

[65] U. Langenbeck, A. Mench-Hoinowski, K.-P. Dieckmann, H.-U. Möhring, and M. Petersen. *J. Chromatogr.* **145**, 185 (1978).

[66] A. Yoshida, T. Yamazaki, and T. Sakai, *Clin. Chim. Acta* **77**, 95 (1977).

[67] M. Ghebregzabher, S. Rufini, M. G. Castellucci, and M. Lato, *J. Chromatogr.* **222**, 191 (1981).

[68] L. M. Bertani-Dziedzic, A. M. Krstulovic, S. Ciriello, and S. E. Gitlow, *J. Chromatogr.* **164**, 345 (1979).

[69] J. Mitchell, and C. J. Coscia, *J. Chromatogr.* **145**, 295 (1978).

[70] N. Fornstedt, *J. Chromatogr.* **225**, 440 (1981).

[71] A. M. Krstulovic, L. Bertani-Dziedzic, S. Bautista-Cerqueira, and S. E. Gitlow, *J. Chromatogr.* **227**, 379 (1982).

[72] D. D. Koch, and P. Kissinger, *J. Chromatogr.* **164**, 441 (1979).

[73] A. M. Krstulovic, and C. Matzura, *J. Chromatogr.* **163**, 72 (1979).

[74] T. Nagatsu, K. Oka, and T. Katsu, *J. Chromatogr.* **163**, 247 (1979).

[75] A. Hausen, D. Fuchs, K. König, and H. Wachter, *Clin. Chem.* **27**, 1455 (1981).

[76] H. Morrison, D. Avnir, and T. Zarrella, *J. Chromatogr.* **183**, 83 (1980).

[77] F. C. Senftleber, A. G. Halline, H. Veening, and D. A. Dayton, *Clin. Chem.* **22**, 1522 (1976).

[78] E. Jellum, *J. Chromatogr.* **143**, 427 (1977).

[79] C. Jakobs, M. Bojasch, M. Duran, D. Ketting, S. K. Wadman, and D. Leupold, *Clin. Chim. Acta* **106**, 85 (1980).

[80] M. Ende, P. Pfeifer, and G. Spiteller, *J. Chromatogr.* **183**, 1 (1980).

[81] B. A. Knights, M. Legendre, J. L. Laseter, and J. S. Storer, *Clin. Chem.* **21**, 888 (1975).

[82] J. Heininger, E. Munthe, J. Pahle, and E. Jellum, in: *Advances in Chromatography 1978*, p. 297. Elsevier Scientific Publishing Company 1978.

[83] E. Jellum, P. Storseth, J. Alexander, P. Helland, O. Stokke, and E. Teig, *J. Chromatogr.* **126**, 487 (1976).

[84] R. A. Chalmers, M. J. R. Healy, A. M. Lawson, and R. W. E. Watts, *Clin. Chem.* **22**, 1288 (1976).

[85] R. A. Chalmers, and A. M. Lawson, *Chem. Britain* **11**, 290 (1975).

[86] R. W. E. Watts, R. A. Chalmers, and A. M. Lawson, *Lancet* **I**, 368 (1975).

[87] R. A. Chalmers, and R. W. E. Watts, *Clin. Chim. Acta* **55**, 281 (1974).

[88] L. Eldjarn, E. Jellum, O. Stokke, H. Pande, and P. E. Waaler, *Lancet* **II**, 521 (1970).

[89] W. Weyler, L. Sweetman, D. C. Maggio, and W. L. Nyhan, *Clin. Chim. Acta* **76**, 321 (1977).

[90] W. Lehnert, and A. Junker, *Clin. Chim. Acta* **104**, 47 (1980).

[91] J. Greter, S. Lindstedt, H. Seeman, and G. Steen, *Clin. Chim. Acta* **106**, 103 (1980).

[92] J. E. Rosenberg, A.-Ch. Lilljeqvist, and Y. E. Hsia, *N. Engl. J. Med.* **24**, 1319 (1968).

[93] S. E. Goodman, E. R. B. McCabe, P. V. Fennessey, B. S. Miles, J. W. Mace, and E. Jellum, *Clin. Chim. Acta* **87**, 441 (1978).

[94] W. Lehnert, *Clin. Chim. Acta* **113**, 101 (1981).

[95] W. Lehnert, *Clin. Chim. Acta* **116**, 249 (1981).

[96] E. J. Norman, M. D. Denton, and H. K. Berry, *Clin. Chem.* **28**, 137 (1982).

[97] R. J. W. Truscott, B. Halpern, S. J. Wysocki, R. Hähnel, and B. Wilcken, *Clin. Chim. Acta* **95**, 11 (1979).

[98] M. Duran, J. P. G. M. van Biervliet, J. P. Kamerling, and S. K. Wadman, *Clin. Chim. Acta* **74**, 297 (1977).

[99] E. Deutsch, and G. Geyer: *Laboratoriumsdiagnostik*, p. 698. Verlag Brüder Hartmann, Berlin 1975.

[100] P. E. Verkade, and J. van der Lee, *Biochem. J.* **28**, 31 (1934).

[101] J. E. Pettersen, *Clin. Chim. Acta* **41**, 231 (1972).

[102] I. Björkhem, *J. Lipid Res.* **19**, 585 (1978).

[103] W. Kam, K. Kumaran, and B. R. Landau, *J. Lipid Res.* **19**, 591 (1978).

[104] J. E. Pettersen, and O. Stokke, *Biochim. Biophys. Acta* **304**, 316 (1973).

[105] P. Felig, E. Marliss, J. L. Ohman, and G. F. Cahill, *Diabetes* **19**, 727 (1970).

[106] H. S. Paul, and S. A. Adibi, *Metabolism* **27**, 185 (1978).

[107] S. Landaas, *Clin. Chim. Acta* **64**, 143 (1975).

[108] S. Landaas, and C. Jakobs, *Clin. Chim. Acta* **78**, 489 (1977).

[109] H. G. Hanley, S. M. Stahl, and D. X. Freedman, *Arch. Gen. Psychiatry* **34**, 521 (1977).

[110] F. A. J. Muskiet, D. C. Fremouw-Ottevangers, G. T. Nagel, B. G. Wolthers, and J. A. de Vries, *Clin. Chem.* **24**, 2001 (1978).

14 Secondary Plant Constituents

by *Kurt Hostettmann* and *Maryse Hostettmann*

14 Secondary Plant Constituents

14.1 Introduction

High performance liquid chromatography has proven to be one of the most useful techniques for the separation of complex mixtures such as crude plant extracts or other biological materials. It has opened unexpected possibilities for all chemists interested in natural products. Due to its high speed and high resolution power, HPLC permits the isolation and separation of unstable plant constituents, closely related compounds and numerous isomers. It is becoming a routine method for the quantitative analysis and the standardization of many drugs.

Thus, in recent years, a tremendous number of papers dealing with the application of HPLC to the separation of natural products have been published. However, the results of these investigations are scattered throughout a large number of journals and it is often difficult for an investigator to find suitable conditions for a particular separation. Kingston [1] published an excellent and very useful review-article which summarizes the literature dealing with the application of HPLC to secondary plant metabolites from 1974 to 1978. Some selected examples of separation of various natural products have been presented by Adams & Nakanishi [2].

Although numerous new types of stationary phases have become available, most secondary plant metabolites are separated on octadecylsilyl bonded phase columns. The estimation made in 1978 by Wehrli et al. [3] that 80% of current separations are done on C_{18}-columns is thus still valid.

This chapter will deal with recent applications of HPLC to the separation of various classes of secondary plant metabolites. In general, the treated examples are posterior to Kingston's review-article. Owing to the large number of published papers and to the diversity of secondary plant constituents, this is not an exhaustive survey of the literature. Typical examples of separation have been selected and hopefully will suggest which conditions to choose for a particular separation problem in the field of plant constituents.

14.2 Plant Phenolics

It is noteworthy that, for plant phenolics, HPLC has mainly been used as an analytical technique, e.g. quantitative determination, purity verification of isolated compounds, chemotaxonomical comparison, etc. For the isolation of phenolics, the full potential of HPLC as preparative-scale separation technique has not yet been exploited. Reviews dealing mainly with the separation of flavonoids have been published by Van Sumere et al. [4] and by Hostettmann [5]. Reversed-phase chromatography on octadecylsilyl bonded columns with methanol/acetic acid/water or methanol/phosphoric acid/water has been employed successfully in many separations of polar aglycones and glycosides. Difficult separations of highly polar phenolics have also been achieved by paired ion chromatography [6, 7]. An alternative method for the separation of polar compounds on buffered silica gel systems has been proposed by Schwarzenbach [8] and applied to the chromatography of beer bitter acids [7, 8].

14.2.1 Flavonoid Aglycones

Silica gel columns are, in general, not often used for the separation of phenolics, but are well suited to the separation of non-polar or weakly polar flavonoid aglycones. HPLC using LiChrosorb Si 60 as adsorbant and a mixture of n-heptane/isopropanol (60:40) as the eluant was found to be a very efficient method for the separation of the most important polymethoxylated flavones from citrus fruits [9]. Tangeretin, tetra-O-methyl-scutellarein, heptamethoxyflavone, nobiletin and sinensetin have been identified in crude extracts of tangerine and orange peels within 25 min. A recent study of the capacity factors of seventeen polymethoxylated flavones by straight-phase HPLC, using four solvent systems with various water contents, showed that n-heptane/ethanol (75:25) and n-heptane/isopropanol (60:40) are the most useful with water contents ranging from 0.05 to 0.02% [10]. Complex mixtures of isoflavone aglycones have been resolved on a µPorasil column using different gradient systems [11]. But isocratic chromatography of *Glycine max* hydrolyzate with [dichloromethane/ethanol/acetic acid (97:3:0.2)]/hexane (8:2) resulted in a rapid separation of daidzein and genistein. The isocratic run does not require solvent re-equilibration for each sample and thus increases the rate of analysis. Silica gel

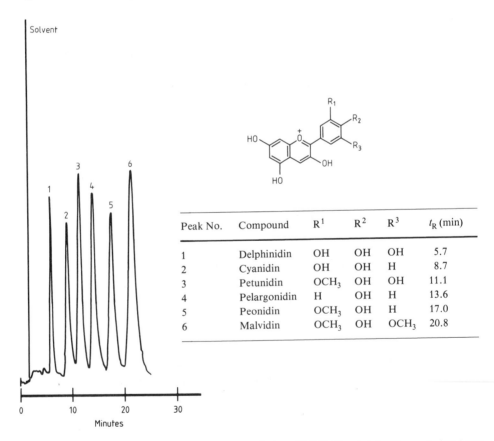

Peak No.	Compound	R^1	R^2	R^3	t_R (min)
1	Delphinidin	OH	OH	OH	5.7
2	Cyanidin	OH	OH	H	8.7
3	Petunidin	OCH_3	OH	OH	11.1
4	Pelargonidin	H	OH	H	13.6
5	Peonidin	OCH_3	OH	H	17.0
6	Malvidin	OCH_3	OH	OCH_3	20.8

Figure 14-1. Separation of anthocyanidins by reversed-phase HPLC. (Reprinted with permission from reference [15]).

has also been used for the separation of flavonoid acetates with benzene/acetonitrile (85:20), benzene/acetone (90:15) or isooctane/ethanol/acetonitrile (70:16:5.5) [12].

For aglycones possessing three or more free hydroxyl groups, the separation can easily be made on octadecylsilyl or octylsilyl bonded columns. A practical application of the reversed-phase technique can be seen in an analysis of isoflavone aglycones in soybeans [13, 14]. An excellent separation of the six most common anthocyanidins has been achieved by Wilkinson et. al. [15]. By using a μBondapak C_{18} column with water/acetic acid/methanol (71:10:19) as eluent, a baseline separation of the six reference anthocyanidins was obtained within 25 min. (Figure 14-1).

The above mentioned separation conditions have been used for the analysis of the anthocyanidins of *Vitis rotundifolia* [15], *Hibiscus sabdariffa* [15], *Vaccinium myrtillus* [16] and to study flower pigment genetics [17].

Flavan-4 α-ol and flavan-4 β-ol epimers which are important intermediates in the biosynthetic pathways of flavonoids could be separated on a μBondapak C_{18} column with methanol/water (1:1) or methanol/water/acetic acid (33:65:2) [18]. Some typical flavonoid aglycone separations are summarized in Table 14-1 (Section 14.2.2).

14.2.2   Flavonoid Glycosides

Glycosides are generally separated on C_{18} reversed-phase columns with acetonitrile/water or methanol/water containing small amounts of acetic acid. These mobile phases are well suited to UV detection and can easily be employed in gradient systems for complex separations [20 to 22]. In numerous reported separations, acetic acid as constituent of the mobile phase has been replaced by very small amounts of phosphoric acid [23 to 26]. Depending on the separation problem, it may be advantageous to replace C_{18} chemically bonded phases by C_8 reversed-phase material. For example, the resolution of isovitexin arabinoside and vitexin rhamnoside was very poor on a LiChrosorb RP-18 column, whereas these two flavone-C-glycosides are well separated on a RP-8 column with a water/acetic acid/methanol solvent system [27]. Becker et al. [28] employed an amino-chemically bonded silica gel column (LiChrosorb NH_2) with acetonitrile/water for the separation of isomeric O-glycosides of glycoflavones. Acylated flavone-C-glycosides from the seeds of *Zizyphus jujuba* were separated on a C_{18} column with tetrahydrofuran/water (4:53) [29].

Isoflavone glycosides can be separated on C_{18} columns with methanol/water [30] or acetonitrile/water [31]. An excellent method for the separation of anthocyanins from fruits and their products on a μBondapak C_{18} column has been reported [23]. Separation of 3- and 3,5-diglucosides of anthocyanidins was achieved with aqueous acetic acid whereas an aqueous methanolic acetic acid solution was used for the p-coumaryl-3- and 3,5-diglucosides. For the separation of highly complex mixtures of anthocyanins containing members of all four above mentioned pigment groups, a programmed, non-linear, gradient elution between aqueous acetic acid and aqueous methanolic acetic acid solution is required. Within the individual groups, the substitution in the B-ring is a key factor in the determination of the retention times. With increasing hydroxylation in the B-ring, the retention time of the compounds decreases. Since anthocyanins can be selectively detected in the region of 520 nm, where few other compounds adsorb, the method can be applied to crude plant extracts without derivatization of the pigments. Strack et al. [32] developed a HPLC procedure for the resolution of mixtures containing low and highly glycosylated anthocyanins as well as 3-deoxy-anthocyanins.

For the separation of peracetylated flavonol glycosides, an isocratic method using LiChrosorb Si 60 with benzene/acetonitrile (4:1) has been proposed [33]. Detection was made by UV at 300 nm. Some separations dealing with different types of flavonoid glycosides are summarized in Table 14-1.

Table 14-1. Typical HPLC Separations of Flavonoid Aglycones and Glycosides.

Separated Compounds	Column	Mobile Phase	Reference
Polymethoxylated flavone aglycones	LiChrosorb Si 60	n-Heptane/isopropanol (60:40) n-heptane/ethanol (75:25)	[9] [10] [10]
Flavone aglycones	μBondapak C_{18}	Water/acetic acid/acetonitrile (68:2:30)	[19]
Flavonoid acetates	LiChrosorb Si 60	Benzene/acetonitrile (40:60) benzene/acetone (90:15) isooctane/ethanol/acetonitrile (70:16:5.5)	[12]
Isoflavone aglycones	μPorasil	Dichloromethane/ethanol/acetic acid (97:3:0.2)/hexane (12:88)	[11]
	Partisil-10 ODS	water/acetonitrile (4:1)	[13]
Anthocyanidins	μBondapak C_{18}	Water/acetic acid/methanol (71:10:19) water/acetic acid/methanol/ acetonitrile (75:10:7:8)	[15] [16] [17] [17]
Flavan-4-ols	μBondapak C_{18}	Methanol/water (1:1) water/acetic acid/methanol (33:65:2)	[18]
Flavone and flavonol glycosides	Zorbax ODS	45% → 100% Methanol containing 0.1% acetic acid	[20]
	μBondapak C_{18}	40% methanol in phosphate buffer	[24]
Flavone-C-glycosides	LiChrosorb NH_2	Acetonitrile/water (1:9 → 9:1)	[28]
Acylated flavone glycosides	COPELL ODS	Tetrahydrofuran/water (4:53)	[29]
Isoflavone glycosides	μBondapak C_{18} Nucleosil ODS	32% → 90% Methanol acetonitrile/water (18:82)	[30] [31]
Anthocyanidin glycosides	μBondapak C_{18}	Acetic acid/water (15:85) methanol/acetic acid/water (20:15:65)	[23]

14.2.3 Xanthones

Xanthones occupy an important position in the chemistry of natural products. Their structure is related to that of flavonoids and their chromatographic behaviour is also similar. The growing interest in these compounds is easily explained by their pharmacological activities (anti-psychotic action, monoamine oxidase inhibition) as well as their importance in chemotaxonomy [34].

A systematic HPLC study of xanthone aglycones has been reported by Hostettmann and McNair [35]. Weakly polar xanthones could easily be separated on a nitrile-chemically bonded phase (Micropak CN column) with n-hexane/chloroform (13:7) or cyclohexane/chloroform (1:4). Aglycones possessing more than two free hydroxyl groups require the use of a less polar phase and have been separated on an amino-chemically bonded phase column with dioxane/dichloromethane (1:9) or isooctane/chloroform (3:17). Chloroform extracts of various *Gentiana* species have been analyzed by HPLC and xanthone aglycones identified by UV and MS [36]. The difficult separation of the isomeric xanthone aglycones gentisin (1,7-dihydroxy-3-methoxy-xanthone) and isogentisin (1,3-dihydroxy-7-methoxyxanthone) was achieved on a C_{18}-chemically bonded phase with methanol/water (1:1) [37]. The same compounds have also been separated on a LiChrosorb RP-8 column with acetonitrile/water [38, 39]. In the course of the isolation of a new xanthone aglycone from *Gentiana corymbifera* Massias et al. [40] used a silica gel column with chloroform containing small amounts of methanol, as mobile phase.

C_{18}-chemically bonded silica gel, used with different methanol/water mixtures as the solvent, was found to be an ideal system for the separation of naturally occurring xanthone glycosides [37]. A base-line separation of isomeric disaccharides was obtained on a µBondapak C_{18} column with methanol/water (45:55). Permethylated xanthone glycosides could easily be purified on a Micropak CN column with isooctane/chloroform (3:7) [36].

14.2.4 Anthraquinones, Quinones and Related Compounds

Several examples of anthraquinone and quinone separations have been reported and summarized in the review of Van Sumere et al. [4]. Since numerous drugs are characterized by the occurrence of these polyphenols, there is a need to have fast and reliable methods for their quantitative determination. Such a method has been elaborated for the separation and determination of arbutin, methylarbutin, hydroquinone and hydroquinone monomethylether in *Arctostaphylos, Bergenia, Calluna* and *Vaccinium* species [41]. A reversed-phase system with a µBondapak C_{18} column using methanol/water (10:90) as mobile phase was developed. All the compounds were separated within 22 min. Detection was made by UV at 280 nm and arbutin could be detected at concentrations as low as 25 ng.

The pharmacologically highly important aloin, a C-glycoside derivative of anthraquinone, was found to be a mixture of two stereoisomers. HPLC investigation of the juice of *Aloe ferox* and *Aloe arborescens* allowed a base-line separation of these stereoisomers [42]. The excellent separation was achieved on a LiChrosorb RP-18 semi-preparative column with methanol/water (45:55) in less than 12 min. Detection was made by UV at 360 nm.

A method for qualitative and quantitative analysis of *Senna* preparations has been described by Görler et al. [123]. By using paired-ion chromatography, the isomeric dianthrone-8,8'-diglucosides sennoside A and sennoside B were readily separated. The best resolution was obtained with a RP-8 column coupled with methanol/acetonitrile/water/PIC A reagent (tetrabutylammoniumphosphate) (15:15:70:1.65). Such a separation is shown in Figure 14-2.

Paired-ion chromatography allows much faster separation of the sennosides than the previously described methods which were all using gradient elution [43, 44]. The anthraquinone aglycone rhein occurs also in *Senna* preparations (extracts of *Cassia angustifolia* or *Cassia senna*) and could be determined by paired-ion chromatography on a RP-8 column with water/methanol/PIC A (42:58:1.65) within 6 min [123].

(96:4), whereas for dihydroxy and monohydroxy monocarboxy triterpenoids the eluting solvent was hexane/ethanol (99:1). For monoketonic and monohydroxytriterpenoids, the less polar mobile phase hexane/ethanol (99.85:0.15) gave a satisfactory separation. More polar triterpenoids such as soyasapogenol A and related compounds were separated on a reversed-phase C_{18} column (Zorbax BP-ODS) with methanol/water (80:20) containing 0.05% of 88% formic acid. Reversed-phase HPLC was also employed for the separation of less polar triterpenoids (lupeol, lanosterol, friedelin, euphol, etc.) with methanol/water (96:4). Because the triterpenoids containing carbon-carbon double bonds have a λ_{max} near 202 nm, this wavelength was used for the detection of unsaturated triterpenoids. It is also suitable for the detection of ketonic triterpenoids and conjugated double bond triterpenoids.

Valepotriates have been separated on a silica gel column with hexane/ethylacetate (20:3) [52]. Adsorption chromatography was also used for the determination of quassinoids of *Quassia amara* and *Picrasma excelsa* with dichloromethane/methanol (98:2) as mobile phase [53].

Recently, it appears that reversed-phase chromatography is being increasingly used for terpenoid separation. Some examples involving different types of terpenoids are summarized in Table 14-2.

14.4 Terpenoid and Steroid Glycosides

Reversed-phase chromatography on C_{18} or C_8 columns with methanol/water or acetonitrile/water mixtures has proved to be indicated for the separation of various types of terpenoid glycosides.

14.4.1 Iridoid and Secoiridoid Glycosides

Iridoid glycosides generally possess only one or two sugars and occur also as esters of benzoic, cinnamic or related acids. They can easily be separated by HPLC on reversed-phase packing material. Detection is made by UV at various wavelengths. A method for the quantitative determination of harpagoside in the roots of *Harpagophytum procumbens* has been reported [60]. Separation was achieved on a µBondapak C_{18} column with methanol/water (1:1). The detection limit for harpagoside was about 0.2 µg/µL at 278 nm and the relative standard deviation was between 2 and 5%. Similar chromatographic conditions have been employed for the analytical and semi-preparative separations of iridoid glycosides of *Veronica officinalis* [61], *Scrophularia lateriflora* [62], *Euphrasia salisburgensis* [63] and other species. Although up to sixteen iridoid glycosides could be separated with the methanol/water solvent system, no base-line separation was obtained for iridoid acids. These rather seldomly occurring compounds could be separated by paired-ion chromatography using tetrabutylammonium phosphate as counter-ion, buffered at pH 7.5 [64].

Secoiridoid glycosides which are responsable for the bitter taste of the roots of *Gentiana* and related plants have been separated by Sticher and Meier [65] on a C_{18} column with methanol/water (1:1). A base-line separation of amarogentin, amaropanin and amaroswerin was realized within 15 min. The bitter principles of various *Gentiana* species have also been determined by Quercia et al. [66] on a reversed-phase packing column by a methanol/phosphate buffer gradient elution. The simultaneous determination of amarogentin, amaroswerin and gentiopicroside in *Swertia japonica* was achieved on a silica gel column with chloroform/ethanol mobile phases [67]. However, the quantitative determination of swertiamarin, which is the main component of this Japanese drug, was made on a C_{18} column with methanol/water (10:90) [68]. The compound was detected by UV at 238 nm and eluted after 15 min. using a flow-rate of 1.0 mL/min. Secoiridoid glycosides of various species of the genus *Centaurium* have been separated on a Spherisorb ODS column with methanol/water (15:85) [69]. But the isolation of sweroside and gentiopicroside by preparative HPLC was achieved on silica gel with ethyl acetate/methanol (95:5).

14.4.2 Saponins

Only few examples of HPLC separations of saponins have been reported. This is partly due to the difficulty of detecting these compounds by UV absorption and to the complexity of their structures. The well-known Chinese longevity drug ginseng (the roots of *Panax ginseng*) has been studied in numerous laboratories. A method for the quantitative analysis of the biologically active dammarane saponins (ginsenosides) was reported by Besso et al. [70]. Ginsenosides, quantitatively reacted with benzoyl chloride in pyridine to afford the respective derivatives, exhibit strong UV absorption. The benzoylated ginseng saponins were separated on a silica gel column with n-hexane/dichloromethane/acetonitrile (15:3:2) and detected at 240 nm. A method for the quantitative determination of ginsenosides without UV-derivatization was elaborated [71]. A silica gel column with n-heptane/n-butanol/acetonitrile/water (1000:446:132:36) as mobile phase was employed. The ginsenosides were detected at 207 nm and separated in 40 min. For the determination of ginsenoside Rg_1, a reversed-phase system using a C_{18} column and methanol/water (44:56) was suitable. HPLC has also been applied to the isolation of ginsenoside-Rf, -Rg_2 and -Rh_1 from a crude saponin mixture [72]. The described procedure involved preparative HPLC on silica gel with the upper layer of n-butanol/ethyl acetate/water (4:1:2), followed by semi-preparative HPLC on a carbohydrate column with acetonitrile/water (86:14). An RI detector was used to determine each compound. A further, large-scale isolation of ginsenosides from leaves and stems of American ginseng *(Panax quinquefolium),* using a combination of silica gel column chromatography and semi-preparative HPLC, was reported [73]. HPLC was performed on two interconnected silica gel columns with the lower phase of chloroform/methanol/ethyl acetate/water (2:2:4:1).

The roots of *Bupleurum falcatum* (Bupleuri radix) are a well known and very important crude drug in traditional oriental medicine. They are characterized by three major oleanane-type saponins named saikosaponins -a, -c and -d (Figure 14-3). An HPLC study of Bupleuri radix has been reported by Kimata et al. [74]. The genuine saikosaponins containing the unstable allyloxide linkage were converted into artificial UV-active diene-saponins by mild acid treatment and separated by reversed-phase chromatography on a column of octadecylsilylated silica gel with methanol/water/acetic acid/triethylamine (75:25:0.2:0.2).

The diene-saponin from saikosaponin-c was eluted before the less polar diene-saponins obtained from saikosaponin-d and saikosaponin-a. However, a base-line separation of these two saponins which differ only in the configurations at C-16-OH could easily be achieved in 20 min. Detection was made by UV at 254 nm and anthracene could be used as an appropriate internal standard for quantitative analysis.

Glc(1-6)Glc-O
3
1
1
Rha

saikosaponin c

R: β OH   saikosaponin a
R: α OH   saikosaponin d

Figure 14-3. Structure of the saikosaponins.

A reversed-phase system using a μBondapak C_{18} column and methanol/water/acetic acid (60 : 34 : 6) as mobile phase was elaborated for the quantitative determination of glycyrrhizic acid in Radix liquiritiae *(Glycyrrhiza glabra)* [75]. A method for the analysis of this drug using ion-exchange chromatography has also been reported [76].

14.4.3 Cardiotonic Glycosides

These glycosides, also called cardiac glycosides, are distributed in several plant families and used therapeutically to strengthen a weakened heart. Some of them have long been used as arrow poisons. Two types of aglycone (genin) may be distinguished according to whether there is a five or six membered lactone ring. These types are known respectively as cardenolides (e. g. digitoxigenin) and bufanolides or bufadienolides (e. g. scillarenin).

Owing to the importance of cardiotonic glycoside-containing drugs and their pharmaceutical formulations, numerous papers dealing with the HPLC separation of these glycosides have been published since 1974 [1]. The modes of separation employed include ion-exchange chromatography, adsorption chromatography and reversed-phase chromatography. In some cases, the glycosides have been derivatized prior to analysis [77, 78], but most separations were carried out on the naturally occurring compounds. Cardenolide glycosides from *Digitalis* species can be separated, either on silica gel or on reversed-phase columns. An excellent comparative study of both separation modes has been published by Erni and Frey [79]. It appears that adsorption and reversed-phase chromatography fulfill complementary functions. As true reversibility of orders of separation is observed, one can, in most instances, choose the mode that is best suited to the particular problem and requirements, i. e., saving of separation time and increasing resolution. For the separation on silica gel, dichloromethane/methanol/water (920 : 80 : 12) was used as mobile phase, whereas acetonitrile/water (37 : 63) and dioxan/water (45 : 55) were ideal solvents for reversed-phase chromatography on C_{18} chemically bonded columns. Detection was made by UV at 230 nm. Reversed-phase systems possess some advantages in regard to sample preparation for analysis of dosage forms.

Bufadienolide glycosides of *Urginea maritima*, of *Scilla* species and *Scilla* preparations have been analyzed qualitatively and quantitatively on reversed-phase columns with acetonitrile/water mixtures as mobile phase [80, 81]. The presence of a conjugated double bond in these glycosides allows an easy detection by UV at 280 or 300 nm.

Some typical HPLC separations of cardiotonic glycosides are summarized in Table 14-3.

For the analysis of bufadienolides and cardenolides, reversed-phase chromatography on a µBondapak column was particularly effective [83]. The best indicated solvent systems are methanol/water (2:1), acetonitrile/water (1:1) or tetrahydrofuran/water (2:3).

Table 14-3. Separation of Cardiotonic Glycosides.

Separated Glycosides	Column	Mobile Phase	Detection	Reference
Digitalis glycosides (lower polarity)	LiChrosorb Si-60	n-Pentanol/acetonitrile/ isooctane/water (175:60:620:10)	220 nm	[82]
Digitalis glycosides (medium and high polarity)	LiChrosorb Si-60	tert-Butanol/acetonitrile/ heptane/water (204:93:712:10.4)	220 nm	[82]
Lanatoside C and by-products	LiChrosorb Si 100	Dichloromethane/methanol/ water (320:80:12)	230 nm	[79]
Digitalis glycosides	Nucleosil C_{18}	Acetonitrile/water (37:63)	230 nm	[79]
		dioxan/water (45:55)		
		tetrahydrofuran/dioxan (2:1)/water (67:33)		
Bufadienolide glycosides (*Scilla* glycosides)	Nucleosil C_{18} or µBondapak C_{18}	Acetonitrile/water (1:3)	280 nm	[81]
	LiChrosorb RP-8	Acetonitrile/water (18:28)		[80]

14.4.4 Miscellaneous Glycosides

By means of semi-preparative HPLC, new monoterpene glucosides have been isolated from the Chinese drug *Schizonepeta tenuifolia* [84]. Separations were achieved on a µBondapak C_{18} column with acetonitrile/methanol/water (1:1:4) and detection made by a refractive index monitor. The structures of the isolated glucosides were elucidated as (1S, 4R, 8E)-9-0-β-D-glu-copyranosyl-p-menth-8(9)-en-3one and a glucoside possessing a dioxan ring formed by the double linkage between glucose and the aglycone (1S, 4R, 8R)-8, 9-dihydroxy-p-menth-3-one, respectively.

14.5 Alkaloids

The separation of alkaloids by HPLC has been reviewed [1, 3, 85, 86] and the number of published papers is still growing. Alkaloids occur in numerous plant families and are the most important natural products from the viewpoint of biological and pharmacological activities.

Thus HPLC is nowadays widely used in the analysis of alkaloids, e. g. pharmaceutical preparations, urine analysis for abuse of drugs, toxicology, metabolite studies and phytochemical analysis [86].

As alkaloids are basic compounds, one requirement for their separation is that the pH of the mobile phase is above 7. Basic conditions are necessary to suppress ionization of the sample and to give narrow peaks. However, at high pH, silica gel begins to dissolve. In most cases, it is preferable to use bonded phase packings but even these packings are not stable indefinitely. Some alkaloids can be separated on C_{18} chemically bonded phases using acidic mobile phases (phosphate buffer at pH 2.7) [87]. Alternative methods involve ion-pair chromatography [87] and ion-exchange chromatography [88]. In recent papers, acidic mobile phases, coupled with C_{18} columns, are reported as the method of choice for the separation of certain classes of alkaloids. Recently developed packing materials, such as styrene-divinylbenzene resin, allow the use of high pH mobile phases and afford good peak symmetry for basic compounds without the use of ion-pairing reagents [89].

Owing to the wide variety of alkaloids and the large number of papers published on their separation by HPLC, only a few recent reports have been selected for discussion in the present review.

14.5.1 Purine Alkaloids

For the analysis of tea constituents in aqueous tea solution, a μBondapak C_{18} column with methanol/0.1 mol/L citrate-phosphate buffer at pH 7.0 (20:80) gave satisfactory results [90]. Theobromine, theophylline and caffeine were separated in less than 10 min. A general method for the determination of caffeine in vegetables and pharmaceutical raw material has been elaborated [91]. Separations were achieved on a C_{18} chemically bonded phase with methanol/water (60:40), detection made by UV at 280 nm and 8-chlorotheophylline used as internal standard. The method allows simultaneous determination of theobromine, theophylline and caffeine.

Theophylline (1,3-dimethylxanthine) is a drug used in the treatment of asthma and its therapeutic value is dependent upon its concentration in the blood. Thus, rapid, quantitative analysis for theophylline is a necessity and numerous HPLC methods have been proposed. One of them uses a C_{18} bonded column (Partisil-10 ODS-2) with methanol/0.025 mol/L KH_2PO_4 (65:35) [92]. The method required only 10 μL of serum which can be injected directly onto a guard column. Detection is made by UV at 254 nm and there is no interference with other xanthines present.

14.5.2 Morphine Alkaloids

Numerous papers dealing with the separation of morphine alkaloids have been published, the first paper, as long ago as 1973, was by Wu et al. [93]. Reversed-phase chromatography using C_{18} columns is well indicated for the separation of opium alkaloids. For the determination of morphine, codeine and thebaine, the following solvent systems were employed: methanol/0.1 mol/L KH_2PO_4 (7:93) [94], methanol/0.3% ammonium carbonate (4:1) [95] and acetonitrile/0.1 mol/L NaH_2PO_4 (1:3) or (1:19) at pH 4.8 [96]. A simultaneous determination of the six major alkaloids in gum opium was realized on a reversed-phase C_{18} column isocratically without ion-pair reagents [97]. A mixture of 1% ammonium acetate buffer (pH adjusted at 5.8 with acetic acid) and acetonitrile, or a mixture of the buffer, acetonitrile and dioxan was used as mobile phase. Detection was by UV at 254 nm. This simple and reliable method is suitable for routine quantitative analysis of crude opium. An excellent separation of morphine and narcotoline has been obtained with methanol/dioxan/0.01 mol/L CH_3COONa on a C_{18} column within 5 min [98]. With this system, morphine is eluted before narcotoline. However, when the same solvent system is used without buffer, an inversion of the retention times can be observed. This second solvent system is well suited to the separation of minor opium alkaloids such as palaudine, papaverine and isocorypalmine.

Hansen [88] investigated the influence on the retention of some opium alkaloids by a gradual change in the polarity of the mobile phase from a straight-phase system containing 1% water to an ion-exchange system containing 90% water using a silica gel column. With acetonitrile/water/glacial acetic acid/diethylamine (10:90:0.5:0.5) as the mobile phase, the efficiency of the column was 6000 plates for thebaine ($k = 2.0$).

14.5.3 Pyrrolizidine Alkaloids

During the last ten years, pyrrolizidine alkaloids have attracted considerable attention owing to their toxic properties. They occur in a large variety of plant families and are of interest for both veterinary and human medicine. Segall and co-workers [99 to 103] published a series of very interesting papers dealing with the HPLC separation of pyrrolizidine alkaloids from various *Senecio* species. One method was based on tetrahydrofuran/0.01 mol/L ammonium carbonate at pH 7.8 (16:84) as solvent system used with a μBondapak CN column [99]. Retrorsine, seneciphylline and senecionine from *Senecio vulgaris* could be separated isocratically on a C_{18} reversed-phase column with methanol/0.01 mol/L potassium phosphate buffer at pH 6.3 (1:1) [103]. This solvent system appears to be excellent for resolving closely related pyrrolizidine alkaloids. Recently, Ramsdell and Buhler [89] employed a reversed-phase styrene-divinyl-benzene resin column for their investigation of the alkaloids of *Senecio jacobaea* and *Senecio vulgaris*. The main constituents of this latter species were nicely separated within 18 min by using acetonitrile/0.1 mol/L ammonia (25:75) as shown in Figure 14-4.

The styrene-divinylbenzene resin column allows use of high pH mobile phases that would destroy silica-based columns. Good peak symmetry for basic compounds is obtained without the use of ion-pairing reagents. The acetonitrile/ammonia solvent system is indicated for preparative work since the solvents can be directly evaporated under vacuum, thus avoiding the extractions necessary when using phosphate buffers. The low adsorbance of HPLC-grade acetonitrile at 220 nm allows gradient analysis of pyrrolizidine alkaloids and high sensitivity without prohibitive baseline shifts. Finally, the problems associated with the use of solid buffer salts are avoided with this system which is certainly suitable for other classes of alkaloids.

For the analysis of pyrrolizidine-N-oxide alkaloids of various *Symphytum* species, Wagner et al. [104[used a μBondapak NH_2 column with acetonitrile/water (92:8).

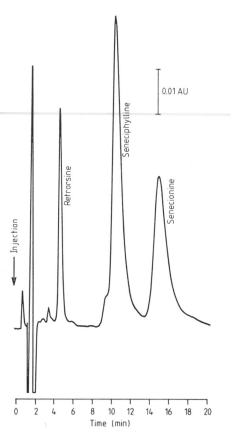

Figure 14-4. Separation of a *Senecio vulgaris* extract.
Solvent: isocratic, 1 mL/min, acetonitrile/0.1 mol/L
ammonia (25:75)
(Reprinted with permission from reference [89]).

14.5.4 Indole Alkaloids

The isolation and separation methods for indole alkaloids have been discussed by Verpoorte
[86], who studied the effect of a basic modifier on the separation of strychnine and brucine. A
very fast baseline separation of these two alkaloids without any tailing was achieved on a silica
gel column with ether/methanol (9:1) containing 1% diethylamine. The alkaloids produced in
Catharanthus roseus cell cultures could be characterized by reversed-phase HPLC with acetoni-
trile/water (62:38) containing 0.1% triethylamine modifier [105]. For the quantitative determination of vincamine, apovincamine and 14-epivincamine, Pietta et al. [106] proposed a method
using bonded octadecylsilane with methanol/0.01 mol/L ammonium carbonate (75:25) at
pH 7.8. Papaverine was employed as internal standard and detection made by UV at 254 nm.
The method is sensitive, accurate and suitable for routine determinations of vincamine in drugs,
pharmaceutical preparations and diluted urine and plasma. Vincamine and closely related
alkaloids have also been separated on LiChrosorb RP-8 or μBondapak C_{18} with acetonitrile/
0.01 mol/L ammonium carbonate (6:4) or (7:3) [107]. The method was indicated for
stereoisomers and ester homologues and for group separation. However, optical isomers and
structural isomers were not separated. The separation of these alkaloids was realized on silica gel

columns with chloroform/methanol (95:5), n-hexane/chloroform/methanol (60:30:10) or (80:10:10) [108]. Using a four component eluent mixture formed of n-hexane/chloroform/acetonitrile/methanol (55:25:20:3), further selectivity of the separation was achieved for cis and trans isomers, namely the trans isomers of apovincamic acid ethyl ester, epivincamic acid ethyl ester and vincaminic acid ethyl ester were eluted before the corresponding cis isomers.

14.5.5 Miscellaneous Alkaloids

The major cinchona alkaloids have been separated on a C_{18} bonded column with methanol/acetic acid/water (25:1:75) [109], but the separation of cinchonine and cinchonidine was carried out using methanol/acetic acid/water (20:1:80). The elaborated method is specific, precise and suitable for the analysis of drugs or formulations containing quinine salts.

Ten different aconitine alkaloids could be separated on a C_{18} column using tetrahydrofuran/phosphate buffer at pH 2.7 (89:11) as mobile phase [87]. An alternative method is involving ion-pair chromatography with tetrahydrofuran/phosphate buffer at pH 2.7 (85:15) and 0.01 mol/L sodium hexanesulphonate as counter-ion. The detection limit was 12 ng for mesaconitine and 15 ng for benzoylmesaconine. When the alkaloids were monitored at 235 nm, the sensitivity was about five times as much as that at 254 nm.

For the analysis of ergot alkaloids, reversed-phase chromatography on C_{18} columns with acetonitrile/0.01 mol/L ammonium carbonate (1:2) or (2:3) was generally employed [1]. But for the isolation and separation of new natural lactam derivatives of ergotoxine alkaloids, a LiChrosorb-NH_2 column coupled with ether/ethanol (96:4) gave excellent results. A mixture of diastereomeric pairs of ergocristine and ergocristam was resolved within 12 min [110].

Colchicine, the major alkaloid of *Colchicum* species, possesses interesting pharmacological properties and thus has attracted several research groups. A first HPLC separation was reported by Forni and Massarani [111], who used a silanized silica gel column and acetonitrile/water as solvent system. More recently, a successful separation of six colchicine derivatives on a C_{18} reversed-phase column with acetonitrile/methanol/phosphate buffer at pH 6.0 (16:7:79) has been achieved [112]. The same conditions were employed for the simultaneous determination of colchicine and colchiceine in microbial cultures [113] and for the characterization of colchiceinamide in the course of the microbial transformations of N-methylcolchiceinamide [114].

14.6 Non Alkaloidal Nitrogen Containing Compounds

Betalains are plant pigments of considerable interest due to their chemotaxonomic significance and to their use as food colorants. A HPLC method for rapid analysis of betaxanthins using a methanol/acetic acid/water gradient elution system on LiChrosorb RP-8 has been described [115]. An improved reversed-phase method was reported by Strack et al. [116]. Seven betaxanthins and seven betacyanins were separated on LiChrosorb RP-18 using the following elution system: within 60 min with a linear gradient from solvent A (1.5% phosphoric acid in water) to 40% solvent B (phosphoric acid/acetic acid/acetonitrile/water, 1.5:20:25:53.5) in A + B. The method can be applied to the identification and quantification of pigments in crude plant extracts. Good resolution of betanin and its isomer isobetanin was obtained on µBondapak C_{18} developed with methanol/0.05 mol/L KH_2PO_4 (18:82) adjusted to pH 2.75 with phosphoric acid or by gradient elution with increasing concentration of methanol in this solvent [119].

For the determination of capsaicin, the pungent principle of chili pepper, in extracts from *Fructus capsici,* reversed-phase HPLC with methanol/water mixtures as mobile phase has been employed [118 to 120]. The detection limit was about 100 ng capsaicin. A more sensitive method was elaborated by Saria et al. [121]. Separation of capsaicin and six analogues was carried out on a C_{18} column with acetonitrile/water (40:60). Fluorimetric detection at an excitation wavelength of 270 nm and an emission wavelength at 330 nm allowed measurement of 3 ng of capsaicin.

14.7 Conclusion and Outlook

It appears from the numerous published papers that reversed-phase HPLC on chemically bonded phases is the most commonly used method for the separation of natural products. Combined with ion-pairing reagents, it is suitable for the analysis of plant constituents with a wide range of polarities. Recently developed packing materials, such as styrene divinylbenzene resin, seem to be highly promising and have been applied successfully to the separation of pyrrolizidine alkaloids [89].

HPLC has mainly been used as a method for the qualitative or quantitative analysis of plant extracts. Although the number of papers dealing with the isolation of natural products is increasing, the full potential of HPLC as a preparative scale separation method has not yet been exploited.

The combination of HPLC with mass spectrometry (MS) is another step forward. Very interesting results have been obtained with an on-line LC/MS interface using a dynamic soft ionization method [122]. A fraction of the HPLC eluate is split into the chemical ionization (CI) source of a quadrupole spectrometer where the mobile phase provides a soft direct-CI of the contained components. This method has been applied to the analysis of *Digitalis* glycosides. Digitoxin could be directly characterized by its molecular ion and the successive diagnostic losses of its three digitoxosyl units.

Mass spectrometry used as detection method for HPLC is particularly suited to polar or thermally labile plant constituents. Since it provides directly important structural information about the separated compounds, HPLC/MS will find numerous applications in the field of natural products.

14.8 References

[1] D. G. I. Kingston, *J. Nat. Prod.* **42,** 237 (1979).
[2] M. A. Adams, and K. Nakanishi, *J. Liquid Chromatogr.* **2,** 1097 (1979).
[3] A. Wehrli, J. C. Hildenbrand, H. P. Keller, R. Stampfli, and R. W. Frei, *J. Chromatogr.* **149,** 199 (1978).

[4] C. F. Van Sumere, W. Van Brussel, K. Vande Casteele, and L. van Rompaey, in: T. Swain, J. B. Harborne, and C. F. Van Sumere (eds.): *Biochemistry of Plant Phenolics, Recent Advances in Phytochemistry,* Vol. **12,** pp. 1 – 28. Plenum Press, New York 1979.
[5] K. Hostettmann, and M. Hostettmann, in: J. B. Harborne and T. J. Mabry (eds.): *Advances in Flavonoid Research 1975 – 1981,* pp. 1 – 18. Chapman & Hall, London 1982.
[6] K. Görler, S. Mutter, and C. Westphal, *Planta med.* **37,** 1 (1979).
[7] C. Dewaele, and M. Verzele, *J. Chromatogr.* **197,** 189 (1980).
[8] R. Schwarzenbach, *J. Liquid Chromatogr.* **2,** 205 (1979).
[9] J. P. Bianchini, and E. M. Gaydou, *J. Chromatogr.* **190,** 233 (1980).
[10] J. P. Bianchini, and E. M. Gaydou, *J. Chromatogr.* **211,** 61 (1981).
[11] R. E. Carlson, and D. Dolphin, *J. Chromatogr.* **198,** 193 (1980).
[12] R. Galsensa, and K. Herrmann, *J. Chromatogr.* **189,** 217 (1980).
[13] L. G. West, P. M. Birac, and D. E. Pratt, *J. Chromatogr.* **150,** 266 (1978).
[14] P. A. Murphy, *J. Chromatogr.* **211,** 166 (1981).
[15] M. Wilkinson, J. G. Sweeny, and G. A. Iacobucci, *J. Chromatogr.* **132,** 349 (1977).
[16] R. Brenneisen, and E. Steinegger, *Pharm. Acta Helv.* **56,** 180 (1981).
[17] N. Akavia, and D. Strack, *Z. Naturforsch.* **35 c,** 16 (1980).
[18] S. R. Udupa, and A. V. Patankar, *J. Chromatogr.* **205,** 470 (1981).
[19] B. A. Charpentier, and J. R. Cowles, *J. Chromatogr.* **208,** 132 (1981).
[20] G. J. Niemann, and J. W. Koerselmann-Kooy, *Planta med.* **31,** 297 (1977).
[21] D. Strack, and J. Krause, *J. Chromatogr.* **156,** 359 (1978).
[22] V. Quercia, L. Turchetto, N. Pierini, V. Cuozzo, and G. Percaccio, *J. Chromatogr.* **161,** 396 (1978).
[23] M. Williams, G. Hrazdina, M. Wilkinson, J. G. Sweeny, and G. A. Iacobucci, *J. Chromatogr.* **155,** 389 (1978).
[24] W. A. Court, *J. Chromatogr.* **130,** 287 (1977).
[25] C. T. Seitz, and R. E. Wingard, *J. Agric. Food Chem.* **26,** 278 (1978).
[26] G. J. Niemann, and J. Van Brederode, *J. Chromatogr.* **152,** 523 (1978).
[27] D. Strack, K. Fuisting, and G. Popovici, *J. Chromatogr.* **176,** 270 (1979).
[28] H. Becker, G. Wilking, and K. Hostettmann, *J. Chromatogr.* **136,** 174 (1977).
[29] W. S. Woo, S. K. Kang, H. Wagner, O. Seligmann, and V. M. Chari, *Phytochemistry* **19,** 2791 (1980).
[30] N. Ohta, G. Kuwata, H. Akahori, and T. Watanabe, *Agric. Biol. Chem.* **44,** 469 (1980).
[31] Y. Akada, S. Kawano, and M. Yamagishi, *Yakugaku Zasshi* **100,** 1057 (1980).
[32] D. Strack, N. Akavia, and H. Reznik, *Z. Naturforsch.* **35 c,** 533 (1980).
[33] W. Henning, and K. Herrmann, *Phytochemistry* **19,** 2727 (1980).
[34] K. Hostettmann, and H. Wagner, *Phytochemistry* **16,** 821 (1977).
[35] K. Hostettmann, and H. M. McNair, *J. Chromatogr.* **116,** 201 (1976).
[36] K. Hostettmann, and A. Jacot-Guillarmod, *J. Chromatogr.* **124,** 381 (1976).
[37] M. J. Pettei, and K. Hostettmann, *J. Chromatogr.* **154,** 106 (1978).
[38] K.-P. Hupe, H. H. Lauer, and K. Zech, *Chromatographia* **13,** 413 (1980).
[39] R. Schuster, *Chromatographia* **13,** 379 (1980).
[40] M. Massias, J. Carbonnier, and D. Mohlo, *Phytochemistry* **20,** 1577 (1981).
[41] O. Sticher, F. Soldati, and D. Lehmann, *Planta med.* **35,** 253 (1979).
[42] M. Grün, and G. Franz, *Pharmazie* **34,** 669 (1979).
[43] B. Christ, T. Pöppinghaus, and F. Wirtz-Peitz, *Arzneim.-Forsch./Drug Res.* **28,** 225 (1978).
[44] F. Erni, and R. Frei, *J. Chromatogr.* **125,** 265 (1976).
[45] D. A. Cairnes, D. G. I. Kingston, and M. M. Rao, *J. Nat. Prod.* **44,** 34 (1981).
[46] D. Strack, G. B. Feige, and R. Kroll, *Z. Naturforsch.* **34 c,** 695 (1979).
[47] S. A. Abou-Donia, J. M. Lasker, and M. B. Abou-Donia, *J. Chromatogr.* **206,** 606 (1981).
[48] N. Asakawa, M. Tsuno, T. Hattori, M. Ueyama, A. Shinoda, Y. Miyake, and K. Kagei, *Yakugaku Zasshi* **101,** 374 (1981).
[49] S. E. Moring, and J. D. McChesney, *J. Assoc. Off. Anal. Chem.* **62,** 774 (1979).
[50] S. B. Mahato, N. P. Sahu, and S. K. Roy, *J. Chromatogr.* **206,** 169 (1981).
[51] J.-T. Lin, W. D. Nes, and E. Heftmann, *J. Chromatogr.* **207,** 457 (1981).
[52] G. Tittel, Ph. D. Thesis, Ludwig-Maximilians-Universität, Münich, 1978.
[53] T. Nestler, G. Tittel, and H. Wagner, *Planta med.* **38,** 204 (1980).

[54] D. Strack, P. Proksch, and P.-G. Gülz, *Z. Naturforsch.* **35 c,** 675 (1980).

[55] E. G. Heisler, J. Siciliano, E. B. Kalan, and S. F. Osman, *J. Chromatogr.* **210,** 365 (1981).

[56] I. Ganjian, I. Kubo, and T. Kubota, *J. Chromatogr.* **200,** 250 (1980).

[57] W. Kraus, and R. Cramer, *Liebigs Ann. Chem.* **1,** 181 (1981).

[58] F. Bohlmann, J. Ziesche, R. M. King, and H. Robinson, *Phytochemistry* **20,** 263 (1981).

[59] F. Bohlmann, J. Jakupovic, H. Robinson, and R. M. King, *Phytochemistry* **20,** 109 (1981).

[60] O. Sticher, and B. Meier, *Dtsch. Apoth. Ztg.* **117,** 1431 (1977).

[61] F. Ü. Afifi-Yazar, and O. Sticher, *Helv. Chim. Acta* **63,** 1905 (1980).

[62] O. Sticher, B. Meier, D. Lehmann, and L. Swiatek, *Planta med.* **38,** 246 (1980).

[63] O. Sticher, and O. Salama, *Helv. Chim. Acta* **64,** 78 (1981).

[64] B. Meier, and O. Sticher, *J. Chromatogr.* **138,** 453 (1977).

[65] O. Sticher, and B. Meier, *Pharm. Acta Helv.* **53,** 40 (1978).

[66] V. Quercia, G. Battaglino, N. Pierini, and L. Turchetto, *J. Chromatogr.* **193,** 163 (1980).

[67] Y. Takino, M. Koshioka, T. Miyahara, H. Tanizawa, Y. Ishii, M. Kawaguchi, M. Higashino, and T. Hayashi, *Planta med.* **38,** 344 (1980).

[68] M. Koshioka, Y. Takino, and T. Hayashi, *Planta med.* Supplement 64 (1980).

[69] W. G. van der Sluis, and R. P. Labadie, *Planta med.* **41,** 221 (1981).

[70] H. Besso, Y. Saruwatari, K. Futamura, K. Kunihiro, T. Fuwa, and O. Tanaka, *Planta med.* **37,** 226 (1979).

[71] O. Sticher, and F. Soldati, *Planta med.* **36,** 30 (1979).

[72] T. Nagasawa, J. H. Choi, Y. Nishino, and H. Oura, *Chem. Pharm. Bull.* **28,** 3701 (1980).

[73] S. E. Chen, and E. J. Staba, *Lloydia* **41,** 361 (1978).

[74] H. Kimata, C. Hiyama, S. Yahara, O. Tanaka, O. Ishikawa, and M. Aiura, *Chem. Pharm. Bull.* **27,** 1836 (1979).

[75] O. Sticher, and F. Soldati, *Pharm. Acta Helv.* **53,** 46 (1978).

[76] Y. Akada, and Y. Tanase, *Yakugaku Zasshi* **96,** 1035 (1976).

[77] F. Nachtmann, *Z. Anal. Chem.* **282,** 209 (1976).

[78] J. Gfeller, G. Frey, and R. W. Frei, *J. Chromatogr.* **142,** 271 (1977).

[79] F. Erni, and R. W. Frei, *J. Chromatogr.* **130,** 169 (1977).

[80] J. Jurenitsch, B. Kopp, H. Kirchner, and W. Kubelka, *Planta med.* **39,** 272 (1980).

[81] G. Tittel, and H. Wagner, *Planta med.* **39,** 125 (1980).

[82] W. Lindner, and R. W. Frei, *J. Chromatogr.* **117,** 81 (1976).

[83] K. Shimada, M. Hasegawa, K. Hasebe, Y. Fujii, and T. Nambara, *Chem. Pharm. Bull.* **24,** 2995 (1976).

[84] H. Sasaki, H. Taguchi, T. Endo, I. Yosioka, and Y. Iitaka, *Chem. Pharm. Bull.* **29,** 1636 (1981).

[85] R. Verpoorte, and A. B. Svendsen, *J. Chromatogr.* **100,** 227 (1974).

[86] R. Verpoorte, in J. D. Phillipson, and M. H. Zenk (eds.): *Indole and Biogenetically Related Alkaloids, Phytochemical Society of Europe Symposium Series* No. **17,** pp. 91 – 112. Academic Press, London 1980.

[87] H. Hikino, H. Konno, H. Watanabe, and O. Ishikawa, *J. Chromatogr.* **211,** 123 (1981).

[88] S. H. Hansen, *J. Chromatogr.* **212,** 229 (1981).

[89] H. S. Ramsdell, and D. R. Buhler, *J. Chromatogr.* **210,** 154 (1981).

[90] A. C. Hoefler, and P. Coggon, *J. Chromatogr.* **129,** 460 (1976).

[91] F. Baltassat-Millet, S. Ferry, and J. Dorche, *Ann. Pharm. Fr.* **38,** 127 (1980).

[92] D. J. Popovich, E. T. Butts, and C. J. Lancaster, *J. Liquid Chromatogr.* **1,** 469 (1978).

[93] C. Y. Wu, S. Siggia, T. Robinson, and R. D. Waskiewicz, *Anal. Chim. Acta* **63,** 393 (1973).

[94] W. D. Gupta, *J. Pharm. Sci.* **65,** 1697 (1976).

[95] F. F. Wu, and R. H. Dobberstein, *J. Chromatogr.* **140,** 65 (1977).

[96] C. Y. Wu, and J. J. Wittick, *Anal. Chem.* **49,** 359 (1977).

[97] Y. Nobuhara, S. Hirano, K. Namba, and M. Hashimoto, *J. Chromatogr.* **190,** 251 (1980).

[98] B. Proksa, and J. Černy, *Pharmazie* **36,** 380 (1981).

[99] C. W. Qualls, and H. J. Segall, *J. Chromatogr.* **150,** 202 (1978).

[100] H. J. Segall, *Toxicol. Lett.* **1,** 279 (1978).

[101] H. J. Segall, and R. J. Molyneux, *Chem. Pharmacol. Toxicol.* **19,** 545 (1978).

[102] H. J. Segall, and T. P. Krick, *Toxicol. Lett.* **4,** 193 (1979).

[103] H. J. Segall, *J. Liquid Chromatogr.* **2,** 429 (1979).

[104] H. Wagner, V. Neidhardt, and G. Tittel, *Planta med.* **41,** 232 (1981).

[105] W. G. W. Kurz, K. B. Chatson, F. Constabel, J. P. Kutney, L. S. L. Choi, P. Kolodziejczyk, S. K. Sleigh, K. L. Stuart, and B. R. Worth, *Helv. Chim. Acta* **63,** 1891 (1980).

[106] P. Pietta, A. Rava, and E. Catenacci, *J. Chromatogr.* **210,** 149 (1981).

[107] G. Szepesi, and M. Gazdag, *J. Chromatogr.* **204,** 341 (1981).

[108] G. Szepesi, and M. Gazdag, *J. Chromatogr.* **205,** 57 (1981).

[109] M. A. Johnston, W. J. Smith, J. M. Kennedy, A. R. Lea, and D. M. Hailey, *J. Chromatogr.* **189,** 241 (1980).

[110] M. Flieger, M. Wurst, J. Stuchlik, and Z. Rehacek, *J. Chromatogr.* **207,** 139 (1981).

[111] G. Forni, and G. Massarani, *J. Chromatogr.* **131,** 444 (1977).

[112] P. J. Davis, and A. E. Klein, *J. Chromatogr.* **188,** 280 (1980).

[113] A. E. Klein, and P. J. Davis, *Anal. Chem.* **52,** 2432 (1980).

[114] P. J. Davis, *Antimicrob. Agents Chemother.* **19,** 465 (1981).

[115] D. Strack, and H. Reznik, *Z. Pflanzenphysiol.* **94,** 163 (1979).

[116] D. Strack, V. Engel, and H. Reznik, *Z. Pflanzenphysiol.* **101,** 215 (1981).

[117] S. J. Schwartz, and J. H. von Elbe, *Agric. Food. Chem.* **28,** 540 (1980).

[118] O. Sticher, F. Soldati, and R. K. Joshi, *J. Chromatogr.* **166,** 221 (1978).

[119] J. Jurenitsch, E. Bingler, H. Becker, and W. Kubelka, *Planta med.* **36,** 54 (1979).

[120] J. Jurenitsch, M. David, F. Heresch, and W. Kubelka, *Planta med.* **36,** 61 (1979).

[121] A. Saria, F. Lembeck, and G. Skofitsch, *J. Chromatogr.* **208,** 41 (1981).

[122] D. J. Dixon: *The Application of the Direct Liquid LC-MS Interface to Problems in Biochemistry.* Hewlett-Packard Technical Paper 1981.

[123] K. Görler, S. Mutter, and C. Westphal, *Planta med.* **37,** 308 (1979).

Index